THE BROAD
SCOPE OF
PSYCHOANALYSIS

THE BROAD SCOPE
OF PSYCHOANALYSIS

Selected Papers
of Leopold Bellak

EDITED BY

DONALD P. SPENCE

New York University

GRUNE & STRATTON ———— NEW YORK · LONDON

Library of Congress Catalog Card Number 67-19253

Printed in U. S. A.

Contents

Section V: Psychoanalysis and Creativity

Acknowledgments

THIS VOLUME consists of a group of individual papers which share a common conceptual viewpoint. Most of them have already appeared in widely scattered publications which are sometimes difficult to obtain. Several of these previously published papers have been condensed and integrated with each other. A few have hardly been altered from their original form. We are indebted to the *Annals of the New York Academy of Sciences, International Journal of Psycho-Analysis, American Journal of Psychotherapy, Psychoanalytic Quarterly, American Psychiatric Association Research Reports, American Journal of Orthopsychiatry, Journal of Nervous and Mental Disease, Journal of Projective Techniques, Archives of General Psychiatry, Psychoanalytic Review,* Logos Press, Williams & Wilkins & Co., Grune & Stratton, Appleton-Century-Crofts, and the Atherton Press, for permission to use material previously published by them.

In instances of joint authorship, the coauthors are acknowledged in a footnote, and we wish to express our gratitude to them for their previous collaboration. They are Bertram Black, Joseph Chassan, Ruth Cooper, Timothy Dineen, Florence Haselkorn, Abraham Lurie, Eva Meyer, Joseph Miller, Max Prola, Sidney Rosenberg, David Rosenhan, Renate Safrin, Lee Salk, M. Brester Smith, and Marvin Zuckerman.

We are also greatly indebted to Miss Suzette H. Annin and Mrs. Ann Noll for their editorial contributions toward integrating some of the papers and toward increasing the readability of the volume.

The book is divided into an introduction and five main sections. The main introduction was written by Bellak; the introductions to each section and to each chapter were written by the editor.

DONALD P. SPENCE
LEOPOLD BELLAK

Introduction

ONE MEASURE OF A MAN'S GENIUS might be said to derive from the length of time his contributions continue to prove valid before they are replaced or expanded by others. By this measure alone the genius of Sigmund Freud is established beyond question, for the clinical and theoretical concepts he evolved have endured well beyond the half-century mark.

The many volumes which comprise Freud's papers on the development and structure of personality attest to his tremendous creativity, as do his countless other contributions. It is almost impossible to overestimate the extent of Freud's influence. Those who have read and understood his theories, and who perhaps have then tried to carry his thinking in some areas one step further, are well aware of the depth and *Prägnanz* of his comments.

Freud's efforts to formulate a general theory of personality began as early as 1895 (1895b). The brilliance he demonstrated in his early work stems not only from the comprehensive approach he brought to his subject, but also from his ability to anticipate future developments: for these initial efforts also included some tentative formulations regarding ego psychology, although he did not return to this subject until many years later. Scientist that he was, he created working hypotheses and then tested their validity in terms of what he learned from his patients in the course of their treatment. He reshaped his model when he felt that it was not broad enough to encompass the additional information he had acquired. Occasionally, at such times, he attempted to integrate his earlier concepts with these newly found insights—and thereby trace the evolution of his formulations. This is particularly evident in his successive theories of anxiety. But, more frequently, he did not make a systematic effort to integrate one concept with another; nor did he try to develop an over-all synthesis of his concepts. Moreover, Freud was not concerned with the formulation of textbook definitions; nor did he attempt to define his concepts operationally. Freud himself was well aware that concepts are merely approximations of the truth, and that if they are to be of value they require gradual—but continual—elaboration, expansion, and revision. In the opening paragraphs of "Instincts and Their Vicissitudes," which was published in 1915, he says: "It is only after more thorough investigation of the field of observation that we are able to formulate its basic scientific concepts with increased precision, and progressively so to modify them that they become serviceable and consistent over a wide area. Then, indeed, the time may have come to confine them in definitions" (1915a, p. 117).

In brief, Freud's theoretical constructs—from his first tentatively formulated hypotheses, through the continued expansion of a gradually evolving body of lawful propositions—were intended to provide us with a foundation on which we could continue to build. His great contribution was to bridge the gap between conscious and unconscious thought, between childhood experiences and adult behavior, between waking thought and dream content, between normal and pathological behavior, between man and the world he has created. It is

NOTE: From *Conceptual and Methodological Problems in Psychoanalysis*, edited by L. Bellak, *Annals of the New York Academy of Sciences, 1959, 76, 971-1134.* Reprinted by permission of the publishers.

amazing how often carping criticism of psychoanalysis ignores the real, basic contributions it has made which include: the continuity in personality we have just indicated and the basic formulations concerning this continuity: that child-hood events have a definitive structuring effect so that the adult can be under-stood in terms of his development; that psychoanalytic treatment is simply a systematic attempt to undo earlier learned apperceptions and reactions; that it is useful to look for cause and effect in psychology as in other sciences. All the rest are details of theory—details which are subject to change: about just what kind of childhood experience will lead to what kind of an adult personality and just what are the best ways of reversing early effects or sources of motivation. The basic propositions will probably endure for as long as anything can be ex-pected to. But, despite the importance of these basic concepts and their in-calculable impact, the gap Freud left cannot be ignored. For, although he con-tinued to add to his knowledge of personality through the years, he could not succeed in formulating an integrated theory of the psychology of personality in carefully defined psychoanalytic terms and internally integrated forms.

Thus, in spite of our continued reliance on Freud's basic concepts, to all in-tents and purposes the first crucial phase in psychoanalysis has come to an end. And it has become increasingly evident that we must now devote our efforts to the methodological refinement of those concepts. Yet, contrary to other dis-ciplines, where such clarification and expansion would have represented an ini-tial, and continuing, effort, psychoanalysts have been slow to develop a system-atic presentation of the hypotheses which comprise the tools of their trade.

To a degree, this difficulty may stem from the fact that inevitably Freud's life—and his work—came to an end. And, as is true of all great men, it is hard to deal with their legacy rationally and constructively. Some discarded most of what he taught. Others, perhaps because it considerably simplified matters merely to stand fast, have been all too eager to disregard Freud's plea for con-tinued "thorough investigation," so that the scientific concepts underlying psy-choanalysis may "become serviceable and consistent over a wide area," on the pretext that the psychoanalytic process is so subtle and complex as to be im-measurable. Accordingly, the "scientific approach" has been considered by some antithetical to our discipline and has been barred from its forum. As a result, more than fifty years after Freud stated his position in "Instincts and Their Vicissitudes" (1915a), we find ourselves sloshing around in a bog of unevenly developed ideas, haggling endlessly over misunderstanding of termin-ology and meanings in his original work, suspicious of innovation, with ambiv-alent feelings towards theory and therapy, and with frustrating problems of teaching.

Obviously, the utilization of the orderly, systematic, and experimental ways of science could alleviate these ills and deficiencies. Clearly, then, if we are to safeguard the present status of psychoanalysis and assure its further growth and development, we must reformulate, validate, and—where possible—define con-cisely the concepts on which it is based.

The success of this attempt will depend first on our ability to clarify the "scientific orientation" of many of the members of this discipline. For the most part, psychoanalysts have adopted one of two possible philosophies: they are "orthodox" Freudians, or they are the "rebels" among our colleagues; only a few well-trained psychoanalysts are "eclectics."

The orthodox psychoanalyst is convinced that little of significance has happened in the field since Freud. And—admittedly—this is true to a great extent. Nevertheless, one wonders whether this allegiance to Freudian concepts would not preclude the capacity to assess the value of innovations with an open mind in any event. On the other hand, the unquestioning, conforming psychoanalyst has certain advantages which, in fact, accrue to orthodoxy in any field— religious, political, or scientific. In the manner of the authoritarian personality (Adorno, Frenkel-Brunswik, Levinson and Sanford, 1950), the ready-made distinctions between "good" and "evil" with which he has been provided are a source of security and guidance. There is safety and pleasure in being a member of the in-group, approved by peers. Thus, he derives comfort and satisfaction from the conviction that God is on his side, while the other side is ruled by the Devil. But, inevitably, although he may not be aware of it, this enviable position carries with it certain disadvantages, such as constricted vision, rigidity, and impaired creativity.

Conversely, the rebel has set for himself the task of revision, modification, and reformulation. And again, this goal has some validity. Unfortunately, however, the rebel is frequently carried away by impulses which are less than rational. And in the process of adding a brick to the Freudian theoretical structure, ostensibly for its improvement, he may tear the house down. Many Neo-Freudians have done just about that. Moreover, when they lose the approbation of the "establishment" as a result, they often react with excessive and inappropriate aggression which further endangers the foundations of the structure. Typically, this aggression precludes their return to the "fold." Instead, they join with other rebels to create what soon becomes still another school of orthodox theorists.

One is reminded here of the apocryphal account of the discussion between Freud and Adler, during which Freud had become particularly annoyed with Adler's rather petty objections. Adler protested in self-defense that even if he were but a dwarf on the head of a giant, he might see more than the giant. And Freud is supposed to have replied that in all likelihood the dwarf on the head of the giant would have expanded his range of vision only to the extent that he would see the lice on the giant's head.

The scientific eclectic must fulfill several rather stringent intellectual requirements. Above all, he must have a thorough knowledge of the field, so as not to talk in shallow generalizations. Then he must be able to accept some hypotheses without reservation, to reject others, and to reserve decision on still a third group. Like the independent voter, he must make his own decisions without guidance from the official party line; nor can he count on the support of his party—whether this involves the assurance of a secure berth through patronage, or the approval of his peers, for he is convinced that an objective viewpoint precludes the formation of alliances.

Yet he too pays more than the price of subjective discomfort for the aloofness he has taken such pains to achieve. All too often his position is a sterile one, for without some degree of emotional commitment, there may not be sufficient motivation to follow whatever hunches come along. The eclectic is in danger of trading his potentially creative climate for the objectivity he prizes so highly.

Nevertheless, although the eclectic's position may be a sterile one because of his lack of emotional commitment, he may attempt to find a compromise position somewhere between rigid acceptance and excessive critique in a stance comparable to the psychoanalytic phenomenon of regression in the service of the ego. Repeatedly, an initial positive phase of temporary cessation of any attempt at critical evaluation can be followed by a second phase of emotional disengagement, accompanied by sharpened perspective and cognitive acuity. I believe that a consistent oscillation between these two phases can constitute the most fruitful approach to psychoanalytic hypotheses, and to other scientific propositions as well.

The scientific apathy with which psychoanalysis appears to be afflicted cannot be attributed solely—or even primarily—to the prejudices or personal predilections of its disciples. Many other factors are involved as well. For one, psychoanalysts have not customarily engaged in academic research; on the contrary, until very recently, almost all psychoanalysts devoted the major portion of their professional lives to clinical practice. And, as clinicians, their efforts and interests are focused on the treatment process. Unfortunately, too few of these dedicated therapists realize that psychoanalytic practice and theory are as inextricably bound to each other as are conscious and unconscious thought processes.

Another difficulty stems from the nature of psychoanalytic training. Contrary to postgraduate educational programs in other sciences, which underscore the importance of logical thought and a well-organized approach, the primary goal of psychoanalytic training is the development of clinical competence. Consequently, the psychoanalyst has not received adequate training in methodology or concept formation either at medical school or in the course of his postgraduate studies in psychiatry or psychoanalysis.

Typically, the psychoanalyst who has been tempted briefly to organize an orderly presentation of psychoanalytic theory has been deterred by other stumbling blocks as well, which he may consider even more treacherous. Most clinicians and psychoanalysts in particular have good reason to be wary of the strictly academic orientation.

The difference between the clinician and the theoretician is aptly illustrated by the story of the attempts of two men to learn to swim. The first jumps into deep water almost at once and flails about desperately, trying to keep his head above water and barely keeps himself from drowning. The other remains on land to prepare for his experience. He takes endless lessons from the best teachers and spends years perfecting his stroke but never gets into the water at all.

I believe we can find a reasonable compromise between these two attitudes. At this point in the development of psychoanalysis, it is clear that the gap between clinician and theoretician must somehow be closed—to our mutual advantage.

The lack of definition of basic psychoanalytic terminology stands in the way of necessary verification, modification, or rejection. Also, to some degree, analytic nomenclature is no longer adequate for our growing needs, and this represents still another crucial deterrent to scientific progress.

From time to time one of the results of progress in most sciences is the concomitant realization that the established terminology of the past has become incongruous with new developments. And, at that point, it becomes necessary to evolve a set of terms which are appropriate to the new facts which have been incorporated into its theoretical and practical framework. To illustrate, scientific advances made the use of the term "ether" obsolete; another example was the replacement of the term "perityphlitis" with "appendicitis." The classification of "fevers" is still a third example. And the usage of "humoral pathology" versus "cellular pathology" was a hotly disputed issue.

Psychoanalysis may be suffering from just such a deficiency. Despite our inability to replace Freud's original concepts with anything better, our present clinical and theoretical knowledge extends well beyond the terminology which served us so well in the past, to the extent that this traditional terminology has taken on the character of a Procrustean framework: it prevents comfort and inhibits development.

However, it is no easy matter to replace the terms one has become accustomed to, and this is particularly true in psychoanalysis. Certainly, one would be hard pressed to replace the elegance and simplicity of the tripartite model, and other basic terms have stood up equally well over the years. To illustrate, while the term "cathexis" may appear anachronistic and better suited to an hydraulic or hydrodynamic model, it conveys a unique meaning, and we have not yet found an adequate substitute.

My own experience along these lines may be of interest here. I have attempted to substitute the term "stimulus value" (*Anspruchswert*) for "cathexis," so that the hedonic implication would focus first on the "stimulus" and then on the internalized object in turn. I felt that this terminology might lend itself to the experimental investigation of certain economic aspects of the libido theory, e.g., the comparison of various zones, aims, and objects with regard to their stimulus value and the investigation of maturational sequences in terms of libidinal stages. This substitution has not been an entirely satisfactory one, however. All too frequently I am tempted to revert once more to the use of the term "cathexis." My efforts to expand Freud's definition of the term "projection," because it seemed to me to be too limited, proved even more futile. In this instance, I devoted two years to experimentation and cogitation (see Chapter 2), only to discover at the end of this time that Freud had conceptualized projection in the broadest possible terms, and that his insights into the nature of this phenomenon had been tucked away in what amounts to little more than a footnote (1913). Moreover, I do not believe we can attach any value to Sullivan's neologisms or to the efforts of other Neo-Freudians to update Freudian terminology.

After fifty years of Freud's theory of personality, it must still be regarded as the most internally consistent and comprehensive approach available.

Nevertheless, only because we have become accustomed to these terms do we use them *as if* they had a precise, universally acknowledged meaning. In fact, when we compare individual interpretations of many of the key concepts, we are startled by the ambiguity they acquire in the process. For example, in a recent paper Holt (1962) points out (with numerous supporting examples) that Freud varied his definition of "bound cathexis" twelve times in the course of his writings. Furthermore, the flexibility of the individual interpretations contributes to their popularity and reinforces our reluctance to replace them with other terms.

This ambiguity was well illustrated in a research experiment, described in Chapter 8, in which some colleagues and I participated in an attempt to judge and conceptualize recorded psychoanalytic sessions. We found that although we were all properly trained psychoanalysts and had, in fact, graduated from the same psychoanalytic training institute, we were unable to agree about the precise meaning of such basic phenomena as "identification," "transference," "acting out," etc. This is borne out by the fact that, typically, in the course of his everyday clinical practice, the good psychoanalyst works with concepts which vary according to his individual predilections, and which—while they are sound enough—are never anchored to specific behavior. While we had no doubt about what was occurring in the patient, or what needed to be done, or what to expect in the future, and although the patient's progress was satisfactory, it was clear to all of us that psychoanalytic concepts needed to be systematically restated in scientific terms. Only then can we verify what is useful and what is not, and progress toward further valuable formulations.

To the degree that Freud's conceptualizations may be considered constricted in scope, this may be attributed in large measure to the fact that he was forced to work in a hostile social and scientific climate, isolated from other scientific developments. Conversely, today, psychoanalysts have sufficient professional status to enable them to participate in the active interchange of ideas among academic psychologists, sociologists, psychopharmacologists, experimental psychiatrists, etc. This is a comparatively recent development, first, because the members of these other disciplines were slow to realize the implications of psychoanalytic theory for their own work and second, because the development of methodological procedures which might permit interdisciplinary collaboration was a gradual process.

These events will have far-reaching consequences which can only be estimated. But some of the advantages of this new scientific orientation are immediately apparent: hopefully, as a result of these developments, we will be able to draw upon the relevant contributions of other disciplines in order that we may expand psychoanalytic hypotheses to formulate a general theory of personality which, ultimately, will constitute the basic foundation for the efforts of workers in all of the behavioral sciences. Second, where they are applicable and useful, we would hope that contributions from other disciplines will be incorporated into psychoanalytic theory and practice. Some examples immediately come to mind: psychoanalysts may have to take into account such fascinating phenomena as imprinting and investigate the extent to which this can be said to determine later behavior, and modifications in theory may be required on the basis of their findings. Again, as learning theories become more sophisticated, psychoanalysts will have to acknowledge their significance and incorporate them into clinical practice. They may play a crucial role in the psychoanalyst's approach to the core problem of psychotherapy, namely, the most efficient way to reverse the faulty "learning" the patient acquired during the early years of his life, and thereby modify the resultant pathological personality structure.

On the other hand, in the course of their efforts, workers in public health and preventive medicine have become increasingly aware of the importance of mental health concepts. The heightened interest in community psychiatry and the participation of these disciplines in such programs throughout the country is evidence of this increased awareness. As this movement gathers momentum—and increased support from other allied professions—we can expect a spate of social legislation which, inevitably, will have to incorporate psychoanalytic theory of the psychogenesis of personality disturbance, as well as theoretical and clinical concepts. This heightened focus on mental health and illness may be attributed to social and technological factors. Recent events—dictatorships, atomic energy, war, the perils of ineffectual leadership, the assassination of President Kennedy —all have served to underscore the fact that if our civilization is to survive we can no longer afford to tolerate the "authoritarian personality," or the delinquent, or the bigot, or any number of other pathological personalities who seem to possess an incredible capacity for psychological contamination.

Thus, it is essential that we clarify existing terminology and, where necessary, evolve new terms and concepts which can keep pace with our recent advances. However difficult this may be, the ever-increasing influence of psychoanalysis in every area of human relationships makes it imperative that we put our house in order.

Each era of a science has its unique relationship to the general historical process in the surrounding world on the one hand, and to the preceding events in its development on the other. At present, in almost all sciences, the work of individual pioneers has been replaced by the efforts of teams of specialists. Similarly, now that Freud and his contemporaries have laid the foundations for psychoanalysis, there is a need to pool resources for a period of methodological refinement, as well as for broadest social application. It is necessary to validate and redefine hypotheses, to test limits, and thereby extend our theoretical and clinical horizons once again.

The goal of validation is to determine the degree to which a given theoretical formulation is substantiated by empirical data. However, it is axiomatic that the fit will never be perfect. Scientific work must therefore be concerned with the repeated checking of consistency, and with reformulation where indicated. A common-sense empirical approach is likely to become particularly inadequate when many factors enter into a given situation. Ideally, then, experimental methods will be designed to permit controlled manipulation and observation of the many variables under study, so that hypotheses regarding the interrelationships among these variables may be evaluated objectively. As a discipline, methodology is concerned with devising techniques for obtaining unbiased data and with evolving procedures to check the compatibility between these data and the theoretical models on which they are based.

This volume attempts a small step toward the goal of better integration as well as broad application of the psychoanalytic concept. More precisely, I have attempted to restate and define basic psychoanalytic concepts and terminology. I have also described my initial efforts to validate several of these concepts. Hopefully, I will have contributed thereby to the efforts of those of my colleagues who have long sought to remove psychoanalysis from the ranks of the pseudo sciences—those based solely on intuition, vague concepts, and even more vaguely defined procedures—and to elevate it to its rightful position.

In summary, I should like to elaborate briefly on the considerations which governed the choice and organization of the material presented herein. The function of every hypothesis is to promote understanding and to enable the prediction and control of events. And similarly, it is the function of psycho-analytic hypotheses to permit us to understand human behavior; to permit pre-diction based on factors which are implicit in the treatment situation; and to permit the limited control of human behavior, either by means of carefully formulated interpretation, or through therapeutic intervention. But an attempt to restate hypotheses merely so their ability to fulfill these requirements can then be validated experimentally would be sterile labor indeed. This criterion must be met, of course. However, it is equally important that the reformulation and consequent clarification of concepts lead, in turn, to the formulation of system-atic, workable generalizations; to the constant elimination of inaccuracies; and to the discovery of new vistas for possible exploration.

The chapters contained in this volume are the result of my own efforts—spanning about two decades—to apply a systematic, orderly approach to clin-ical phenomena and clinical theory.

Section I: Some Basic Clinical Concepts

IN THE LONG-STANDING ARGUMENT between basic and applied research, history has usually favored the former. If the fundamentals are understood, their application is infinitely accelerated. Human nature, on the other hand, has tended to favor the latter because it is always more tempting to rush into a field before all the basic problems have been solved.

Psychoanalysis might at present be characterized as starting to return to fundamentals after a long detour in the field. The clinical theory which worked so well for so long is now getting extensive scrutiny; the basic work of Freud's *Project for a Scientific Psychology* (1895b) has recently attracted wide attention; research training in psychoanalytic institutes has received renewed support; and such basic concepts as psychic energy are being looked at in a critical way (see Holt, 1966). Indeed, the swing away from the clinical-applied end of the spectrum has been such that the field is crying out for the old-fashioned case study; no one seems to write them any more.

In a sense, the movement has come full swing and returned to asking the fundamental questions posed in Freud's metapsychological papers. This series was never finished; besides the five published papers, Freud had brought seven others to varying stages of completion but stopped short of publication. These seven treated consciousness, anxiety, and related topics; if finished, the twelve would have represented an impressive underpinning for the clinical theory. Now it appears that the field is attempting to replace them.

The papers in this section represent one such attempt. The first two chapters concern themselves with basic issues of the theory in general, and the unconscious in particular. The next two chapters describe the ways in which unconscious material is often expressed in the treatment situation: either by the "basic rule" of free association or by a primary resistance to the basic rule—acting out. The fifth chapter describes a clinical concept (state of consciousness) that also has particular reference to the treatment situation, and the last chapter, a discussion of hypnosis, describes a more extreme form of this state.

Throughout these chapters, the principle of continuity-discontinuity runs like a semivisible thread. It was partly to make up for the discontinuity in the data of consciousness that Freud proposed the concept of the unconscious. Similarly, the analyst in the treatment situation is constantly trying to put the dream or the symptom into its proper relation with the rest of the patient's life (see Chapter 1). And in the ideal sense, free association is expected to provide the links between the dream or symptom and its dynamic surround.

Discontinuity, on the other hand, is implied in the last three chapters. Acting out is disruptive because it interrupts the verbal continuity of the treatment and/or substitutes for verbal communication; depersonalization and hypnosis both entail a loss of self-awareness and constitute a break with one's usual thoughts and feelings. Where discontinuity is uppermost, we have psychopathology; where continuity reigns, we have health. One of the aims of treatment, after all, is to understand how a diverse mixture of behaviors all fit together.

In a broader sense, we could say that psychoanalytic thinking is trying to reduce its own discontinuity by returning, at long last, to fundamental questions.

I

A RESTATEMENT OF SOME ASPECTS
OF PSYCHOANALYTIC THEORY

Psychoanalytic propositions can be seen as primarily descriptive in that they merely attempt to summarize complex behavior; or they can be seen as responsible members of an interlocking theory. The test of any theory is its usefulness, and to be tested fully, it must be pushed to the limit and to an extent that may at times seem ludicrous. Although its defenders may cry that the theory is not meant to be taken literally, they forget that unless it can stand this rough usage, it is useless as a theory.

This chapter attempts to stretch psychoanalytic theory to its limits. It does this in two ways: by stating propositions in the form of predictive statements, on the one hand, and in very concrete, almost oversimplified language, on the other. To the extent that certain propositions do not lend themselves to this translation, they may be seen as representing a class of statements that are more descriptive than theoretical. By putting all parts of the theory to what is, essentially, a linguistic test, it may be possible at some future time to distinguish between the purely descriptive and the more operational elements.

Such a distinction would have several consequences. In the first place, the purely descriptive elements cannot be tested as such; they form a kind of context for the theory, much as Freud's personal affairs in Vienna provide a context for *The Interpretation of Dreams* (1900). The more operational elements could be tested very seriously, confronted with whatever inconsistencies might arise, and, in general, strengthened by the strictures of sceptical criticism in the usual procedures of science.

The distinction between descriptive and operational elements is similar in some ways to the distinction between clinical theory and metatheory. The former gathers together the descriptive statements which the working clinician uses constantly in practice; the latter is a structured pattern of axioms and "if-then" statements with testable consequences. Currently before us is the task of moving easily from one level to another, a task which amounts to putting the clinical theory into a testable form. This chapter takes a large step in that direction.

SOME BASIC PRINCIPLES OF PSYCHOANALYSIS

DETERMINISM

FREUD WAS PROBABLY THE FIRST to apply the principle of causality in a truly thoroughgoing way to the psychology of personality. His attempt took the form of psychic determinism: the axiom that each behavioral act is determined by a specific cause or causes (and is itself a cause of other effects). His theory of free association is based on the assumption of causal connections via uncon-

NOTE: From *Psychology of Personality,* edited by J. M. McCary, New York, 1956. Reprinted by permission of the Logos Press.

scious motivations. Freud's genetic viewpoint is a function of the consistent application of the law of causality to the shaping of the personality. As Kaufman (1943) suggests, it may be better to speak not of a law of causality, since "the principle of causality is 'no law at all' but rather a declaration of the resolution not to renounce the search for causes in any instance and of the belief that this search will not be in vain." The laws of classical physics, including the statements about causality, still hold for macroscopic events, while quantum physics is said to need some special treatment. Einstein still held, though, that "God would not have played dice with the world"; classical principles are still useful for the new science of psychology.

The entire theory and practice of psychoanalysis is in fact predicated upon determinism, which in turn, is related to a number of allied propositions. This does not necessarily mean rigid one-to-one relationships; restatement in terms of probability theory is possible. Logically, the next step is a concern with the nature of determining factors. They may be divided into two principal classes: sociopsychological-environmental determinants on the one hand, and genetic-constitutional-prenatal-somatic-maturational ones on the other. Between these two sets of factors are countless and complex interactions.

Determinism is a necessary assumption for therapy, which is predicated on the proposition that the contemporary "neurotic personality" is a result of early events, and that it can be restructured.

OVERDETERMINISM

Overdeterminism is but a special case of determinism. A given event, for example, a dream, or a spoken sentence, is the final result of many genetically and contemporaneously derived forces. Strange as this concept may sound at first, it is, of course, also true of the physical world: the course of an object through space is determined by its weight, its size, space, air currents, the impetus given, gravity, etc., and its history—e.g., whether it was magnetized or exposed to a radioactive field. In a sense, of course, all forces are contemporary ones, in psychology as well as in physics, but as a convenience in description and for the best understanding of the interrelation of forces, a historical viewpoint can be adopted. The entire concept of "working through" is predicated upon the principle of overdeterminism.

METAPSYCHOLOGICAL PRINCIPLES

The metapsychological principles are also predicated upon the principle of determinism. Each psychological event, in order to be understood, must be examined from the dynamic, structural, and economic points of view. Of all these dimensions, we will concern ourselves here only with the economic.

Economic assumptions are part of libido theory. Libido itself is the form of energy of the system, and its cathexis (investment, charge) in various libidinal aims and the countercathexis (in the defensive system) are a fundamental part of psychoanalytic theory and practice. Metaphorically, a person can be considered as having a closed energy system to which the law of conservation of energy may be applied: that is, if libido is withdrawn from one area, the psychoanalyst asks himself to where it becomes diverted or in what reinvested.

This is fundamental to the theoretical understanding of narcissism and object cathexis, and of symptom formation.

A very mechanistic application of the economic viewpoint can be found in Freud's (1907) theories concerning wit, humor, and the comic, and may be stated briefly as follows: a certain saving of expenditure of energy, which was previously used for repression, becomes available by the use of the trigger mechanisms of wit, and the amount of energy thus available is "laughed off" and expended in somatic activity of the diaphragm and the facial muscles. Similarly he conceived of humor as due to a saving of expenditure of energy for affective tone and thought of the pleasure of the comic as the saving of expenditure of energy incidental to the fact that the spectator feels that he could perform the "comic" task with much less exertion than the comic.

It has been impossible so far to measure quantities of cathectic energy in any direct way, but I do not believe that this affects the heuristic importance of the concept. The most notable attempt along the lines of "libidometry" has been made by Bernfeld and Feitelberg (1934). The problem of measurement may be simpler than it seems. When we speak of measurement generally, we have in mind reference to a metric scale. We know, however, that there are other types of scales, of which the simplest is the nominal scale, where we do not deal with more than the identity of the sign ascribed to an object; in other words, where we deal only with naming things. The next type of scale is the one we feel is useful and meaningful for libidinal energies, namely, the ordinal scale. In such a scale the statement made concerns the identity and the position in the scale of the datum dealt with. All one can say is something is greater or lesser than something else. This type of scale has been useful in various forms of sensory psychology and in the psychology of hedonic tone, and it could be used in experiments on libidinal cathexis, e.g., in ranking the liking of different people at different times (Bellak and Ekstein, 1946).

A possible way of actually submitting the libido theory to quantitative measurement will be discussed later. From the evidence of Ernest Jones' biography (1953), there can be little doubt that Freud practically grew up with the formulation of the thermodynamic laws. In fact, he relates the controversial theory of the death instinct to the concept of entropy (the second thermodynamic law).

THE REALITY PRINCIPLE—PLEASURE PRINCIPLE

The term "pleasure principle" is probably a particularly unfortunate one from the standpoint of the academician, but peculiarly enough, Freud from the very earliest days of 1892 (Hartmann, Kris, and Loewenstein, 1949) had about as broad and academically acceptable a concept of this principle as one could imagine. Freud was then already speaking of "constancy" and the tendency toward constancy of organismic and psychic phenomena, anticipating broadly the later physiological concept of homeostasis advanced by Cannon and present-day applications of the concept of homeostasis and von Bertalanffy's stables states (1955) to psychological phenomena.

In essence, the pleasure principle implies that the organism has a tendency toward drive gratification, or even more broadly, toward a state of equilibrium, perceptually, physiologically, and otherwise.

The reality principle, so dramatically opposed to the pleasure principle in Freud's system of polarities, is nothing more than the fact that the learning of detour behavior by the ego inhibits the immediate and direct gratification of drives. As has been pointed out by Freud (1905a) and Hartmann et al. (1949), instincts lead to gratification and survival in animals, while in men the ego needs to mediate between drives and reality to achieve this aim. Freud's contention in "Civilization and Its Discontents" (1930) can briefly be summarized here by saying that increasing civilization implies increasing interaction between individuals, increasing regulation of individual behavior and therefore increasing conflict which requires more frequent and more complex detours for drive gratification.

Symptom formation, in this sense, may be seen as resulting from unstable compromise efforts at drive gratification on the one hand and inhibition of the drive by learned (ego and superego) behavioral patterns on the other.

Unconsciousness and Continuity of Personality

Unconsciousness is partly a necessary construction, subsidiary to another basic principle, the continuity of the personality. The interpretation (of the unconscious content) of a dream involves ordering the dream thoughts into a continuum with the thought processes of the preceding day (the day residue) and the subsequent day (e. g., that the patient got up tense and with a headache, etc.), as well as relating the other aspects of the dream to genetic and dynamic material. In other words, the concept of unconsciousness was necessary to bridge the discontinuity of manifest behavior. Additional hypotheses are concerned with the nature and explanations for unconscious material and its fate. Parapraxes (misnaming, misspelling, etc.) are among the simplest examples of continuity-discontinuity.

The concept of continuity of personality was never stated explicitly by Freud. Implicitly, he stated it in his contention that all the essentials of the personality are established by the fifth year of life. Manifest differences of behavior in later life are presumably explained by shifts in the intrapsychic system, a quasiclosed system in that the person is in constant interaction with the environment. It is better to say then that the theory of continuity of personality implies that, after age five, responses to the environment take place only over a certain range or in a finite number of variations predicated upon established intrasystemic variables.

These assumptions become most conspicuous in the concept of the *repetition compulsion* which can be formulated as the *return of the repressed*. Clinically, it is met most frequently in the problem of marriage, where repeated choice of mates is likely to be made along the same personality patterns (with some dynamic variations, e.g., a masochistic choice instead of a sadistic choice, but definitely a sadomasochistic relationship each time).

Theories of testing, e.g., with the Rorschach and the TAT, are founded upon such a concept of the continuity of personality. Testing is an experimental sampling of behavior based on the assumption that the personality is continuous and that the sample obtained will be representative. If one uses a rough analogy, and compares psychological testing with public health assays of the waters of a stream (by taking a pailful of water at regular intervals for analysis), one can easily see why tests sometimes fail: if one test samples the surface water (paper and pencil tests) and another the ground current, they are likely to come up with different contents. Similarly, if a pailful is taken very near to the entrance of even a small tributary (such as a disturbing recent event, including a not properly structured testing situation), one is likely to be woefully wrong.

SOME BASIC CONCEPTS

THE LIBIDO THEORY

The pre-Freudian meaning of libido in medical science referred to a person's sexual interests, in the sense that a patient suffering from some endocrine disorder associated with gross pathological effects on his sexual life was and is referred to as suffering from increased or deficient libido. It is probably from this usage that Freud took one of the two major aspects of the psychoanalytic meaning of libido, namely, the concept of libido as drive energy.

The second major aspect of the libido theory was shaped by Abraham. A well-trained embryologist before he became a psychiatrist and psychoanalyst, Abraham applied some concepts of segmental development to his new field and conceived of an orderly sequence of stages of libidinal development, from the oral zone (active and passive) to the anal zone (retentive and aggressive-ejective) to the genital zone. Thus, to a certain extent, the libido theory is concerned with maturational processes. To this is added the effect of upbringing and relative emphasis or frustration of the various zones and aims, the timing of the stimulation (earlier or later in life), the subsequent effects upon the personality in terms of fixation, regression, symptom formation, and object relationships, and the reversibility of any adverse effects.

The libido theory can be described as a series of interlocking propositions:

(1) Propositions concerning the sequence of maturation of bodily zones with a positive hedonic tone (erotogenic zones) and specific aims of gratification (libidinal aims).

(2) Propositions concerning the perception of oral, anal, and genital stimuli, and the reaction of significant figures to such stimulation (early anal training, masturbation, and prohibition).

(3) Propositions concerning specific effects of the maturational and learned aspects on later development (object relations, character formation).

(4) Propositions concerning the timing of maturation and learning (the same maternal act at different times in the child's life will have different effects); in discussions by Anna Freud and others at the Arden House Conference in 1954, these propositions were discussed under the term of "phase specificity" of child-mother interactions.

(5) Propositions concerning the interaction of events learned at different times (the relationship of trauma sustained in infancy to trauma sustained in latency to trauma sustained in puberty).

All the above propositions are conceived in quantitative terms; that is, a conception of constitutional variation of the strength of drives, variations in the strength of stimulation or lack of stimulation, and quantitative differences in the nature of learning.

Psychoanalytic therapy is predicated upon propositions concerning the reversibility of perceptual learning and its effects of behavior.

Let us now examine the propositions about libidinal zones, aims, and objects more closely and attempt to restate them further.

THE LIBIDINAL ZONES

The earliest stage of libidinal investment is very appropriately conceived of as a diffuse cathexis of the whole body, inner (visceral) and outer (skin) (Mahler and Elkisch, 1953). This is increasingly focused (in a way that has not yet been specified) into a greater specific sensitization of the oral zone (oral stage) to be followed and overlapped by the anal zone (stage). This stage is superseded at the end of infancy by a focus on the genital zone (phallic stage) to be interrupted by the latency period and later matured into the genital stage, at which time the genital zone is the preferred zone of pleasure seeking coinciding with the end of puberty. To be sure, the sequence does not imply that the earlier zones are entirely abandoned.

These propositions can be stated as *an orderly maturational sequence of preferred loci of stimulation.* These propositions still need clear-cut observational verification and more specific statement; e.g., if oral, anal, and genital preferences were to be drawn as curves, how would the relationship of each curve to the other have to be drawn, if time were the abscissa and "libidinal units" the ordinate?

Experiments would have to be devised wherein standard oral, anal, and genital stimulations are provided at given intervals during the years of childhood and some criteria chosen for determining the preference. Aside from the fact that it would have to be made certain that such experiments not be detrimental to the subject's development, it is not easy to think of the proper experimental design. Recording of infants' reaction to standard stimuli is, however, by no means a new or difficult idea. Among others, psychoanalysts like Spitz (1945a), as well as Fries and Woolf (1953), have studied children's reactions to various stimuli in connection with the investigation of congenital activity patterns (in response to a loud noise, etc.).

LIBIDINAL AIMS OR MODES OF PLEASURE FINDING

Aside from defining the somatic areas which are preferred as foci of gratification, the libido theory includes statements concerning the *nature of the operations involved in gratification* of libidinal aims at various stages of development. These are also spoken of as partial or component sexual aims, since they may be parts or components of later adult genital activity. Thus the theory of libidinal aims is a set of propositions concerned with the sequence, interaction, and fate of preferences for gratifying operations throughout life. These operations may be in part a function of maturational processes of the endocrine-nervous system and in part related to learned stimulus-response patterns. With Lashley (1938), one might think of these aims as perceptual choices *in response to deficit states.* "Perceptual choices" and "stimulus-response" should not be understood in primitive conditioned-reflex terms but rather in the form of complex interactions of configurations (Gestalten), as will be discussed further below.

(1) Corresponding to the earliest *undifferentiated* zone (which for purposes of classification is included in the oral phase, since the relationship between feeding and skin sensation at the mother's breast has been shown) are un-

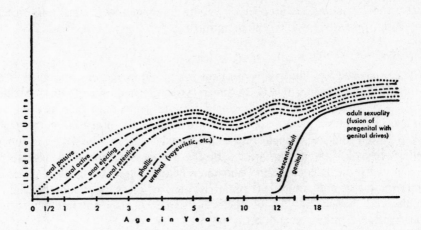

FIG. 1. The early oral (passive) phase is presumably present at birth. Suckling movements of a nonnutritive nature have been observed soon after birth. The active oral (aggressive, incorporating) phase is probably associated with the eruption of the teeth. Inasmuch as the eruption of the first lower incisors usually occurs at about six months, it is arbitrarily entered at that point. Similarly, the retentive phase of the anal period is entered later, roughly related to the time of voluntary control of the anal sphincter.

The phallic phase is generally conceived as developing fully somewhere between the third and fourth year, possibly closer to the end of the third. The urethral phase is not separately represented here, nor are other partial drives.

Greenacre has suggested that it is useful to conceive of the various phases of the partial drives as being more or less accentuated at certain times rather than as being absent and suddenly emerging or re-emerging. Therefore, the drives are presented as starting parallel to the baseline.

The latency period, usually considered as lasting from five to ten, is subdivided again by Bornstein into a period from five, to eight and one-half, to ten. In the first part, the superego is considered by her to be still extremely severe and to hinder the ego and those sublimations which are associated with latency: only between eight and one-half and ten can the ego really function freely.

The area of prepuberty is drawn as it is in the figure because, as Anna Freud has stated, no qualitative changes happen during this time; there is only a reinforcement of the pregenital drives (children becoming dirty, unruly, etc.) after the lull of latency.

From the period of adolescent-adult-genitality on, not only the truly genital impulses and cathexes of the genital area should be considered, but also the admixture of the pregenital drives. In accordance with psychoanalytic theory, the adult sexual drive includes the partial or pregenital components, and for this reason the lines converge in our figure. Only when the pregenital drives become primary and supersede the genital one as a goal do we speak of a sexual disturbance.

It must be remembered that this graph is only a schematic approximation of psychoanalytic theory and has all the limitations and falsifications of this kind of oversimplification.

differentiated aims of skin stimulation, rhythmic muscular activity, and of splanchnic gratification, already related to the aim of sucking of the oral phase.

(2) More specifically, the *oral* aims are subdivided into the passive (sucking) subphase and the active oral (incorporating, biting) subphase.

(3) The *anal* phase is subdivided into the aim to retain and the aim to expel (aggressively). Sadistic-masochistic aims are considered characterological derivatives of this phase.

(4) The *early genital* or *phallic* phase, including urethral phase, was added by Freud to his pregenital and genital conceptions (1905a) with these words: "I later (1925) altered this in that I interpolated a third phase into the development of the child after the two pregenital organizations, one which indeed deserves the name of a genital, one which reveals a sexual object and a measure of convergence of the sexual strivings upon this object, but which differs in one essential point from the definitive organization of sexual maturity. That is, it knows only one sort of genital, the male. I have therefore called it the *phallic* stage of organization."[1] Its biological prototype according to Abraham is the homogeneous genital *Anlage* of the embryo undifferentiated for either sex.

It is of interest to note again the reference to Abraham's suggestion of the biological equivalent, to which one might add the cultural correlate of phallic worship as the symbol of productive activity in many religions.

The basic assumption of the phallic phase of libidinal development is that the aim and modes of gratification are now focused on the penis and its biological equivalent, the clitoris. (Clinically there are many forms of an illusory phallus; the fecal mass is a common example, and adult female patients often seem to conceive of the cervix as an indwelling phallus.) The implication for object relations is that in contrast to the autoerotic pregenital phase, phallic gratification is desired from an external object, from one specific object originally.

From the standpoint of learning, the phallic phase may be of particular importance for the development of a girl. If the little girl has a brother who is greatly favored, she may feel that it is better to be a boy and she may become "fixated" at the phallic level. Not only is she a tomboy as a child, but she stays identified with masculine activities, viewpoints, and aims into adulthood. She may be overassertive, denying the lack of a phallus, she may be particularly aggressive toward males of whom she envies the phallus and wants to "castrate," or she may make male object-choices (of boy friends, husbands) who have a large feminine component. Other learning experiences may also fixate[2] a girl at the phallic phase of gratification: if the role of the mother is a particularly suffering one, e.g., at the hands of a sadistic husband; or if the child is particularly exposed to parental intercourse (primal scene) or has realistic reasons for a sadistic conception of things done to the mother; if the situation is so structured that the child becomes particularly aware of menstrual bleeding and connects this with ideas of genital traumatization of the female. All these learning experiences may tend to arrest her at the level of attempts to maintain that she is a boy rather than a girl. In extreme cases, this may culminate clinically in her becoming a Lesbian who wears or uses rubber phalli.

The *urethral* phase is sometimes treated as an independent intermediary stage between the pregenital and the phallic and sometimes as part of the phallic. The latter designation seems more appropriate clinically and logically.

The urethral phase is usually conceived of as twofold: the active form, accompanied by fantasies of penetration and exhibitionism, and the more passive form of "letting flow." The latter is clinically often seen related to the oral phase, e.g., in cases of premature ejaculation in which the patient reports a

---

[1] The clitoris may play the role of the phallic organ for the girl.

[2] The term "condition" or "fixate by conditioning" could be substituted for this usage of "fixate."

pleasant feeling of the penis being enveloped by the vaginal walls "like a body being embraced" and has associations of being fed and loved by the mother. Ejaculation in such cases frequently takes place from an unerect penis and without a feeling of climax, the patient reporting that "it really was more like urinating."

In more detail, the aim of the urethral phase of gratification is not only to urinate, but also often to urinate competitively (seeing who can aim higher), and to be admired for one's prowess. To be sure, the intermediary position of the phallic phase is also borne out by the fact that some of the urinary pleasures may be more of an autoerotic nature, while others are definitely object related. On the other hand, the more definitely phallic connotations appear in the fact that little girls at this time often want to "urinate like boys" standing up and by this activity stake their claims to having phalli.

Surrounding conditions enter in here as well; for instance, early and severe urinary training or a general overemphasis on urinary functions will leave their mark. Again, frequent occasions for comparison with an older male, or reasons for excessive masculine identification in a female child (e.g., in a strong homosexual relation to a sister) may reinforce urethral aims to the point where they predominate in character formation or in the creation of neurotic syndromes.

Characterologically, the psychoanalytic proposition is that urethral aims will later manifest themselves in the wish to be looked at (exhibitionism) and to look (voyeurism, e.g., for comparison of genitals). If such aims are sublimated, acting on the stage, or looking, as does a microbiologist, may be the result. More diffusely, a urethral character can be one who is very ambitious, competitive, show-offish.

The degree to which this aim is expressed in behavior depends alike on how early the urethral aim was strengthened by the mother's conditioning and other environmental circumstances. That is, if the urethral aim is excessive, it is considered likely to produce pathological manifestations (from perversions to premature ejaculation, to character disorders, to sublimated character traits). However, the isolated event of increased urethral aims must be seen in the total pattern of the personality. Similarly, other statements concerning libido theory have to be qualified. For instance, even if a mother should particularly stress urethral performance but should otherwise afford the child a "healthy" psychological climate, the urethral problem might appear only in a sublimated or at least nondisturbing characterological form (e.g., a voyeuristic hobby such as collecting opera glasses in an otherwise well-functioning person), while the same maternal behavior in an otherwise pathogenic environment might lead to a specific urethrogenic psychopathology, while again in a third environment of extreme pathogenicity a schizophrenic syndrome might be produced in which the urethral pathology is among the least of the patient's troubles.

(5) The *latency period* is one of the more embattled psychoanalytic concepts. This is mostly because Freud originally ascribed it to phylogenetic influence. Nearly all psychoanalysts have given up this speculation and hold that ontogenetic propositions adequately explain its existence. Another point of contention has concerned its lawful appearance: there are those who maintain it reflects ontogenetic maturational processes, and those who maintain that the latency period is strictly the result of cultural learning.

In short, the proposition concerning aims of gratification in the latency period (roughly from the fifth to the tenth year) means that there is an inhibition of direct pregenital or phallic aims; i.e., these aims are not observed or are observed less than before and after this period. Instead, what is observed and is presumed to be causally related to the erstwhile manifest phallic aims (now inhibited by the superego) are sublimations of this aim, manifesting themselves in intellectual curiosity. The infantile aims are also sublimated in part, and in part reaction formations take place. The ego is strengthened, possibly by a maturational ebbing of active striving and resultant better control, in part by the emergence of the superego (out of the resolution of the oedipus complex).

Thus, the concept of the "latency period" involves at least the following:

(a) The assumption of a biological, endocrine, maturational process characterized by a decrease of a sexual drive (in all its psychoanalytic submeanings).

(b) A strengthening of the ego, partly secondary to the weakening of the id drives and partly due to the perceptual, motor, and intellectual growth of the ego (a strengthening of the "autonomous functions," as Hartmann calls them). The secondary strengthening of the ego is itself predicated upon a set of propositions: namely, that it is among the ego's functions to mediate between drive demand and reality, and to exercise control generally, and that such control is "easier" when the drive demand is decreased. The further proposition involved is that if the ego can "spare some energy" from controlling the id, it can use this energy for other tasks, e.g., that of sublimating the drive.

(c) The concept of sublimation: drives may change their mode of gratification, their aim from direct gratification to some detour behavior which is more consistent with the entire set of cultural demands and maturational change. For example, the wish to look at someone's genitals may be generalized into curiosity concerning the nature of the universe and learning generally which leads to mastery of the environment.

(6) *Adolescent-adult genitality.*[3] The aim of this phase is the one ordinarily associated with sexuality, namely, that there eventually be a union of the genitals in copulation. It is important for the concept of adult genital aims that psychoanalysis recognizes all preceding pregenital and early genital aims as appropriate components of the genital aim per se, provided the components play a secondary role and terminate in the genital union. Perversion, psychoanalytically, exists where any component pregenital aim supersedes the genital aim.

It should be pointed out that the mere fact of copulation with apparently good function and orgasm in either sex is not *ipso facto* evidence of genital sexuality. Psychoanalysts frequently find that such manifest genitality is accompanied by conscious, preconscious, or unconscious fantasies of a homosexual or anal nature, that these factors contribute the main aim and pleasure, and that therefore dynamically speaking, the manifest genital activity does not represent genital activity. If frequency and even intensity of genital activity and orgasm were the criterion of psychodynamic maturity, manics would doubtless win the prize. However, such a criterion would be the result of fallacious reasoning which could only be compared to the proposition that if being married is a cri-

---

[3] Preadolescence, roughly ages 10-12, shows an increase again of pregenital drives and interests, sloppiness, and general unruliness.

terion of maturity, then being married five times means being five times as mature.

It is part of the concept of sexual aims that there may be not only *progression* as described up to now, but also *regression*. Under adverse circumstances regression to any earlier level may take place. Clinically, it is of the utmost importance diagnostically and prognostically for a psychoanalyst to know whether a patient ever reached the genital level and, having reached it, regressed again, or never reached it. The prognosis in the latter case is generally less hopeful.

LIBIDINAL OBJECT-CHOICES AND THEIR CATHEXIS

The third major proposition of the libido theory is concerned with the nature of the object that is chosen for gratification at various stages of maturation. Implicit in this proposition are the quantitative economic formulations concerning libido as energy. The proposition concerning object choices states that the first object is the infant's own body (as yet undifferentiated from the rest of the world) and designates this first state as *narcissistic*. The second type of object choice is described as anaclitic (meaning "leaning against"): the child relates first to that figure which supplies him with gratification of his needs, and only the final achievement of cathexis of a person outside the family is considered true *object cathexis.*[4]

The economic implications are involved in the idea that the "amount of libido" which was originally invested in the self is decreased by the amount invested in, say, the mother figure. To speak facetiously, if baby John started out with a total narcissistic libido of 100,000 Freudian units, he may be investing 20,000 units in the mother. Thereupon baby John would be left with only 80,000 Freudian units with which to keep house. John may be expected to invest some of these in his father, his siblings, his teachers, etc., but incidentally can never go completely bankrupt, according to another proposition never quite explicitly stated. In the first place, some units always stay invested in his body and in the various libidinal zones. Furthermore, some units are intricately bound up in his defenses and countercathexes and his entire intrapsychic system (ego, superego).

However, John's progress in libidinal object-choices could very well be traced quantitatively. For instance, with the final adolescent resolution of the oedipus constellation, John is expected to withdraw a considerable, not specified, number of units—say 15,000 of the 20,000 originally invested in the mother, and some 5,000 of those invested in sister, and an equal amount from those invested in brother and father, and now briefly but richly endow a series of objects (girl friends), and finally settle 30,000 Freudian units on his wife, at least during the active courtship, further increased by a withdrawal of 10,000 units from his own narcissistic reserves. Upon the birth of his first child, some further reinvestment from the family, from his own narcissistic pool, and possibly some withdrawal from the original heated investment in his wife may be expected to be placed upon the account of his baby. As he lives on he can be expected to decrease

---

[4] Probably the most significant advances in psychoanalysis in recent years have to do with the increasingly detailed study of the development of early object relations, and the related development of the ego, such as M. Mahler's work on symbiotic psychoses, Spitz's research on anaclitic depressions, and the work of Kris, Katherine Wolf, and others.

his narcissistic supply to the safe minimum necessary for intact operation, self-protection, and self-esteem, much as any good business venture may be expected not to deplete its reserves below a safe minimum. At the same time, for maximal health, all expendable units should be freely circulating, expended on his own family, friends, the community, and his work.

The above roughly and very schematically constitutes the quantitative picture of the propositions concerned with choices and investments of objects of libidinal aims. It is an inherent part of psychoanalysis that health exists only in such circumstances. Again, the concept of progression is paralleled by a concept of lack of progression. There are a great number of propositions concerned with the lack of progress from the narcissistic stage, which, if complete, will result in the narcissistic neurosis (i.e., psychosis); or if less marked, and possibly in the presence of greater ego strength and other variables, may result in a narcissistic character disorder; or if even less, in a neurosis of the familiar common or garden variety.

Again, progression to true object cathexis may be achieved, only to be followed by regression due to disappointment or other adversity, for example, enforced separation in illness, war, jail, etc. Thereupon, reinvestment of the individual's own person and earlier aims and zones may take place.

Of crucial importance again will be the propositions concerning severity of interference with the progression of object cathexes or their forced regression. Aside from constitutional defects, as recently posited most clearly by Mahler and Elkisch (1953), who state that the mother-child relationship may in part be determined by characteristics of the newborn, and in part by qualities of the mother (frustrating, punishing, giving, sadistic, affectionate), this interference will determine the early object relationship, and according to further propositions, all later ones. Spitz has spelled out most succinctly the devastating effects of early disturbance of object relationships in nearly quantitative terms (1945a, 1946a).

So far we have hardly touched upon the crucial processes involved in the shifts of object cathexis during the oedipus complex and its resolution. In our schematic presentation, it will have to suffice to point out the quantitative assumptions involved. In terms of our hypothetical example, the propositions concerning the oedipus complex can be illustrated by the following: John has invested 20,000 units in his mother as the object of his aim for genital (and other) gratification. He also has a considerable investment in his father (the nature of which we will not stop to specify here) and also in his own penis as the vehicle of his aim. Let us assume that the penis is invested with 30,000 units, and John feels he is in danger of losing it, plus the investment in his father, if he does not forego—or rather withdraw—most of his investment in his mother. This obviously would be very bad business. He thereupon resolves the dilemma by withdrawing 15,000 from his mother, and changing his economic ambition from that of primary control over the mother to that of sympathetic participation in a small way; he reinvests some of the units in the superego (those internal police forces which should protect him from getting so much out on a limb again), and some in his father (making friends with an enemy); he keeps the bulk of libido as ready working capital for a series of transactions of object cathexis. This finally may alight more permanently in the wife, etc., as stated before.

The transactions are more complex in the case of the girl, but in our schematic discussion this need not concern us.

A great number of further propositions are related to those of the oedipus complex. Learning experiences, such as overseductive behavior on the part of the mother, may so increase the investment in her as to make withdrawal and reinvestment impossible without endangering the whole economic structure. A very frightening father may so discourage investment in the mother and, by the same token, in the penis as the vehicle of the aim, that either this stage of the transactions is never reached, or if reached, there is regression to earlier investments of autoerotic aims and objects (zones).

To these propositions concerning the oedipus complex are tied even further propositions concerning the future pathology resulting from a great number of constellations of variables as briefly indicated above, pathology ranging from an inability to marry or to stay married to a general avoidance of competitive striving. If all attainment of success, for instance, is identified with possession of the mother, as it frequently is, any number of other clinical syndromes may result, such as a "success neurosis."

THE EGO

The novelty of psychoanalysis was originally its introduction of the unconscious in the sense of the unconsciousness of feelings, the unawareness of previously experienced events, the covert nature of motivations, and the hidden meaning of dreams and symptoms. Slowly, attention focused on the forces responsible for this unconsciousness, notably repression. Particularly with Anna Freud's book, *The Ego and the Mechanisms of Defence* (1936), a new era started in psychoanalysis, dedicated to the analysis not only of the unconscious but of the ego and its defenses. The pendulum has swung nearly full cycle, in that there is so much talk about ego psychology today that the forces of the unconscious are possibly already somewhat in disrepute. Many a psychologist who would not want to be found reading Freud will quite happily write about the study of the ego—as if the latter alone could be at all sensibly studied without the entire dynamic psychoanalytic context. It seems that ego psychology is the part of psychoanalysis most easily found socially acceptable.

Theoretical assumptions concerning the ego are twofold, being in part based upon constitutional, genetic, maturational processes, and in part upon principles of learning. Even though Freud stated quite clearly that there is no reason why there should not be primary, congenital ego variations, it is only now that these two basic assumptions are being made somewhat overt, e.g., in Hartmann's paper (1952) and Anna Freud's discussion of it (1952).

Enlightened behavioral science has a certain reluctance to consider the significance of genetic and congenital factors; this is in part a reaction to earlier overemphasis on genetics and in part an aspect of our cultural era. Birth and heredity were so all-determining in past centuries that the Declaration of Independence found it necessary to proclaim that "all men are created equal." Much of the sentiment in American psychology against the genetic orientation of psychoanalysis, its determinism and biological orientation, is influenced by these cultural trends.

The ego can be described by its history, by its functions, and possibly best by the extent to which it fulfills its functions in a quantitative way. Spitz probably has put historical events most clearly. There is observational evidence, and it seems likely on neurological and general developmental grounds (Melanie Klein notwithstanding), that there is little differentiation of psychic function in the infant prior to the sixth month (Spitz, 1945a, 1946a). The infant at first probably has only poorly defined sensory impressions, without a differentiation of its own body from the rest of the world or differentiation of its proprioceptive and other subjective perceptions from reality per se. There is in fact observational and experimental evidence that body and mind are one in the sense that perceptual stimulation seems necessary for somatic development: Spitz speaks of the "somatopsyche" up to the sixth month (1945a, 1946a), and has shown hospitalism and anaclitic depressions as clinical syndromes related to this construction.

Only when the perceptions become well-enough differentiated into figure and ground for the child to be able to differentiate the surface of his own body from the rest of the world can he be expected to tell the difference between subjective and objective phenomena. It is, then, presumably, that one may speak of an ego. Freud (1923) in *The Ego and the Id* said: "The ego is first and foremost a bodily ego; it is not merely a surface entity, but is itself the projection of a surface" (p. 26).

Thus, starting with the perception of the body as figure and the rest of the world as ground, psychoanalysis refers to the ego as that aspect of mental functioning concerned with the ordering of reality into figure and ground and the awareness of this and other intricate relationships between apperceptions and their memory. In the most severe disturbances of mental functioning, the psychoses, this differentiation of body and the rest of the world breaks down. As Federn (1952) has pointed out, the ego boundaries are disturbed in psychosis and thus cosmic delusions and hallucinations of any kind are possible.

This function of the organism has recently been interestingly related to the brain. Linn (1954) has studied perceptual functions in the brain-injured and observed defenses as Freud described them. Subscribing to the concept of "scanning" of Pitts and McCulloch (1947), Linn believes that the ego tests apperceptions (in a scanning operation) as long as it is intact but that the efficiency of that scanning may be interfered with by brain defects. He does not say so, but one might surmise that this takes place in accordance with Lashley's concept of mass action and equipotentiality of the brain. Linn leaves the relationship to "functional" ego defect open, though this seems unnecessary. The scanning function of the ego can easily be understood as interfered with if circumstances so strongly revive past apperceptions as to distort each contemporary apperception to a point where it may no longer be perceived clearly as figure and ground. The phenomenon of *déjà vu*, in normals at times of anxiety in a new environment, or in certain schizophrenics who feel about every person they meet that they have seen him before or that he looks like somebody seen before, most clearly illustrates this function. Wilder Penfield's reported eliciting of discrete memories, inclusive of affect, upon electrical focal stimulation of the brain, also supports the entire psychoanalytic theory of memory.

Thus the *reality-testing function* can be seen as a structural capacity of the ego; namely, its ability to keep to a minimum the effect of all but a few selected pertinent past apperceptions upon the contemporary apperception (selective inattention); that is, to apply those apperceptions which have been learned as useful in dealing with a reality situation only. If inappropriate apperceptions gain access to the conscious perceptual and motor apparatus, feelings and behavior inappropriate to reality may result.

We speak of this reality-testing function as associated with a structural aspect of the ego for this reason: if the personal history is of such a nature that apperceptions were clearly articulated (good configurations), and if the child developed good object relations, was exposed to consistent handling and not persistently disturbed by libidinal and aggressive stimuli, then the *structural* organization of the apperceptions is a firm one and not easily disrupted by disturbing contemporary apperceptions or drives. The healthy ego, because of the "good" organization of the memory traces and past apperceptions, keeps a firm grip on reality even in adversity or in monotonous circumstances. (Related to the reality-testing function is the ego's function as a barrier against excessive external and internal stimuli.)

It is consistent with the psychoanalytic theory that all structured mentation starts with perception. The ego comprises those apperceptions which are conscious or can easily become conscious—although some aspects of ego functioning are unconscious—and which are continuously part of the contemporary apperceptions in a way which permits one to differentiate (by experience) various figure and ground judgments, e.g., external versus internal, and permits one altogether to exercise "good judgment" founded upon past experience (memory traces of past apperceptions) as to what is safe and what not, what is probable and what not. In this context there can be no doubt that intelligence may enter in as the ability to form new "wholes" out of old "parts" and to find solutions to new problems never before met as such. In that sense intelligence truly becomes an organizing function.

It is part of the assumptions made about the ego that certain maturational factors are involved, correlated to the maturation of the motor and neurological apparatus. That the ego is correlated to the brain was always implied without much overt statement. Freud did think of it as primarily akin to the cortex. Recent psychoanalytic work in connection with lobotomies, as well as the previously quoted observations of Linn, suggest to us the quantitative relations to mass action of the brain previously mentioned.

Only lately have constitutional differences between egos been clearly stated by Hartmann (1950a), though Freud made reference to them. Hartmann speaks in this context of "autonomous functions of the ego," a concept including intelligence and in essence providing a conceptual basis for the assumption that some inherent nonspecified organismic qualities, possibly genetically transmittable, may also influence "good" organization of apperceptions (and thus in our terms, a strong ego). The study of epileptics with their ego disturbances (of perception, of the muscular apparatus, of impulse control, and obsessive defenses against the impulses and hypothesized synaptic disturbances) might be the best link between the neurological and the psychological level.

The ego is also said to have *executive functions* concerning the motor system. Presumably they are related to the early apperception of kinesthetic stimuli and to their differentiation from external and other stimuli and the reactivation of kinesthetic memory images in the process of bodily manipulation.

Thinking, considered by Freud a form of trial action, can at least in part be conceptualized as the recall of past apperceptions—visual, auditory, etc. Problem solving presumably occurs by closure concerning past apperceptions and the contemporary apperceptions of the "problem." Intuition, so long a matter of speculation, probably simply refers to the fact that a new configuration may occur on the one hand as more than just the sum of the parts that went into it, and on the other hand, without conscious awareness of the process of restructuration or even conscious awareness of the parts that went into it, just as any visual stimulus may be apperceived as a whole without conscious awareness of the parts that make up the total picture.

Into the ego's development go many learning experiences, inasmuch as the reality that is tested differs greatly in different cultures. In fact, even the degree of differentiation of contemporary apperception from past apperception and of that of subjective and objective differs in different cultures. Probably people without psychosis could have hallucinations in other cultures, since what may be socially acceptable behavior in one culture has to be rejected by the ego as unacceptable by another culture.

Ego Strength

Ego strength can be briefly defined as being measured (on an ordinal scale) by the degree to which the ego manages to perform its many functions of reality testing, stress tolerance, motor functions, etc.

Many, if not all, phenomena of ego weakness can be shown to be primarily characterized by perceptual disturbance, specifically a disturbance of the differentiation of past apperceptions from contemporary ones. For instance, in the normal weakening of ego strength associated with falling asleep we speak of hypnagogic phenomena, following Varendonck (1921) and Silberer (1909). There the apperception of reality is distorted by the memory traces of past apperceptions. Dreams themselves may be so understood, particularly if we consider the case in which an external stimulus, e.g., pressure on the body, becomes apperceptively distorted by past apperceptions into some nightmarish imagery.

The diagnosis of conditions characterized by extreme ego disturbance—that is, ego weakness—is primarily based on phenomenological characteristics, whether clinical or by tests. Clinically, phenomena of unreality, and evidence of the primary process in apperception, are evidence of structural weakness—i.e., lack of clear definition of the apperceptions disturbed by the past. The Rorschach diagnosis is of course predicated precisely on the apperceptive disturbance of the contemporary images of the blots by past apperceptions. If images are seen poorly, i.e., if the response is obviously more determined by memory traces than by what consensus agrees to be "reality," the diagnosis of ego weakness has to be made.

The concept of strength or weakness of the ego, in terms of its apperceptive clarity, can be further likened to physical structures. Just as stability of apperception constitutes ego strength (a matter unwittingly demonstrated by experiments of optical ambiguity by Eysenck et al.), so does rigidity constitute an aspect of weakness, and flexibility an aspect of strength. The simile that comes to mind is the architecture of bridges, or even of steel and concrete skyscrapers, which are built to allow a certain flexibility and thus fare much better than structures built as rigidly as possible. The rigid apperceptive construction of the obsessive-compulsive sacrifices adaptability for the sake of stability. The firmness of organization of images may be overdone, particularly in the obsessive. The ego of the hysteric, with its fluctuating ego boundaries in conversions and hypochondriasis, stands on the other side of the center. Alcohol and other anesthetics in their effect on brain function may loosen the arrangement— "weaken the ego."

For a number of normal functions a measure of flexibility of apperception is necessary. Creativity—artistic or scientific—can come about only if figure and ground relationships can change freely. This is most easily observable, of course, in the painter and photographer, but holds true even for functions such as telling stories in the TAT, or being able to free associate (Bellak, 1954b). Kris (1952) has spoken of regression in the service of the ego, which is closely related to Hartmann's (1939) concept of self-exclusion. In both cases a measure of control is relinquished. This is a measure of strength.

For free associating it is necessary that one permit a vague definition of the contemporary apperception, precisely in order that past images may emerge. In what the writer has called the "oscillating function" of the ego (see Chapter 3) it is at the same time necessary that one be able to compare the past apperception with the contemporary apperception (in reality testing in analysis) and observe the differences. Similarly, the ability of the ego to exclude itself and permit a "soft focusing" is necessary for falling asleep, intercourse, and creativity (see also Kris's discussion of regression in the service of the ego (1952).

THE DEFENSES

The defenses were originally entirely anthropomorphized concepts, particularly the concept of the "censor" responsible for repression in dreams, etc. Defenses can probably be entirely conceptualized, however, in terms of apperception. *Repression,* as the main and oldest form of defense, is truly inherent in the entire concept of unconsciousness. It has already been stated that unconsciousness, in the meaning of unawareness of parts that go to make up the new configuration, is a basic proposition of Gestalt formation. Thus, the fact that some characteristics of mother or some memories of her behavior are "repressed" is part of the construction of the composite photograph.

The idea of "defense" has a perfectly good correlate in the "buffer systems" of the bodily organism, viz., the alkali reserve. Cannon's concept of homeostasis had its early forerunner in Freud's thinking (Hartmann et al., 1949; Jones, 1953), and is now freely used by psychoanalysis (Menninger, 1954). It is probably consistent with the perceptual principle of the tendency toward the "good Gestalt" (*Prägnanz*) which on the other hand finds its equivalent in the formation of crystals and the formation of globules in fluid in such a way that the most stable form is the one where all forces are "equalized." The psycho-analytic concept of defense can probably be understood as the organism's tendency to achieve the most stable system, or to permit minimum disturbance of an established system of forces in an apperception. The latter embodies in essence the concept of the ego as a barrier to excessive external or internal stimulation.

One may also state it this way: defense mechanisms are the selective and structuring effect of certain past apperceptions on present apperceptions. Each separate defense mechanism formulated by psychoanalysis constitutes a hypothesis concerning some lawfulness of interaction of events in certain circumstances.

The mechanism of *denial,* for example, can probably most easily be understood as the apperception of a contemporary situation in a way least likely to upset a precarious apperceptive balance. For some of the other defenses, psychoanalysis has actually covertly laid down principles of Gestalt formation which are probably experimentally verifiable, as, for instance, in the concept of reaction formation. When a mother has aggressive feelings for her child along with affectionate feelings, one of the possible results of this conflict of sentiments is described by psychoanalysis as *reaction* formation: the aggressive feelings are repressed and become unconscious and only excessive affection is manifest. It is possible to restate this analytic concept in Gestalt language: when a "good" image and a "bad" image are simultaneously experienced, the resultant will be a reinforced "good" image modified by some aspects of the "bad" image. But mother love as the result of the reaction formation has the destructive features of overprotectiveness; i.e., some of the originally coexisting aggression manifests itself in the new guise. This was experimentally investigated upon the writer's suggestion by Finn (1953). *Projection* also can be best understood as a phenomenon of apperceptive distortion of contemporary images by past apperceptions (Bellak, 1954b).

THE ID

The id was Freud's term, borrowed from Groddeck, and it originally stood for all that was felt as ego alien—"it makes me feel like crying." Conceptually speaking, the id became the hypothetical locus and mainspring of the drives and, covertly, the psychoanalytic concept of the id is part of the psychoanalytic theory of *motivation.* It is not, however, the entire theory of motivation, as some would mistakenly have it, since psychoanalysis deals very complexly with a motivational system that takes into account not only the complex assumptions concerning drives, but also their genetic and dynamic and economic interaction with each other, with the superego, the ego, and the environment.

The concept of the id first of all implies the assumption of primary organismic drives. Psychoanalysis then formulates specific hypotheses concerning maturational changes of these drives, and the impact of environmental learning upon them and interaction with them. As far as the primary drives are concerned, we can safely expect biologists, experimental psychologists, and neurologists to advance the soundest hypotheses, which should then lend themselves to the additional specific hypotheses of psychoanalysis.

However reluctant psychologists may have been to acknowledge any strictly biological nature of drives, it is impossible to form a sound theory of per-

sonality without doing so. Perhaps most helpful will be the formulation of inherent *Anlagen* which react to deficits with a certain neural pattern, as Lashley
(1938) demonstrated experimentally.

Again, psychoanalysis has made a few formal statements of a principle often
implied, namely, that there are probably congenital id variations, primarily in
the strength of the drives.[5] Thus, one person's ego may be predestined for a
more difficult time simply because that particular person starts out life with a
more vigorous id than the next. The excellent observations of Fries and Woolf
on congenital activity patterns come closest to this formulation (1953). They
rightly suggest that this activity pattern may be one of the early determinants of
ego activity and, in particular, help to determine the choice of symptoms,
defenses, and character structure.

Beyond the most basic conception of the nature and functioning of drives,
and aside from the theory of aggression, the psychoanalytic theory of libido and
its vicissitudes constitutes the conception of the id.

THE SUPEREGO

The superego is the structural concept of psychoanalysis concerned with
"moral" behavior, insofar as this moral behavior is based upon unconscious,
early learned behavioral patterns. Alexander's suggestion to speak of conscience
in contradistinction to superego when we speak of conscious, ego-syntonic
precepts of social behavior is probably a widely accepted one.

There are analysts who maintain that the superego also has genetic, constitutional aspects aside from what we can readily identify as learned components. This
seems difficult to accept unless it be made part of a broader concept; namely,
that some organisms seem to have less drive demand than others and that this
is not primarily a function of lack of drive but of excess of control (if the two
can be differentiated). The difficulty lies in the assumption that "moral control"
would be constituted separately from those control factors usually identified with
the ego.

From a learning standpoint, the superego is the totality of a great number of
complexly learned inhibitions of drive aims. Psychoanalysis posits, for instance,
that the earliest and most severe learned inhibitive behavior (often appearing
self-punitive) stems from the anal phase, related to excessive cleanliness training. That is, a child severely trained to be clean may be excessively afraid of
any "dirtiness" including verbal abuse, may grow up to be an adult always feeling "dirty" (guilty), and may in essence suffer from an "inner voice of conscience" which is the persistent unconscious apperception of the nagging and
reprimanding voice or look of the mother. In this sense "moral masochism"
may be understood as a continuous effect of apperception of such an "anal-
sadistic" mother upon one's apperception of one's contemporary feeling, thinking, and behavior.

One should hasten to emphasize that of course psychoanalytic hypotheses are
by no means so naïve or oversimplified as to assume that cleanliness training is
in a one-to-one relationship to the formation of the superego, or for that matter

---

[5] Greenacre (1952) has discussed this topic in a paper on "Some Factors Producing
Different Types of Genital and Pregenital Organization."

that it constitutes all of the causal factors. On the contrary, it assumes many additional factors—e.g., that the learning involved in the correct apperceptions of the dangers of the oedipus constellation and the related inhibition of aims directed toward mother as object become powerful further contributions to the set of regulators.

The apperceptions pertaining to the superego appear in pure culture in the hallucinations of a schizophrenic whose voices may accuse him, frequently in a clearly parental voice, of any number of infractions, and in the self-accusations of the melancholic.

AGGRESSION

Psychoanalysis is generally considered to advance a dual theory of drives— sexual (equated with libidinal) and aggressive. This is another instance of un- necessary semantic confusion because each drive can be fragmented into many partial drives. This is particularly true of the libido theory; e.g., the wish to see, to exhibit, etc. Murray's (1938) need system probably constitutes the best elaboration of the covert diversity of drives subsumed under psychoanalytic libido theory.

The theory of aggression has been in an even less satisfactory state than the libido theory. Freud came to be concerned with aggression belatedly, and first in terms of his concept of the need for mastery as one aspect of sexual wishes; then later as part of the concept of ego drives (which had to be abandoned when the id was considered the locus of drives; what Freud considered the ego drive of self-preservation is really the concept of the ego as the testing aspect of mental functioning), and finally in the concept of the death instinct, which is rejected by the majority of analysts.

The only major systematic paper on aggression in psychoanalysis is the paper by Hartmann et al. (1949). Freud's conception is interpreted and extended into a systematic statement in essence paralleling the conceptualization of the libido. These authors, with Freud, say that beginning in the undifferentiated phase of infancy the self becomes differentiated from the "not-self" by virtue of the latter's being identified with unpleasure and the former with pleasure. By such means the "not-self" becomes invested with aggression and becomes the object of aggression. Hartmann et al. also say that aggression may be described by stating impetus, source, aim, and object, similar to libido theory.

By impetus is meant the amount of force, the quantity of aggression. There seems to be some difficulty in identifying the source of aggressive drive (in the libido theory drive is closely linked with zone). Freud described the strong rela- tionship between skeletal musculature and aggression, but Hartmann et al. point out that the muscular system is also related to libidinal discharge. It would seem that we are not dealing with a specific drive but instead with one aspect of an organismic reaction to environment (ordinarily subsumed under cathexis) which only later becomes more specific by maturation and learning, e.g., specif- ically aggressive. There is some support for this notion in the physiological fact that adrenalin release and the related biochemical changes (blood sugar, clotting time, etc.) are responses as much tied to aggression as to any simple work or any additional demand made on the organism by the environment.

The same basic tenet seems to hold for a discussion of the aim of aggression. Just as the source is nonspecifically organismic, so is the aim originally a non-specific relationship to the environment, only later modified into mastery, involving acquisition as much as rejection, removal, or destruction. The object of aggression (Hartmann et al. quote from Freud, and one can only heartily agree) "is the most variable thing about a drive and is not originally connected with it but becomes attached to it only in consequence of being peculiarly fitted to provide satisfaction."

Hartmann et al. also provide a beautifully systematic discussion of four types of conflict through which the aims of aggression are modified: (1) "Instinctual conflict—aggression and libido may be involved in conflict when the cathexis of both drives is vested in the same object" (that is, when one object arouses both aggressive stimuli and libidinal ones, either by conditioning and/or by memory traces of past apperceptions). (2) "Conflict with reality" (when there is a co-existence of an aggressive drive and learned inhibition related to self-harm). (3) Structural conflict, involving the ego. "This danger (to the individual) may be anticipated by the ego, which is in part already identified with the object, and the ego might be opposed to the completion of aggressive acts" (when there is a coexistence of an aggressive drive and learned inhibition, the latter being predicated upon apperceptions of the self, superimposed on and integrated with apperceptions of the object). (4) Structural conflict involving the superego: "The conflict may involve moral values" (which to me means a coexistence of aggressive drive and learned apperceptions concerning culturally acceptable modes of behavior.)

These authors also speak of four types of processes which modify the impact of aggression, and which hardly need any redefinition: (1) displacement of aggression to other objects; (2) restriction of the aims of the aggressive impulses; (3) sublimation of aggressive energy; and (4) fusion of aggressive drives with libidinal drives. The only point needing further elaboration is the one dealing with sublimation of aggressive energy, for which incidentally the authors suggest the term "neutralization" (as equivalent to "sublimation" of libidinal energy). Either concept—involving the redirection of an aim to a socially acceptable object, or the inhibition, restriction, or modification of the mode of gratification—is difficult to redefine in terms of learning except in terms of conditioning, which still is not quite satisfactory.

As stated, these propositions parallel the libido concept by insisting that a form of sublimation must be posited for the aggressive drive; Hartmann et al. speak of it as "neutralization of aggression" and of neutralized aggressive energy, paralleling the concept of sublimation and sublimated energy of the libido theory. They believe that the ability to neutralize aggressive energy is as much an aspect of ego strength as the ability to sublimate, and as necessary for the creation and maintenance of permanent object relations.

Clinically, this assumption makes excellent sense. One is reminded of Schopenhauer's parable of the porcupines: Two porcupines met on a cold winter day and decided to move close together to give each other warmth. They soon found that they stung each other with their quills and so moved apart, only to find that they became cold again. Moving back and forth, they finally found that optimum distance at which they could give each other some warmth and yet find the sting of their quills bearable. This may serve as an excellent parable on social relations, involving both the libidinal needs (warmth) and the interfering aggressions (and fear of libidinal needs). Actually, it seems that selection of mates may be as much influenced by the amount of distance or tolerance of closeness that two people can bear as by their libidinal needs. (Clinically, this is often primarily a function of their narcissism). At any rate, the disturbance in social relations is frequently related to a lack of neutralization of aggressive energy. The paranoid frequently has to change positions because of his tremendous hostility. In fact, a research program dealing with posthospital psychotics shows how the tolerance of ambivalence can be important in their work rehabilitation (see Chapter 17).

One can probably state the psychoanalytic theory of aggression fairly easily in academically acceptable terms. Aggression as described by psychoanalysis is at first one aspect of oral (aggressive, incorporative) behavior (later also anal). More generally, all movement is related to contact with and mastery of the environment, either in the form of acquiring or pushing away. Hoffer (1949) has suggested that in a disturbance of ego development, the hand, instead of being an instrument of aggressive mastery in infants, may be an object of oral aggression, as in the self-biting he observed in a mentally deficient child of one year. Aggression can be conceptualized as the direct outcome of motility—anal expulsion might be seen as an extension of the body—moving to grasp by mouth or otherwise. The frustration-aggression hypothesis as a sole explanatory principle has already been roundly discredited. It again was an attempt to deny primary biological mechanisms for the sake of an all-inclusive learning theory. If aggression is originally identical with any outward-going movement—as appears in Mira's and other expressive techniques—it may again be related to the activity patterns studied by Fries and Woolf (1953) and possibly even to the somatotypes of Sheldon et al. (1940).

Psychoanalysis states that in the beginning libidinal and aggressive behaviors are inextricably fused (A. Freud, 1949). This means that we are really introducing a conceptual artifact when we speak of aggressive aims and libidinal aims of gratification toward an early object. Only as the child clearly perceives the outside world and learns frustration of a more specific and clearly perceived aim to incorporate, to reject, to be warmed, to be held, to be free from discomfort, does he differentiate specific movement in the service of producing the desired effect. In other words, in the theory of aggression too we must differentiate a basic motor and perceptual, organismic factor, and a series of later learned behaviors.

The organismic perceptual factor is again a nearly protoplasmic one of reaction to stimuli. The human nervous system is so constructed that we can learn to react discriminatingly. Part of the acquired discrimination has to do with the differentiation of body from the outside world, and, as Hartmann et al. (1949) suggest, the identification of the outside world as the source of nonpleasure. Further learned behavior, in the nature of both trial and error and better perception of figure and ground, then deals with differentiation of movements toward or away from these objects—acquisitive, rejecting, destructive. The psychoanalytic theory of aggression, as we can now state again, is concerned with the maturational order of progression of differentiated response and with the formulation of specific learning of aggressive responses and their effect on adult personality. The primary existence of the reaction to stimuli refutes a simple frustration-aggression hypothesis. On the other hand, it seems to make unnecessary the postulation of a specific primary aggressive drive. As stated in the libido theory, we assume a reaction to stimuli which becomes modified by maturation *and* by learning into aggressive and other forms of behavior.

In that sense it may be easily acceptable that, after the oral-aggressive phase, expulsion of the feces may acquire an aggressive meaning in the sense of rejecting by the ejection of material causing proprioceptive tension. Psychoanalysis assumes that if anal-ejecting behavior is severely punished, an early learning of nondirection of aggression toward outside objects is established and redirection of aggression toward the child's own body (headbanging, etc.) is the first substitutive behavior. This is later modified into aggression against the ego. Thus, there is the psychoanalytic theory of the anal, obsessive-compulsive character trait with its inhibition of overt aggression and severely moral character. One hardly needs to caution again that this is a schematic representation and that psychoanalysis does not posit such a one-to-one relationship. This has been isolated for the purpose of description but is intricately bound up with hundreds of other apperceptions, each having a modifying character, as discussed in connection with other concepts.

THE THEORY OF DREAMS

The dream theory is indeed justly considered the cornerstone of Freud's theory. Significantly enough, none of the Neo-Freudian schools has been able to alter substantially or to contribute to Freud's dream theory. None, in fact, could advance any cogent theory in terms of their supposedly novel formulations.

Any dream theory has to explain the nature of the manifest content. It has to explain the specific lawful relationship between the manifest and the latent content and the relations of both to other aspects of the person—i.e., it must order the dream behavior into a meaningful sequence within the continuity of a personality and that person's contemporary situation. To date, this has been accomplished only by Freud's theory.

Freud's formulation lends itself with particular ease to a restatement in terms of learned apperceptive distortion. Dreams consist primarily of pictures, sometimes of auditory, olfactory, or kinesthetic apperceptions; for purposes of simplicity we will speak of pictorial apperceptions only, though it will be apparent that any other dimensions could as readily be used as a model.

In this case, the dream pictures can best be understood as configurations structured by a series of learned earlier apperceptions and a contemporary apperception (the genetic aspects of dreams and the day residue). It is inherent in our previously stated concept that the dream will be overdetermined, since a whole series of past apperceptions will structure the imagery. The primary-process quality of the dream—its nonsensicalness—is predicated upon decreased ego functioning and thus the lessened tendency toward formation of "good Gestalten." The secondary elaboration is indeed precisely the structuring of the primary process by the waking ego into "good Gestalten." The wish-fulfilling element can simply be restated as being the expression of drive aims in apperceptions consistent with the principle of achieving an equilibrium of forces.

The translation of the latent content into the manifest content is one major use of free association.

FREE ASSOCIATION

"Free association" is probably rarely "free," or, for that matter, strictly "association" in the clinical situation. It is a complex and little-discussed phenomenon which will be considered in detail in Chapter 3.

Suffice it to say here that by means of association, the contemporary composite apperception of a male superior figure, for example, is shown to be the result of all previous apperceptions of male superior figures (father, older brothers, uncles, teachers, policemen, grandfather, phallic mother or aunts, etc.). In analyzing a patient's neurotic anxiety or aggressive behavior toward, say, his boss, we arrive by means of association at the various genetic constituents of his contemporary Gestalt. Associations, as it were, lead to and constitute the component parts of our contemporary composite.

PSYCHOANALYTIC THEORY CONCERNING PERSONALITY "TYPES" AND "TRAITS"

Generally, the formulation of personality types and traits is inconsistent with the dynamic approach to personality; however, within the dynamic framework of psychoanalysis there are actually a number of concepts which constitute "types" and "traits" as syndromes or clusters of variables associated in a way that assumes certain principles of psychodynamics. This fact actually permits an infinitely richer understanding and prediction of personality characteristics than, for instance, a factor-analytic approach.

The main dynamic syndromes which one may lift out as constituting psychoanalytically formulated personality types are: the oral, the anal, the phallic, and the urethral personalities. This classification is primarily founded upon the genetic dynamic propositions of the libido theory. However, on the basis of the outstanding pathological trait, personality types are often also referred to by analysts as the "phobic type," or the "obsessive-compulsive type" of personality, or the "voyeur," or the "exhibitionist." Similarly, "oral," "anal," "phallic," are used as adjectives to refer to personality traits; these, incidentally, need not imply a clinical disorder. These traits may be integrated aspects of the character structure which may lead neither to subjective discomfort nor to objective impairment, but simply constitute modes of operations which are discernible as having more of an organizing effect on a person's behavior than other characteristics which he also possesses. Psychoanalysis has advanced the concept of "anal character," for example, to describe a personality in which anal traits are outstanding in a nonpathological way. Such "character types" can be clearly differentiated from "character disorders," in which the same traits are sufficient to cause difficulties to the environment—for example, to the patient's wife or husband or employer—and get the patient into difficulty with the environment without in themselves causing him subjective discomfort. The psychoneurosis (e.g., a compulsion neurosis), on the other hand, is characterized primarily by subjective difficulties. The word "primarily" has to be stressed, since mixtures of character disorder and psychoneurosis are very frequent clinically.

In essence, the concept of "oral personality," for example, permits one the following minimum of propositions (we are not differentiating further into active and passive oral):

(1) *Behavioral propositions:* an excessive response to food (usually overeating, with anorexia under specific circumstances); impulsivity; passive-dependent behavior with a great need for affection; low frustration tolerance; little patience; mood swings; flexibility, often including inventiveness, going hand in hand with carelessness.

(2) *Pathological propositions:* tendency toward depression; use of mechanism of denial and elation; obesity, frequently premature ejaculation in males; great sensitivity of feelings; easily hurt, etc.

(3) *Genetic propositions:* a childhood deprived of affection in any number of ways. This may be difficult to quantify except by rank-ordering a number of people. It should then be possible on the basis of such rank-ordering of deprivation (all other things being equal) to predict degree of oral characteristics, which could easily be experimentally investigated (frustration tolerance, etc.). The plain fact of the existence of the syndrome has been experimentally confirmed by Goldman (1948).

Actually, the above is but a short schematic presentation; much more complex propositions can be derived simply from the diagnosis, "severe oral type." Lewin (1950) has formulated the oral triad which has already been abundantly confirmed clinically: the wish to devour, the wish to be devoured, and the wish to sleep constitute a syndrome. Thus, oral people usually like to sleep, may in adversity take to sleeping long and frequently, and if depressed may wish to be dead. This last idea is almost always one of sleeping peacefully. Diagnostically, this can be of the greatest importance, since this type of suicidal idea, in the absence of other characteristics, is usually benign.

In a similar way, the other character types involve complex propositions which interlock with other concepts concerning defenses, relations to objects, and every other variable of personality. Research establishing the clustering as postulated by psychoanalysis will not be enough. Prediction of complex experimental behavior should go further to verify and enlarge the usefulness of the character-type concept.

PSYCHOANALYTIC TREATMENT

Psychoanalytic treatment, schematically speaking, can be said to take place in a situation with a minimal apperceptive structure: the patient knows little about the psychoanalyst, the office may be nondescript, and the patient does not see the analyst sitting behind him. In this setting, in which the attempt is to treat the situation as a constant and the patient as the only variable, one may differentiate these processes: communication, interpretation, insight, and working through.

Communication from patient to analyst in classical psychoanalysis is primarily carried out by free association, but also by bodily expression and other behavioral variables. By such means the analyst becomes acquainted with the patient's history of apperceptions and his contemporary distortions.

For instance, if a patient in the first hour lies down on the couch with the feet dangling to the floor and head turned back as far as possible, the analyst may roughly infer that the patient perceives the analytic situation as dangerous, is keeping a lookout on what possible attack to expect from his rear, has some passive anal wishes and fears, and is ready for flight. If the patient then associates and says that there is a funny smell in the room that reminds him of the time he had his tonsils out when he was five years old, the analyst further knows that this patient associates the situation with one in which one might be made unconscious and hurt. This patient will lead the analyst to postdictions and predictions totally different from those elicited by the patient who lies down on the couch comfortably, states that the couch suits him well, that he feels like falling asleep, and hopes that when he wakes up all his troubles will be over. In the second case we have a patient with a great deal of oral passivity who will expect the analyst to help him by magic, as he always wished his mother (or father) would do things for him, etc.

It is the job of the analyst to wait until evidence accumulates for a particular pattern of behavior and then, following a set of complex rules, tell the patient about those aspects of his behavior which it seems best to point out at that moment. We call this latter step *interpretation,* the analyst pointing out to the patient a certain common denominator in the apperceptive distortions related to his behavior. Now it would be just as inaccurate to say that interpretation is the only way in which the analyst communicates with the patient as to assume that free association is the only way the patient communicates with the analyst. Actually, silence or an impassively friendly tone or facial expression upon the patient's leaving may also be a means of communication. Also, the analyst makes many preparatory statements which serve as stimuli to which the patient reacts and only these secondary responses may lead to interpretation on the part of the analyst.

At any rate, the interpretations follow an intricate pattern. In essence, one starts with the minor apperceptive distortions relatively close to consciousness and the contemporary scene and slowly progresses, in many a back-and-forth movement, to the genetically earliest and the least conscious apperceptive distortions. The process of tracing the constituents of each apperception leads to a loosening of the figure-ground relationships in the patient. That is, he cannot any longer deal with contemporary situations using his stable apperceptive distortions as he had learned to deal with them, and this process leads to anxiety and attempts to use even earlier learned responses. This is the process classically called analysis of the defenses in the analytic situation. The interpretations by the analyst may pertain to behavior and perceptive distortions in relation to the past, to the present contemporary scene, and, most often, specifically to the relationship to the analyst. In the process of analyzing apperceptive distortions into their constituents, the patient's attempts to deal with the environment in terms of earlier learned responses also involve the analyst. Analyzing the patient's distortion of the analyst by means of earlier genetic apperceptions is classically called the *analysis of the transference situation.*

Insight is the word we use when the patient is able to apperceive a new figure and ground relationship, specifically, if he is able to apperceive some form of contemporary behavior in relationship to earlier learned apperceptions. In this

process he indeed learns, or in other words comes to restructure his apperceptions. It is almost as if an operation had repaired an ocular defect and the
previously astigmatic patient were now able to see things in proper proportions.
Making the unconscious conscious means to trace the figure constituents, make
the patient aware of their contribution to the total (almost as in a Müller-Lyer
figure), and thus break up the particular destructive Gestalt formation. It is
because of the long history of the adult patient that analysis takes so long: a
long time is required to restructure such a multitude of images.

Insight again will have to take place with regard to contemporary, genetic,
and transference distortions. It must be remembered that the affective tone of
an apperception is part of its Gestalt, and that unless the appropriate emotion
accompanies the analytic process, it will not lead to real restructuring in a
stable new system.

Working through is the term connoting a repeated attempt on the part of the
patient to try out his new optical correction in a variety of experiences. Just as
a previously blind person or someone disturbed kinesthetically or in any other
sense modality will try out his newly gained learning in a variety of situations,
so the analytic patient will try to fit his new apperceptions on contemporary
figures, e.g., his boss, his wife, etc. He will also try to apply the newly gained
insight to his analyst and attempt to understand the apperceptions he had of his
analyst in the light of the new discovery. Similarly, an apperceptive distortion
into which he has gained insight concerning, say, his relationship to his father,
may be extended to apperceptive distortions concerning his older brother, a
high-school teacher, a local policeman, etc. Again, the affective tone must be
considered an integral part of the apperception and the corrective experience.

By such means, psychoanalytic treatment may be perceived schematically as a
long process of studying apperceptive distortions in all their complexity and
attempting to change them by interpretation, insight, and working through.
Thus, problems of technique could profitably be viewed in the light of facilitating or interfering with this aim. Technical considerations can be reduced to discussions of the best means to restructure apperceptive distortions most efficiently and lastingly. Questions of diagnosis involve the nature and extent of
apperceptive distortions (considered genetically, dynamically, and economically),
and prognosis is concerned with estimating the likelihood and the extent of
restructuring and the probable stability of such new Gestalten.

2

TOWARD CLARIFICATION OF THE
CONCEPT OF THE UNCONSCIOUS

This chapter presents a view of the unconscious as a collection of superimposed photographs, some in and some out of focus. This model is in accord with the experience of the patient in treatment: certain scenes that were hitherto vague or fuzzy gradually become clearer in both a perceptual sense ("I see the house where I lived when my sister was born") and in a conceptual sense ("We could never have moved to Utica until I was 6"). As a model, the idea of superimposed photographs is clearly preferable to the standard seething cauldron. It has the further advantage of putting unconscious ideas on a continuum with remembered ideas; in other words, it treats the unconscious as an inefficient part of the memory system which holds ideas in storage but does not make them systematically accessible to retrieval.

The unconscious as a dimly perceived apperceptive mass must be sharply distinguished from what is described later in the chapter as the physiological unconscious. There are countless sensations of which we are unaware, such as the secretion of insulin and the absorption of sugar into the blood; in contrast to repressed ideas, these activities were never consciously experienced. Because aspects of the physiological unconscious were never cognitively labeled, in contrast to past memories, they can never take their place alongside the contents of consciousness. To the extent that one is aware of bodily processes, it seems likely that these processes have been coded in some explicit way; the extreme example of this is found in the hypochondriac.

The same considerations can be applied to awareness of defenses and drives. One is normally not aware of using a certain defense; indeed, much of the work of therapy consists in making it possible for the patient to recognize a defense as such. The lack of awareness stems not only from dynamic concerns (although these play a part), but also from a lack of learning; the particular defensive function has never been explicitly articulated. Teaching appropriate labels is part of the work of therapy.

"UNCONSCIOUS" IS A WORD of wide usage and many meanings. To avoid weightiness in the present discussion, we refer, for a consideration of its many usages (in addition to the psychoanalytic ones), to James G. Miller(1942), who defines altogether sixteen meanings in academic, clinical, and popular use.

Everyone, of course, is aware of the fact that the concept of "unconscious" in psychoanalytic theory has had two different positions. At first, in the topographical model, Freud (1915b) spoke of the systems "unconscious (*Ucs.*), "preconscious" (*Pcs.*), and "conscious" (*Cs.*). He later abandoned this picture of the mental apparatus for the structural model of ego, id, and superego (Freud, 1923). The relationship of the topographical to the structural model has never

NOTE: From *Annals of the New York Academy of Sciences,* 76 (Art. 4), 1066-1097, 1959. Reprinted by permission of the New York Academy of Sciences.

been discussed fully enough. I am concerned with the quality of some processes: unconscious drives and feelings that may or may not remain unconscious. In this sense the "unconscious" continues to play, of course, an important role in the tripartite psychoanalytic model. It is this process, rather than the system unconscious, to which we address ourselves.

If one were to attempt the thankless task of singling out the one most important contribution Freud made, the consensus would probably be that his formulations concerning the unconscious were the most valuable.

Freud's (1915b) theory of the unconscious originally was *primarily a construct*. He observed neurotic symptoms, dreams, and parapraxes; he bridged the apparent discontinuity between rational behavior and symptom, between dream and waking life, between intention and parapraxes by one systematic inference, namely, that all of these seemingly discontinuous forms of behavior were part of a continuous, causally related series of events, some parts of which, however, were not represented in the subject's consciousness and, therefore, must be considered "unconscious." Free association was the means discovered for bridging the discontinuity.

A great number of propositions concerning the various aspects of the unconscious have been developed but hardly ever systematically interrelated. In fact, an aura of near mysticism often surrounds the concept; many psychoanalysts have maintained, quite unnecessarily, that the nature of the unconscious sets psychoanalytic propositions apart from all other scientific hypotheses. Nothing could be further from the truth. By establishing causality in human behavior, Freud automatically opened the door to rational, causal investigation of mental processes, ranging from relative unconsciousness to relative consciousness.

Once Freud had discovered unconsciousness as an inference, he formed concepts concerning the nature of the unconscious material, its origins, the dynamics of repression, and certain formal characteristics of unconscious ideation. Accordingly, we shall consider the genetic, formal configurational, and physiological aspects of unconsciousness, as well as its energic-economic, dynamic, and motivational characteristics within the structural model. These thoughts must be considered both tentative and rudimentary. Many of the metapsychological implications of unconscious functioning will not be mentioned at all; others, at best, will be touched upon and briefly illustrated. The intention here is not to present new data, but rather to suggest systematic formulations that might be the basis for heuristic use.

It is generally held that the newborn infant is not able to differentiate itself from its environment. Before there are well-articulated self-boundaries, the hand-mouth zone may be one figure on a dim ground, the mouth-breast area another. Whether we refer to Bertram Lewin's (1946) dream screen or to René Spitz's (1957a) primary cavity, it is certain that for a long period both figure and ground are poorly defined. The child has difficulties not only with visual, auditory, and kinesthetic perception, but also with the concept of time and causality. Only slowly does the "secondary process" come about, the ordering of events into time and place and sequence to each other.

In other words, unconscious ideation does not "come" from anywhere: the unconscious ideational content to a large extent is precisely this poorly defined apperceptive mass (C. P. Herbart; see Runes, 1942) of infancy that remains forever in the person's mind.[1] It is as though an infinite number of photographs had been taken, the vast number of which were unfocused, in various stages of infancy and childhood, and only a relative few in sharp focus; these are later superimposed upon earlier fuzzy objects as in a tremendous kaleidoscope.

If unconscious ideation is the history of ideation (that is, if the content of the unconscious is formerly—and poorly—perceived experience),[2] it is already clear that consciousness-unconsciousness must lie on a continuum. Since the ordering of time, place, person, and causality occurs gradually over the years of childhood, it is clear that consciousness-unconsciousness must lie on a similar transitional continuum that is characterized by content from transitional genetic phases and from primary process to secondary process.

In part, the poor Gestalt formation of childhood is presumably due to immature neurological status, and the perceptual progress must then be considered as predicated upon continuing physiological maturation; in part, a learning process of cause and effect, of association, of conditioning enters into the emergence of the rational world of the secondary process.

Every contemporary apperception must be considered as a configuration which is the resultant of many genetic parts. For example, the apperception of a contemporary woman is like a composite photograph into which reality and past apperceptions have merged, as of the mother in many different roles at many different times; of nurses, sisters, grandmothers, and, of course, as is common psychoanalytic knowledge, features of male figures also. The relative influence of past apperceptions upon a contemporary apperception varies from subject to subject and from instance to instance in a given subject. By and large, the less effect past apperceptions have on organizing a contemporary apperception, the more firmly established is the secondary process. Clinical psychologists are well aware of this process: for example, E. H. Weisskopf (1950) has elaborated the "transcendence index" which bears on this issue. She established the fact that different patients will introduce varying percentages of apperceptive distortions beyond the mean number of apperceptions introduced by an experimental population. We know that relatively healthier people do better at "reality testing," that is, they are less influenced by past apperceptions (and drives) than are less healthy ones. Moreover, this particular ego function of reality testing not only varies from person to person, but it may be influenced by fatigue, sleepiness, and drugs. Most interestingly, experiments with perceptual isolation have shown that a lack of external apperception will lead to an emergence of past apperceptions of a primary-process nature. Also, we know that rigid exclusion of past apperceptions from contemporary ones may occur particularly in obsessives, precluding the regression in the service of the ego that Kris (1952) has described as essential to the creative process.

The formal characteristics of the unconscious process are the features of the primary process described by Freud. They are usually referred to as condensa-

---

[1] To be sure, adult perception can also become part of unconscious ideation, becoming aggregated to the earlier apperceptive mass; such adult perception may be originally preconscious as, for instance, in the experiments of Fisher (1954) and Klein (1951).

[2] A variation of David Hume's *"Nihil est in intellectu quid non antea fuerit in sensu"* (there is nothing in the mind which was not previously in the senses), if one speaks of content, not of organic processes or *Anlagen*.

tion, symbolization, and displacement, although on various occasions Freud also referred to other aspects, such as the lack of causality, the lack of references to time, the opposite meanings of one and the same word, and others. Freud's formulations are complemented by the characterization of children's thinking by Jean Piaget (1923) as concrete, syncretic, anthropomorphic, and animistic. Kraepelin (1919), Bleuler (1911), and other psychiatrists described schizo-phrenic thinking in formal terms overlapping in meaning those of Freud and Piaget. Werner (1948) illustrated the formal similarities in the thinking of children, psychotics, and primitive tribes. Many, if not all, features of the pri-mary process can also be observed in oligophrenics. Linn (1953) illuminated the primary-process thinking of patients with brain injury—as Hartmann (1950a) has done previously—a process that often includes the use of *pars pro toto* (the part for the whole) or associative substitution by contiguity or sim-ilarity. Drugs, metabolic toxicity, and perceptual isolation can also produce the same characteristics; whenever ego functioning is poor, the primary process can be observed. Some day it will be possible to write a textbook of human be-havior, including the whole range of pathological variations, from the stand-point of ego functioning and its disturbances; for the present, it still must be emphasized that the same primary process can be observed in a variety of condi-tions. Much of the field has simply not been brought up to date, including the extension of ego psychology to epilepsy and other organic disorders. A differen-tial diagnostic clustering of specific types of primary-process constellations is needed to replace "signs" in clinical and testing practice.

Holt (1956) has most clearly addressed himself to the formulation of the primary process in connection with Rorschach testing. He, too, stresses the idea that thought processes may be arranged from the most primary to the most secondary. Following Freud, he considers thinking to be more primary the more it is organized by and compelled by drives, and the less it is sublimated and neu-tralized. Aside from this characterization, that of preoccupation with instinctual aims, he discusses the formal aspects, including autistic logic, loose types of associative links, and other distortions of reality, in addition to the basic processes of condensation, displacement, and symbolization.

Discussing a continuum of primary-secondary-process thinking, Holt then goes further: he formulates 25 content variables and 27 formal characteristics that he considers indicative of the primary process. The 25 content variables are grouped into ideational and affective drive derivatives with the stipulation that the latter are scored "only in instances where a display of affect occurs in-stead of the response" (Holt, 1956, p. 18). Ideational drive representatives are divided into the libidinal and aggressive, and a residual nonspecific "anxiety or guilt about drive expression." Each of these is further subdivided for the pur-poses of a check list.

Among such formal characteristics as "fusion of two separate percepts"; (as in classical contamination) and "partial fusion of separate percepts," one category deserves particular attention because it enables us to illustrate a basic point; namely, that in the category of image fusion (Holt's term for a condensation manifested in the Rorschach test situation) he describes the fusion of "internal-external views of something," and gives the following example: " 'Could be part of a woman's breast with a bow in between . . . this might be the lungs . . . she might be wearing the bow around her neck.' "

Again, Holt's examples clearly illustrate that in the formal characteristics of the primary process we may recognize the problems a child has in perceiving and organizing the world, including the establishment of the body image, the separation of inside and outside of the self—I and the outer world (Federn, 1952). In this sense, it again becomes clear that the formal aspects of the unconscious that are represented by the characteristics of the primary process contain traces of the gradual organization of experience into what is finally secondary process. It is in this sense that I can understand K. Eissler's statement (1953a) that "with each act of perception ego structure is formed," and that his and my own theories on schizophrenics can be related to these hypotheses.

It is in the nature of the development of any science that there is a good deal of semantic confusion in its early stages. As already indicated, unconsciousness has many meanings; it is necessary to examine two sources of frequent lack of clarity.

The first of the two meanings of unconsciousness, other than the strictly Freudian one, refers to physiological unconsciousness. By that we mean not total unconsciousness, as in a coma, but the unawareness of most vegetative and neurological processes in the individual. For instance, one is not aware of secretion of insulin by the islands of Langerhans, or of the nervous system's neuronal processes. For that matter, gastric or intestinal secretion and motility or cardiovascular, pulmonary, and dermatological processes are accessible to awareness only to the smallest degree, and only to the extent that kinesthetic or proprioceptive data from them can enter consciousness, or to the degree to which these visceral processes are related to the voluntary neuromuscular apparatus. Visceral manifestations may be related directly to the symbolic unconscious process when they are at least partially under the influence of voluntary muscles such as the rectal sphincter or those of respiration. Consequently, it is important to make clear that some physiological processes are "unconscious" in the sense that they never have been conscious, cannot be accessible to consciousness, and are not characterized by symbolic (semantic) mentation in the sense in which the "psychoanalytic" unconscious is so distinguished.

From this it follows that these autonomous processes can be influenced only by their relationship to the cerebral cortex and its symbolic conscious and unconscious processes. We can therefore speak only of an indirect effect of psychodynamic conflicts upon the visceral and circulatory apparatus; the intestine does not express thought content per se, but it may react to thought content in certain rather nonspecific ways.

By virtue of this indirection and related nonspecificity it would be difficult, if not impossible, to conceive of specific neurotic problems or character traits as translating themselves by a one-to-one relationship into such syndromes as hypertension, peptic ulcer, colitis, and dermatosis. Thus, some of the propositions of psychosomatic medicine were probably largely misconceived as specific expressions of unconscious imagery in autonomously functioning parts of the body. These, however, are in principle related neither to imagery nor to verbal thinking. It might be said that some of the early specific psychosomatic propositions advanced were possibly predicated on a mistaken equation of the unconscious in the psychoanalytic sense (of experience which, at least, was once perceived and much of which consisted of imagery related to verbal representation) with unconsciousness (that is, the unrelatedness to and inaccessibility from consciousness) of vegetative autonomic nervous processes.

Much of any learning process is characterized by an increment in performance, the attainment of which itself is not conscious and, for that matter, not accessible to verbal conscious understanding. Take, for instance, the acquisition of expressive or mechanical skills. A teacher of social dancing or automobile driving may need to make his pupil conscious of steps in the learning process, but the result would be poor indeed if some "unconscious" automatization did not take control. The gradual steps of the learning process of any experience merge subtly into each other.

It is this unawareness of the blending of one experience into others to form a Gestalt that is referred to here as "configurational" unconsciousness. In part, it is probably predicated upon neuronal interaction and integration; as such, this process is not of a symbolic nature, and, for the most part, it is not accessible to consciousness or insight on the psychoanalytic couch. If we say that psychoanalytic unconscious mentation consists of data that have passed through the perceptual apparatus at some level of organization in some form and at some time—some of it consciously, some of it preconsciously or unconsciously—we must qualify the statement: each unit, each element of experience has passed through the perceptual apparatus, but the final result, the final configuration of attitudes or object relations, may emerge as a uniquely different whole that never passed through consciousness as such. The process of Gestalt formation is unconscious; this observation is not without clinical significance.

It is likely that some of the merged experiences can be reconstituted into their constituent parts, others cannot. Psychoanalysis as a therapeutic method is, after all, largely predicated upon the proposition that configurations of experience can be "analyzed" or, in other words, reduced to their component parts so that, with the help of the adult ego, they can be "better" reconstituted. In this sense, the accessibility of certain materials and the reversibility of the learning process are crucial problems in psychoanalysis, suggesting its therapeutic limitations; some configurations cannot be successfully reduced to historical component parts because they were obscure (for example, preverbal or overdetermined) or because some memories retain such a decisive organizing effect, have been so thoroughly learned, or have such firm engrams that the present technique of classical psychoanalysis (that is, making the component parts conscious) does not suffice to make them reversible. It is possible that some day certain auxiliary techniques may be devised to enable us to deal with some of these particularly stubborn problems. "Reliving," à la Ferenczi and Sechehaye (1956), constitutes an attempt in this direction (albeit of very limited usefulness) for use in severely regressed schizophrenics, for example. "Fractionated analysis," with "dispersal of training," is becoming more popular without having been given an explicit name as yet; the process simply manifests itself in the higher frequency of second and third analyses. In the long run the interruption of analysis for a year or more may become a specific tool for dealing with personality components that are particularly difficult to reverse.

Forgetting, in many instances, may not be a matter of repression in the usual psychoanalytic connotation, but rather a configurational problem; that is, the merging of figure and ground. One might suspect that the important psychoanalytic concept of infantile amnesia is, to a certain extent, predicated upon an erroneous concept; namely, that of considering configurational unconsciousness and dynamic unconsciousness as identical, the latter, of course, being motivated by the unacceptability to consciousness of certain materials. There is no question that dynamic infantile amnesia of traumatic or unacceptable instinctual material is often important, but I have yet to hear of an analysis that uncovered memories of the normal process of learning to walk! Configurational unconsciousness plays a particularly important role in infancy and childhood because, of course, experiential boundaries of mostly primary or early secondary processes are especially poor. Many clinical analytic attempts to recapture early childhood material probably fail, not because of dynamic interference, but because of the configurational unconsciousness of these poorly defined and merged experiences.

The configurational merging of experiences into the apperceptive mass is the strongest reason for not accepting a traumatic theory of neurosis. The present apperceptive distortion (for example, in a neurosis) is of necessity a function of all past experiences, not of only one.

This fact expresses itself in the clinical psychoanalytic experience that there is no one-to-one relationship between any characteristic of the patient and his experiences, and there may be a relative barrier to insight into the connection between some specific characteristics and earlier experience. Only a few insights relevant to certain analyzed characteristics can be concentrated on and integrated at one time. Fortunately for therapeutic success, restructuration need not be a more conscious process than the original emergence into neurotic configurations. The patient need not leave the analytic couch capable of delivering a dissertation on his psychoanalytic development, as is so often popularly believed.

Previously apperceived experience is accessible not only to psychoanalysis, but also in such clinical procedures as projective testing. The content-analytic techniques employed with the Rorschach and such projected tests as the TAT and the CAT produce data that are comparable to the unconscious and preconscious levels reached in psychoanalysis. Formal analysis of levels of functioning in projective techniques may give insight into autonomous functions not accessible to consciousness. However, it is probably the expressive techniques in particular, such as graphology, the Bender Gestalt test and, especially, Mira's myokinetic psychodiagnostic test (1951) that might reveal unconscious myoneural, constitutional-organizational levels of functioning entirely beyond the reach of consciousness. At least some of this functioning may be "configurational" in an experiential sense and stem from preverbal experience.

The level of unconsciousness of expressive movement has a direct bearing on problems of unconsciousness in relation to artistic talent or other giftedness. It now appears likely that certain gifts originally considered entirely innate may be the results of early variations in ego synthesis. Thus far psychoanalysis has been mainly preoccupied with unconscious content elements of artistic creativity, but it may now be possible to analyze formal and expressive features related to giftedness; these features are specifically the result of synthesis of autonomous functions of the ego, a configurational synthesis that never had conscious representation and, therefore, never appeared as direct psychoanalytic content material and can only be inferred as having taken place by emergence into a Gestalt of units of experiences.

The motivational theory of the psychoanalytic psychology of personality is still often improperly equated with the concept of the id, that is, the instincts or drives. It needs hardly more than a reminder that, of course, psychoanalysis conceives of motivation not only in terms of maturational organismic processes, but also as a series of object-related learned behavior patterns as well as the interaction between biological maturation and environmental experiences at various times. Thus, the psychoanalytic theory of motivation consists not only of the libido theory per se, but also of formulations concerning the ego and superego. Superego forces often motivate behavior; outstanding examples are such pathological conditions as moral masochism, the success neurosis, and a host of other normal and pathological circumstances.

Freud himself formulated some relationships between his topographical model of the systems—unconscious, preconscious, and conscious—and his structural model of ego, id, and superego. It is generally agreed that not only the id but many functions of the ego and superego must be considered as unconscious. Indeed, it might be best to say that in general, all functions as processes per se are unconscious. It is the results of ego functioning of which we are aware, strictly speaking. Only in rare instances, as in a hypercathexis of thinking in the obsessive or schizophrenic, for example, is the process itself conscious.

It would probably not be amiss to say that psychoanalysis sees the roots of all motivations as unconscious. When one speaks of instincts or drives as unconscious, it would be well to remember that drives or instincts are processes that are unconscious not in the strictly psychoanalytic sense but rather in the physiological sense mentioned, and for the most part not accessible to consciousness. The unconscious, in the psychoanalytic sense, may refer to the aims, nature of objects, or the motives for modes or preferences of zones of stimulation. These roots may be related to the drives themselves (the original concept of the id as an "energy reservoir") or to the functioning of the ego and superego.

A major conceptual problem in psychoanalytic theory arises when one considers the relationship of unconscious motivation to conscious behavior. Traditionally, determinism has been the guiding principle of motivational psychoanalytic theory. The proposition holds that free association will unfailingly provide the links between conscious mentation and behavior on the one hand, and unconscious motivation on the other, provided there is no undue interference with free association by insurmountable anxiety, inhibition, or lack of motivation for surmounting the resistance to free association.

The psychoanalytic concept of determinism as originally formulated by Freud is one of those tenets that have so far remained virtually unchanged. This is the more surprising in that determinism is one of the concepts most clearly anchored in the scientific tradition of the end of the nineteenth century. It implies a concept of causality that sets rather rigid links in a chain of events, as is shown in the clinical attitude of the orthodox psychoanalyst who assumes that if the patient will only free associate and the analyst interpret it, "it will all come out in the wash."

The fact is that many analyses end in what Glover (1955) calls a stalemate; undoubtedly they do so for many reasons, but one might suspect that a good percentage of them do not end optimally because of poor strategic and tactical planning on the part of the analyst. Orthodox analysis, by and large, frowns on such mapping out because it seems governed by too mechanistic a concept of cause and effect. But when applied to cause and effect in human behavior and to the relationship between unconscious and conscious variables, the probability theory is likely to be a more useful model than is classical determinism.

Why should this be so? To begin with, the theory of free association as a link between unconscious and conscious processes would be on a sounder basis if we stated, with a specific estimate of probability, that we expect certain events to lead to certain other events, or that certain currently observed phenomena have a highly probable relationship to certain historical events. Psychoanalytic theory is thereby brought up to the level of the rest of contemporary scientific methodology, and may more easily avail itself of the advantages of statistical procedures, as Chassan (1956) has pointed out. All statistics are, after all, predicated upon the theory of probability. In connection with certain past work that some of my colleagues and I have done, described in Chapters 8 and 14, it has seemed entirely feasible to apply to psychoanalytic propositions the method of statistical prediction customary in all the rest of science. Meehl (1954) has discussed the general problems of clinical and statistical predictions; I, for one, see no difference whatsoever between the two forms.

Application of probability theory to the psychoanalytic concept of motivation may have useful implications for psychoanalytic practice. It implies that the analyst may have to be systematically active to bring about certain effects, more active than he feels is desirable on the basis of his general theory. I believe that it makes untenable the concept of a rigidly followed classical procedure and militates strongly for the considered introduction of parameters, to use Kurt Eissler's (1953b) term for variations in analytic technique. Although I favor the use of parameters, I also wish to align myself clearly with Eissler's strict rules concerning the justification of the introduction of parameters. I do not believe that the probability theory gives one a brief for wild psychoanalysis, or anything but the most careful procedure. On the other hand, I do believe that realization of the shortcomings of the concept of determinism (as an example of the theory of causality of classic physics) may lead to explicitly stated variations of psychoanalytic technique.

If the probability theory suggests relatively more active behavior on the part of the analyst (that is, behavior designed to increase the probability of a predicted therapeutic effect), it may be entirely true that the analyst becomes less of a detached observer than he used to be. The myth that he is such an observer has, I believe, been abandoned by nearly everyone. "Participant observer" is probably the most felicitous term (although undoubtedly the participation is overdone by some analysts because of a lack of proper theory or discipline). Nevertheless, the idea of the analyst's being simultaneously effective as therapist and as scientist is certainly a fallacious one. If the analyst is really primarily an observing scientist, he may have to forego intervention for the sake of research. To be a therapist means to be an applied scientist, a professional with a task to perform on an already primarily established empirical basis.

Certain dynamic and energic-economic propositions are inextricably tied to the psychoanalytic concept of the unconscious: for instance, the beliefs that certain drives and feelings and perceptions may become unconscious after having reached consciousness, that some psychic elements may be "kept" unconscious, that unconscious elements may become conscious, wholly, in part, or in the form of a derivative and, further, that energy exchanges are involved in these processes. Unconscious psychic elements can be cathected, and countercathexes keep them from becoming conscious. If unconscious elements become conscious, energy reallocation takes place (for example, symptom laughter). A corollary hypothesis states that the cathexes and ideas in the secondary process are firmly bound together, while, in the primary process, idea and percept are loosely cathected, and cathexis and idea are easily separated from each other, making for the typical Alice-in-Wonderland confusion of ideas and their values. These parts of theory and modes of energy relate to important propositions, notably those of Hartmann (1950a) and of Kris (1955), concerning neutralization and sublimation.

In a theory as closely knit as Freud's theory of personality it is always difficult to discuss any part of the theory without either hopelessly losing one's specific point in a general discussion or without doing violence to it by oversimplification or excessive extrapolation. I shall attempt to solve this problem by presenting the nature of the general propositions in the barest outline and then enlarging on some more relevant aspects.

The Freudian model of energy can probably be characterized as a quasi-open system.[3] Libido itself is the system's form of energy and its cathexes in various libidinal zones, aims, and objects (and the countercathexis in the defensive system) are a fundamental part of psychoanalytic theory and practice. Each person seems to have a certain amount of energy, to which the law of conservation of energy seems to apply. If libido is withdrawn from one area the psychoanalyst asks himself whither it has been diverted, or in what way reinvested, topographically and structurally. We must ignore, for the moment, the fact that not only are different qualities of energy postulated, but also different modes of energy, such as free, lightly bound, strongly bound, sublimated, and neutralized modes in different degrees.

------

[3] I prefer to call it a quasi-open system because it only appears that cathexes are really placed on external objects. Actually, the investment of libido is made in the internal object representations. Even if someone should not agree to this point, it is obvious that cathexes are rather temporarily placed, and can be withdrawn or redistributed. The conceptualization of countercathexis, of hypercathexis of one person or one function *at the cost of* hypocathexis of some other person or the self (as in love) is predicated on the economy of a closed system; this is also true of the transformation of energy into a neutralized or sublimated form and the concept of deneutralization. The death instinct, with its conceptual relationship to the second thermodynamic law, was one possible exception to Freud's model being really a closed one. An argument can be made for calling the Freudian energic model a quasi-closed one rather than a quasi-open one; there are merits on both sides, but because I believe that it is the object representations that are cathected, I prefer to describe it as quasi-open.

The concept of repression may provide us with the simplest and at the same time the most important example of dynamic and economic aspects of unconsciousness. Brenner (1957) has extensively reviewed Freud's varying concepts of repression. The physical analogy suggested by the concept of repression is that some surface object is submerged in water and that it takes some energy to submerge it and to keep it submerged: when the countercathexis is removed, the repressed material comes to the surface like a cork, with concomitant disturbances in the surroundings. The submarine area corresponds (in our very simplified analogy) topographically to the unconscious, the surface to conscious mentation, following the characteristics of the primary and secondary processes, respectively.

Corresponding to the change of fashion in physical models, the contemporary tendency is to see a defense such as repression less in terms of hydrodynamics and more in electronic terms of computers and scanning. Linn (1954) discusses the discriminating function of the ego in these terms. He formulates the hypothesis that the ego recognizes a stimulus in two operations: first, it focuses attention on the appropriate cluster in the psychic apparatus, and then it scans the cluster for further yes-no decisions until it settles on the appropriate one. In effect, the ego matches up the presenting stimulus with a series of memories until it arrives at the one that corresponds best to the stimulus. Although Linn then discusses defects in the scanning of the cluster's individual elements in brain disturbances, we may turn to another aspect of his paper. He links the scanning operation to the motivational theory of psychoanalysis by hypothesizing that the scanning process "turns first to those elements in the cluster capable of evoking the greatest pleasure, then to those elements associated with less pleasure, and finally to those which evoke anxiety. Indeed, if an element is capable of arousing a quantity of anxiety intolerable to the individual, it may be skipped completely by the scanning process. In that case, we say the element in question has been repressed."

Linn's formulations are internally consistent with the current perceptual orientation of dynamic psychology, and to some extent are amenable to experimental verification. Sanford (1936) performed some of the earliest tachistoscopic experiments on the influence of hunger on perception. Levine, Chein, and Murphy (1942) showed that food-deprived subjects not only saw food where there was none (as Sanford had illustrated), but also recognized correctly food depicted tachistoscopically more often than did nondeprived subjects—their scanning was more efficient. Later, others showed that stimuli with a positive cathexis needed shorter tachistoscopic exposure than stimuli without it. The experiments of Klein (1951), Fisher (1954), and others have highlighted the sensitivity and intricacy of preconscious scanning.

Linn suggests solving the economic-energic problems of consciousness-unconsciousness by a neurophysiological model suggested by Pitts and McCulloch (1947), wherein a volley of afferent impulses may pass a synapse depending on the intensity of the elements of the afferent impulse and the frequency with which the critical synapse is fired by simultaneous impulses from the scanning circuit. Linn (1954) hypothesizes that the intensity of the elements of a volley is a function of the cathexes of ideas.

Linn (1954) concludes that brain injuries may be understood as impairments of the discriminating function because the organic scanning functions are disrupted. I suggest that scanning may be poorly performed on a psychogenic basis if scanning was never properly learned. In this sense, I relate scanning ability to reality testing. A child consistently exposed to the confusion of incorrect information and inconsistent reward and punishment learns to scan but poorly. From another viewpoint, one might say that the child's clusters and the elements within the clusters do not have good boundary lines, are not good Gestalten and, therefore, are poorly scanned; that is, they are brought into imperfect relationship with the already poorly apperceived contemporary stimulus. In addition, we may remember that an overstimulated child (and the later adult) will have excessive cathexis in some elements, with a poor hierarchy of cathexis in general; ego psychology, as Holt (1956) points out, is also predicated upon a complex hierarchy of relatively stable, sublimated, and neutralized object relationships. The orderly selection of choices is also impaired by excess drive discharge (as in acting out, for example, or infantile psychotic behavior).

The perceptual model of selective scanning predicated upon neuronal activity permits one to relate observed psychoanalytic phenomena of consciousness and unconsciousness to experimentally observable data of the physiological processes of visual perception and auditory stimuli.

However useful this model may be for the understanding of certain aspects of repression, it leaves much to be desired for the understanding of empirically observed and even experimentally substantiated phenomena posited by psychoanalysis. As we have previously stated, there seems little doubt that the "lifting" of a repression may cause "symptom laughter," or "symptom crying" during analysis; no better hypothesis has replaced Freud's conceptualization of wit, humor, and the comic. If the electronic model is to maintain itself, it must accommodate these phenomena within its framework. It may be possible to relate the quasi-open energic model of psychoanalysis to a finite number of electric elements of the nervous system, and both to the interchangeability of symptoms so often observed clinically; that is, to the disappearance of subjective anxiety in connection with the emergence of vegetative disturbances or the replacement of a conversion symptom by an obsession.

Quite problematical are the defense mechanisms which are more complex than repression, e.g., projection—a process by which drives, feelings, and thoughts can become unconscious by a process that itself is unconscious. This is further discussed in Chapter 11.

3

FREE ASSOCIATION: THE CORNERSTONE
OF PSYCHOANALYTIC TECHNIQUE

As this chapter makes clear, the concept of free association formed a bridge between academic psychology and psychoanalysis. Prior to Freud, the laws of association were considered to be the laws of thinking. Once free association became part of analytic technique, its rationale was greatly expanded and it was observed—largely because of the loss of reality imposed by the analytic situation—that a wide variety of associations had nothing to do with normal thinking. It also became apparent, as this chapter makes clear, that the patient not only generates linked ideas, but he can also look back on what he has said and arrive at an over-all understanding of it. Both activities have come to be expected in the clinical situation, and if either is absent for very long, the patient is not working in optimum fashion. Further experience in the analytic setting has made it clear that free association is more honored in the breach than in the observance, and that when the patient can freely associate and reflect on his associations, he is usually close to the end of treatment. By the same token, disturbances in the associative process are to be expected and, in fact, constitute one of the major diagnostic indices used by the analyst. It is only at the end of treatment—as it should be—that this tool is taken away from him.

A key concept in this chapter is the oscillating function of the ego. It is seen as underlying the dual role of the patient just described, enabling him at times to associate freely without explicit direction or control, and at other times to synthesize his ideas and look back over what he has said. To the extent that similar oscillations are seen in the creative process, there is reason to see free association as less ordinary and more demanding than is usually assumed; it clearly goes some distance beyond Freud's "passenger-in-the-train" analogy. Changes in state of consciousness are also implicated; the patient's mode of thinking and feeling when he is reporting can be quite different from what it is when he is synthesizing.

Not discussed here but worth further consideration is the oscillation on the part of the analyst, and the problems that arise when patient and analyst are out of phase. Difficulties of understanding are one clear consequence of this asynchrony; another may be a subtle kind of reinforcement in which the patient turns to the mode of speaking that the analyst "hears" best, with the result that other aspects of free association are severely curtailed. Ideally, the analyst must oscillate in phase with the patient, lagging just enough behind to follow his lead.

FREE ASSOCIATION IS THE BASIS of psychoanalytic technique and the main instrument of psychoanalytic research. It is, in fact, known as the "fundamental

NOTE: From the *International Journal of Psychoanalysis*, 1961, 42, 9-20. Reprinted by permission of the publishers.

rule"; nevertheless, literature dealing with it is scanty and a systematic meta-psychological consideration is nonexistent.

The concept of association is defined in a recent psychological dictionary (English and English, 1958) primarily as follows: "a functional relationship between psychological phenomena established in the course of the individual experience and of such nature that the presence of one tends to evoke the other; or the establishing of such a relationship; or the process whereby the relationship is established.—*Syn.* **Connection.**"

The history of the concept of association is a long one. Aristotle, in his discussion of logic, was the first to speak of associations and to formulate laws governing the interrelationship of associative elements (association by identity, similarity, and contrast). Associations played a primary role in the English school of sensualism and in what Boring (1950) calls British Associationism; Hobbes (1588-1678) is generally considered the first to deal with them, followed by Locke, Hume, Berkeley, James Mill and his son, John Stuart Mill, Thomas Brown (see Wyss, 1958), Hartley, Bain, Spencer, and finally, Brentano, Galton, Herbart, Lipps and nearly all modern psychology in the wake of Wundt and Freud.

The so-called "sensualist" school considered *sensory* impressions to be primary data which were registered on an innately blank mind. *Nihil est in intellectu quod non antea fuerit in sensu* was superimposed on Locke's concept of the *tabula rasa.* Associations were the building blocks (content), and their laws constituted the formal characteristics of the mind. For example, Boring traces in detail the emergence of the concept of association, from a rather mechanistic level to an holistic one, which relates significantly to today's perceptual theory of personality as well as to learning theory. The younger Mill formulated the laws of frequency and intensity, still basic to conditioning theory; he held that frequency and intensity of repetition bring about associative coupling.

The analytic history of association interrelates with pre-Freudian interests. It is not generally recognized how many of these academic association laws are implicitly part of psychoanalytic theory: suffice it to point out here that the psychoanalytic theory of personality and of neurosis is heavily predicated upon the "law of primacy"—that early "associations," early learning experiences, have a particularly stable character and have a greater organizing effect on the adult personality than events experienced later. Academic American psychology confuses many outside its ranks by referring to all experiential data as "learned"; however, this is a useful term, since it automatically subsumes all experiencing under some potential lawfulness. "Phase specificity," a term brought into prominence by Hartmann, Anna Freud, and others, and particularly stressed in the discussions at Arden House (Hartmann, 1950b), concerns a hypothesis that associations and experiences (e.g., certain parental attitudes) at a particular time of childhood development may have an especially profound effect on personality structure and thus on future perception and behavior.

Boring's account includes only scant reference to Freud; his statement is usefully supplemented in that respect by Wyss (1958), who discusses the philosophical background of association in relation to psychoanalytic theory. He traces Freud's concept of association in "The Aetiology of Hysteria" (1896) and points out that in *The Ego and the Id* (1923) Freud seems to subscribe to a sensory viewpoint, since he relates all knowledge to previous perception. Wyss points out that Freud, in a later discussion of wit, uses Wundt's concept of external and internal associations, implying that "internal" coupling of associative material may take place independently of original perceptual history. Wyss believes that the discrepancy in Freud's thinking of sometimes accepting a straight sensory orientation and at others subscribing to elements independent of external experiences is due to his being influenced by historical trends: the school of associations as well as the school of act psychology. While association psychology was concerned with the lawful nature of the content of the mind, act psychology found "imageless thought," the mental "set" or *Aufgabe* most relevant to psychological acts or behavior. Of course, the two approaches do not mutually exclude each other, despite heated discussions at the time. Wyss particularly emphasizes the fact that Freud was familiar with Lipps' work, and feels that the latter might have had some influence. He also wonders whether Freud had any contact with Brentano, who also lived and taught in Vienna at the time, publishing his *Psychologie vom Empirischen Standpunkt* in 1874. Zilboorg has pointed out that "It has been established that Freud, when a student at the University of Vienna, knew Brentano, who introduced him to Gomperz, who in turn asked him to translate the twelfth volume of John Stuart Mill into German" (1952).

Wyss touches briefly upon the relationship between act psychology and Gestalt psychology and its relation to the concept of free association or association as a foundation of psychoanalytic theory. He does not seem to recognize that the concept of condensation in dream work (which he discusses in this context) is indeed a Gestalt concept; and that, in fact, the idea of displacement, by its very nature, involves a proposition concerning the effect of Gestalt formation in a dream. The role of configurationism implicit in Freud's theories may well call some day for a separate investigation.

Wyss discusses usefully the conflict between the automatism implicit in the mechanistic notions of associations and the conceptual act psychology. We have to remember that the concept of "act" is closely related to the concept of "determining tendency" and to that of *Aufgabe* or "mental set." He points out that Freud knew that so-called "free" associations were influenced by unconscious goal ideas. He states that one may speak of "free associations" only in the sense that the patient attempts to give up *conscious* control of thought so that unconscious goal ideas may be revealed.

In passing, Wyss brings out that even the term "analysis" conveys the historical anchor of Freud's thought: his search for elements, for building bricks; and that, owing to this, he was less concerned with synthesis. A certain inattentiveness in psychoanalytic theory and practice to the process of therapeutic change is related to this historical aspect of psychoanalysis; much thought has been given to the analysis of contemporary distortions by developmental constituents, but much less thought to the optimal formation of new concepts—the optimal production of synthetic therapeutic change. The therapeutic result is still widely considered the "automatic" by-product of analysis, and it is often considered heretical or demagogical to view it otherwise. Yet this attitude seems but a conceptual misunderstanding born out of the history of psychoanalysis and the admirable "libertarian" concept underlying the psychoanalytic therapeutic process (see Zilboorg, 1952). Hartmann, in 1926, discussed free association as "a tool for the broadening of consciousness and as an opening of the road leading to the reintegration of the ego." Zilboorg then traces the development of the method, through Freud and others.

Aside from a discussion of the background already mentioned in connection with Boring and Wyss, Zilboorg stresses the central role of free association in psychoanalysis and the consequent need to understand this role better. Both he and Jones (1953, p. 246) refer to Wilkinson and also to Schiller's correspondence with Körner as well as to the essay by L. Börne on "The Art of Becoming a Writer in Three Days" (". . . . write down, without falsification or hypocrisy, everything that comes into your head . . . you will be amazed what novel and startling thoughts have welled up in you."). Zilboorg and Jones feel that these works might have suggested to Freud that free association was possibly a basic tool for psychoanalysis. Zilboorg, in addition, extensively cites Francis Galton's experiments. These were published in 1879 in *Brain,* and dealt with free association; Galton (1879) concluded that " 'associated ideas' lay bare the foundations of man's thoughts . . . with more vividness and truth than he would probably care to publish to the world . . . and the valid reason they afford for believing in the existence of still deeper strata of mental operations, sunk wholly below the level of consciousness which may account for such mental phenomena as cannot be otherwise explained."

Jones says: "There can be no exact date for the discovery of the 'free association' method. All we can say is that it evolved very gradually between 1892 and 1895" (1953, p. 242). Attempting to indicate the evolutionary stages of the method which followed hypnosis, Jones notes that Fräulein Elisabeth von R., whose treatment Freud undertook in the fall of 1892, was the first patient on whom he used a "concentration technique." "The patient, lying down with closed eyes, was asked to concentrate her attention on a particular symptom and to try to recall any memories that might throw light on its origin" (p. 243). Here, we have evidence that Freud applied what is usually called "controlled associations," a method still used by psychoanalysts, as, for example, when a patient is asked to associate around a specific detail of a dream, some parapraxes, affect, or transitory motor symptom. Freud at that time, however, still urged the patient to associate and felt that he might help by touching her forehead with his hand.

The most significant steppingstone toward making association somewhat freer was arrived at when Freud urged Fräulein Elisabeth von R. to ignore all censorship and to express every thought. In addition, when she reproved him for interrupting her flow of thought with his prompting and questioning, he was able to move still closer to free association, though he did not abandon hypnosis entirely until 1896. The technique of keeping the eyes closed was given up in 1904; controlled associations, however, with the symptoms as a starting point, were retained, "and this habit was reinforced when it became a matter of analyzing dreams, since here one mostly has to start from point after point in the dream" (Jones, 1953, p. 244).

Apart from reference to free association in the *Studies on Hysteria* (Breuer and Freud, 1893-1895), Freud also mentioned it in his "Autobiographical Study" (1925a), in "The Aetiology of Hysteria" (1896), the "Papers on Technique" (1911-1915), "Negation" (1925b), *The Interpretation of Dreams* (1900), *Totem and Taboo* (1913), *The Ego and the Id* (1923), *Inhibitions, Symptoms and Anxiety* (1926), and other works.[1]

The *analytic concept* of free association was originally closely related to the early topological model. In its simplest form, it posited that repression of traumatic events is the cause of neurosis. It was in this context that the "basic rule" was substituted for hypnosis, as a superior tool for arriving at the original therapeutic goal of filling in gaps in childhood memories.

Certain technical problems of psychoanalysis today, notably those concerning patients with other than classical psychoneurosis, are in large part due to the fact that this concept of the "basic rule" has never been restated; it was designed to meet the foregoing theoretical model. At that time, the only conceivable interaction was for the patient to say everything that ran through his head and for the analyst to interpret the repressed content. The concept of therapeutic effect has vastly changed since then, though it suffers, like most other areas of psychoanalytic thinking, from a lack of explicit statement. We know today that the therapeutic effect involves a complex restructuring of various ego activities aside from those of memory, including a dynamic, structural, and energic change in object relationships via "learning" in the transference neurosis. Correspondingly, the ideas concerning the patient-analyst interaction have changed in practice; this has been succinctly described by analytically trained psychologists, e.g., Strupp (1957), who categorizes statements facilitating communications, exploratory operations, clarification, structuring, direct guidance, etc., aside from interpretive operations.

Free association was further predicated on a concept of strict determinism (particularly evident in nineteenth-century physics); Freud "felt intuitively that there must be some definite agency, even if not evident, guiding and determining the course of these thoughts" (Jones, 1953, p. 245).

The unconscious was a *construct* that bridged the gap between the manifestly irrational and the rational. Free association was seen as the path, at one and the same time, to repressed unconscious content and to genetically important events. A motivational theory and a memory theory implied in these propositions has been developed in more recent years by Rapaport (1942) with the important assumption that an affective factor or underlying striving joins the links of the associative chain.

The "freeness" of association, strictly speaking, referred to the freedom of thought processes from the structuring influence of the analyst and from the conscious interference with these thought processes by the patient.

We recall that the role of the analyst was supposed to be that of a detached observer, the analytic situation nondescript, and the analyst a *tabula rasa*. It seems, however, that a number of variables structure the patient's cognitive field as a matter of routine, and that it will be clinically useful to make these factors explicit.

It is clear that one frequent determinant of our patients' associations is that they come to be helped. For some patients this plays a particularly large role

---

[1] The author is indebted to Henry Hart, M. D., for letting him consult his personally compiled index to Freud's writings.

in the beginning of the analysis; in fact, many "have nothing else to say" once their complaints are stated. We say that they have not as yet learned to free associate, and introduce them to the dissociative process of thinking, self-observing, and reporting simultaneously. A subtle process of guidance sets in, largely not conscious even to the analyst. It is one which the patient might interpret as a "reward and punishment" technique, since the analyst responds to certain types of communication and not to others. These clues, which are part of the rarely defined psychoanalytic technique, soon lead the patient to concern himself with his history. He becomes interested in dreams, looks for common denominators in his behavior and also for transference manifestations. As the analysis progresses, the clues are heavily weighted in favor of associations concerning his childhood.

To a large extent, however, analysis often involves "controlled" rather than "free" association. As previously mentioned, this happens most clearly when the analyst asks what such and such a dream detail or parapraxis suggests to the patient. In such cases the analyst supplies the stimulus for the patient to associate to. Then, too, whenever a theme is worked through, in one session or over several weeks, we have largely dealt with controlled associations. They are in part contingent on an unconscious frame of reference—such as a specific childhood object relationship—and in part the result of the analyst's operations. We find no objection to this procedure. On the contrary, its planned and explicit use may be indicated for more frequent employment than at present, particularly in certain types of analysis or at certain stages of the analysis.

It seems that in the "best working" analytic patients *their personal difficulties remain a constant preconscious organizing factor in* their associations, as compared with those whose associations are indeed "freer," even when without specific recognizable denial or avoidance. It seems as if the relatively healthier patient never quite loses sight of the over-all reality situation, as compared, for instance, with the patient whose anaclitic needs structure his thought processes in such a way as to produce a transference resistance. This latter patient will want real love from the analyst as a real person rather than as an interpolated figure or a transitional object. As a result, he reports thoughts without real interest in insight per se, or without considering them as a tool which both analyst and patient must use in the treatment.

Toward the last third of their analysis, patient and analyst usually develop a sort of shorthand language of their own, one mainly concerned with some outstanding molar problems which they work on with certain minimal references to reality events as starting points.

Be that as it may, these observations are not intended as a critique of analytic procedure: they are stated in the belief that these operational modes are necessary. They need to be stated because they are among the numerous influences brought to bear on the patient's thought processes by every analyst, and it is necessary to delineate the process in an orderly and explicit fashion, so that it can be further elaborated upon as a useful and variable technique. Rather than try in vain to be more "passive," it seems that analysts need to take conscious and planned advantage of the operational variants available to them, and to tailor these variants to the needs of different nosological groups, differing patients, and different stages of the analysis of the same patient.

The insistence upon hypothetically uniform behavior by the analyst does analysis a disservice. The basic rule and the legendary "classical" analysis were predicated on the aforementioned rigid concept of determinism; in essence, the position was taken that as long as the patient associated freely, he would recover his childhood memories, and everything would come out in the wash . . . in due time. This type of analytic attitude is, in fact, opposed to psychological testing prior to analysis, and militates against any attempts to formulate a tentative dynamic picture or a tentative treatment plan; such analysts choose to feel that associations must invariably lead the way, and that a free flow will be interfered with by any preconceived notions. There is, of course, much truth in this position, but also much misunderstanding. With the increased scope of its applicability, psychoanalysis must be accompanied by some systematic technical changes concerning communication between patient and analyst, quite consistent with Eissler's paper on parameters (1953b). I believe that there should not be any variation of any aspect of the technique without good, stringent and clearly formulated reasons. Flexibility should not be mistaken for license or for wild analysis. By the same token, the analyst must have an expectant attitude, he must constantly reformulate his conclusions as the treatment progresses, and keep his intrusion as much as possible to strictly technical operations; he must also have clearly conceived reasons for every interaction. However, he must, in addition, be constantly aware of the fact that associations are not free from external clues, particularly those of a preconscious nature; he must also know that the causal connections are not rigid, but follow the principle of statistical probability—all our hypotheses state, in essence, that there is a greater probability that certain acts will take place than others (Nagel, 1939). His technique may have to increase the probability of certain types of patient behavior to produce therapeutic results rather than stalemates (as Glover calls them). In this sense, psychoanalysts finally have to identify themselves clearly as therapists with a primary interest in the treatment process. This still leaves us ample room for learning more about analysis; in fact we shall probably find out more than when we accept a more passive role.

In an erudite paper on free association, Zilboorg reviews the history of the concept and its central position in psychoanalysis, stating that "its nature is still a mystery" (1952).

Thanks to some propositions advanced by Hartmann (1939) and by Kris (1952), it is possible to shed some light on the process of free association. The structural aspects of this process are characterized by a certain type of ego function, called by Hartmann the self-exclusion of the ego; closely related to this concept is Kris's "regression in the service of the ego." In examining the process involved, and in discussing responses to the Rorschach test and the TAT, I have spoken of this particular ego function as the "oscillating function of the ego," to emphasize the heightened acuity of the cognitive and synthetic functions of such a "regression." Kris has pointed out, for the creative act, an oscillation between regression of the ego and full functioning. We would prefer to say that there is a swing from regression to vigilance of cognitive, adaptive, and synthetic functions. This produces emergent qualities which we know as the creative process (see Chapter 22). Vigilance is a concept formulated by psycho-analytically oriented psychologists and so far not given its deserved attention by psychoanalysis: namely, that in certain circumstances the cognitive functions of the ego are *greater* than normal, as in the experiments with the food-deprived subjects perceiving food more accurately than well-fed subjects, when the need to solve a problem is urgent. In a sense, vigilance is antipolar to some concepts of defensive ego functions.

When patients are asked to free associate, we instruct them, in essence, to decrease their external cognitive functions, to focus on the internal (mostly pre-conscious) stimuli, and to exclude as much as possible the judgmental reality testing: the censoring and orderly secondary-process functions. At the same time, we ask them to report their observations, and at certain times, in fact, expect them to perceive common denominators (in the process of insight).

An elaboration of a Freudian simile concerning free association and the patient-analyst interaction may be illustrative. The patient is told of two men traveling in a railroad compartment; only one, however, can look out of the window. As it happens, the one at the window is unacquainted with the scenery, while the man on the inside knows every detail well. They agree that the window-watcher will call out all that he observes (remaining nonjudgmental, descriptive, and focused on his window scene). The man inside then puts all the information together and concludes that the Gothic steeple, the rivulet, and the dairy farm mean that they are at such and such a place.

This parable is meant to convey a little of the interaction of patient and analyst: the patient calls out the details of his internal scenery and the analyst puts it together. Our patient-window-watcher is, in fact, not only asked to observe and call out, but after a while to take over some of the analyst's synthetic role. Also, in the analytic process, we allow progressively better clues to sharpen and broaden the joint observation; it is as if the first details observed through the window leads the man inside to formulate a certain opinion, which he tests by saying: there must also be a railroad track close by. Very often the patient fails to see the tracks, but comments on a little landing platform which can be seen in a widening of the little river; thus, this intersensual validation leads the analyst to conclude that the patient has arrived at X.

The foregoing, like most analogies, has its limitations: in addition to introducing vigilance, it may be useful to reformulate the concept of regression in the service of the ego, as it involves free association, to involve a *relative* reduction of *certain* adaptive functions, including a reduction of secondary-process qualities; thus, the ability to perceive sharply the boundaries of figure and ground, and to see things in hierarchical, spatial, and temporal relationships, is reduced. The length of time for which this relative reduction takes place varies from occasion to occasion, and certainly from patient to patient.

This first phase is succeeded, or sometimes accompanied in individually differing ways, by an *increase* in adaptive and synthetic ego functioning. In associations as in the artistically creative process, the temporarily decreased boundaries permit fusions of new Gestalten, new emergences or hitherto un-perceived relations between ideational content of different temporal, logical, and other orders; *insight* emerges, partly as spontaneous new wholes, partly by trial and error, as a result of oscillation from regression of certain ego functions to an increase in others. The regression facilitates the new synthesis: it is in this sense that we understand it to be "in the service of the ego."

The regressive process itself involves at least two aspects which are difficult to separate: one is the temporal regression of ego function to levels characteristic of earlier ages—to childhood years when the secondary process was weak and when little order could be made out of the primary data of perception (see Chapter 2). The second aspect is that we deal with a topological regression, from primarily conscious functioning to functioning at the preconscious and unconscious levels; the topological regression of certain ego functions is not only accompanied by a temporal regression of these same ego functions, but also often involves a regression in libidinal zones and modes; this, we have stressed above, is alternated with (and possibly accompanied by) an increase in synthetic and some cognitive ego functioning. Children cannot free associate psychoanalytically because of a lack of development of the self-observing and other aspects of the oscillating function.

To make sure that this is more than playing with words, let us attempt to illustrate its clinical usefulness. The patient who associates well is able to oscillate between reduction and increased adaptive functions while exercising synthetic functioning, and thereby producing new insights, working through and reintegrating previous apperceptive distortions. In certain types of associative disturbances, those found in obsessives for example, the patient presents the analyst with a "travelogue," a faithful account of realistic events, but he does not focus upon internal observation, nor does he regress topologically to preconscious levels or give up his cognitive vigilance. On the contrary, he often increases it, much like the sexually disturbed person who becomes excessively aware of every thought, every feeling, and every action during intercourse—even the ticking of a clock.

In other patients, notably hysterics and borderline psychotics, the regression of ego functioning to preconscious levels and early libidinal stages takes place easily, and the material out of which case histories are made pours forth. Often this regression is neither accompanied nor followed by increased perceptual acuity, and the synthetic functioning which leads to the awareness of new configurations, to insight, is lacking. The observations are faithfully reported but no active second phase of the oscillation takes place.

In fact, for some patients, as we know, the absence in the analytic situation of the customarily structuring stimuli of the social situation seems to make it impossible for them to maintain the secondary processes; the adaptive and cognitive ego functions are so reduced that the patient fails to distinguish the boundaries of the self, and tends toward hallucinatory and delusional experiences. Psychoanalytic experience and theory along these lines has been splendidly supported by a series of experiments dealing with perceptual isolation or perceptual "scrambling," which have also led to the emergence of primary-process features, hallucinatory phenomena, and disturbances in body images (Bellak, 1959).

We shall have occasion to discuss further certain specific disturbances in associating. Suffice it to say here that the cognitive ego participation varies in different normal processes: it is highest in purposive planful behavior; it is least involved in dreams (and psychotic phenomena), though often in varying degrees in one single dream, so that a sequence analysis of the dream content may clearly show varying degrees of drive breakthrough and ego control. Hypnagogic and hypnopompic phenomena are vivid and often frightening experiences of decreased ego control. Brenman (1959) has drawn attention to certain hypnotic phenomena of different stages of ego functioning, when she speaks of "the embellished reminiscence," "the static pictorial image," and the "quasi dream." Next in the series of relative ego participation are Varendonck's type of preconscious fantasies (1921); then, following on the continuum, we have free associating with its relative ego participation, the ordinary daydream with its many realistic features, that type of activity involved in responding to projective techniques (attending to stimulus and yet permitting a controlled flight of fancy, if the subject can function well) and, finally, the purposive planning with maximum ego participation which may also involve occasional regression to allow for creative flexibility of planning.

A few additional topological observations may also be in order. Associating means, by virtue of the regression discussed, a sampling of the nonconscious stream of activity. The role of preconscious functioning has received and is receiving increased attention, e.g., by Fisher (1954). The electronic model of scanning is probably most fruitful for purposes of conceptualizing the selective process, provided the motivational link, by affects, is not overlooked.

Undoubtedly, it is true that associating in the analytic process involves, to a great extent, preconscious thinking; nevertheless, it is obvious that this factor should not be overstressed. It is useful to remember that, by definition, we speak of preconscious processes as those which we are unaware of, but can become rather easily aware of by increased attention. Much associating, however, has its affective and other links well beyond possible conscious awareness, though obviously some derivatives have to become preconscious and conscious for the patient to be able to report them.

From the standpoint of the determining factors of mental processes, dreams as well as associative material, Fisher's extension of Pötzl's work is particularly interesting. Freud had already mentioned the day residue (of the last twenty-four hours) as a shaping factor in dream production, but Pötzl, Fisher, and others working with subliminal stimuli have shown more specifically the process of weaving preconscious material into further products. From the clinical point of view, the analyst's behavior, as a source of preconscious clues, has to be constantly checked. Of relatively minor significance is, for example, the fact that one of my patients became aware that my left foot would flex when I thought she had said something significant; for quite some time this behavior of mine, of which I was unaware, had a certain, presumably preconscious, structuring effect on her. Of considerable importance are the mostly preconscious "guide fantasies" (or *Leitfantasien* as I would rather call them, after *Leitmotiv*) which may either be related to the analyst or constitute independent structures. Behavioral mannerisms are often of this nature.

The *dynamic, genetic,* and *energic* hypotheses of the libido theory are also involved, of course, in a metapsychological consideration of associating. The libido theory encompasses dynamic propositions in that it concerns itself with different drives and their interaction; it involves energic statements in that it speaks of the quantitative difference in a drive push. It constitutes a genetic timetable with regard to the maturational sequence of drive aim, drive mode, and bodily focus of different drive aims at different times; in addition, it adumbrates a complex series of statements constituting a specific learning theory (namely, the effect of certain experiential events at various times, such as weaning, sphincter training, etc.) and the "phase specific" interaction of maturational and learned factors already referred to.

The motivational theory enmeshed in psychoanalytic formulations has still never been stated in an orderly fashion; to be sure, motivational forces pertain not only to drives generally subsumed under the id but also pertain to the motivational functions of the ego ("reality principle" and the related motivations for postponing immediate gratification) and the superego which motivates action in accordance with its "precepts." Associations are evidence of this interplay of motivational forces—e.g., if one studies their sequence (when, for instance, the expression of a drive is followed by limitations imposed by prudence and guilt, which are experienced in some indirect form). Strictly speaking, associations are the manifestations, and often the only manifestations (if action is excluded) of the hypothetical constructs we call id, ego, superego. In this sense we can discuss associations as characterized by the structural source of their motivational origin; the genetic level and the libidinal content (voyeuristic, oral incorporative, etc.) of associations may serve as another classification scheme.

The attitude *toward* associating is often clinically important: for some patients it is a passive process of "letting things come into mind" which may be a pleasurable gift for those with little fear of (oral) passivity, while for other patients, those with marked fears of (anal) passivity, it is a threatening invasion or emergence of (dirty or dangerous) forces beyond control. For one patient, a photographer, the meaning of associating was clearly voyeuristic: in a hypnagogic fantasy, on the analytic couch, after having consciously attempted to get himself to associate "better," he obtained an image of a camera moving in for a close-up. The camera was heavy and on rollers, and it was clearly he who was moving into position as the observer, not as the object of observation. A second patient revealed in a dream that being asked to associate was synonymous with being watched while defecating. She was, understandably, very constipated on all levels of functioning. For yet another, associating was like floating in the clouds in the way he had often let his small plane be carried away by airstreams, after shutting off the motor. Needless to say, the active phase of the oscillating function was in this case in abeyance.

An associative abuse, possibly not recognized often enough, is that of recalling biographical events with considerable narcissistic gratification but without either phase of the oscillating function. Comparing this process with the obsessive's recounting of actual events, one might refer to it also as an "internal travelogue" or "narcissistic reverie."

The *dynamic* problems involved in the defenses are best discussed with other clinical problems. From a motivational standpoint it must suffice here to refer again to Rapaport's discussion of the organizing function of affects (and drives) upon the associative "complex."

The problem of energy exchange in topological changes is most important. Not infrequently patients will break into symptomatic laughing or crying (maybe less often while associating and more often in response to an interpretation) upon arriving at a new insight, or reviving a memory. The problems of conceptualizing this energy exchange from bound to free energy pertain, of course, to a much wider field of concern than associating proper. They belong to core problems of personality theory. These problems have been discussed in relation to neuronal-electronic discharge phenomena by Linn (1954) and myself (see Chapter 2).

The *formal* aspects of associating, unless they involve psychotics, are not usually given much attention in clinical psychoanalysis. This subject, usually studied by experimental psychologists, was as already mentioned, originally the domain of philosophy. Boring (1950) gives a most extensive review of the history of conceptualization of associations.

Psychoanalytic interest lies primarily in the qualities of the primary process and the secondary thinking processes. Condensation, symbolization, displacement, expression by opposites, lack of referents in time, causality, location, and a loose connection between an idea and its "energic charge" are among the most frequently considered formal characteristics of primary thought processes; these may also be manifest during associating in the clinical psychoanalytic situation.

These formulations are largely identical with, though also supplemented by, those of Bleuler with regard to schizophrenics and those of Piaget with regard to the thinking of children. Bleuler's concept of autism adds a concept of the direction of thought processes, while his "looseness of associations" describes the instability or absence of the hierarchical orderliness of the secondary process together with the unstable relationship between manifest idea and affective charge (as witnessed in "inappropriate affect"). Piaget, of course, contributes concretism, syncretic quality, anthropomorphization, animistic tendencies as qualities of some thoughts and associations. From Rorschach and Rorschach test literature come such terms as contamination; many other investigators have contributed various descriptive terms for the formal characteristics of thinking; these, too, are useful in a consideration of associating. For a review of the basic literature we must refer to Rapaport's collection of papers on thinking (1951).

Some clinical problems of associating have been discussed in various theoretical contexts. While it is not feasible to exhaust the possibilities of disturbances in associating, a schematic outline can be given which can encompass all; they can all be studied and described as the result of disturbances in different ego functionings. A list of ego functions might serve as a checklist.

Since we have described the process of associating as being specifically predicated upon the *ego's oscillating function*—the ability to oscillate from regression in the service of the ego (as described by Kris) to a heightened acuity of self-observation—it is reasonable to examine disturbances related to this particular aspect of ego functioning.

A disturbance in the ability to regress in the service of the ego is a normal occurrence for the new analysand who is not an artist or a particularly introspective person; for the new patient "learning" to associate means learning to exercise the oscillating function and, usually, learning the regressive phase first. The regressive phase is typically most difficult for the obsessive-compulsive patient who has a tendency to relate concrete events. In an anxiety state, patients who normally associate well lose the ability to regress, and revert, at times, to simply recounting events. Giving "shallow" associations usually means that the patient offers a rather remote derivative of the thoughts of which he first became conscious, and often the defensive counterpart of thoughts relating to drive expression. In *conscious resistance*, the patient expresses only sections of the chain of thoughts of which he becomes conscious, making it difficult to see the continuity in the thought process, continuity being a factor which makes all insight possible.

In some patients we find an excellent ability to perform the regressive phase of the process, but little talent for the active phase of synthesis. It is in this context, of course, that intellectual limitations may be a handicap, since synthesis requires at times the intellectual ability to see common denominators, which may take the form of syllogistic relations between thoughts and actions. Otherwise, good function in the first phase and poor function in the second is probably found in a good many hysterics, and in the extreme, of course, in schizophrenics. This may be so because the second phase requires activity and *intact* thought processes, but also because the synthetic function in hysterics and in schizophrenics is disturbed. We are talking, so far, primarily of a disturbance in the cognitive synthetic function, though affect can certainly not be left out of consideration.

Speaking strictly in terms of therapy, the synthetic function may sometimes be disturbed in such a way that both associating phases under discussion are well performed; insight is achieved but no stable therapeutic accomplishments have resulted. It seems, in such instances, as if there were not enough "binding" power to attain, or if attained, to *maintain* some stable personality organization. It is in such instances particularly that one symptom is no sooner made to disappear than another arises; we are reminded of Janet's example for psychasthenia—of the woman who had more bundles to carry than she could manage, dropping first one, picking it up, only to lose another; her basket simply did not have the necessary capacity.

A lack of synthetic functioning may sometimes be induced by the analyst who interprets too much for his patient instead of letting the patient arrive at part of the insight himself. The patient is then content to play a passive role; he does not "learn" as well.

A special condition of disturbance in the second phase is probably too often not recognized, owing to the lack of analytic interest in formal thought processes: the patient who, more or less psychotic or severely obsessive, suffers from a concretization of thought processes, with a real semantic disturbance of abstract symbolic thinking. The best interpretations are lost on such a patient. Such concretization occurs frequently in patients with severely hypochondriacal complaints, who use organ language either in psychosomatic or hysterical fashion. The somatic expression of the conflict may well be related to the semantic primitivity of these patients.

A specific type of second-phase disturbance may occur particularly in patients with severe transference resistances: the real preconscious goal of the patient is to win the analyst, rather than to use the analyst as a catalytic agent or as the transitional object of transference neurosis. While the first phase functions well, the patient simply has no interest in synthesis, since the goal is to maintain a symbiotic or anaclitic relationship rather than to improve. Regression and re-porting are really a pouring out, orally or anally, to please the analyst. In these patients particularly, though of course in all patients with a positive transference who have acquired some familiarity with psychoanalysis, we find "courtesy association": things are said which fit well with the analytic textbook but have no real meaning to the patients. The mental set "to please" and "to be liked," rather than the wish for cure, governs the stream of thought. The mental set "to understand" often interferes similarly, as a defense against affect.

The entire psychodynamics of defense mechanisms is, of course, applicable to the associative process. Denial is, in many ways, the most fascinating to watch, and has been most specifically described by Lewin (1950) (for affective dis-orders) by its centrifugal quality. In the same way that one might make in-ferences about the size or weight of an object that causes circles in the water, the analyst has to infer the denied but central thought and affect from the centrifugal thoughts.

It is hardly necessary to discuss the well-known associative disturbance pro-duced by inhibition, repression, emotional isolation, etc.

Certain aids to associating have generally been more appropriate for psycho-therapy than for psychoanalysis. The main objection to hypnosis is predicated, in essence, upon the fact that hypnotic recall permits the first phase of the oscillating function—regression—but interferes with the synthetic and increased cognitive function of the second phase. Recently, analytically trained hypnotists have taken cognizance of this fact by giving their patients the posthypnotic order to recall the hypnotically experienced material in suitable fragments in the con-scious state. In this way, the waking ego may contribute to the function of the second phase.

Oral or intravenous barbiturates have encountered the same justified criticism from analysts; it is my impression though, that, at least in psychotherapy, first-phase facility is possible without significantly affecting the second-phase per-formance if the barbiturates are combined with stimulants, such as desoxy-phedrine; the acuity of the cognitive process, particularly, may be increased while barbiturates facilitate the ability to regress. We generally think of a synergistic action on the ego rather than an antagonistic one.

The combination of psychoanalytic psychotherapy with ECT has been held disadvantageous because ECT either tightens the controls so as to interfere with the first phase, or so affects the synthetic powers that it makes the second phase impossible.

Tranquilizers, like chlorpromazine, may decrease the affective charge enough to permit the patient more phase-one activity without dulling him so much as to make a part of phase-two activity impossible.

4

ACTING OUT: SOME CONCEPTUAL
AND THERAPEUTIC CONSIDERATIONS

The preceding chapter has described the primary investigative method of the analyst: he learns about unconscious mental processes through the unchecked and extended verbalizations of the patient. The present chapter describes another expression of unconscious material, this time represented in activity. The two sets of data—associations and actions—tend to be reciprocally related, for it is clinically assumed that acting out (in the strict sense of the term) reveals what is *not* expressed in the patient's associations.

Several definitions of acting out are supplied in this chapter, ranging from a colloquial use (he is acting out his wish to be loved) to the more technical use of acting out as an expression of transference feelings, usually discharged outside the treatment setting. In the first and more common usage, acting out is frequently made synonomous with drive discharge and tells us little more; in the second sense it has an explicit reference to resistance; the patient is not complying with the "basic rule" of expressing his thoughts in words. In the second sense we expect that the conflicts will eventually be verbalized and analyzed; in the first sense, we are not so sure. We are in a better position to understand the second because it takes place within the analytic setting and often represents a continuation of a theme that has been partially verbalized and understood; we are unable to do more than guess about the dynamics of the first and thus can never say whether it is truly acting out in the sense that the present is being reacted to in terms of the past.

Both kinds of acting out should be distinguished from sheer id activity. As this chapter makes clear, acting out is a carefully orchestrated medley that combines past fantasies with resonating parts of present reality; the parts are skillfully coordinated and extended over time. We are not dealing with a momentary breakthrough of impulse but with a long series of actions that have an impressive internal coherence. Its very complexities make us realize that it is broadly overdetermined; aspects of past fantasy and present reality are combined in the person's characteristic style. The last point is worth additional emphasis. In the midst of acting out, the person is still behaving as we expect him to, in a semipredictable way. Impulsive behavior (when it in itself is not a style of life) frequently takes us by surprise; it is uncharacteristic and represents an uncoordinated breakthrough of drives.

ENGLISH AND ENGLISH (1958) have defined acting out briefly as "manifesting the purposive behavior appropriate to an older situation in a new situation which symbolically represents it." Hinsie and Campbell (1960) have defined it as "the partial discharge of instinctual tension that is achieved by responding to the present situation as if it were the situation that originally gave rise to the

---

NOTE: From the *American Journal of Psychotherapy,* 1963, 17, No. 3, 375-389. Reprinted by permission of the publishers.

instinctual demand." While both definitions are useful, neither fully encompasses the scope of this phenomenon.

CLINICAL VARIETIES

The usage of the term and the concept of acting out in clinical discussions cover a wide range of phenomena. Sometimes the term is used to characterize brief acts of a circumscribed and merely episodic nature; for example, an obese person is sometimes said to be acting out his sense of frustration and his need for gratification by overeating. Of course the dynamics may be much more complex, but the essential implication here is that such a person, feeling frustrated, disappointed, and unloved, translates these usually unconscious feelings into the act of feeding himself. The act of eating symbolically represents the unstated verbalization, "Nobody loves me, nobody feeds me. Therefore I have to feed myself," or "I feel empty, I feel deflated. I wish to have the feeling of being full and solid." It is obvious that drinking may have the same unverbalized meaning. One might say that, in such instances, the *term acting out is used when certain behavior seems to make a simple unconscious statement*. It is this quality of making an unconscious statement that differentiates acting out from other neurotic behavior of a phobic or obsessive nature, as well as the fact that acting out is usually ego syntonic, at least at the moment of action. (Overeating, however, as a simple form of acting out, is often ego alien and may be perceived as compulsive by sophisticated people.)

Another conceptually simple use of the term acting out is frequently encountered in discussions of psychotic behavior. An assaultive attack may be considered as the acting out of delusional and hallucinatory distortions: the behavior is consistent with and caused by the distortions and has little or nothing to do with reality. When we ask ourselves in dealing with psychotics, "Is this patient likely to act out?", we are wondering what the chances are that he will act upon his unrealistic perceptions and impulses. The question is one that has enormous therapeutic and social import, and it is an urgent task that we understand and develop reliable criteria about why certain persons are able to sustain indefinitely paranoid feelings and vicious notions without ever doing harm, and others are sometimes pressed and overrun by similar impulses into the performance of dreadfully destructive acts. Fortunately, only a small percentage of psychotics translate their distorted perceptions into action.

Another rather simple form of acting out is also the classic characteristic of the hysterical personality. What impresses one most strongly about such persons is the tremendous mood swing, from love to hate, from depression to elation, with actions correspondingly extremely different, in rather short time intervals.

In a sense, some of the behavior typical of fugues and multiple personalities belongs in the area of acting out: in these major disassociated states, one split-off part of the personality is permitted to act out ordinarily unacceptable impulses.

Psychopaths or sociopaths, unlike psychoneurotics, are characterized by alloplastic reactions. They tend to translate their conflicts and drives into behavior rather than into the symptoms of the autoplastic neurotic. Addiction, itself a form of acting out, among other things, leads to further acting out under the influence of the drug.

The nuclear concept of acting out, however, may perhaps best be seen in the behavior of often apparently normal people suffering from character disorders who tend to react to certain situations in a stereotyped way. Their behavior patterns do not appear stereotyped to them, but do to the observant onlooker. There are those who act in an inappropriate or ill-advised way as an unconscious invitation for aggression against themselves. There are others who persistently respond pathologically and self-destructively by being greatly attracted to those whose main aim is to exploit them sadistically; there are men and women whose empty promiscuity is an acting out of certain childhood conflicts and frustrations in their lives. It is as if all of these persons, when presented with a certain set of stimuli, responded with a whole sequence of behavior wrongly programed by an electronic computer. Although discordant to everyone but themselves, their behavior is concordant with their unconscious subjective set of realities and therefore does not change with realistic experiences: they do not see a cause-and-effect relationship between their behavior and its manifest results (as they ascribe the results to accident or fate) and therefore do not profit from ordinary learning. In effect, the situation works out entirely as it is supposed to according to the unconscious set, and the defenses make their maladaptive behavior appear appropriate and ego syntonic to them. This clinical situation has often been misconceived as a "repetition compulsion," although there is no more compulsion in it than in any other act related to a mental set. The manifest absurdity of this acting-out behavior makes it appear like a compulsion.

In these character neuroses and the character disorders, the acting out is less episodic, more diffused through the entire "life style." To borrow another useful phrase from Adler, one could say that their character structure evolves around some "fictive, unconscious goal." Similar to the simpler forms of acting out, their entire behavior seems to make a statement, for example, "I am going to be bigger than anybody else," or "I will show everyone what a self-effacing person I am." A special and serious form of acting out in terms of the whole character structure is seen in the so-called fate neurosis or success neurosis: the person always seems the unwitting victim of apparently uncontrollable circumstances, is always disappointed, always fails. Analysis reveals that such person actually constructs his life in order to fail, in order to inflict self-harm, in order to suffer. Like the proverbial *Schlemiel* he always finds a banana peel to slip on, even if he has to place it there himself.

Some people make acting out a style of life by which they become, to some extent, known: for example, the playwright best remembered for his drinking excesses and uninhibited statements, the actress who remains an *enfant terrible* well into old age, the absent-minded professor who actually lives that particular conception of his role.

Another type of personality, related to the one just discussed, but much less well integrated, is the one found in excitable people, who constantly blow off one kind of affect or another, in one form or another: from ticlike twitches to volatile verbal expressions to hasty acts of all kinds. These people's behavior is not identical with the impulse disorder in its usual sense. In the case of the impulse disorder, there are often long quiescent periods, characterized by a seeming calm before the blow-off. The excited person has no quiet period, and acting out is but one of the many overactivities.

It becomes apparent, then, that acting out involves phenomena of somewhat different complexity, different clinical syndromes, and may have episodic or more diffuse temporal characteristics. There is tremendous variation in the extent to which it dominates a personality.

METAPSYCHOLOGY OF ACTING OUT

Freud first mentioned acting out in *The Psychopathology of Everyday Life* (1901), in which he describes various kinds of symptomatic and faulty actions within the range of normal behavior. In his "Fragment of an Analysis of a Case of Hysteria" (1905b), the well-known study of Dora, he refers to her premature termination of her analysis as an acting out of certain childhood recollections and fantasies. In a paper on technique (1914), he uses the term acting out in still a third context, that of its relationship to transference and resistance.

Some time later, Fenichel (1945a) attempted a more systematic discussion of acting out. He describes people in whom

an unconscious misunderstanding of the present in the sense of the past is extraordinarily strong; the patients repeatedly perform acts or undergo experiences, identical or very similar ones, that represent unconscious attempts to get rid of old instinctual conflicts, to find a belated gratification of repressed impulses (instinctual demands as well as guilt feelings), or at least to find relief from some inner tension. For these persons the environment is only an arena in which to stage their internal conflicts. The patients appear as restless, hyperactive personalities, or their activity may be hidden and their life history may give the impression that they are the toys of a malicious fate, the repetitions being experienced passively and rationalized as occurring against the person's will.

Elsewhere in the same volume, Fenichel describes these patients as having an intolerance for tension, as being unable to perform the step from acting to thinking: they exhibit an immediate yielding of reasonable judgment to all impulses. He feels that their aim is the avoidance of displeasure rather than the attainment of pleasure; that oral fixations and early traumata play a significant role; and that acting out is often associated with cyclic moods. He quotes Alexander as stating that this type of problem is closely related to what Alexander first described as "neurotic character."

In another paper (1945b), Fenichel emphasizes that the *quality* of action in itself is especially conspicuous in acting out as compared to other neurotic activity, that it is generally a fairly organized activity and not merely a single movement, gesture, or mimicked expression. Fenichel further characterizes acting out as being ego syntonic, and as being an alloplastic rather than an autoplastic defense: people who act out tend to change their environment rather than themselves, and while their behavior seems appropriate to them, it seems implausible and inappropriate to others.

After reviewing Fenichel, Greenacre (1950) brings forward major considerations of her own. She says that in acting out "there may be special problems in accepting and understanding current reality either because of (1) specific problems in the immediate real situation; (2) special persistence of memories of earlier disturbing experiences; or (3) an inadequate sense of reality. . . . In the case of acting out there is a compulsion to reproduce repetitively a total experience or episode rather than to select some small part of it as a token representation." She notes that acting out is relatively more frequent in persons undergoing analysis, and as such, constitutes a special technical problem. Acting out creates reality situations of a detrimental nature and discharges tensions outside of the therapeutic milieu which makes it impossible to analyze them. She limits her discussion to habitual neurotic acting out which she sees as a selective distortion of reality.

In contrast, she sees psychotic acting out as characterized by a complete taking over of the current situation by early unconscious memories which severely affect reality perception and bar conscious memories and attitudes. She also differentiates "isolated, occasional, really symptomatic acting out during the course of analysis from those conditions in which the acting out is frequent, habitual, or characteristic of tendencies evident in the entire life of the patient." According to her, "the impulsiveness is based on an inability to tolerate frustration, a special disturbance of reality and of self-criticism, the quality of marked motility or activity often of a dramatic character—all especially characteristic of the extremely severe neuroses, which sometimes appear perilously close to psychoses and the psychopathies."

Both Greenacre and Fenichel consider part of the genesis of habitual acting out an oral fixation, a great narcissistic need, an intolerance of frustration, a constitutionally heightened motility, and the presence of severe early traumata which cause repetitive abreactive acting out similar to that found in the traumatic neuroses. Greenacre, however, adds a special emphasis of visual sensitization which produces a bent for dramatization (she sees it as related to exhibitionism and scoptophilia), and an unconscious belief in the magic of action. She thinks that the need for dramatization may be crucial in converting plain neurotic action into acting out. She feels that the important role of acting out is due to disturbances of the development of speech in the second year. When such is the case, motor action is used to take over some of the communicative functions. She feels that this also accounts for the prevalence of body language in people who act out. The capacity to verbalize and to think in verbal terms (which she sees as having an important function in the integration of emoinadequate ability to organize and control emotion results.

In order to discuss acting out more systematically, it may be useful to consider it genetically, dynamically, adaptively, structurally, economically, and tions with appropriate thought content) is interfered with and therefore an topographically, even at the risk of being repetitive.

GENETIC ASPECTS

Fenichel says that oral fixations and marked traumatic experiences play a large role in this phenomenon. Greenacre adds that difficulties in the second year of life, specifically interference with speech development and compensatory motility as a substitute for verbal communication, also play a part. She considers visual sensitization, which may derive from exhibitionism and scoptophilia, as producing a bent for dramatization and an unconscious belief in the magic of action. *Expression* of impulse and emotion rather than *organization* carries over into the secondary process.

I believe that multiple diverse identification coupled with a lack of synthesis of ego nuclei also play a role. Some patients intermittently act out highly diverse roles which seem patterned on identification with one or the other parent. Low frustration tolerance, which is also considered as a dynamic aspect of acting out, is frequently related to a developmental interference: inconsistent rearing, overindulgence, insufficient discipline, general overcharging with sexual and aggressive impulses (beyond those specifically mentioned by Greenacre) predispose to low frustration tolerance and acting out.

Blos (1962) discusses acting out in the adolescent as operating in the service of ego synthesis as a phase-specific mechanism. He states that "the adolescent process proceeds from a progressive decathexis of primary love objects through a phase of increased narcissism and autoerotism to heterosexual object finding." He goes on to say that these changes are "accompanied by a profound sense of loss and isolation, by a severe ego impoverishment which accounts for the adolescent's frantic turn to the outside world, to sensory stimulation and to activity." In the sense that action and motion are normal adolescent means for resisting the surrender to primal passivity, "action assumes the quality of a magic gesture: it averts evil, it denies passive wishes, and it affirms a delusional control over reality." Still discussing normal adolescent development, Blos says "the adolescent process can be accomplished only through synthesizing the past with the present and the anticipated future . . . [through] constantly striving to bring the past into harmony with the terminal stage of childhood, with adolescence. Is it surprising to find among the instrumentalities of remembering the one called acting out?"

In the more diffuse type of acting out a much broader genetic basis than the ones mentioned so far needs to be considered. In such persons' lives, we find not the subtlety of mere visual sensitization described by Greenacre, but a general overstimulation and sensitization for all stimuli—in the sense of a much lowered threshold for both input and output. It may be that the concept of lower stimulus barrier advanced by Bergman and Escalona (1949) describes some congenital differences. More often, such people seem to have been exposed to tremendous overstimulation of nearly all sense modalities, starting out with a mother with hypermotility during rocking and nursing and continuing into frequent exposure to aggressive and sexual stimulation. Much as I believe that an infant needs a certain amount of sensory input for development (best conceptualized by means of Magoun's concept concerning the function of the ascending reticular system), it also seems that a "system" may get a permanent overload; such a person then has a lifelong excessive stimulus hunger, matched only by the inability for containment and the constant need for discharge.

DYNAMIC ASPECTS

Both Fenichel and Greenacre agree that the acting-out person inappropriately permits past experience to dominate his perception of contemporary stimuli. The more rigidly such distortions occur and the broader the scope of contemporary stimuli so affected, the more serious is the condition.

Some authors have discussed the defensive aspects of acting out as a cathartic and abreactive experience: the patient blows off steam and reduces the tension. Sometimes acting out, even when violent or self-harming, wards off the more anxiety-laden feeling of depersonalization (see Chapter 5). The defensive function of acting out lies in keeping certain forms of behavior ego syntonic with the help of denial and repression. Jacobson (1957), writing on denial and repression, says that the resistance against remembering effected by acting out constitutes a form of denial. "Acting out," Jacobson says, "appears to be regularly linked up with a bent for denial." "That this persistent denial goes hand in hand with a distortion of reality is borne out convincingly by patients of this kind. The function of acting out is denial through action; the magic of action and of gesture appear in such cases in great clarity."

In the very complex forms of acting out, though, as in character neuroses, I would think that repression also plays a large role. The complex forms of acting out may be highly overdetermined, and unconscious (not preconscious, as in denial). One sequence of patterns is actually designed defensively to counteract another sequence of behavior patterns; a series of masochistic and passive seductive acts may be followed consistently by active sadistic reactions, and vice versa.

An interesting proposition, although in part a genetic one, deserves some thought. Fries and Woolf (1953) have suggested that there are definite congenital activity types, and that the more active type may be predisposed to a choice of alloplastic rather than autoplastic defenses. One wonders, then, if some of the dynamic determinants of acting-out behavior might not be predicated on a congenital basis.

As yet, we have no information on the possible relationship of *imprinting* to acting out and other forms of character development. Very likely, this discovery of the ecologists will play a significant role in future psychological considerations.

ADAPTIVE ASPECTS

Sometimes acting out which is not directly in the interest of the person may have certain social advantages. Revolutionary behavior, which may contain instances of individual acting out, is an example. Needless to say, when individual acting-out features become predominant, the "cause" suffers by hindrance of realistic goals.

Blos (1962) has pointed out the adaptive aspects of acting out specific in adolescence.

A controlled use of acting out is not infrequent among actors, perhaps especially among "method acting" devotees. The relationship between dramatic acting and acting out may account for the higher incidence of this phenomenon in the theatrical world. The same features of dramatization, scoptophilia, and exhibitionism that Greenacre mentions as being related to a tendency to act out are also related to dramatic performances on the stage. Depersonalization, often related to acting out, is met among theatrical people: some actors feel "real" only when acting on the stage and feel depersonalized at other times. Such people have a tendency to carry over stage roles into real life. On the other hand, certain highly type-cast performers, for example, the villain, the tough guy, the milksop, often portray only those roles which they act out in real life.

STRUCTURAL ASPECTS

A lack of fusion of ego nuclei has been mentioned from a genetic standpoint. In acting-out persons, it is often as if the left hand knew not what the right hand was doing. The actions of the one bear apparently little relationship to those of the other. Indeed, it is almost as if one were dealing with different persons at different times. A deficiency in the synthetic function of the ego seems crucial.

Other ego functions are involved in the poor impulse control, low frustration tolerance, and poor reality testing which are all integral aspects of acting out. An inability to attain object constancy, or a reasonable degree of sublimation and neutralization also play a major role. The logic implicit in secondary-process functioning and the detour behavior which is essential in the hierarchical relationships of goals are other structural defects related to acting out.

ECONOMIC ASPECTS

Fenichel and Greenacre have pointed out the general role of narcissism in acting out. Action is overinvested in acting out: it has magic connotations, subjective symbolic meaning, and thus remains highly personalized and noncommunicative; the statement the acting-out person seems to convey fails in its communicative purpose by virtue of the highly subjective nature of the expressed act. Along with the narcissistic overinvestment of certain ego functions including those of action and motility, there is also often a narcissistic overinvestment of the self.

TOPOGRAPHICAL ASPECTS

Complex acting out is usually largely unconscious. In those instances where it is part of rapidly fluctuating hysterical behavior or of a brief episodic nature, it is preconscious, with denial related to the instability of the performance. A combination of preconscious denial and unconscious repression plays a role in the immediate triggering and in the basic "programing," respectively.

SOCIOLOGICAL ASPECTS

It is frequently overlooked that the manifest form which acting out assumes is often determined by cultural milieu, social factors, and other contemporary determinants. Certainly metapsychological considerations determine the predisposition and potentiality for acting out, yet social factors may be critical with regard to the form it follows or even to its actual emergence. Drug addiction may be the symptom of choice among the Spanish population in New York City, alcoholism among the Irish. Relatively crude forms of acting out may be consistent with one socioeconomic level whereas more subtle forms characterize a higher level. War and mob situations may lead to acting out of a socially contagious nature in otherwise reasonably controlled people. Foreign and other unaccustomed settings may facilitate acting out which is carefully controlled in the familiar milieu.

THE THERAPEUTIC MANAGEMENT OF ACTING OUT

In view of the diverse complexity of behavior covered by the concept of acting out, and in view of the many psychological features and social aspects, the therapeutic management of this phenomenon will obviously vary a great deal from patient to patient. The strategy and tactics of a well-planned therapeutic program impose their own individual structure (see Chapter 9). Within this framework, it is often useful to differentiate between immediate and long-range techniques, although at times both may be needed concurrently. Among the short-range measures to be considered (see Chapter 16) are:

(1) *Removing the patient from the situation* which precipitates or triggers acting out. In some cases, a change of social milieu is possible and indicated; in others, plain prohibition of certain contacts may be indicated. However, Greenacre points out how limited the use of such prohibition is, not only from the standpoint of immediate effectiveness, but because of its potentially detrimental effect on the conduct of the analysis or therapy.

Where environmental factors are important in sustaining the tendency to act out, it may be prerequisite for successful treatment to effect a change, if possible, before treatment begins. This may involve changing the geographic milieu, insisting that the patient move out of the parental home, altering the arrangement by which a son works for his father-in-law, and the like. I find it infinitely more useful to make such changes in advance, if necessary in consultation with the others involved, than to try to analyze in an untenable atmosphere.

(2) *Cathartic interpretation* dealing directly with the drive expressed in acting out may sometimes be useful, provided necessary precautions are kept in mind.

(3) The attempt to make the *behavior ego alien* is perhaps the most useful instrument. One points out the repetitive and harmful nature of the behavior patterns, and above all, indicates to the patient that he is really a victim of his unconscious distortions. By making apparent the passive role he plays in relation to his own impulses, one can remove much of the feeling of omnipotence and magic which is inherent in acting out.

(4) Since immediate action is a large factor in all acting out, *any delay*, of itself, will tend to interfere with this behavior. The patient who wants to get married today, who wants to break off treatment now, who wants to initiate divorce proceedings instantly, may sometimes be deterred by an agreement to wait a day, a week, a month. The benefits of such an agreement are twofold: in the first place, the urgency of the moment may be bypassed; in the second place, one gains time to interpret usefully.

(5) In extreme cases, it may be necessary to enlist the *help of others* to curb harmful acting out.

(6) A *strengthening of the superego* may be immediately helpful. One appeals persistently to the patient's conscience and points out to him the social implications of his behavior and the detrimental effect it may have on others. One attempts to ally with the part of the patient's personality which wishes to control the impulses. At those times when the danger of acting out is acute, it is necessary to be available to the patient by telephone or personal contact in order to delay or deter the episode.

LONG-RANGE MEASURES

Among the long-range measures for dealing with acting out, Greenacre (1950) considers the three basic techniques of prohibition, interpretation, and strengthening the ego. She is highly cognizant of the shortcomings of prohibition as a long-range technique. She sees interpretation as the method of choice, but applicable primarily to those patients with a reasonably well-integrated ego who act out only occasionally. It is her feeling that interpretation of id content is usually contraindicated, but that extensive interpretations of narcissism are helpful. Provided that there is a strong positive transference, she feels that one can soon acquaint the patient with the relationship of his tendency to act out and its use in warding off anxiety. She also feels that, in general, an early intellectual outlining of the meaning of the patient's behavior may be useful in increasing self-scrutiny and self-criticism. Her long-range goal is to convert into verbal or thought-out expressions the preverbal material that has been previously acted out. She reports success in changing the general manner of expressiveness from acting out to verbalization, although some patients may always have to remain on guard against the possibility of tensions that might become unbearable. Greenacre also takes cognizance of the important fact that occasionally a quality of the therapist's own behavior may encourage acting out. He himself may tend to act out either overtly or in more subtle form, or he may choose patients as a medium for his own acting out much as some parents trigger acting out in their children.

I have found a few other techniques useful additions in dealing with this problem therapeutically. One is the systematic and intentional use of prediction: if the therapist is able to tell the patient in advance that he is very likely to act out because of an approaching set of circumstances or particular situation, it will go a long way toward aborting the behavior. It may be pointed out to the patient that the purpose of the prediction is the hope of proving it false. If the analyst repeatedly predicts correctly, it will have a marked effect on the patient's conduct.

Another tactical procedure which has proved useful in my experience is to further the synthetic abilities of the patient by a great deal of reviewing and by routinely tying together dissociated events in interpretive statements. Acting-out patients, particularly the hysterical ones, have a tendency to forget completely what mood they were in the day before, or what last week's most urgent problem was. Such patients must be reminded of the state of affairs of yesterday and the week before, and shown the relationship of today's need for action to those just past. To this effect, I have found it useful to insist that such patients start off their therapeutic hour recalling by themselves the main dynamic gist of the previous session, or maybe several previous sessions, and intentionally and actively relating current material to previous material. This technique, coupled with extrafrequent review and overview, seems useful for important integrative development.

I feel that it is important to prevent acting out as a form of repeating a "learned" behavior pattern. I explain to the patient that in a sense every act, every phase of acting out, fortifies the wrong response, much as does the repetition of a poorly executed dance step or a wrong driving maneuver. I use a simple explanation of conditioning to drive home the importance of avoiding repetition of acting out both for short-range control and long-range therapeutic attainment.

From the same standpoint, I consider the periodic use of appropriate drugs strongly indicated to avoid repetitions of acting out. Drugs that will decrease the predisposing anxiety and tension will give one the breathing spell necessary for therapeutic attainment, and at the same time hinder further strengthening of pathological patterns. It is possible that some drugs, especially of the phenothiazine group, interfere with acting out by decreasing the affective drive directly, thus increasing the synthetic functions indirectly. It is also possible that phenothiazines directly increase the synthesizing capacities of the ego. It is Ostow's (1962) opinion that energizers have this ability. It remains for future experimental approaches to establish the processes involved, but the clinical effects of anxiety reducers, tranquilizers, and energizers in different acting-out patients seem evident.

In some patients, the amount of unlearning and relearning by the purely verbal means available in individual therapy is limited. In such cases, the judicious use of group therapy with its unique opportunity for learning and unlearning in actual social situations may prove a useful adjunct to individual psychoanalysis or analytic psychotherapy.

There are many cases in which acting out remains refractory: a large percentage of such persons do not enter treatment even if they have sought one consultation, or they break off very soon, long before one has had a chance to make ego alien what is ego syntonic. Even if they stay in treatment, progress may be slow or may not occur at all.

The person who is constantly excited, who has had a sensory overload in early childhood and now lives on a high level of tension, with a great need for stimuli *and* immediate discharge, remains largely unreachable psychotherapeutically. Some totally new, possibly physiological, forms of therapy must be searched for.

Even for the control of some forms of acting out in neurotics, some new and totally different treatment approaches may have to be devised; possibly a technique predicated upon a combination of learning theory and the understanding derived from psychoanalytic psychodynamics would be useful: that is, varieties of conditioning, not concerning manifest aspects of behavior but rather the unconscious sets we know about, techniques for acquiring frustration tolerance, and so forth.

Much of the difficulty in treating acting out is related to the fact that its genetic roots lie in preverbal experiences. No wonder acting out shares its therapeutic problems with other pathological syndromes of a nonverbal nature and preverbal origin, and is often even an exchangeable symptom: it is useful to keep in mind that acting out is often closely related to hypochrondriasis, psychosomatic conditions, and hysterical phenomena. In all these instances, we deal with a variety of body-language expressions rather than with verbal communication appropriate to the secondary process. Greenacre, in closing her paper (1950), asks why symptomatic acting out is so very common in conversion hysteria. I believe the answer is that although sometimes acting out takes the complex form of interpersonal behavior patterns, at other times it makes its own preverbal statement in the form of migratory hypochondriacal concern over one organ or another, for example, "there is something wrong with me; I find my body deficient, decaying, inferior, liable to invasion." Of course, it is well-known that the conversion symptom also makes a somatic statement of repressed material. It is by this common denominator of somatic statement of nonverbal content that I believe acting out, hypochondriasis, psychosomatic phenomena, and hysterical phenomena are linked.

If problems remain in the successful treatment of neurotic acting out, it seems to me appropriate to derive a few notions concerning the treatment of the more severe forms of acting out, involving major social pathology.

In the first place, the difficulties of treating relatively minor forms of acting out in otherwise well-integrated personalities make me pessimistic about success with severe and especially asocial forms of acting out. It seems to me often wishful thinking to expect that addictions and major asocial and antisocial forms of acting out will respond to our current psychiatric therapeutic armamentarium (often very thinly spread), except with a relatively small percentage where the severity of acting out is primarily related not to the degree of psychopathology but to social and other situational factors.

In instances of sociopathic or psychotic acting out of major violence, I do not feel that psychiatric treatment alone can take the place of other forms of humane management which offers society more immediate protection until the effectiveness of our diagnostic and therapeutic attempts has increased generally or has been proved extensively in each individual case of a social offender.

5

DEPERSONALIZATION AS A DISTURBANCE
OF SELF-AWARENESS

From free association and acting out we turn to depersonalization, and the transition is less abrupt than it might seem. When freely responding, the analytic patient achieves a novel kind of self-awareness; he listens to himself speak from afar, as it were, with something of the same detachment that we see in stage fright (although with much less anxiety). Acting out, similarly, is frequently accompanied by a loss of awareness of one's action, particularly in the extreme forms represented in the fugue state. In a sense, then, we might say that depersonalization is a necessary antecedent for both free association and acting out; conversely, they both may be used as defenses against it. The literal ruminations of the obsessive are often a protection against falling into a free-floating reverie state with its correlated changes in self-awareness; a violent and painful outburst, as the last part of the chapter makes clear, may be a way of diverting attention from the anxiety produced by a change in self-awareness.

Fears associated with depersonalization become of particular importance in the analytic situation which strives, by definition, to bring about a change in self-awareness. Oversimplifying somewhat, we could say that real changes in self-knowledge can come about *only* through changes in self-awareness and when these cannot be tolerated, the patient cannot be analyzed. When these fears are overcome, we have such regressive states as the Isakower phenomenon and extreme transference reactions, each involving substantial changes in self-awareness. A similar toleration is required on the part of the analyst; listening intently, he may momentarily lose his sense of self and feel completely identified with the material.

BECAUSE PSYCHIATRY, AND PARTICULARLY PSYCHOANALYSIS, derives its theories from empirical data which are obtained from relatively few patients, it frequently happens that hypotheses are at first conceived from a narrowly clinical point of view. Only gradually, and sometimes reluctantly, are these hypotheses broadened into general propositions dealing with a general psychology of personality.

The concept of depersonalization is a case in point: identity, depersonalization, feelings of unreality, and feelings of loss of identity occupy an important place in modern psychiatry. In many ways, the currently flourishing existentialism revolves almost entirely and excessively around variations of these feelings. Yet, in clinical psychiatry and in psychoanalysis, depersonalization has traditionally been considered primarily a major pathological syndrome.

The clinical concept of depersonalization has been defined as "a state in which a person loses the feeling of his own reality, or feels his own body to be un-

---

NOTE: From *Unfinished Tasks in the Behavioral Sciences,* edited by A. Abrams, Baltimore, 1964. Reprinted with permission of the Williams & Wilkins Co.

real." Everything seems dreamlike, and actions of oneself or of others are watched with indifferent detachment. There may be delusions such as that the body is hollow or does not exist.

Hinsie and Campbell (1960) define depersonalization as "The process of being dissolved, of losing the identity, personality, the I. A mental phenomenon, characterized by loss of the sense of the reality of oneself. It often carries with it loss of the sense of the reality of others and of the environment."

Hinsie and Campbell make it clear in an extension of their discussion that Freud, and later Fenichel, differentiated between depersonalization and estrangement. Fenichel stated that in estrangement there is an increased cathexis of the body and the self (at the cost of loss of cathexis of the environment), while in depersonalization there is an increased narcissistic cathexis of mental processes (at the cost of cathexis of the body).

Usage in the literature suggests that *feelings of unreality* often refer to conditions involving a loss of personal identity, whereas *depersonalization* more usually refers to the feeling of unreality of one's body. *Feelings of unreality* are, however, also often used to describe the sense that the world around one and one's self too are not real. Sometimes the self is mostly experienced as real and primarily the world around as unreal—a state that tempts the person to pinch himself to make sure all is not a dream.

Yet these definitions do not entirely encompass the experience of depersonalization and its associated feelings as one sees them clinically. Let me suggest as a descriptive definition that: depersonalization is a state of *heightened and changed* awareness of the self and/or the body in relation to the world; it is usually accompanied by an unpleasant feeling of unrealness of oneself, sometimes with anxiety; it may involve the whole or only parts of the body; and in varying degrees it is accompanied by a feeling that the environment, and one's relationship to it, is strange. There is a feeling of loss of frame of reference in time, in place, in person, or perhaps in all three. Functions that are ordinarily performed unconsciously or preconsciously are performed consciously and often poorly (e.g., one walks awkwardly when one is "self-conscious"). Subjective descriptions of depersonalized feelings include being on the outside and looking in, being surrounded by a thick wall of glass, being wrapped in cotton.

So far, the discussion has centered entirely upon feelings involving the *total* person—the whole body. Depersonalized feelings that involve only parts of the body are frequent, however; they seem most often, in my observation, to concern the mouth and the hand. Anesthesialike numbness of the perioral zone or the sensation that the hand does not belong to one have been reported. Feelings of unreality concerning only certain actions are also not uncommon. For instance, marked acting out is often followed by incredulity and feelings of unreality. "It doesn't seem possible that that was I" is a mild form of the phenomenon. This feeling may also be encountered after alcoholic bouts, or any other disruption of the experiential continuity. Hysterical dramatizations and overaffectivity, with rapid switches from anger to affection, are often accompanied by the feeling that the "other mood" was not real; such hysterical people are often amazed that others take their outbursts seriously.

Depersonalization has been ascribed by Schilder (1950) to withdrawal of libido, by Nunberg (1956) to loss of love or love object, by Bergler and Eidelberg (1935) to a defense against anal exhibitionism, and by Oberndorf (1950) to a means of containing anxiety. Spiegel (1959) mentions the papers of Reik (1927), Fenichel (1928), and Hartmann (1922) as stressing the defensive function of depersonalization and feelings of unreality. He also discusses Freud's paper, "A Disturbance of Memory on the Acropolis" (1936), as describing a defensive alteration of perception related to feelings of unreality.

The concept was further broadened by Blank (1954) when he suggested depersonalization to be a defense against rage, anxiety, and deprivation. He added that depersonalization takes over as a defense only where hypomania fails. Stamm (1959) further extended the concept when he related it to hypnagogic states, to twilight experiences, and even to the wish to sleep. With Lewin (1950), he felt that depersonalization was a phenomenon one might expect to occur more commonly in persons with marked oral trends and passive strivings.

Jacobson (1959) has offered the broadest consideration of depersonalization so far. She takes Federn's contributions into account (1926) and acknowledges the fact that depersonalization is an experience which occurs in normal people as well as in neurotics and psychotics. She lists a number of factors which precipitate this subjective experience and formulates depersonalization as *a process wherein an intact part of the ego observes an unaccepted part*. She distinguishes depersonalization from depression by saying that in the latter, the conflict lies between the identifications of the sadistic superego and the self-image, while in the former, the conflict is between the various identifications in different *parts* of the ego. Although Jacobson believes that depersonalization may occur in normal people, and may be accompanied by changes in the perception of the environment, she too views it primarily as a clinical phenomenon. However, she, and particularly Spiegel (1959), take a perceptual frame of reference into etiological consideration.

Arieti (1961) uses this term to encompass the much broader problem of loss of reality testing which, with its ensuing phenomena, comes about by a process of active concretization, and Kaywin's ideas of the concept of the self (1957) are worth noting here.

The difficulty of defining and differentiating from each other feelings of depersonalization, estrangement, or unreality, suggests that there may be little reason for differentiation: these disturbances are probably more or less extreme points on a continuum of change in self-perception and an accompanying change in the perception of the world which takes place constantly in everyday life. In part, if we view depersonalization as a special aspect of the general problem of perception, it becomes possible to broaden our understanding of this specific phenomenon, to see its dynamic and genetic relationship to other variants of perception, and to see it as part of a general theory of personality rather than as a form of psychopathology per se.

Everyday life forces a multitude of varying roles upon each individual, and with it, concomitant changes in self-awareness, self-concept, self-feeling, and relation of self to environment. These changes may often be on a preconscious level; the degree of consciousness depends on circumstances and on individual variations of introspectiveness and dissociation. Changes in self-perception, especially quantitative changes in the observation of one part of the self by another, are a daily and nearly constant phenomenon of the functioning self in different roles. Some of the changing roles are those of peer, subordinate and superior, public figure and parent, buyer and seller, etc. In fact, in subtle ways, our role changes in relation to every person we deal with, every setting we move in. There are, of course, the more dramatic changes of roles: from health to illness, from civilian to soldier, from free man to prisoner, from youth to age.

Even mild feelings of "self-consciousness," with their altered self-perception, may be accompanied by a perceptual distortion of the outside world as well as the person's reactions and self-observations, marked enough to be considered mild states of depersonalization. In such instances, depersonalization and projection are inextricably linked as a general perceptual distortion of the self and of the environment. Annie Reich's comments (1960) illuminate the relationship between self-consciousness and ideas of reference.

Another everyday example of mild depersonalization, in which the simultaneous change of role as well as change of perception of the self and of the environment is clearly evident, can be seen in stage fright. The affected person not only feels as if someone else is doing the talking or acting and that the voice does not sound like his own, but also that minutes seem like hours, and that a few steps on stage are like miles. The perception of self, as well as of time and space, is altered.

Several definite advantages are gained by seeing depersonalization as a variation on a continuum of self-awareness. The first advantage is that it obviates the tendency to identify depersonalization only with specific psychiatric disorders. One may merely say that more severe or less severe feelings of depersonalization may occur in certain circumstances and may be related to varyingly severe degrees of pathology. This formulation permits one to make an important point: a patient's history of experience with feelings of depersonalization is, by itself, of no specific diagnostic value. The severity of depersonalization probably relates to the extent of the perceptual disruption and the predisposition to depersonalization. These, in turn, relate more or less directly to the severity of the neurosis or psychosis.

A second advantage to be gained by considering depersonalization as a general perceptual phenomenon is that it obviates the tendency to define it too narrowly as a specific psychic process or even simply as a defense.

A third advantage is that we are enabled to see the many pathways that lead to this phenomenon. Feelings of depersonalization may be produced by a wide variety of drugs, particularly by the psychotomimetics (e.g., LSD, bulbocapnine, etc.). They may also come about by simple physiological mechanisms. A very anxious person with rigid neck muscles may get enough disturbances of proprioception from the nuchal rigidity with consequent dizziness and disorientation to account for a feeling of estrangement. A patient who hyperventilates may get a feeling of lightheadedness with paresthesia and other sensory peculiarities aroused by alkalosis. He may get sufficient muscle spasticity to effect a change in proprioception. These changes may lead to a change in self-perception and to feelings of depersonalization. Feelings of depersonalization associated with dizziness may be produced by nonfocusing of the eyes. Hysterical patients frequently look at near objects as though they were far away. The resulting diplopia and blurring may cause a feeling of unrealness. Internal perceptual change most often produces depersonalization in the strictly endopsychic and clinical sense: a surge of aggression, of a feeling of deprivation, and of the defenses attempting to deal with them, disrupt normally synthetic ego functioning and produce perceptions of change of part of oneself by another part of oneself, with a disruptive and disorienting effect. To the traveler accustomed to spending several days en route to Europe, the first jet trip is very likely to produce some disorientation and slight depersonalization. Sudden changes of role (e.g., Jacobson's prisoners [1959], sweepstakes winners), drugs, changes of proprioception, all may produce feelings of depersonalization. Of course, sensory deprivation can also produce these feelings.

We must conclude that any change in the usual perceptual frame of reference (of all five senses, and of proprioception, and of time and role, too) may cause sufficient disorientation to create varying degrees of change in self-perception and perception of environment. Such changes may induce feelings of depersonalization, especially in the presence of predisposing factors, such as poor ego boundaries, poor identification, and poorly controlled strivings.

The fourth and main advantage of the formulation proposed is that it may permit us further formulations which can be experimentally verified, modified, or rejected.

(1) In a population composed of some people with a clinical history of depersonalization and some without, we should be able to differentiate the groups by

  (a) their history of less stable identification figures
  (b) poor individuation
  (c) greater orality (rated on a 5-point scale)
  (d) prevalence of denial
  (e) greater aggressivity.

(2) We should be able to produce depersonalization by a wide variety of ways of inducing severe perceptual changes with an ease positively correlated with the syndrome mentioned above.

(3) We should be able to abolish experimentally produced (or other) depersonalization by: revising perceptual disorganization with drugs that control anxiety, aggression, and feelings of deprivation, or with drugs that increase synthesis.

(4) We should be able to prevent it when necessary in personnel likely to experience it, e.g., astronauts, atomic submariners, etc.

The *déjà vu* phenomenon, in which the person feels that a scene he has never witnessed before has a sense of unreasonable familiarity, seems to occupy a place somewhere between depersonalization and projection. The experience has an over-all quality of strangeness: it seems uncanny, may arouse anxiety, and often makes the person feel odd to the point of depersonalization. In such cases, external perception may be affected by past fantasies or by congruity with earlier experiences. One might consider this as Federn does (1926), to be the emergence of an ego state or to be a form of projection. Since *déjà vu* is particularly likely to occur in states of mild anxiety (for example, in foreign places), it may have the defensive function of making something strange and disturbing seem familiar and more comfortable. Arlow (1959) specifically discusses the defensive function of this feeling of familiarity. In its extreme form, as is sometimes seen among schizophrenic patients, everybody and everything seems familiar. This is due to the contamination of *all* perception by past perception.

In severely pathological states of depersonalization, micropsia has been observed. Lewy (1954) considers this to be a projection of the self-feeling of dissolution. One wonders if micropsia may not also reflect self-feelings of smallness and inadequacy. (See the experiments by Bruner and Goodman (1947) on perceptual changes of size with valence). A patient of mine had "perspective dreams" in childhood. The images appeared as if viewed through the wrong end of a telescope. These dreams reflected his feelings of smallness, helplessness, and emotional isolation.

Savage (1955), experimenting with LSD, found that the drug produced feelings of depersonalization as well as hallucinations and other perceptual changes of the environment. Experiments in sensory deprivation (Hebb, 1958) and perceptual isolation (Lilly, 1956) have produced similar phenomena. Also, some experiences of obsessive thinking, or ruminations, produce ego-alien feelings and those of "overawareness," both closely related to depersonalization. Experiences of dissociation—having thoughts run simultaneously on several channels, as one patient put it (with TV as a model), may also produce such feelings. We have already mentioned experiences of unreality associated with hysterical hyperaffectivity, acting out, with and without the help of alcohol, as leading to similar clinical phenomena. Most generally put, any disruption of continuity in experience may produce a dreamlike feeling or other feelings of unreality. The dreamlike feeling is most pronounced in the state of oneirophrenia, related closely to either catatonic or marked depressive episodes.

The metapsychology of depersonalization has to include: the structural, the adaptive, the genetic, the dynamic, and the economic aspects. Each of these factors may contribute to the degree of susceptibility to the feeling of depersonalization or feelings of unreality induced by perceptual changes.

The *structural* point of view is most succinctly expressed by Jacobson (1959), who suggests that we are dealing with a conflict among different identifications within the ego, and that various self-concepts conflict with each other. One may add schematically that the more conflicting representations there are in the ego (as established by history and analytic observation), the more a tendency to depersonalization there will be. This should be an experimentally testable hypothesis, and could lead to the prediction that a group of patients suffering from depersonalization will have a history of less stable identification figures than will a control group. Many different identifications, particularly in early life, may lead to insufficient synthesis of various ego nuclei, a poorly integrated self-image, poorly defined self-boundaries, and perceptual disturbances. Kaywin (1957) has discussed this point most instructively. Billy Rose (1948), the millionaire showman whose rags-to-riches life has swung a wide arc, vividly described such strong feelings of incredulity and unreality when he visited his country estate that he was afraid the butler might throw him out.

The ability to integrate one's various roles is probably best seen as an aspect of the *synthetic* function of the ego. Most of the process of role playing takes place automatically. In fact, if it is not automatic, it may interfere with functioning, as is often the case with certain motor performances. Yet many changes of role involve at least a preconscious, if not a conscious, awareness for constant checking and reality testing. Sensitive, insightful social behavior certainly necessitates oscillations in consciousness of self-awareness.

Self-awareness and its myriad variations are not related in a simple way to a continuum of health-pathology. There is probably no single ego function which relates simply to an over-all state of mental health. I have had occasion before to discuss a model of ego functions which resembles the original conceptual model of intelligence used for the Wechsler-Bellevue Scale. There are as many different ego functions as facets of intelligence, all of which can be subsumed into the global concept of ego strength or I.Q., respectively. Individual functions, however, may be markedly greater or less great than the rest of them.

Ego syntonicity is excessive in persons with a narcissistic or an obsessive character disorder with little subjective awareness of their illness. In their object relations, they suffer from what one might describe as "impersonalization"—the counterpoint to excessive self-awareness and depersonalization. In the "organization man," impersonalization may serve certain defensive functions and may not be a stable state. In a genuine character disorder, the trait of impersonalization is stable. At the other extreme are the hysteric and the schizoid whose dissociative tendencies include a proneness to excessive awareness of all changes of role and frames of reference with concomitant marked changes in self-awareness. Somewhere between these two poles is the range of the normal, with its sufficient object constancy and sufficient neutralized energy to be goal directed and automatically acting under most circumstances, yet able to respond to changes, including changes in self-awareness, sensitively, both subjectively and objectively.

That the nature of the object relations, and by implication, the process of identification, is involved in variations of self-awareness and feelings of identity is obvious.

This fact has a bearing on the current social scene (see Chapter 15). In our world of tremendous social and geographic mobility, with the constant impact of communications media, identification with people, places, and events is increasingly transitory and shallow. The "lonely crowd" and those with existentialist preoccupations are people who still mourn lost involvement and respond with variations of self-awareness, often reaching feelings of depersonalization. Some future generation, I suspect, may have such shallow identifications that they will be characterized by genuine impersonalization rather than depersonalization. Object relations may become smoother but will be of a shallow and more transitory nature with little lasting commitment.

The *genetic* viewpoint is closely interrelated with the structural. One might say, to use Glover's terms (1955, p. 404), that the less fusion of ego nuclei, the more likely the tendency toward depersonalization. (However, additional hypotheses are needed to delineate such a prediction from one concerning fugues and other related conditions.) Depersonalization is more likely to occur if parts of the self, the oral strivings in particular, have not been clearly separated from the mother figure. The failure of separation and individuation engenders a feeling of incompleteness and of nonexistence as an independent whole. Such a formulation places depersonalization genetically in relation to the process of individuation. The whole development of the secondary process, the clear organization of experience and speech as a focusing point for emotions, deserves consideration here.

Certainly a poorly established self-boundary would predispose to severe states of depersonalization. Stamm (1959) mentions a woman suffering from depersonalization who, as a child, was plagued by the feeling that she did not know what her mother looked like when her mother was out of sight. This is probably a case of a symbiotic relationship which interfered with the establishment of good self-boundaries. Such a situation could predispose toward feelings of depersonalization because some of the infantile self may have remained unintegrated with the various parts of the adult self.

Dynamically, depersonalization is a complex process. It involves, at first, repression and/or isolation and denial of the pertinent libidinal or aggressive impulses. When this fails to accomplish control, withdrawal of cathexis from the outside world or from the self takes place. (I prefer to speak of this cathectic process as a shift in the affective valence from one set of stimuli to another.) The process involves a further variety of defenses: libidinal regression toward orality, and then an ego regression with changes of intrapsychic awareness. The changes of the cognitive functions with regard to the devalued part of the ego is considered a form of denial by Jacobson (1959). She suggests that we speak of *repression* when ideas become unconscious, and of *denial* when ideas remain preconscious. Because preconscious ideas are more readily accessible to consciousness, denial is the less stable and more easily reversible process. She considers repression as a means of dealing with instincts and denial as a negation of reality (although she allows that the two processes interact, and that denial may be a forerunner of repression in some instances). The same point is implied by Blank (1954) when he says that depersonalization occurs when hypomania fails to afford an equilibrium. By further implication, denial affects thought processes and reality testing much more severely than does repression. Denial plays an insufficiently appreciated role in the "grand hysterias," for example, fugues, and other amnesias. The *belle indifference* of old is a hypomanic by-product of the denial. (Fugues have been restudied by Fisher and Joseph [1949] and by Geleerd, Hacker, and Rapaport [1945].)

In my own conceptualization, I suspect that repression and isolation are usually attempted first. Denial of one part of the self, or of reality, follows, and is accompanied by an overawareness of other parts of the self (or rather, of other ego functions, specifically the self-observing ones) which leads to the feeling of depersonalization.

Certain phenomena loosely grouped under the heading of somatization may involve a mixture of denial and repression. When a patient complains of numbness of a body zone, I think we are dealing with repression and a conversion symptom. The feelings *accompanying or resulting from* the sensations themselves are more specifically those of depersonalization. The impairment of cognitive functioning involved in denial of part of the self is accompanied by an increase in the self-observing function which is trained onto another part of the self. It is in this way that a *change in self-feeling* results. We have already stressed that perceptual changes and distortions affect not only the self but, in varying degrees, perception of the outside world including perception of time and space. By the same token, changes in the perceptual frame of reference may induce feelings of depersonalization. Lilly (1956) and Hebb (1958) have described such reactions in experiments involving extreme sensory deprivation and isolation. The reaction to an altered frame of reference, or rather, to no frame of reference, is one of the most important considerations in the qualifications of men being trained as astronauts. The candidate's ability to withstand the "strain" of extreme sensory isolation (in water tanks, etc.) is tested. It is noted, for example, how well he is able to perform certain mental tasks under these conditions. Some people are unable to function at all after a very short time: they begin to hallucinate, become disorganized, lose all sense of time, and experience varieties of depersonalized feelings and panic (Lilly, 1956).

Stamm (1959) has called attention to the relationship between the dynamic processes involved in depersonalization and those involved in hypnosis. My description of the dynamic relationship of hypnosis to other forms of regression in the service of the ego, including the process of free association, will be found in Chapter 6. The spontaneous fluctuations in depth of hypnosis and their implications for ego function are traced by Brenman, Gill, and Knight (1952). The greater likelihood of depersonalization in instances of marked oral fixation is empirically well founded and theoretically well anchored in Lewin's triad (1950).

Various authors have stressed the *defensive function* of depersonalization. It is interesting to observe, in this context, that depersonalization may be an alarming symptom to one patient and a matter of no concern to another. Jacobson believes that the nonanxiety-arousing type is associated with severe pathology and especially with psychotic withdrawal. While this holds true in some cases, I believe that the degree of threat in depersonalization may also be related to the degree of fear of passivity: people with little need for control may hardly complain of their feelings of depersonalization or unreality—they may even enjoy them.

Topographically, the process obviously takes place in the conscious, the preconscious, and the unconscious, with the relative prominence of denial giving emphasis to the preconscious nature of the phenomenon.

The adaptive aspects of depersonalization have been stressed by Jacobson (1959). She describes, for example, how political prisoners found the drastic change in their personal lives somewhat more bearable as emotional isolation and depersonalization came into play. Combat situations in wartime may lead to similar experiences. These reactions apparently serve to divorce the person from the whole experience and thereby preserve some identity. Most often, however, depersonalization and estrangement must be considered forms of adaptive malfunction under the impact of perceptually confusing stimuli.

Economically, it is clear that depersonalization involves a shift of cathexis. It may be a withdrawal of libido from objects, from ego representations, from certain parts of the self, to other parts of the self. It may be a withdrawal of investment from certain normal ego functions, specifically the synthetic ones, to an exaggerated investment of self-observing ones with a resultant change in self-feeling. Occasional violent outbursts such as breaking a pane of glass with the bare hand have, in my experience, been related to sudden panic associated with feelings of depersonalization. The pain and danger serve to disrupt the altered self-feelings much as crises and emergencies do. Thinking may become overinvested in some forms of depersonalization: it stops being an automatic function and becomes unpleasantly similar to obsessions, and in some clinical instances becomes delusional.

In depersonalization, one must speak not only of a decathexis of some, and a subsequent hypercathexis of other parts of the self, but also of shifts of cathexis of ego functions.

6

AN EGO-PSYCHOLOGICAL APPROACH
TO HYPNOSIS

The ego function of "self-exclusion," described in this chapter, is one pole of the oscillating function described in Chapter 3, and refers particularly to the productive phase of free association. It seems less applicable to the synthetic phase. In this chapter, hypnosis is conceptualized as a special form of ego exclusion and is aligned with such phenomena as creative regression, day-dreaming, and the like. Despite their over-all similarities, there is one important difference between these states: hypnosis is not always reversible by the hypnotic subject and the feeling held by some that they can regain control at will is frequently illusory. In this respect, hypnosis differs from the other examples of self-exclusion which are more under the ego's control.

OF THE MANY FUNCTIONS OF THE EGO (Hartmann, 1952; Bellak, 1952a, 1954a), the function of "self-exclusion" (Hartmann, 1939; Kris, 1952; Lewin, 1950) is least generally understood. In certain circumstances, the ego is able to exclude or to decrease some or nearly all of its functions. The cognitive function needs to be excluded in the process of falling asleep. In hypnagogic phenomena, especially in Silberer's functional phenomenon (1909), we deal with a self-observation of the process of falling asleep and, as it were, a self-observation of the decrease and exclusion of perception. Varendonck (1921) has cited a number of interesting examples which occurred to him when he was struggling to stay awake. A patient of mine, following a small operation, was nightly given codeine as a sedative and experienced a vision of a window being closed as the last thing before falling asleep. I have myself experienced the image of a closet door closing and darkness ensuing. Such phenomena are easily recalled either if one trains oneself, as Varendonck did, to awaken again, or when circumstances bring about a chance noise that penetrates the perceptual field and reverses the process.

Not infrequently, people report a final awareness of muscular relaxation as the feeling of falling, in going to sleep, only to awaken with a start if they happen to be anxious and the muscular relaxation is incomplete, and if passivity is a threat. Similarly, the process of awakening from a deep slumber frequently involves a temporary disorientation with only gradual perception of the entire field.

I suggest that the hypnotic state—in the past frequently described as a "state of narrowed consciousness"—can be better understood as a state of partial self-exclusion of the ego similar to the process of falling asleep, but not identical with it. In enumerating the differences, I hope also to contribute to a clarification of the long-standing discussion of comparisons between sleep and hypnosis.

NOTE: From the *International Journal of Psychoanalysis,* 1955, 36, 375-378. Reprinted by permission of the publishers.

Consciousness, and therefore ego activity, is not an "all-or-none" proposition, but is a state ranging on a continuum from a hypothetical maximum to a hypothetical minimum. This is known both popularly and clinically, and finds its conceptual expression in psychoanalysis in the formulation of "preconsciousness" (mental processes that are not conscious but can with minimal intent be made conscious) and in such clinical psychiatric terms as "cloudy states" (*Dämmerzustand*), depersonalization, etc.

For a variety of functions it is necessary that the ego be able to exclude itself. Kris (1952) speaks of "regression in the service of the ego" in connection with the artist who must be able to relax ego control in order to "create" and yet must maintain the degree of control which makes his art product socially acceptable (requiring the service of the ego).

I have referred to the need for self-exclusion and control in relation to such productions as Thematic Apperception Test stories (Bellak, 1954a). The subject must be able to let his fantasy go and yet maintain enough perceptual and conceptual control to adhere to the stimulus and to fulfill the task of telling a fairly structured story. In free association also the patient is asked to let his mind wander "freely," i.e., without exerting the usual ego control, and at the same time or successively to switch back to observing his own stream of thought in order to report to the analyst. One might speak of this ability to switch back and forth as the "oscillating function" of the ego which, if good, allows for great "flexibility" (and thus, sensitivity, creativity). On the negative side, one usually speaks of "rigidity." If the self-observation itself becomes a compulsive act, as in the obsessive or the psychotic, it is a phenomenon of ego weakness: the self-observing function has replaced the cognition of outside stimuli to a pathological extent.

In the struggle to remain awake, the oscillating function may also be involuntary. One may switch from external cognition to hypnagogic reveries.

It is postulated here that *hypnosis is a special case of self-exclusion of the ego*. In many tasks the ego activity is voluntarily limited to *some* functions. Problem solving is often not possible without complete repression of external stimuli other than those of the problem at hand (the typical "absent-minded professor").

In well-functioning sexual relations consciousness is limited to awareness of the sexual partner, and, in the orgasm, a state of clouded consciousness is achieved, in which there is awareness only of the orgastic process; the person who still hears the clock ticking or wonders about the pimple on the partner's cheek is disturbed.

In hypnosis some ego functions of reality testing are delegated to the hypnotist. This can probably still be best understood in the terms advanced by Ferenczi, namely, that the hypnotist is a parental figure. This need not be taken too literally as repetitive of the childhood situation wherein the child falls asleep to the sound of the mother's or father's soothing voice. It may be taken in a broader sense, i.e., we all constantly defer some actions to one parental figure or another, be it teacher or boss. Such a relationship is frequently compared to a transference relationship. It must not be overlooked that the wish to fall asleep or to be passive in relation to the hypnotist plays a decisive dynamic role in the child or the adult respectively. The sleepy child wants to be cuddled, held close, cared for, and wishes to relinquish control much as a passive adult may prefer to have someone else set a course of action for him. The relationship of this wish to sleep to oral wishes has been particularly elucidated by Lewin in connection with his oral triad (1950).

In this sense it is of course not more correct to speak of an ego-psychological theory of hypnosis than it would be to speak of an id-psychological theory of phobias. As in any psychoanalytic hypothesis, the dynamic interplay of a wish or drive demand with other constituents of the personality and reality must be an integral aspect of any consideration of hypnosis. The wish to fall asleep or to be hypnotized need not be conscious. The person struggling against falling asleep is in fact a much more frequent phenomenon than the one struggling against "going under" in hypnosis, and in either case the struggle involves a conflict between the passive wishes and the defenses against them. In the case of the insomniac who wishes to fall asleep the fear of passivity and the fear of emergent phantasies of castration keep him awake. A tired sentry may struggle against the wish to sleep, possibly induced by still unknown physiological stimuli related to fatigue.

However, a person who uses sleeping as a form of withdrawal may fall asleep in undesired company also against his conscious wish and without any physiological need for sleep. Similarly, a person in an audience undergoing mass hypnosis may fall asleep against his conscious wish to stay awake, and a person consenting to lie down on a couch to be hypnotized may struggle against following instructions and yet become hypnotized, or may consciously struggle to submit, and like the insomniac, never become hypnotized because of unconscious fears.

The degree of self-exclusion of the ego varies with what are known as "stages" of hypnosis. Brenman, Gill, and Knight (1952) have presented some excellent experimental evidence of varying levels of ego activity in hypnosis. They used the increase or decrease in depth of hypnosis as a means of studying regressive changes in ego functioning. Elsewhere I have discussed (Bellak, 1954a) how preconscious fantasies may have a certain autonomy of life: a preconscious fantasy may exist without one's being aware of it. Only suddenly, because of some interruption, may one "snap out of it," as the expression goes. Often such preconscious fantasy starts with some conscious thought which trails off into "daydreams" and sometimes actually into hypnagogic states or sleep.

A similar phenomenon obtains in the process of being hypnotized from the standpoint of decreased ego control (from conscious thought to preconscious thought to hypnagogic reverie to that special state wherein nearly all reality testing is relinquished except the sensory contact with the hypnotist). Some subjects interrupt the hypnotic process by "snapping out of it" as one does in reverie.

Two phenomena well-known in hypnosis may also be easily explained by the ego theory. One has to do with the disturbing fact that sometimes subjects throw off the control of the hypnotist and act out a hypnotic trance of their own. This probably resembles those preconscious fantasies which become autonomous in a state of sleepiness or in more or less psychotic people who find these fantasies intruding and taking over consciousness against their will. Hypnotic subjects who demonstrate this phenomenon are probably people with a particular propensity for dissociation of ego functions, and are better not hypnotized.

In hypnosis the self-exclusion of the ego is probably not as complete as in sleep: cognition of the hypnotist is maintained. However, a similar phenomenon occurs in sleep when one is geared to awaken at specific noises. Such an instance is the case of a mental set to awaken at a certain time, because some time-estimating function of the ego is maintained, or because of noises such as the arrival of the milkman, etc. A similar selective phenomenon occurs in the mother who may sleep through any number of louder noises, but awakens at the merest whimpering of her child. In other words, some selective perception occurs in every sleeping person. While one person may be unable to sleep in the noises of a new environment, another may have become "accustomed" to them, i.e., have acquired a selective inattention to certain stimuli which occur while he is asleep.

The case in which the hypnotic fantasy becomes autonomous and the hypnotist's control is lost comes as close as possible to the normal state of sleeping and dreaming and to spontaneous somnambulistic experience. It must be concluded that psychodynamically there are no systematic differences between sleep and hypnosis except the quantitative one of degree of ego exclusion. This ego exclusion may, however, be of a relative minimum in light sleep, or in sleep geared to special noises: or it may be at its maximum in deep hypnosis with autonomy of hypnotic trance.

Toxic deliria are states of ego weakness induced by various agents, such as alcohol, infectious agents, etc.

Another factor has to do with the much-debated question of performance of extra-aggressive or intra-aggressive acts under the influence of hypnosis. This can probably be restated thus; in fairly healthy people, enough ego function (of reality testing, etc.) remains intact to avoid such acts if normally ego alien to them. However, it is not inconceivable that individual persons with weak egos may be guided to harmful behavior, in hypnosis as well as under the influence of other ego-weakening or ego-directive forces, e.g., of group-psychological nature (viz. Redl's concept of resistance to "group contamination" as a function of ego strength; Redl and Wineman, 1951).

The process of "going under" again resembles the hypnagogic phenomenon. The feeling of many subjects that they were not "really under" and could have acted differently resembles the feeling accompanying all preconscious phenomena—namely, that one could gain complete control of them if one wanted to.

The ego-psychological theory of hypnosis can finally explain why some subjects are not hypnotizable: psychotics do not have an ego integrated enough for the selective regression involved in hypnosis. Similarly, anxious people—all those to whom being "passive" means "being vulnerable to attack"—cannot relinquish ego control. The person suffering from insomnia suffers from inability of the ego to exclude itself, the ego remaining on guard against phallic attacks, usually of primal-scene fantasy origin. It follows then that people with insomnia will usually not be able to be hypnotized.[1] In those who can be, we should keep in mind that for some the presence of a benevolent parent figure (the hypnotist) may well be the one condition under which they do dare to give up the control. (Many a child whose fantasies clearly reveal that fear of the father's aggression prevents him from falling asleep will be able to fall asleep when his fear is no longer of the *fantasy* father: as soon as the real father is in the room, he may fall asleep—possibly because he is reassured about his own destructive wishes.)

All the phenomena produced in hypnosis are under the control of the ego. Motility is as much an ego function as is perception or its lack. The increased recall under hypnosis, which has been put to psychotherapeutic use, is due to a decrease of ego control which can also be produced by such ego solvents as barbiturates and alcohol. The carrying out of a posthypnotic order does not differ from the "mental set" to carry out other tasks under the ego's control, while perception of pain and fatigue can be dissociated and excluded from perception by the ego.

The "compelling" aspects of hypnotic orders do not differ from other compulsive acts such as tics, hysterical anesthesias, obsessions, and the like, which have, to misuse Allport's terms, become functionally autonomous parts of the ego in that the path from the unconscious motivation to the executive muscular function has become a one-way street. Similarly, the hypnotist's posthypnotic order artificially inserts an autonomous set of determining principles which usually remains effective only as long as the amnesia for the giving of the order persists.

I believe that continued systematic conceptualization of the hypnotic process as a special function of self-exclusion of the ego will finally make hypnotism a fully understood phenomenon.

To summarize: in the past, id-psychological theories of hypnosis were outstanding, as Brenman, Gill, and Knight (1952) point out: Freud, Ferenczi, and others compared the relationship of the hypnotic subject to the hypnotist to that of child to parent, lover to beloved, patient (in transference) to analyst. I agree with Brenman et al. that such a theory does not encompass all the features of hypnosis.

Brenman et al. observed spontaneous fluctuations in the depth of hypnosis and concluded that these changes represent defensive maneuvers on the part of the ego when an existing psychological equilibrium is threatened by drives of various natures or by the defenses against them.

I would like to go further, to the elaboration of a framework of an ego-psychological theory of hypnosis: hypnosis is defined as a special case of the self-

---

[1] In this context there may be an opportunity for an experimental verification of this hypothesis. A group of insomniacs should have a significantly greater number of people who are not hypnotizable than a group of people who habitually sleep soundly. The difference could be increased if the insomniac group were further selected by the results of the administration of a number of TAT cards, namely 12M and 18BM, than including only those subjects who seem to feel threatened by an attack from the rear and who exhibit a great deal of anxiety concerning passivity. (By the same token, any group exhibiting strong traits of oral passivity ought to be wonderful hypnotic subjects in contrast to the anal type of the other group.)

excluding function of the ego. A topological regression takes place from conscious perception to preconscious functioning similar to the performance of routine tasks. As in the routine task, a small aspect of cognitive function persists, in the case of hypnosis directed toward the hypnotist.

Further regressions similar to those in hypnagogic reveries are discussed, and the relationship to sleep and dream is mentioned. Various perceptual, motor, and other executive phenomena associated with hypnosis can also be understood in terms of ego functioning.

Hypnosis, as well as other behavioral functions, needs to be integrated with our more recently acquired knowledge of ego psychology. However, the libidinal factors should not be ignored; a complete theory of hypnosis must take into account the libidinal relationship between hypnotist and patient, as stated earlier, and in addition the aspects of ego functioning involved, and all these factors integrated with the total psychodynamics.

Section II: Research in Psychoanalysis and Psychotherapy

IT HAS BEEN FASHIONABLE to speak of psychoanalysis as having its own research method and to argue that the treatment situation as such is essentially a series of small-scale experiments that can yield highly significant data; if these data—the complete transcription of each session—were only properly recorded and coded, many questions could be answered.

This is a misleading analogy; it confuses the detachment of the analyst with the dispassionate distance of the scientist, and it forgets that whereas the analyst typically shies away from manipulation, it is the scientist's stock in trade. Worst of all, it discourages the search for new approaches and can lead to the fallacious argument that data gathered outside the treatment situation are somehow suspect and unrepresentative. A vicious circle has thus been closed: the only legitimate data come from the treatment situation which is not, in any essential, way, a research instrument.

One way out of this impasse is illustrated by the papers in this section. Their general strategy is to gather material in the usual treatment setting and then code it in a systematic way; once coded, the material is used to generate predictions which can then be checked against future behavior.

The essential difficulty with this method is that while positive results are encouraging, they do not add much in the way of systematic knowledge. Negative results add even less, and one or two negative outcomes may often discourage the researcher from ever trying again, so great is his investment in time and effort. Furthermore, the results of several studies are rarely additive, because diagnosis, treatment setting, and history all vary from one study to the next. Further data reduction is necessary so that experiments of the kind described here may be expressed in some consistent way with a common set of terms.

In these and related efforts, we are paying the price for our neglect of basic research. Problems of unit, definition, measurement, hardware—all the unglamorous underpinnings of a science—are simply not solved and must be faced anew in each enterprise. The rare solutions, moreover, are frequently buried or lost because the focus of the final report is on the findings rather than on the procedure. We might find that the methodological yield of the past ten years has been far greater than we realize.

With these thoughts in mind, the chapters in this section should be read with an eye to procedure as well as to outcome. The advances are in procedure, and Chapter 12, on the single case, is a good example of how a new method is potentially more useful than a new finding. As methods accumulate, standard procedures will emerge and then the stage will be set for significant discoveries.

7

PROBLEMS AND GOALS OF
PSYCHOANALYTIC RESEARCH

This chapter deals with the general problem of research strategy in psychoanalysis and comes out boldly for a predictive model. Since this paper was written, an increasing number of researchers have tried to base short- and long-range predictions on analytic materials; such attempts range from trying to predict what the patient will say after an intervention to what he will do in the next hour or next week. In some studies (such as the one described in Chapter 8) the predictions are made on the basis of recorded material, after the event has occurred; in others (such as the work of Knapp, 1960), the predictions are made by the treating analyst to events in the next hour, before the event has occurred; in still others (such as an ongoing study by Gill and Simon), the analyst attempts a specific intervention which is designed to produce a certain response, with a prediction implicit in the intervention.

The success of this method has been mixed, and Escalona's critique, quoted in this chapter, has been recently joined by Meissner (1966). Writing about the general problem of psychoanalysis and the scientific method, Meissner asks whether the two approaches are perhaps incompatible, and suggests that because overdetermination is basic to so many clinical phenomena, the predictive method is necessarily impossible to apply. Briefly stated, his argument runs as follows: If $A, B, C \ldots N$ all combine to produce a particular piece of behavior, Z, then a predictive model based on the paradigm *If A, then Z* is obviously too simple. If the predictive model is to be applied, a more sophisticated contingency paradigm is needed; provision must be made for the simultaneous assessment and differential weighting of many variables. Research on the ego, as described in the present section, calls for such a paradigm; other examples are suggested in Chapters 10 and 13.

RESEARCH IN PSYCHOANALYSIS falls naturally into three areas according to the three definitions: (1) psychoanalysis is a body of interlocking hypotheses; (2) it is a form of therapy; and, as the avenue which joins them, (3) psychoanalysis is a process or method. The three areas are closely related, for the therapy is predicated upon the body of psychoanalytic propositions. The psychoanalytic process is based on the theoretical formulations and is an implement for exploration, validation, refutation, and discovery.

The definition of research in psychoanalysis is not simple. Research is a "searching for something with especial care or diligence." It has been and is pursued fruitfully in clinical research where observation, hypothesis formation, and verification are performed by one person with no means of checking results other than that person's own subjective empirical findings. This type of re-

NOTE: From the *Psychoanalytic Quarterly*, 1961, 30, 519-548, and *Psychology of Personality*, edited by J. M. McCary, New York, Logos Press, 1956. Reprinted with slight revision of text and references by permission of the publishers.

search is probably the best method for developing heuristic hunches which can lead to further investigation. Creative insight usually develops more fruitfully in individual reflection than it does in teamwork. Teamwork, although invaluable in checking and elaborating individually conceived great ideas, has been quite sterile in producing great discoveries. Individual clinical research, on the other hand, is insufficient for verifying theory, for testing the limits of a hypothesis in a scientifically acceptable way, or for establishing the necessary differentiations and variations which then often lead to new and broader generalizations.

The main training of analysts is that obtained in medical schools, that is, in applied science as compared to methodological training in graduate schools. Not only has analysis suffered from a lack of incentive to research, as Bandler (1960) has pointed out, but perhaps even more from a basic lack of orientation to research or to thinking in methodologically useful ways. An approach such as M. J. Johnson Abercrombie's (1960) might well be the most useful one in the curriculum of analytic institutes. She is disappointed in the effects of scientific learning on habits and thinking. Specifically, she quotes a report of a committee of the Royal College of Physicians: "The average medical graduate tends to lack curiosity and initiative; his powers of observation are relatively undeveloped; his ability to arrange and interpret facts is poor; he lacks precision in the use of words." Hence she decided to teach what one might well call a scientific attitude through discussion among small groups of students. Her main hypothesis was that we may learn to make better judgments if we become aware of some of the factors that influence their formation. The course consisted of eight discussions, each lasting about one and one-half hours, and the students attended them in groups of twelve. An investigation some years later seemed to support Dr. Abercrombie's thesis that the students who had taken this course did better than others in discriminating between facts and conclusions, drawing fewer false conclusions, considering more than one solution of a problem, and being less adversely influenced in their approach to a problem by their experience of a preceding one; that is, they were more objective and more flexible in their behavior. They succeeded better in what the author defines as the process of judgment: making a decision or forming a conclusion on the basis of indications or probabilities when the facts are not clearly ascertainable.

It is obvious that the psychoanalysts share these same problems. Instead of using X-ray pictures and words as Dr. Abercrombie did in her brief course, analytic concepts themselves might be used—perhaps in the second year of training—and in a continuous case seminar in the third year.

Training such as is described in Abercrombie's book, used judiciously with psychoanalytic candidates, might result in the habit of carefully evaluating past teaching and evidence and encourage more independent and productive clinical work, as well as research. Examining different concepts and impressions gained by participants in a continuous case seminar, and doing so systematically by repeated predictions and judgments, would illustrate not only individual distortions but also the need for improvement in expression of our concepts, leading to better formulation of our hypotheses.

I should like here to restrict the term *research* to "systematic investigations with methodological safeguards for the soundness of conclusions," the search moreover to be carried on by more than one person (with guarantees for independent judgment) and in a form which permits the basic operations to be generally demonstrable. Such research is possible in psychoanalysis and it is essential that it confirm the insights of clinical research if it is to have the benefits of lawfulness.

The personal characteristics of the researcher are worthy of note. It is easily understandable that people attracted by the meticulous demands for the order and correctness of research are likely to have the obsessive-compulsive traits which are very useful in such work. The distinction between the clinician and the experimenter,[1] the tender minded and the tough minded, is psychologically that between a relatively hysterical and a relatively obsessive character. The researcher's methodical, statistical, and neatly conceptual bent is likely to be joined with a feeling of arrogance for being a little "cleaner" and better than his clinical colleagues. The more intuitive, more spontaneous clinician is apt to feel that the other fellow may have the "higher" type of mind but does not know what he is talking about. Methodologists, however, bring to mind Freud's patient who washed the bank notes to avoid passing on germs, but seduced the children of his friends. Beneath the reaction formations of the purist may lurk an element of anal-erotic laxity. The "dirty" flaw in a methodologist's pure culture may be in the form of a loose assumption; e.g., a parameter, or taking "too narrow a slice," while the details of work and computation are meticulously clean. Even more often the sterile precautions are so excessive as to have killed all germs of ideas.

Part of the difficulty with the methodologist is the use of a secret language of special terms, spurious distinctions, and flights into numbers, when the problem could be stated simply and (except for computational details) in readily understandable words. It may require much effort to understand the jargon well enough to realize that the frighteningly complex problem is not only simple, but also often enough irrelevant. Methodology can be learned by anyone and a cleavage between the clinical and the systematic experimenters is unnecessary.

THE NEED FOR DEFINITIONS

The first step in the verification of a theory has to be a clear statement of the theory. To the logical positivists we owe the idea that to be properly answered a question must be properly asked. Logical positivism has undoubtedly been misused for pedantic purposes, but it does force us to start our research by formulating definitions and hypotheses in a semantically clear way. Years of work are needed for us merely to achieve this first step.[2] Psychoanalytic hypotheses are rarely clear, concise, and well defined. Freud, too creatively involved to stop and codify, admittedly used terms loosely with different meanings, and psychoanalytic literature has often followed his example.

For purposes of research any psychoanalytic hypothesis needs first to be clearly stated. As an example, I have previously attempted to restate the molar

---

[1] A distinction extensively discussed in a volume by Erika Chance (1959).

[2] The indexing project currently being conducted at the Hampstead Clinic in London, and reported by J. Sandler at the 1961 meeting of the International Psychoanalytic Association in Edinburgh, is one such step in the direction of basic definitions.

aspects of the libido theory as a series of interlocking propositions (see Chapter 1).

(1) Propositions concerning the sequence of maturation of bodily zones with a positive hedonic tone (erotogenic zones), and specific aims of gratification (libidinal aims), and specific objects.

(2) Propositions concerning the interaction of the perception of oral, anal, and genital stimuli, and the reaction of significant figures to such stimulation (early anal training, masturbation, and prohibition).

(3) Propositions concerning specific effects of the maturational and learned aspects on later development (object relations, character formation).

(4) Propositions concerning the timing of maturation and learning. (The same maternal act at different times in the child's life will have different effects.)[3]

(5) Propositions concerning the interaction of events learned at different times. (The relationship of trauma sustained in infancy to trauma sustained in latency to trauma sustained in puberty.)

Even the first set of propositions concerning the libidinal zones is not adequately proved. Is it true that there is indeed an orderly maturational sequence of preferred loci of stimulation? If so, does the interaction with a great number of other factors correspond approximately to the additional hypotheses advanced by psychoanalysis?

The task of defining psychoanalytic concepts is beyond the capacities of one person. Such a study should be carried out by teams, including analytically versed methodologists, and should continue for many years. It should include the collection of the relevant literature and make bibliographies available. The participants should act as an advisory body, coördinate psychoanalytic research performed in various locations, and stimulate or originate research considered necessary. I believe that it should be one of the tasks of the American Psychoanalytic Association to undertake a study of conceptual and methodological problems, much as it set up a survey of training, and as long ago as 1954 I suggested such a study.

THE NEED FOR METHODOLOGY

The second basic necessity for bringing the analytic house into order is to teach analysts more methodology, not necessarily to make methodologists or statisticians of them, but to acquaint them with methodological ways to help them collaborate comfortably and usefully with methodologists and to think along their lines. Ernst Kris (1947) has said that we need "trained clarifiers," and to have trained clarifiers one must train them. Every psychoanalytic institute should have a basic course in methodology as it applies to psychoanalysis. Such a course would be most suitable for candidates in the last year of training, although a broad methodological perspective should be maintained in all the courses. Among other things, it should address itself to psychoanalytic hypotheses from the vantage point of other sciences, and notably to general psychology. This would lead to a salutary broadening of perspective. For instance, psychoanalysis might be considered from the point of view of motivational theories, or some of Freud's propositions might be considered from the point of view of

---

[3] In *The Psychoanalytic Study of the Child,* Vol. 9, these propositions were discussed under the term of "phase specificity" of child-mother interactions.

learning. Candidates should be made thoroughly conversant with the formal problems of methodology. To this end there should be some training in research and a solid acquaintance with the research point of view.

In a way, psychoanalytic training suffers from the same shortcomings as medical training in general. This is not surprising. In both instances, the student must be prepared to become a practitioner. However, because analysts may be the only people qualified to do psychoanalytic research, they must rise above this limitation in their training. My suggestion for such a course in analytic institutes is to develop a research attitude and to concentrate on basic methods and problems. Technicians can be hired for the technical problems. It is important that the clinicians understand enough to make sure that they do not engage in insignificant and irrelevant hair-splitting to the detriment of the clinical problem. (A statistician not well acquainted with the clinical problems is as useless or dangerous as a research clinician not sufficiently acquainted with methodology.)

ASPECTS OF VERIFICATION—APPROACHES AND SCOPE

Verification of analytic theory takes place subjectively in every analysis. Verification can also be achieved by systematic, controlled observation of the psychoanalytic process itself and of other situations which lend themselves to psychoanalytic hypotheses, such as group behavior.

The experimental technique of creating reasonably controlled settings for the examination of one variable is applicable and has been employed in various ways; for example, by creating experimental analogues to human or animal subjects, or Mowrer's method in his study of regression (1940).

Psychologists' early attempts at verification, as reported for instance in a monograph by Sears (1944), used techniques of reduction to the point of absurdity, took concepts unduly out of context, and often completely misunderstood them. Today's psychologists—often well analyzed themselves—are more comprehending and promising. The statistical analysis of the oral syndrome (Blum and Miller, 1952) and the study of the authoritarian personality (Adorno et al., 1950) are two examples of this valuable work. The experimental work of such analysts as Fisher, and of such analytical psychologists as Klein and Brenman, shows the obvious value of elucidating and testing psychoanalytic hypotheses outside the clinical situation (Fisher, 1954; Klein and Schlesinger, 1949; Brenman, Gill, and Knight, 1952). It is probable that the nature of defenses will be most usefully established in some such extraclinical setting. Such concepts as body image or the genesis of delusions and hallucinations can be fruitfully examined in psychoses experimentally induced by drugs or perceptual isolation.

The close and systematic study of infants and children is another useful approach to the formulation, validation, reformulation, and expansion of psychoanalytic hypothesis. The work of Spitz, Lois Murphy and associates, and the Kris group in New Haven are fine examples (Spitz, 1951a; Murphy et al., 1956; Coleman, Kris, and Provence, 1953).

The scope of a research project has much to do with its useful outcome. Defining a problem too finely entails an artificial isolation and may lead to distortion. To include too much may be self-defeating, since investigators die, move away, run out of money, or lose interest when, with the passing of time, parts of the project are solved elsewhere. The design should permit flexibility while assuring comparability of the results. There are projects with a frozen design which were known to be failures within the first few months of their existence but went on for years anyhow, nourished by grants and little else.

THE CONCEPT OF VALIDITY

The testing of analytic hypotheses is technically one of *validation*. In recent years this concept has undergone refinements, particularly by the psychologists who were trying to validate the analytically conceptualized process of projective techniques. Four types of validity are generally included: content validity, predictive validity, concurrent validity, and construct validity.

Guided by the manual of the American Psychological Association (1954), one may say that *content validity* is evaluated by showing how well the content of an experimental situation samples the class of situations about which conclusions are to be drawn. For instance, an experiment designed to test the concept of orality should clearly involve oral problems in order to test the hypothesis. Many psychological investigations of psychoanalytic problems do not have content validity. For example, experiments designed to investigate the concept of repression did not really deal with situations involving repression.

Predictive validity is evaluated by showing how well predictions made from sample behavior are confirmed by evidence gathered later and judged independently; for example, predictions of response to therapeutic interventions.

Concurrent validity is evaluated when we compare the performance of a patient in a psychoanalytic interview with the performance on projective tests. In essence, we are predicting that a patient judged to be of a certain nature will show the same characteristics when tested projectively at the same time. As we know, this does not always appear to be the case, and the discrepancy between test results and clinical diagnosis involves interesting problems of the intervening variables or the invalidity of test or theory.

Construct validity is properly concerned with validating a theory underlying behavior. It involves two steps. First, the inquiry: what predictions may we make regarding variations of behavior from person to person or analytic session to session? Second, the confirmation: are we able to obtain data to confirm our predictions? If we predict that a patient admiring objects in the analytic office feels positive transference, we want to see if positive transference is apparent in other ways.

The different forms of validity overlap considerably and are, to a certain extent, arbitrary and artificial separations. As the authors of the manual say (p. 15), "Concern for validity is in no way a challenge to the dictum that prediction of behavior is the final test of any theoretical construction."

The term "hypothesis," incidentally, we usually reserve for sophisticated intuitions, the term "theory" for such of these as have a reasonable factual support. When we speak of "propositions," we may mean "formal propositions" which must be consistent only within their own theoretical system, or "empirical propositions" which, by themselves, are not directly verifiable, but relate to statements which can be verified.

An excellent discussion implicitly concerned with problems of validity and control was recently published by The Group for the Advancement of Psychiatry (1957).

Many psychoanalysts still feel somewhat disdainful of experimental validation, feeling that they already have proof enough, or that to validate theories is in essence merely to restate what is already known; or they feel that psychoanalysis cannot be validated by scientific methodologies designed for other sciences.

To the first point, let me say that clinical observation has often proved fallacious and is not sufficiently reliable. To be sure, scientific methods are also subject to error, but in the long run greater certainty lies with careful methodology. Those who believe that validation is dull and has only academic interest do not appreciate its full merits. In validating, we attempt an approximation of theory and facts, and we are as interested in those facts that do not fit as we are in those that do. Almost every attempt at validation leads to new questions, additional hypotheses, and eventually, to new answers. It is the essence of scientific progress and, as such, is the direct opposite of academic boondoggling. The third and most prevalent objection arises from a misunderstanding of one of Freud's basic contributions. It has often been said that the unconscious is irrational, and therefore not subject to scientific validation. Freud, to the contrary, developed the construct of the unconscious to bridge *rationally* certain discontinuities between the child and the adult, between dreams and the waking state, neurosis and normal life. He formulated rational hypotheses concerning unconscious processes, and each of these is testable by scientific methods.

RESEARCH CONCERNING THE LIBIDO THEORY

Interestingly enough, attempts to investigate the libido concept belong to the earliest of any attempts to verify psychoanalytic concepts experimentally: Bernfeld and Feitelberg (1934) attempted extensively to derive measurement of libido from the Weber-Fechner law and from thermodynamic processes. Unfortunately they failed.

Some useful experiments include the one by Sears (1936, 1943) investigating the existence of the syndrome stinginess-obstinacy-orderliness as posited by the analytic concept of the anal character. Sears found low correlations but all positive and in the expected directions. Similarly, Goldman (1948) investigated the existence of the trait cluster associated with the concept of the oral character and in essence confirmed the theoretical expectations. The most ambitious experiment bearing upon the theory of libidinal stages was made by Blum (1949) by means of his Blacky pictures. This provided a flexible scheme and permitted verification of several sets of psychoanalytic hypotheses.

An even more systematic way of investigating the libido theory might involve a combination of the Szondi and the Blacky test principles. One might construct a series of pictures: One picture would depict gratification of a partial drive; e.g., a person looking through a keyhole might be a representation of voyeurism, while a nude near a window might be a picture of exhibitionism, and a wolf devouring an animal a picture of oral incorporation, while a picture of a land of milk and honey might constitute a representation of oral passivity. Erector sets might be representations of phallic drives, and water cascades stand for urethral wishes. It would not be too difficult to represent the genital aims. Aside from the aim presentations, there should also be representatives of the defenses against each drive aim. For instance, a blindfolded person (defense against voyeurism), a meticulously clean, orderly room (defense against anal-erotic drive), a picture representing anesthesia (defense against sadism—while a picture of medieval torture might stand for expression of sadism), and a picture of a nun or a monk (might indicate defense against genital drives), etc.

Actually, the pictures would have to be chosen with great care; the rather haphazard suggestions above are merely meant to illustrate the idea. Also, each drive and the defense against it should be presented several times, say five times at least—ten times including drive aim and defenses against it. If there should be an agreement on the use of fifteen or twenty variables, the set would have to include 150-200 pictures. These should be presented in groups with the request that they be selected and rank-ordered for their esthetic value or artistic merit.

The hypothesis is, of course, that each person would select those pictures representing his aims, or his defenses against them which would be most important in his personality. Since each variable is represented several times, it should be possible to study internal consistency—e.g., a person might pick all (manifestly different) pictures relating to anal sadism in the set of 150 as the worst and those representing defense against anal sadism as the best. If each subject is asked to rank-order the whole set several times at some intervals, validity and over-all reliability could be established. One might think of this as a Szondi on a rational basis, viz., the libido theory. The crux is concerned with establishing a rank-order system of hedonic choices representative of the zones, aims, and objects of the libido theory.

External validation could proceed by first choosing subjects who have been studied psychoanalytically. The analysts would have to fill out a chart corresponding to the variables tested by the pictures and state which drives are most important, secondary, tertiary, etc. By this means, their judgment—which is in effect a prediction of the subjects' performances—could be used as the validating factor. Again, in other cases, analysts acquainted only with a detailed history of the subjects should again be able to predict the pictorial choices, within the framework of the libido theory.

RESEARCH CONCERNING THE EGO

The ego and its functions can also be experimentally investigated. If the ego is defined by its functions, one can investigate experimentally how well it performs the functions; that is, design tests for reality testing, frustration and anxiety tolerance, rigidity, motor functions, etc.

A.   The ego as defined by its *functions:*

(1) The ego organizes and controls motility and perception.

(2) The ego serves as a protective barrier against excessive external and internal stimuli. (Here we might also include a statement made by Hartmann (1939) that it is part of the function of the healthy ego to *exclude itself.* For instance, in order that we may be able to fall asleep, the ego must be able to relinquish most or all perception, including subjective awareness, motility control, etc., or else insomnia ensues. In this context E. Kris's concept of "regression in the service of the ego" in artistic creativity, etc., has found wide usefulness and acceptance.

(3) The ego tests reality and engages in trial action (Freud's formulation of thinking), and sends out danger signals (anxiety).

(4) The ego is responsible for detour behavior in gratification.

(5) Under "organizing and self-regulating functions," we comprise character, defenses, and the integrating function of the ego.

B.   The ego can also be defined by its *development*. Its development is characterized by:

(1) *Primary, genetic, congenital,* and/or *constitutional ego endowments:* Hartmann speaks of autonomous factors in ego development, apparently referring to motor, perceptual, intellectual, and maturational equipment. He quotes from Freud's "Analysis Terminable and Interminable": "We have no reason to dispute the existence and importance of primal, congenital ego-variations."

(2) *Environmental forces:* the child learns the control of id drives at first possibly by conditioning and later by more complex processes of identification with parental figures. Inconsistent training or impossibility of identifying with parental figures for purposes of integration (either because of their absence or because of their own inconsistency or inadequacy) may make for a weak ego, a factor to be discussed more fully below. A seductive environment may so strengthen the id drives as to make control of them (by the ego) very difficult, thus indirectly influencing or weakening the ego development.

(3) *Influence of the id drives:* there probably are hereditary, congenital, constitutional, physiologic, pathologic, and psychogenic variations of the nature and strength of id drives. A psychogenic influence (a seductive environment, for example) has already been mentioned. Pituitary or thyroid deficiency might be instances of pathologic influences; latency, adolescence, and involution are examples of physiologic influences which affect the ego.

C.   The ego could be defined by the *quality of its function,* or possibly by the *quantitative aspects of its performance* (often spoken of as *ego strength*).

Ego strength can be principally defined by the effectiveness with which the ego discharges its functions, namely, of coping with the id, the superego, and reality, and of integrating (as described earlier), and by the energy remaining to permit self-exclusion of the ego for purposes of creativity and *ad hoc* needs. This latter, one might call flexibility (in distinction to rigidity of the personality when the ego is very capable of mediating between id, superego, and reality, but only at the cost of utter impoverishment of its resources).

Ego strength must be considered a resultant of the developmental factors mentioned above.

The ego will be strong:—

(1) If its *congenital, genetic, and constitutional equipment is "good."* If there are any hereditary aspects to the presence or absence of mental disease then it would seem that ego strength or its lack is what is inherited rather than specific psychiatric disorders. If statistics have shown anything at all convincing, then it is a greater incidence of all kinds of psychiatric disorders than of particular ones in certain families. It would also seem that actual libidinal and generally psychopathologic constellations would be secondary to the primary inherited defect (of ego strength) in such instances.

(2) *If the environmental circumstances are such as to permit consistent learning.*

(3) *If the id drives are not overwhelming.*

(4) A fourth factor affecting ego strength may be the so-called *secondary factors* of physiologic, pathologic, environmental nature. The most obvious effects on ego strength were, for example, discussed by Bychowski in a paper on the study of the brain wounded, and can be observed as well in lobotomies. Physiologic variations are encountered in sleep, dream, hypnagogic phenomena (Silberer's functional phenomena) and in exhaustion (Varendonck's preconscious fantasies).

Ego strength must be seen as something *global* in the way in which, for example, Wechsler conceives of intelligence. No single ego function can be appraised by itself without consideration of all the other functions at the same time. Any attempt to test ego strength would actually have to consist of many subtests such as in the Wechsler-Bellevue Intelligence Scale, each item being properly weighted to afford meaningful final data. Ego strength can then be measured by the effectiveness of the organism in various aspects of ego functioning, as revealed in the study of the integrative capacities under the impact of disorganizing events (experiments by Luria (1932), and Haggard (in Tompkins, 1946) and under the influences of frustration (Holt, 1943).

Experimental procedures would have to involve the hypothesis of quantitative factors and would have to take the following directions:

A. *An appraisal of libidinal status* (object relations):
   (1) A weighted scale of data consisting of a psychoanalytic appraisal of the history and symptomatology.
   (2) A weighted scale derived from projective test data.
B. *An appraisal of ego strength.*
   (1) A weighted scale of data concerning history and symptomatology with regard to ego strength (study of defenses, etc.). In such a scale different weighted scores would be given to the history of a psychotic mother or a psychotic aunt: having had a psychotic mother would be weighted in such a way as to decrease the total degree of ego strength more than the presence of a psychotic aunt not closely related to patient.
   (2) A weighted scale concerning medical history and somatic aspects of ego functioning.
   (3) Psychologic tests concerned with frustration tolerance and anxiety tolerance (Luria, Tomkins, Haggard, Holt, et al.) as well as integration and flexibility.
   (4) Physiologic tests of ego strength, such as hyperglycemic index, adrenergic response to stress, autonomic balance tests, a study of "mental set" under sodium amytal, the behavior in the Baranyi chair, etc.

All these test data will have to be weighted so as to allow summation and conversion into what one might call a Diagnostic and Prognostic Index.

In order to construct the aforementioned tests and scales, each subtest will have to be tested for its validity and its reliability; like items in an intelligence test, each part will have to be validated for its ability to differentiate crucially. For this purpose each item will have to be administered to normals, neurotics, manic depressives, patients with organic brain diseases, and schizophrenics. The ability of these items to differentiate between those more ill and less ill must be assured. For this purpose, exchange and substitution of items will frequently be necessary.

All measurements are based on an ordinal scale.

QUANTIFICATION

Any discussion of quantification as related to methodology in psychoanalysis is somewhat difficult. It seems to be a particularly objectionable idea to some psychoanalysts although quantitative terms are part of all psychoanalytic propositions.

A recent casual conversation with a colleague illustrates this point. He thought it impossible to consider positive transference in terms of "amount." However, when he was asked whether he ever thought of a patient as having a stronger positive transference one week than the week before, or of the possibility that the week after the transference would be stronger still, he agreed that such was frequently the case. I then suggested that this would constitute a scale: little transference, medium transference, greater transference. He found this readily acceptable and it was pointed out that it was merely a matter of agreement or convention (and convenience) to express this judgment by numbers: transference 1, 2, 3.

Most of us nonmathematicians have never got over the very concrete "how many apples will you have left?" way of thinking. Our scale, *transference 1, 2, 3,* does *not* imply that 2 is twice as much transference as 1, and that 3 is three times as much. The "ordinal scale" which methodologists use says that 1 is smaller than 2, and that 3 is bigger than 2 without stating any proportion between the numbers (Stevens, 1951). Such a scale, which we can and must construct for psychoanalytic concepts, has been very useful in other sciences.

PREDICTION AS A TOOL

If a hypothesis permits us to understand even one link in a chain of events, to predict accordingly and therefore to control therapeutically even a small part of human behavior, it must be considered useful. Statistical measures of validity are one way of telling us just how useful a hypothesis may be and what the probability is that a certain type of event will be followed by another certain type of event. Reliability, or the ability to repeat the same course of predicted events time after time and in a concretely demonstrable way, is another basic demand of science. Prediction is the central core of it all. I believe that the royal road for research, and one which is accessible to any group of psychoanalysts who will take the trouble, is the proper use of prediction and postdiction[4] on the basis of explicit and clearly formulated hypotheses.

Prediction is *the* tool of the scientific method and the one to which other techniques (e.g., repeat-reliability, manipulation) refer. Escalona has some misgivings about the applicability of prediction in clinical psychoanalytic investigations (1952). She says:

It is important to realize, however, that even the most successful predictions can do no more than lend strong support to a hypothesis; they cannot prove the truth of an assumption. This is because prediction from one analytic hour to subsequent ones, or from analytic hours to behavior in life situations, is not prediction in the same sense as when this term is used in reference to experimental work. The

---

[4] A term of G. W. Allport's which applies to statements referring to what must have happened in the past to account for presently observed facts; in essence, prediction in reverse.

crucial point about an experiment, the circumstances which allow us to accept experimental results as conclusive, is that prediction is made for a controlled situation. In clinical research we do not know what the relevant environmental influences are going to be at any future time, we do not know what is going to happen to the patient and what it is he will be reacting to at the time for which prediction is made.

Unlike Escalona, I believe that prediction is as strictly applicable to psychoanalytic hypotheses as it is to any science. We are not concerned with proving the truth of an assumption, but rather with testing the probability with which we can predict a certain kind of event. If strong support is given a hypothesis frequently, the reliability and validity of the hypothesis is increased in a very desirable way. Causality is only a conventional way of viewing the frequent temporal sequence of two events. Nobody has ever proved more than that.

When Escalona says, "We do not know what the relevant environmental influences are going to be—what is going to happen to the patient—and what it is he will be reacting to," it seems to me that she forgets the central proposition of all psychoanalytic theory: namely, that in personality and character we are dealing with a relatively stable and persistent structure which can be relied upon to maintain a great degree of sameness of responses to stimuli. Without such a proposition, there could be no psychological work, no testing, in fact, no living. The psychoanalytic theory particularly was originally predicated upon determinism and even now is especially committed to the notion that there is great probability that a person will react within a rather circumscribed choice of responses representing drive, defense against that drive, or a mixture and neutralization of these two variables, in an individually characteristic way. The daily work of the psychoanalyst is based upon this central theoretical assumption; very exceptional events excluded, it is only reasonable to test psychoanalytic hypotheses within this framework of relative stability in time.

Admittedly, the passage of time may make it quite difficult to predict minor psychological variables. In practice, the research analyst's task may be made easier by making major long-range predictions or intrasession predictions, not only predictions from the first half of the session to the second half, or from one small segment of the session to another, but ultimately perhaps from sentence to sentence. This might mean successive sentences of the patient, or successive statements of patient, analyst, patient. In any case, time is reduced to the same minimum as in any classical laboratory experiment. In a nonexperimental situation, I have tried a technique that might easily be extended for investigatory purposes. In the teaching of psychotherapy to residents, I have used one of Hans Strupp's (n.d.) movies of an initial interview as well as *The Initial Interview* record of Gill, Newman, and Redlich (1954) in the following way. After each sentence I asked, what is your judgment of the situation, what hypotheses are involved in your thinking, and, based on those hypotheses, what is your prediction for the next sentence? This was a teaching device, but there is no reason why such a device cannot be used in a controlled way. We should undoubtedly find that for some sentences there are hypotheses that permit us to predict successfully and for others not. The discrepancies would lead to further useful exploration.

Escalona expresses another reservation about prediction in her publication with Heider (1959, p. 5). She says: "We are impressed by the circumstance that, although an event may be predicted correctly, it may have occurred for reasons altogether different from those which led to the prediction. The fact that X is really followed by Y does not prove that Y occurs for the reasons we assign to the sequence, and this applies whether the theorizing is done retrospectively or in advance."

Their objection to the usefulness of prediction seems predicated upon a misconception of the process. The prediction that X will be followed by Y is meaningless. It may be based on intuition, prophecy, or plain guesswork. A prediction is useful scientifically if it is based upon clearly and explicitly stated steps, each of which can be independently verified and repeated and understood in a sequence of events. The patient, for example, is looking around the room approvingly and making complimentary remarks about the things in it. This behavior is consistent with a positive transference which at this moment is not consciously acceptable to him. Therefore, he displaces these feelings upon inanimate objects associated with the analyst; in the near future we may see in dreams or manifest behavior further indications of this positive transference. However, when we find no further evidence of positive transference the hypothesis is not sustained, either because it is wrong or because the feelings were too transitory (in which case it might be possible to support the hypothesis in some other patients); or we may accumulate evidence that this particular patient's looking around and making complimentary remarks was related primarily to other motivations.

The above prediction of unconscious positive transference involves such concepts as displacement, projection, a certain personality type, etc. as well as transference. Without complicating matters by bringing in a variety of intervening variables that are also involved, we can say that such a clinical hypothesis repeatedly and independently made by different analysts, who clearly relate the observed facts to interlocking hypotheses in making their predictions, will have fulfilled the scientific criterion of validation by successful understanding and prediction (and eventually control) of certain subsequent events.

Naturally, the method is not foolproof and does not necessarily establish the truth. What predictions permit is a probability that event A will be associated with B. The quality of the hypothesis will be ascertained by some such measure as the coefficient of correlation which indicates the extent of the probability. If it is of a certain magnitude we will be satisfied unless and until we have better approximations.

Prediction as a scientific method has attained increasing attention (Benjamin, 1959; Escalona and Heider, 1959; M. Kris, 1957). As a general source Meehl, on clinical versus statistical prediction, gives a broad background of the topic (1954) which is richly supplemented in an excellent critique by Mann (1961). I do not believe there is a difference in principle between clinical and statistical prediction. Such differences as do exist are those that exist between abstraction and reality. Clinical predictions are likely to involve more contaminating factors. The most effective safeguard is to be continually more explicit in all the inferences involved. It is as easy to be precise about an actuarial prediction that involves, for example, the life expectancy of male residents in New York as it is about any mathematical speculation. It is as difficult to be explicit and precise about a clinical prediction concerning, for instance, the transference of a patient in analysis as it is when one deals with any reality.

The broad problem of psychoanalysis and scientific method has been discussed in a volume edited by Hook (1959). Among many thoughtful contributions is this statement by Nagel: "Psychoanalysis falls short of the scientific tenet which holds that a credible theory must not only be confirmable by observational evidence but must also be capable of being negated." This is in line with Hook's attitude; he asks what evidence psychoanalysts would accept which would lead them to state that a certain child did *not* have an œdipus complex. The reply is that there is no such thing as an "œdipus complex." The philosophers here have done more to reify Freudian concepts than have the more enlightened psychoanalysts. There are only certain observations concerning the relationship of a child to his parents under different circumstances and at different times, made with sufficient frequency to have become lawful propositions. What one wishes to make amenable to scientific inquiry is whether different manifestations of these parent-child relationships occur according to analytic expectations or not. One would have to study a broad variety of child-parent groups and make widely divergent predictions which might be proved or disproved.

One way of attempting to utilize prediction systematically in an analytic setting is described in the following chapter. This includes use of a tape recorder.

Two principal ways are open to improve the means of studying and predicting actual change by the method described. One is by making longer-range studies (a year or two at least) which would permit the very small daily variations to be canceled out; the other is by making shorter-range predictions (on an intrasession basis) which would increase predictive validity by precluding the environmental contamination of which Escalona speaks.

Increasingly better definition of analytic concepts, longer experimental training, and closer acquaintance with the problems of quantitative rating on the part of participating analysts would be beneficial.

Some useful psychoanalytic research can be done by analysts who need to know only enough methodology to be able to consult intelligently with an expert methodologist. One may take any fragment of a psychoanalytic session, ask for predictions, and see how they are borne out. Suppose, on playing back the tape recording, the experimenter feels that a valuable piece of information has been imparted in the communications of the first ten minutes. He might play these ten minutes to a group of analysts and then ask questions in both unstructured and structured form, to wit: What went on? What will this lead to? What should the analyst say? What do you expect the patient to say in the next few sentences, in the rest of the hour, in the next session? The structured questionnaire might be a variant of the one described in Chapter 8 in multiple-choice form or a rating scale, making certain that the starting point is always anchored in a clearly defined segment of an analysis, and that the reasons for prediction and judgment, that is, the hypotheses concerning the concrete piece of information and the hypotheses for further inference, are clearly spelled out. Such a process would often lead to a very useful point of departure for further definition of terms and processes, and would lead to a sharpening of hypotheses. What is more, I cannot think of a better teaching and learning process than careful scrutiny of such recorded material.

This method of prediction might likewise make pathographies and biographical analyses more scientifically acceptable. As it stands now, they are usually extremely interesting and plausible to the analyst, but are often, and understandably, suspected of being *post hoc, ergo propter hoc* types of reasoning. Consider, for example, an extremely interesting paper by Niederland (1959) in which he proposed to relate certain biographical facts of Schreber's life to his psychotic symptoms. Niederland did a tremendous amount of excellent work in obtaining these new data, but instead of being descriptive or using the method of clinical intuition, he might have employed systematic predictions and judgments. He might have postulated certain facts about Schreber's childhood and *then* searched the material. He might then have attempted to link each of his initial expectations or postdictions to his actual findings, noted which conformed and which did not, and for which of his clinical facts and hunches he was able or not able to find corroboration. If two or more analysts would independently do the same thing with the material, and a few others were willing to try to match presented statements of observed symptomatological fact[5] with historical data, and would state their concept for linking one with the other, we could see how much concurrence there would be. By this matching technique we might get a measure of interobserver agreement. We would also learn where there was no agreement and have an opportunity to refine our hunches about the relationships between experience and symptom.

A STUDY OF THE PSYCHOANALYTIC PROCESS

A study of the psychoanalytic process itself is, to a certain extent, involved in any experimental study. Insofar as independent observers formulate, test, and compare opinions concerning the interaction between patient and analyst, they are studying the process itself.

A study of the process was more specifically intended in an experiment designed several years ago, entitled Hypothesis Formation in Psychoanalytic Supervision.[6] In this study, the sessions of a patient were again to be recorded. This time the analyst, who was to be a recent graduate of the institute, would report to an analytic supervisor as is the usual procedure. However, his sessions with the supervisor were to be recorded too. Three independent judges and three independent predictors were again to judge and predict from their observations of the patient's session material. Some intrasession material was also to be used. Each predictor and judge would, at first, receive only that part of the session prior to a major intervention by the analyst; he would then be asked what his intervention would be. Then he would be given the recording of the treating

---

[5] This method leaves the door open for biased selection and is therefore of limited usefulness unless it is further refined.

[6] This project was originally submitted to the Research Committee of the New York Psychoanalytic Institute in 1956 but has not been realized. Some years later Kubie independently published a paper dealing with the same problem area and made suggestions for similar research (1958).

analyst's intervention and asked to predict how the patient would respond. Finally, judges would be given the last part of the session and asked to state what, in their opinion, did happen.

By this means it was hoped to illuminate the personal equations: how much difference was there from analyst to analyst, and how much agreement was there in what they saw, predicted, and judged? Furthermore the supervisor was to be asked to record his impressions and predictions. Among other things the study would have permitted some insight into the amount and kind of material that is lost by transmission from candidate to supervisor.

The study provided for a number of refinements and ramifications including a provision to use analysts geographically far apart and trained in different institutes. The fundamental hypotheses of analysis were to have been examined again, a content analysis was planned, and some check on the effect of recording analytic material by comparing the trends prior to with those after recording was to be made.

Be that as it may, our present main interest in the study is that this method allows a close examination of the process of interaction, of personal distortions by the analyst, and of the distortions in transmitting to a supervisor. I believe that this method of short-range prediction and judgments, including intrasession prediction, enables one to study much that is of importance to analysis and to validate it in the best sense of the word.

RESEARCH IN PSYCHOANALYSIS AS A THERAPY

Psychotherapy (of which psychoanalysis is one specific form), unfortunately, is still too often all things to all men. I will define it as broadly as is possible while still maintaining it as a useful concept: psychotherapy is the systematic interaction of a "therapist" with a "patient" by intervention through symbols; this process must follow a framework of clearly stated hypotheses related to personality, and have as a stated goal, in the broadest sense, the metapsychological restructuring of the "patient" for his benefit.

This definition has its weaknesses, as every definition has that attempts a symbolic approximation of empirical data, but it serves to delineate psychotherapy from friendly advice, religious council, etc. The intervention is primarily by means of verbal symbols, although other signs such as silence, facial expressions, giving a placebo, or even a cigarette may have their effect. In group therapy we view the group as an extension of the therapist. Other forms of treatment concerned with the restructuring of the personality exist; for example, by effecting changes in the somatic substratum with drug therapy or psychosurgery.

Our goal as psychotherapists must be to find the most effective ways of bringing about beneficial changes. For this purpose we need increasing clarification of all the factors involved in the process. This attempt at increasing effectiveness must go on clinically *and* theoretically—experimentally, with mutual enrichment. Here, we are exclusively interested in the experimental approach and offer first a brief review of the aspects involved and of the related literature.

The first point concerns the major variables involved in psychotherapy. Of these, there are at least five, to wit: *the patient; the situational factors; time; the therapist;* and *the therapeutic method.* Under proper experimental conditions, we would want to create a situation in which the first four factors can be held constant, and the therapeutic method be the only variable and the only factor the effect of which we want to examine. The difficulties one encounters in attempting to meet these ideal laboratory conditions are legion. For instance, it would be statistically advisable that more than one patient be used, but then it would be necessary to match patients so as to keep them constant. Any clinician knows that people cannot really be matched. (While we may call five different people phobic, they vary tremendously individually.) Again, the situational factors can never be kept constant. People we treat are in the stream of life, and therefore infinitely varying factors enter in. Time itself is a troublesome variable because there is always the possibility of some spontaneous change in the psychodynamic equilibrium of patients. (The burden of proof will be on the experimenter to establish what changes are due to the influence of the therapeutic method and what are due to accidental variations or simply the passing of time.) As to the therapist: we know that one of the most frequent questions asked of anyone who has been treated is: "Who was your therapist?" This is no idle question. From the answer we form an idea of what sort of treatment it might have been, based on the notions we have about the particular therapist. The therapeutic method itself is not the least variable: we know from surveys that even among orthodox psychoanalysts there are divergencies in their daily practice (Glover, 1955; Oberndorf, 1949; Oberndorf, Greenacre, and Kubie, 1948).

In the past most investigators of psychotherapy have concerned themselves with *criteria for success.* The clinical criteria used were, for example: (1) loss of symptoms; (2) adjustment socially, occupationally, and sexually; (3) patient's satisfaction with outcome of therapy; (4) doctor's satisfaction with outcome of therapy. Some of the experimental criteria predicated upon the use of rating of recorded protocols are: (1) a ratio of negative and positive attitudes toward the self, the idea being that as therapy progresses there should be an increase of positive attitudes toward the self with a great shift in that ratio at the end of treatment (Miller, 1951; Raskin, 1949; Seeman, 1949; Sheerer, 1949); (2) an increase of insightful solutions (Raskin, unpublished); (3) an increase of acceptance of others (Sheerer, 1949); (4) a decrease in defensiveness (Haigh, 1949); (5) linguistic changes—an increase in adjectives and in subordinate clauses has been claimed by some as a good indicator of therapeutic success (Grummon, unpublished; Mowrer, 1953); (6) a discomfort-relief quotient as has been developed in connection with social work (Dollard and Mowrer, 1947); (7) the McVickers Hunt Movement Scale (Hunt and Kogan, 1950); (8) changes in the voice and in breathing technique (Finesinger, 1944).

Extensive efforts at rating psychotherapeutic events were made by Watson and Mensh (1951) using detailed reporting forms worked out with meticulous care. The "Q" technique of Stephenson (1953) has been put to recent, ambitious, and in a way, most sophisticated use to test progress in analysis and in other therapeutic situations. Of course, projective tests have been used extensively (Snyder et al., 1953), and content analysis deserves a special place among the evaluations of criteria and events in psychotherapy (Auld and Murray, 1955).[7]

The earliest attempts to gauge the success of psychoanalysts were simply concerned with the percentage of success. The survey of the Berlin Institute was one such attempt. Several investigators accumulated data to demonstrate that psychotherapists other than psychoanalysts were more efficient. Their lack of comparable criteria was obvious. Curiously enough, one of the crudest efforts along these lines in recent years was made by Eysenck (1952) who prides himself on being a particularly pure scientist. However, he seems to have lost all judgment when facing his favorite bête noire. The detailed reply by Rosenzweig (1954) demonstrates ably some of the pitfalls in this type of unsophisticated and uncontrolled comparison.

It has always been difficult to define "health" from a general medical or psychoanalytic point of view (Jahoda, 1958). Does it mean: "greater health than was possessed on starting psychotherapy or analysis"? Does it mean better functioning? Such general statements as "the attainment of genitality," "sublimation," or lately, "neutralization" and "object constancy," or "the resolution of the œdipus complex" are all terms sorely in need of definition.

I believe that a schematic approach to a definition of success in the *completion* of an analysis is possible but not very practical except as a frame of reference against which to check. One could postulate the ideally completed psychoanalysis as one in which all significant object relationships on all levels of development have not only been discussed but also, briefly at least, recapitulated in the transference neurosis. Success would lie in having "worked through" the affective and cognitive parts genetically in the transference and with regard to realistic contemporary relationships. (In this context, it is hard to resist thinking of psychoanalysis as a corrective recapitulation of previous history somewhat as Haeckel thinks of ontogenesis as a recapitulation of phylogenesis.)

Another approach to the measuring of health and increment of health during an analysis might be an extensive individual and over-all appraisal of all ego functions at different points of the treatment. I have elsewhere set out a scheme for doing just this; of arriving at some over-all measure of ego strength on the basis of subscores of each individual ego function (Bellak, 1958).

However, I believe that progress in psychoanalytic treatment could best be studied by using the method of short-range prediction: by postulating explicitly all the criteria; by making carefully hypothesized predictions; and by checking thus many serial sections of the analysis to see if the process conforms to expectations. To start with, one might state hypotheses concerning the transference relationship. Then one might make specific hypotheses concerning the analysis of defenses and feel that treatment was progressing satisfactorily even though the patient was feeling subjectively worse: it is in conformity to the hypothesis that the analysis of defenses often causes a transference regression. One might predict, and have independently judged, hypotheses concerning the resolution of

---

[7] In preparing a bibliography on Research in Psychotherapy, taught by Robert Holt and the author to graduate students of psychology at New York University, we accumulated, with heavy borrowing from the works of others, a bibliography of 462 items exclusively concerned with individual adult therapy.

conflict in dreams, fantasy, free association, and reality. By this method of prediction and judgment, one could scientifically study the nature and success of psychoanalytic treatment; each step in the analysis would be directly related to hypotheses which form part of the (largely unwritten) technique of psychoanalysis.

By this method, I believe, lies our best hope for making rational decisions on the advantages and disadvantages of the various schools of psychotherapeutic thought. By submitting the propositions of Klein, Sullivan, and Rogers to such serial study by short-range prediction and judgment, we may obtain reasonable clues about the validity and advantageousness of the one or the other form of theoretical or practical orientation. Group therapy should lend itself to the same kind of investigation. Last, but not least, it should enable us within the psychoanalytic house itself to develop those parameters for different types of patients which have become so necessary with the widening scope of psychoanalysis.

8

AN EXPERIMENTAL EXPLORATION
OF THE PSYCHOANALYTIC PROCESS

The experiment described in this chapter broke new ground in several ways. First, it made clear that recording analytic sessions, if done in a tactful and responsible manner, need not interfere with the treatment process. Second, it showed that judges could agree on the basic themes running through an hour or a series of hours, although their consensus was undoubtedly enhanced by their common training. Third, it showed that a predictive method, tied to a multiple-choice procedure, had particular merits for this kind of material. Subsequent studies have undoubtedly been influenced by this initial attempt.

The findings are somewhat more ambiguous. The good agreement between prediction (what will happen) and judgments (what has happened) is very likely an artifact of the method and does not represent any new information. The high correlations in Table 8 probably indicate that both judge and predictor could agree on the basic structure of the case and therefore used the same categories for their judgments. They do not indicate that psychoanalytic theory can or cannot be used to predict behavior. Thus, the findings speak more to method than to anything else; usefulness of the theory *qua* theory must be tested elsewhere by other means.

Despite these faults (which are, in large part, a function of its pioneering status), the study described here has not been appreciably bettered. Research using clinical materials must still depend on a laborious coding of latent and manifest content; reliability of the coding usually varies inversely with its clinical significance because the most interesting themes are those that lie several levels beneath the surface and, consequently, are the hardest to sift out clearly. Until this problem has been solved, the researcher is faced with the heartbreaking choice between the reliable and the significant. It is to the great credit of this chapter that it opted for the second.

CLINICAL PSYCHOANALYTIC STUDIES need to be supplemented by systematic experimental investigation of the psychoanalytic process. The psychoanalytic situation can be regarded as an experiment in which the attempt is made to study the patient's behavior in interaction with the analyst's behavior as the two principal variables. The analyst behaves in accordance with certain analytic hypotheses and the patient reacts correspondingly. Then the analytic session itself permits one to investigate the power of the hypotheses in helping us to understand, to predict, and to control behavior.

The general purpose of this study was to investigate the nature of communication between psychoanalyst and patient so that what is implicit in practice may be made explicit and consonant with theory. The degree to which understanding,

NOTE: From the *Psychoanalytic Quarterly*, 1956, 25, 385-414. Reprinted by permission of the publisher and M. Brewster Smith, co-author, whose collaboration is gratefully acknowledged.

prediction, and therapeutic control of behavior can be achieved through application of psychoanalytic hypotheses was explored.

· To do this psychoanalytic sessions were recorded. Two psychoanalysts were asked certain questions about what occurred in these recorded sessions. Two other analysts were asked to attempt to predict, independently, what the nature of subsequent analytic sessions would be. Statistical comparisons of agreements and disagreements were made. Recording permits making of a psychoanalysis what scientists call "a publicly demonstrable and repeatable experiment." Another group of analysts could study these same records and arrive at comparable conclusions.

The kind of study undertaken here forces the participants to attempt to describe more accurately what they see, to agree on definitions of phenomena, and to make more explicit the hypotheses under which they operate. The participants were surprised to find that an implicit prediction was part of their every interpretative statement.

It was decided to record the analytic sessions because only in that way could an objective record available for independent inspection be obtained. Traditionally analysts have felt critical of recording because they have felt it might destroy the necessary conditions of privacy and freedom from extraneous stimuli essential for the proper conduct of an analysis. It must be agreed that there probably are some patients, notably those who are very suspicious, with whom the procedure could not work. The patient discussed in more detail in this experiment was not at all suspicious. Five hours were recorded as a trial more than half a year before the actual experiment started and no disturbance was noted; furthermore, there seemed to be no change in trend before or during and after the trial run of recording.

During the actual experimental recording there was no indication of disturbance. And the patient was treated by analysis for eighteen months after the ending of the experimental recording. Special attention was paid to any changes when the recordings stopped. The procedure of recording was apparently so unobtrusive that the patient was unaware of its discontinuance for two or three hours after it was stopped. No change in trend was observed, and no significant influence of the recording has been discovered to date. The one effect caused by recording seemed to accord with the character of the patient and could be analyzed. This rather oral and exhibitionistic man enjoyed the idea that his analysis was being recorded. He felt that some extra investment was being made in him and that maybe the analyst would sit up for hours relistening and editing. In one dream a reference to recording appeared: the patient found himself part of a movie being shown to a large audience. This was analyzed with other evidences of exhibitionism. No unduly disturbing secondary gains were observed, nor was the transference significantly distorted.

It has also been objected that recording may interfere with the freedom of action of the analyst. It must be confessed that the recording of the first few sessions produced a discomfort in the analyst somewhat as does being under supervision or reporting to a seminar. There was some concern with the criticisms the other participant analysts might entertain. These feelings were described to the participants by the analyst as part of his dictated comments following each hour. During the first week of recording the analyst suffered an anxiety dream, the content of which was primarily concerned with the thought that the recorded hours were being nationally syndicated (a problem of exhibitionism on the part of the analyst, no doubt).

Others have feared (Kubie, 1952) that recording alone may not convey all the processes of communication between analyst and analysand. Screens permitting one-way vision and sound movies have been suggested. Even these procedures, however, do not guarantee that the significant communications have been observed or recorded since much that is of significance may occur on first encounter in the waiting room; furthermore, such a procedure is of course much more difficult, much more costly, and probably much more likely to create a really disturbing situation.

Comments were dictated by the treating analyst after each hour to provide supplementary data not readily apparent from the recording or transcript. These comments took note of changes in facial expression, posture, and voice, or of circumstantial factors such as that the patient came in through the hallway door as an attractive woman left. Care was taken to exclude from these comments any interpretation that might tend to bias the evaluations of the recorded material by the other participants.

One of the great problems in the study of psychoanalytic hypotheses has been the fact that nonpsychoanalysts have had to judge the relevance of data. It was justly felt by analysts that no one but a psychoanalyst can equitably judge the psychoanalytic process. This "criterion problem" was solved for the purpose of our study by using psychoanalysts as independent judges and predictors.

In order to be sure that the quantitative concepts had meaning, we always tied them to qualitative statements.

Throughout the experiment, the greatest care was taken to avoid "contamination" of judgment. The recorded material of one week at a time was distributed to each participant. Whenever the analyst also recorded some of his own interpretative impressions, they were withheld from the rest of the group. When the group met for discussions, care was taken to limit the discussion to such points as would not influence predictions or judgments (the discussion was usually limited to problems of method and concept and to the records of hours on which predictions and judgments had already been recorded). These group meetings were also recorded.

We recorded, with the explicit permission of the patients, a series of entire sessions of two patients. Patient A was recorded first, from his first through his sixtieth session. Thereafter, patient B was recorded for fifty sessions. The treating analyst, five other analysts, and a psychologist (as consultant on methods) participated. The recorded material was typed, with identifying data deleted,[1] and was then distributed to all participants.[2] The trial recording for five hours of another patient was first submitted to the group for discussion of procedures to be followed, and for trials of prediction and judgment. After this the experiment itself was carried out as follows.

---

[1] Except during a very brief period, the typists were analyzed psychologists.

[2] All analysts participating in this study (Andre Allen, M.D., David Epstein, M.D., Bertram Gosliner, M.D., David Kairys, M.D., and the late Adolph Zeckel, M.D.) are graduates of the New York Psychoanalytic Institute, and belong approximately to the same academic generation.

TABLE 1

PART I: STANDARD PREDICTIONS (QUANTITATIVE)

The patient's	Present Status		Next Hour		Next Week*		Next Month*		Other	
	Consc.	Uncon.	Consc.	Uncon.	Consc.	Uncon.	Consc.	Uncon.	Consc.	Uncon.
Transference										
positive										
negative										
Acting out	XXXXX		XXXXX		XXXXX		XXXX		XXXXX	
Insight		XXXXXXXX		XXXXX		XXXX		XXXXXXX		XXXX
Working through										
Resistance										
Anxiety										
Aggression										
Extra-										
Intra-										
Passivity										
Guilt										
Depression										
Elation										
Oral strivings										
Anal strivings										

Phallic strivings							
Oedipal strivings							
Genital strivings							
Homosexuality							
Scoptophilia							

DEFENSES:

Repression							
Projection							
Rationalization							
Isolation							
Denial							
Intellectualization							
Displacement							
Reaction formation							
Regression							
Reversal							
Identification with aggressor							

* Refers to the hour after this week's material, week after this material, etc.

Please rate intensity in appropriate columns by 0-10.

Date material rated:

Sessions rated:

Name of rater:

(1) A consecutive series of analytic sessions of patient A was recorded. The necessary explanation and reassurances were given to the patient regarding anonymity and other problems. The matter of recording was discussed with the patient even though his agreement was immediate. Several hours were permitted to elapse for him to have an opportunity to change his mind and to have a chance to analyze any problems that might arise in connection with the recording.

(2) A secretary picked up the recordings daily and typed them. If, for example, the last recording was picked up on Friday, the typed transcripts of all sessions were available to both predictors and judges Saturday noon and were delivered by the secretary. One of the four or five weekly hours was retained in recorded form; the other tapes were re-used after two weeks and only the transcripts were kept. (After each hour had been typed, the secretary submitted it to the treating analyst for any necessary correction of errors, before distribution.)

(3) On the basis of each week's records, two members of the group made predictions of what would happen in this analysis in the next session, in the next week, and in the next month. (All participants could listen to all or any part of the recordings, if they wished, though in fact predictions and judgments were based almost entirely on typewritten transcripts.) Predictions and judgments were made with the help of forms provided for this purpose.

(4) Starting one week later than the "predictors," two members of the group judged what had in fact happened in the succeeding analytic sessions, using forms basically the same as those of the predictors.

(5) The treating analyst also made predictions which, however, were not communicated to the participants. Comments of the analyst necessary to supplement the auditory record (noting, for example, changes of position and voice of the patient) were added to the transcript.

(6) After four weeks, a meeting was held. The statistical findings on the first four weeks of comparisons of predictions and judgments were presented to the group. If necessary, modifications of method were adopted as a result of general discussion.

(7) Those who were "judges" next served as "predictors" and vice versa. After four weeks, another meeting took place, followed by another four-week period of exchanged functions; this plan was continued for a total of twenty-four weeks. Different analysts were paired as predictors and judges in these periods, systematically varying the possible combinations. After the end of the project, a general evaluation took place wtih particular emphasis on the nature of hypotheses confirmed and those unsuccessful, and with an attempt to differentiate artifacts from genuine shortcomings of hypotheses. Attempts to reformulate the hypotheses were made.

(8) The same procedure was followed for patient B. Additional prediction and judgment sheets covering the main themes of sessions were introduced.

Aside from the initial trial period of two weeks, patient A was followed over three periods of four weeks each. After that, patient B was recorded. He was a patient of mine. I did not want to know the judgments and predictions of the group. (This was possible by the time patient B came under consideration, since the study was running smoothly and I could isolate myself somewhat from the mechanics of the experiment.)

Quantitative results are here presented for both cases, but the present discussion will be of patient B. The group was given data of the case history after an attempt to delete any dynamic formulations that the analyst had already formed on the basis of his experience. The meeting at which these data were presented was recorded, for later scrutiny.

TABLE 2

PART I: STANDARD JUDGMENTS

The patient's	Previous Status*		First Hour**		Current Week	
	Consc.	Unconsc.	Consc.	Unconsc.	Consc.	Unconsc.
Transference						
positive						
negative						
Acting Out						
Insight						
Working through						
Resistance						
Anxiety						
Aggression						
Extra-						
Intra-						
Passivity						
Guilt						
Depression						
Elation						
Oral strivings						
Anal strivings						
Phallic strivings						
Oedipal strivings						
Genital strivings						
Homosexualtiy						
Scoptophilia						

TABLE 2 *(Continued)*

DEFENSES:

Repression					
Projection					
Rationalization					
Isolation					
Denial					
Intellectualization					
Displacement					
Reaction formation					
Regression					
Reversal					
Identification with aggressor					

* Status of the previous week.

** Status first hour of current week.

Please rate intensity in appropriate columns by 0-10.

Date material rated:

Session rated:

Name of rater:

To make clear the actual procedures followed, the prediction and judgment sheets with which each of the participants worked are presented (Tables 1 to 4). The first sheet required predictors to rate variables agreed upon. On the second or qualitative sheet, predictors were asked to give their reasons for expecting change in each variable so rated. They were asked to name the variable with respect to which they had predicted a change; to summarize the observed facts relevant to prediction of change; to state the hypothesis underlying their predictions; and thereupon to state the predicted changes of that particular variable. Using the form illustrated in Table 3, the predictors made "postdictions"— G. W. Allport's term—and here applied to statements of what must have happened in the past of the patient to account for the currently observed clinical facts. Finally (Table 3) predictors were asked to write a thumbnail sketch of developments in the week's analysis, unhampered by quantitative ratings and formal argument. The judges were also given similar forms to fill out. The reproductions in Tables 3 and 4 constitute condensations of three pages each. One complete page (or two, if a participant chose) was devoted to specific predictions, one to postdiction, and one to a thumbnail sketch.

TABLE 3

	Page 2

Part II A: Specific predictions (Qualitative)
(1) (a) Variable considered
    (b) Reason for predicted change:
        Observational
        Theoretical
	This blank is meant to supplement Part I: Standard Predictions. Please select variable for prediction from there, stating here the observed fact and hypothesis leading to prediction.

	Page 3

Part II B: Specific *Post*dictions
(1) (a) Observed Clinical fact:
    (b) Hypothesis:
    (c) Postdiction:	

	Page 4
Part III: Thumbnail sketch Please write any number of statements about what you believe went on in this week's analysis, what will result from it, what accounts for it (genetic propositions, dynamic propositions). Please use this sketch to give you all the freedom of expression that was so limited by the questionnaires.	

A few brief examples of each experimental category may make the process clearer. For instance, Dr. X wrote the following under "judgment":

(a) *Variable considered:* Acting out (Dr. X indicated that he believed there had been a change in this variable).

(b) *Observed clinical fact:* Patient compulsively seeks sexual relations with women right after he returns from a visit home, and again later when material has come up pointing to passive homosexual strivings.

(c) *Please state explicitly rationale for judgmental change, in detail:* I consider this behavior to be an acting out; it shows a defensive purpose, attempting to alleviate anxiety stemming from œdipal conflict, both in positive and negative aspects. The relationships to women were oral and this might indicate oral regression from incestuous wishes.

TABLE 4

	Page 2A

Part II: Specific Judgments (Qualitative)
(1) (a) Variable considered:
    (b) Observed clinical fact:
    (c) Please state explicitly rationale
        for judgmental change, in detail:
	This blank is meant to supplement Part I: Standard Judgments. Please select from there *each variable* which you have judged as *changed from previous status*.

	Page 3A
Part III: Judgments (1) (a) Significant genetic data found: (b) Presumed psychological significance of above:	

	Page 4A
Part IV: Thumbnail sketch: Please write any number of statements about what you believe went on in this week's analysis, what will result from it, what accounts for it (genetic propositions, dynamic propositions). Please use this sketch to give you all the freedom of expression which was so limited by the questionnaires.	

What was not made quite explicit (it was not really necessary since the group had agreed upon a definition of acting out) was the metapsychological concept of acting out as "recreating an infantile impulse rather than recollecting it." But the analyst gave his reasons for judging acting out to be increased.

In a similar way, Dr. Y, from his reading of the preceding week's material, predicted as follows:

(a) *Variable considered:* Acting out (he predicted an increase).

(b) *Reason for predicted change (observational-theoretical):* With the upsurge of oral pregenital material observed this week and the homosexual material becoming evident and the castration fears and desires coming to the foreground, I predict the patient will once again act out by showing his virility and his aggressive maleness by promiscuity: this will serve to cover up the above and will shield him (and his analyst, he hopes) from awareness of basic passivity.

A specific postdiction was made by Dr. Z, as follows:

(a) *Observed clinical fact:* The patient compares his present position with that of his brother and shows how much better off he himself is.

(b) *Hypothesis:* The above is the result of a feeling earlier in life that the reverse was true.

(c) *Postdiction:* The patient felt rivalry and inadequacy in his relationship to this brother, particularly with regard to sexual strivings.

As I worked with this patient, I found that my implicit predictions were often concerned with the nature of the theme of the sessions and its relationship to previous hours and to predictions of coming sessions. I therefore made up specific questionnaires (Table 5) concerning the main theme of sessions since this seemed to be the most obvious and frequent problem in understanding and prediction and control (by interpretation). I then asked predictors and judges to select, out of a number of themes listed, the theme they judged or predicted to be the actual theme of the period under consideration. The participants were also asked to rate the relative importance of each theme, if they felt that more than one theme appeared in the material (this latter task was not regularly fulfilled by the participants).

This method of multiple choice was used in order to preserve the context of the analytic situation. The method would be valueless if the themes from which choice was made were not equally plausible. Therefore themes perceived in this patient by me and themes current in the analyses of other patients of mine were offered to the predictors and judges. In later weeks earlier themes of the experimental patient (not current during that particular week) were also included with the theme considered by me to characterize the patient in the week under study. This made the task more subtle and difficult.

TABLE 5A

PREDICTORS: ON THE BASIS OF HAVING READ HOURS 20–24, WHAT WOULD YOU PREDICT WILL BE THE MAIN THEME OF HOUR 25?*

False	1	2	3	4	5	6	7	8	9	10	True
1. Aggressive oral wishes for possession of mother in competition with siblings and father, the analyst appearing as mother in transference situation.											
2. Identification of all sexuality with masturbation and being observed at it. Fears punishment and attempts always to meet standards of behaving well to avoid it.											
3. Lethargy as a result of anger turned inward and meant originally for mother who is seen as withholding.											
4. Concern with watching (primal scene) and resulting (homosexual) castration anxiety and orality, also apparent in transference situation.											
5. Resistance and anger at analyst who is seen as not giving enough and loving others more, and resultant sulky withdrawal.											

TABLE 5B

PREDICTORS: ON THE BASIS OF HAVING READ HOURS 20–24, WHAT WOULD YOU PREDICT WILL BE THE MAIN THEME OF HOURS 25–29?*

False	1	2	3	4	5	6	7	8	9	10	True
1. Deals with many-faceted problems of sex differences (and pro-generation) and particularly their violent origin. Pregenital material abounds partly as defense, as in repression, denial, and reaction formation (to his own phallic wishes).											
2. Primal-scene material leading to feeling that it is as dangerous to be a man (who gets hurt inside vagina) or hurt by other man, as to be a woman who gets hurt. Repression, denial, and depression are aspects of his attempts to manipulate his fears and own impulses.											
3. Sadistic wishes and fear of punishment for them and voyeuristic wishes fused with them being acted out and rousing anxiety over being accused of misdeeds.											
4. Competitiveness as an attempt to ward off passive wishes, with fantasies of greatness and availability of overflowing oral gratification as attempts to allay anxiety.											
5. Intellectualization and isolation as main forms of resistance to anal-erotic wishes in transference situation.											

* Identical multiple-choice questionnaires were given to the judges, asking what in their opinion were, in actuality, the main themes of the hours concerning which the predictors had made their predictions.

QUANTITATIVE RESULTS

The degree of agreement among judges, among predictors, and between predictors and judges, was assessed by correlation coefficients.[3]

A. AGREEMENT AMONG JUDGES

Before one can evaluate the adequacy of prediction, it is necessary to determine how well the judges agree with one another. If there should be little agreement on what the data *are,* there would be no way to determine how well others have predicted what the data *will be.*

Table 6 shows that there was considerable agreement among judges on the variables to which they assigned relatively high or low ratings. Correlation coefficients between judges were all positive, and ranged from .11 to .78. It should be added that the data were tabulated only for variables on which both raters made a rating in a given week. These results therefore represent the degree of agreement in judgment in those instances in which both raters felt that a

TABLE 6

AGREEMENT BETWEEN JUDGMENT RATINGS*

Comparison		Previous Status		First Hour		Current Week	
CASE A	Weeks	Cs.	Ucs.	Cs.	Ucs.	Cs.	Ucs.
		r (n)	r (n)	r (n)	r (n)	r (n)	r (n)
C vs. M	V–VIII	.35 (53)	.30 (60)	.67 (53)	.32 (59)	.57 (53)	.67 (59)
E vs. G	I–IV	.73 (46)	.58 (47)	.55 (45)	.56 (46)	.11 (45)	.57 (46)
F vs. C	IX–XII	.37 (56)	.62 (56)	.45 (62)	.74 (62)	.31 (62)	.70 (63)
CASE B							
G vs. F	V–VI	.70 (36)	.62 (36)	.75 (36)	.53 (36)	.64 (35)	.73 (35)
M vs. G	I–IV	.78 (33)	.38 (32)	.47 (52)	.76 (49)	.60 (52)	.60 (49)

* Correlations were computed between the ratings assigned by each pair of judges. Ratings of the defenses and of intra-aggression were omitted. All other instances in which a pair of predictors rated the same variable were tabulated. The number (n) of such instances on which correlation is based is given in parentheses.

---

[3] Such coefficients can range from −1.00 to 1.00, the former expressing complete disagreement and the latter expressing perfect agreement, while a zero correlation represents a completely random relationship. The method used here is that of "tetrachoric" correlation, which involves classifying the data into four categories: high-high, high-low, low-high, and low-low. This method sacrifices accuracy for ease of computation; since the numbers of cases on which each coefficient is based are also small for the most part, it is the general picture that is significant rather than any particular figure. Since there is little systematic change in ratings from week to week, a high degree of agreement reflects agreement on the dynamic structure of the case (which variables are high, which low) rather than agreement on change. The degree of correlation obtained obviously depends also on the particular variables selected for study, especially on the number of these variables on which judges and predictors gave 0 ratings. Yet the variables selected for rating seemingly include a representative variety of psychoanalytic concepts; and agreement on the absence of a variable, while perhaps less difficult to achieve than agreement about the degree to which it is present, nevertheless provides evidence of consistency among predictors and judges in formulating the dynamic processes in the patient in terms of analytic constructs. The bearing of the data on the prediction of change is discussed hereafter.

judgment was possible. If ratings had been required on all variables, lower figures would have resulted. Such required ratings would be logically and clinically entirely meaningless. It is well understood that any scientist addresses himself to a limited area of functioning; to variables which, at the moment, seem important to him. The statistical picture would be rather more distorted than truthful if he were forced to rate variables he considered irrelevant at the time.

B. AGREEMENT AMONG PREDICTORS

Table 7 shows the degree of agreement among predictors. Correlation coefficients are all positive and range from .07 to .95. The moderate to strong agreement shown in most of these correlations is subject to the same qualifications discussed above. Predictors agree, for the most part, as well with each other in regard to next hour and next week as judges do in regard to first hour and current week (it will be remembered that present status and previous status both represent a judgment). Although the data are scanty for case B, there seems to be no appreciable difference in this regard between case A and case B.

C. AGREEMENT BETWEEN PREDICTORS AND JUDGES

Only those instances in which the judges' ratings were in close agreement were used to evaluate the degree to which predictions were substantiated by the judgments. Prediction, that is, was tested in instances in which the facts seemed reasonably clear.

Table 8 represents data on the relationship between predictions and judgments. Fewer instances are available for analysis than in Tables 6 and 7, since both judges' ratings had to be available for a variable, and in substantial agreement with each other, before a case could be tallied. Since each tally is based on the average of a pair of ratings by judges and in many cases by predictors, the data are more stable than in Tables 6 and 7. Here the prediction of one or

TABLE 7

AGREEMENT BETWEEN PREDICTION RATINGS*

Comparison		Present Status		Next Hour		Next Week	
CASE A	Weeks	Cs.	Ucs.	Cs.	Ucs.	Cs.	Ucs.
		r (n)	r (n)	r (n)	r (n)	r (n)	r (n)
E vs. M	I–IV	*** (13)	.62 (32)	*** (3)	.43 (19)	*** (6)	.40 (18)
F vs. G	V–VIII	.81 (45)	.69 (46)	.85 (44)	.73 (45)	.87 (43)	.64 (43)
M vs. G	IX–XII	.80 (46)	.60 (43)	.94 (44)	.61 (41)	.95 (43)	.49 (41)
CASE B							
C vs. F**	I–IV	.88 (24)	.37 (35)	.95 (22)	.40 (34)	.90 (22)	.41 (34)
M vs. G	V–VI	.55 (29)	.50 (27)	.66 (27)	.65 (22)	.40 (24)	.07 (20)

* Correlations were computed between the ratings assigned by each pair of predictors. Ratings of the defenses and of intra-aggression were omitted. All other instances in which a pair of predictors rated the same variable were tabulated. The number (n) of such instances on which each correlation is based is given in parentheses.

** Data for Week IV were omitted since the records left some ambiguity as to whether G had acted as a predictor or as a judge.

*** Correlations not available.

TABLE 8

RELATIONSHIP BETWEEN PREDICTIONS AND JUDGMENTS*

Type of Variable Rated	Case A			Case B	
	Weeks I–IV r (n)	Weeks V–VIII r (n)	Weeks IX–XII r (n)	Weeks I–IV** r (n)	Weeks V–VI r (n)
Present Status					
conscious	.62 †(38)	.87 (40)	.73 (54)	... (0)	.73 (34)
unconscious	.30 (26)	.17 (49)	.62 (60)	... (0)	.75 (46)
Next Hour					
conscious	.45 (30)	.96 (41)	.65 (57)	.93 (48)	.68 (34)
unconscious	.64 (43)	.26 (42)	.78 (53)	.73 (50)	.62 (38)
Next Week					
conscious	.77 (27)	.97 (35)	.62 (58)	.53‡(47)	.70 (33)
unconscious	.89 (53)	.22 (48)	.51‡(54)	.56 (56)	.60‡(30)

* Only those instances rated by both judges in which their ratings did not differ by more than three scale points are considered. Correlations were computed between average ratings assigned by the pair of judges and the corresponding average ratings made by the predictors. To obtain sufficient instances for statistical analysis, instances in which only one predictor made a rating are included. Ratings on unconscious variables in this table are not strictly comparable to those on conscious variables, since they include ratings on the various defense mechanisms. Ratings on intra-aggression are omitted from the analysis, since the variable was dropped during the course of the study.

** The correlations in this column are based on the assumption that rater G functioned as a predictor in week IV. The records are ambiguous in this respect.

† Chi-square tests corresponding to boldface figures indicate significant association at better than the .01 level.

‡ Chi-square tests corresponding to italic figures indicate significant association between the .01 and .05 level.

both predictors is matched against the combined judgments of a pair of judges. The same logic of correlation described for Tables 6 and 7 applies here.

Again, with considerable variability to be expected with so few instances for comparison, the correlations are all positive and for the most part moderately to strongly so. Most of them represent relationships that have a high degree of statistical significance.

It would be easy to misinterpret these findings. They mean that predictors and judges generally agree in the variables they rate relatively high or relatively low. They do *not necessarily* mean that the predictors are predicting them accurately in regard to *changes* in the dynamics of the case. In fact, there is other evidence that they do not predict change accurately (in terms of how change is rated by the judges). The quite respectable degree of agreement reflected in Table 8 is essentially agreement on the *persisting* structure of the case, which appears in fairly good predictor-judge correlation as well as in consistency among predictors and judges (Tables 6 and 7). No impressive differences appear between the two cases, or between agreement on conscious or unconscious variables. Similarly, agreement is not systematically different between present status (a matter wholly of *judgment*), next hour, or next week.

Additional analysis of the data was undertaken to determine whether there was significant agreement between prediction and judgment of change. Whether the variables were grouped or taken separately, the analysis indicated a virtually random relationship, if all variables were considered.

To summarize the results so far, then, one might say that there is no doubt that the participating analysts were able, quantitatively, to agree on the structure of a case. While they were able to predict the absolute status of the patient on the several variables with considerable success, they were unsuccessful in predicting the variables in which positive or negative change would occur in a given period in this part of the experiment. Such change, of course, is likely to represent minor variations on underlying consistent themes. It nevertheless poses the severest test of a theory's predictive power.

This result is closely related to the question previously raised: is it reasonable to expect analysts to make required, or forced, judgments? It may well be more appropriate to expect them to restrict their judgments to those variables that they consider relevant at a given time. That would, of course, necessitate initial agreement upon which variables are to be considered relevant at the time. A second judgment would then involve the specific status and change in direction of each relevant variable within the given period.

In effect, the method of judgment of main themes discussed in the following pages is one attempt to deal with this problem, without being quite as systematic.

Another approach to the problem of prediction might be to carry on studies for at least a year or two to permit longer-range predictions. Many smaller individual variations might cancel each other out and bring out quantitatively the essential agreement which was quite obvious qualitatively in the present cases.

There is no doubt that increasingly better definition of analytic concepts, longer training for experiments, and better acquaintance with the problems of quantitative rating on the part of the participants would be beneficial.

D. THE SPECIFIC PREDICTION-JUDGMENT QUESTION

On the specific questions (multiple choices) put to predictors and judges during each week of case B, there was striking agreement and success, with only one minor exception.

Table 9 presents synoptically the principal data with respect to the specific prediction-judgment problems with which the raters were confronted during each of the six weeks of case B. The data are of a sort that do not lend themselves to statistical analysis, but happily they are so straightforward that statistics would add little. This table must be studied in conjunction with the questions posed to the raters, as these questions were actually worded. The questions define the nature of the task; the table enables one to see how successfully it was accomplished.

The first observation is that whenever all judges, including myself as the treating analyst, are in complete agreement (Weeks I, II, IV, VI) about the best answer among the alternatives, the responses of the predictors also agree with them with only one clear exception. This degree of agreement is of course striking. And it is the acid test, for unless the judges agree it can be argued that the questions and alternative answers were ambiguous or otherwise inadequate.

TABLE 9

RESULTS OF SPECIFIC PREDICTION-JUDGMENT QUESTIONS*

Case B

Question No.	Answer Categories	Week I		Week II		Week III		Week IV		Week V		Week VI	
		Pdrs.	Jgs.**	Pdrs.	Jgs.	Pdrs.	Jgs.	Pdrs.	Jgs.	Pdrs.	Jgs.	Pdrs.	Jgs.
1.	1												
	2	CF	MGB	CF	GB			DF	MGB			MC	GFB
	3												
	4					F	B	F	B	N	F		
	5					G	B			G	CB		CFB
2.	1	CF				F							
	2					C	G			G	C	G	CFB
	3	CF	MGB	CF	MGB		B						
	4												
	5												
3.	1	CF				F		CF	MCB	M	FB	M	
	2		MGB										
	3												
	4												
	5												
4.	1												
	2		M										
	3												
	4												
	5	CF	MGB										

* Only first choices (including tied first choices) are recorded. Letters stand for the several predictors and judges.
** My own judgments, made when I devised the questions, are recorded with the responses of the other judges (B).

The findings for Weeks III and V show some agreement even in these weeks in which judges disagree, agreement that appears more satisfactory when second choices are taken into account, as they are not in Table 9.

In most weeks, the "wrong" alternatives among which selection was to be made were formulated from other cases I was treating. A correct prediction or judgment, in such circumstances, is likely to mean that the predictor or judge recognizes one particular formulation as more congruent than others with the nature of the case in hand. It need not mean that he has distinguished what is true this week from what was true last week but is not at this moment characteristic of the case. In other words, it seems likely that these findings represent the same sort of success as is reported in Tables 6, 7, and 8, and do not necessarily imply an ability to make correct short-range predictions. On the other hand, the task was a more complex one than mere recognition of one formulation as more congruent with the case than others. Since material from earlier sessions of the experimental patient was included with material from the patient's current week, one might argue that the choices are indeed identifications of particular themes at particular points. Altogether, these cautious statements represent the most rigorous view that can be taken of the results. This should not obscure the fact that the results of the study show a gratifying measure of agreement in the description by four or five analysts in psychoanalytic language of the psychodynamics of a patient. This alone is more than has ever before been established experimentally and statistically, as far as I know.

QUALITATIVE RESULTS

From the qualitative studies of our data we learned some additional facts, which I commented upon in the Introduction.

(1) There was great divergence in the conception and definition of variables among the participants. Though clinically each seemed to know what he was doing and talking about, it became strikingly clear that analytic concepts are poorly defined and not so useful for communication as they might be. This state of affairs doubtless results from the fact that Freud, a pioneer, formulated hypotheses that helped him at a particular time to understand, predict, and analyze. As he advanced in clinical understanding, he reformulated his hypotheses to achieve progressively more fitting models of what he observed. Sometimes he remembered his earlier formulations and integrated them with later ones, sometimes not. The result is that at best one can use a concept by stating its date, but even then there are divergences. We suggest that a team of psychoanalysts and social scientists be formed for attempts at definition of the basic vocabulary.

(2) As the analysts studied the material, their preferences became apparent. One, for instance, seemed to refer much more to the facts of the patient's current life (as this was related to the internal dynamics), while another expressed more interest than others in a rejecting mother figure, and a third obviously gave more attention to the superego than did the others. It became apparent, however, that seeming differences in conception, as expressed quantitatively and qualitatively, were much greater than actual divergences. In the first place, some-

times the participants seemed to refer to the same thing but called it by different names,—for example, "resistance" or "repression." At other times they actually saw and discussed different aspects, but in time analyst B discussed what analyst A had discussed two weeks before, and vice versa. This fact suggests that personal characteristics of the analyst make him proceed in his own way, but that frequently his subjective preference is corrected so as to produce considerable agreement in the long run. The thumbnail sketches tend to support this observation. The basic problem to be studied is, of course, the interaction between patient and analyst, and the hypothesis concerning this interaction on which each analyst based his prediction.

9

AN EXPERIMENTAL STUDY OF

BRIEF PSYCHOTHERAPY

The study described in this chapter is an extension of the experiment described in Chapter 8. Again using the predictive method, it attempts to determine, from a list of specific personality variables, direction of change from one session to the next. To the extent that the predictions (in case B) were statistically significant, one can say that the persons participating in the study were correct in their assessment of the patient's dynamics and in a position to make meaningful estimates of how behavior would change during therapy.

MOST OF THE RESEARCH IN PSYCHOTHERAPY has been in relation to long-term psychotherapy. Experimental investigations of brief psychotherapy are few (Butler, 1953; Harris and Christiansen, 1946; Lord, 1950; Morton, 1955; Strupp, 1960) despite the fact that brief psychotherapy offers a number of research advantages, such as the brief time span involved, the identification of a specific treatment goal which reduces some of the difficulties in evaluating outcome (i.e., the "criterion problem"), and the fact that many different treatment techniques may be explored.

In another paper (Prola et al., to be published) we reported an extensive study of a large number of patients in brief psychotherapy, of not more than five sessions of fifty minutes each. It appeared, by means of self-ratings and independently reported ratings by the therapists, and administration of a Symptom Check List, that a successful outcome of these brief interventions could be demonstrated.

The intensive study of two of the patients included in the large sample is reported in this chapter.[1] Six psychoanalytically trained therapists used the method of short-range prediction and independent judgment, within carefully defined frames of reference, in an attempt to gauge the nature, process, and success of dynamic appraisal, formulation of a treatment plan, and outcome of brief, psychoanalytically conceived psychotherapy.

In long-term psychotherapy or psychoanalysis, the therapist generally tends to place less emphasis upon the immediate, day-to-day problems of the patient

NOTE: From *Emergency Psychotherapy and Brief Psychotherapy,* by L. Bellak and L. Small, New York, 1965. Reprinted by permission of Grune & Stratton and L. Small, whose collaboration is gratefully acknowledged and appreciated.

[1] This study was carried out at the Trouble Shooting Clinic of City Hospital Center at Elmhurst, with the aid of Project Grant 5-R11 MH-0915 of the National Institute of Mental Health.

and addresses himself more to the analysis of transference and resistance phenomena, dreams, free association, fantasies, etc., as a means of gradually uncovering infantile wishes and conflicts, making them conscious, and assisting the patient to "work them through." The therapist's technical activity in this kind of therapeutic process tends to focus upon reflection and interpretation and may be characterized as a generally passive or, better, expectant attitude; there is usually sufficient time for the patient gradually to become aware of genetic, dynamic material and to learn new ways of behaving. Freud remarked that, in some instances, the analyst "must behave as 'timelessly' as the unconscious itself."

In contrast, the aims and the corresponding methods of brief psychotherapy are designed to mobilize effectively the resources of the patient to help him deal with an immediate, pressing psychological difficulty which may also have reality implications. The primary aim is symptom removal; a secondary objective is that, having been able to work through this problem, the patient may become better able to deal with future conflicts, possibly because of some delayed structural changes.

I have described six basic techniques which are employed in brief psychotherapy (1952b): cathartic (and illuminating) interpretation, environmental manipulation, increasing drive repression, fostering the defensive use of intellectual understanding, increasing the strength of the superego, and increasing self-esteem. I emphasized the importance of obtaining a very thorough understanding of the genetic and dynamic roots of the current symptom picture before any therapeutic intervention is attempted, particularly with respect to drive interpretations.

Similar points of view have been discussed elsewhere; one paper was presented by Bibring (1949). Alexander and French (1946) also stress "the value of designing a *plan of treatment,* based on a dynamic-diagnostic appraisal of the patient's personality and the problems he has to solve. . . . The analyst must decide in each [case] whether a primarily supportive or uncovering type of treatment is indicated or whether the therapeutic task is mainly a question of changing the external conditions of the patient's life."

In 1956 Brewster Smith and I published the first systematic experimental study of psychoanalytic sessions by independent judges and predictors (see Chapter 8). Chapter 7 discusses a general topic which is also relevant to the present consideration: namely, the problems of quantification, of obtaining ratings which are meaningful as well as uncontaminated and treatable statistically, and especially the use of short-range predictions as a test of hypotheses and a criterion of validity. One of the cases in the present study was investigated with the help of predictive statements of a very simple nature. This method of repeated short-range predictions and judgments is probably particularly applicable to the profitable study of brief therapy—and brief therapy is probably particularly valuable for the systematic investigation of dynamic hypotheses and the treatment process because the shorter duration is so convenient.

THE PRESENT STUDY[2]

The specific method employed in this study involved repeated independent judgments by six raters on a complex series of increasingly detailed variables in the first case, and of repeated judgments on the same variables and ad hoc questions, specifically designed, in the second case, as well as independent short-range predictions concerning a series of variables.

The main goals of the project were: (1) to evaluate the efficiency of brief psychotherapy; and (2) to illuminate the process of obtaining successful therapeutic change.

The general approach was a partial replication of the study described in Chapter 8 in which psychoanalysts made judgments on a conceptual level about what transpired in one psychoanalytic session and made predictions, also on the same level, about future sessions. They were able to reach a high level of agreement on judgments but were not able to predict successfully.

The present study involved a modification of these techniques. In order to focus upon some of the following aspects of brief psychotherapy, we conceptualized our steps as follows:

(1) Obtaining a general understanding of the patient, his complaints, and his present life situation.
(2) Selecting and defining the problem area to be worked on.
(3) Formulating a dynamic appraisal of the problem which describes how reality, dynamic, and genetic factors converge to produce the presenting problem.
(4) Devising a plan of treatment to alter the balance of these forces so as to eliminate the symptom or reduce its severity. Implied in this plan is an "if . . . then" kind of prediction.

For the purpose of attaining these goals, a complex system of variables was defined in a manual and listed on rating sheets (pp. 134 to 140). A number of modifications were necessary in the preliminary tryouts with patients not part of the experimental design. The group had some practice sessions and discussions. To begin with, skepticism among several of the participants concerning the possibility of corralling significant data was high. Also, doubt that brief therapy could indeed be successful was expressed by those members of the research group who had not had previous experience with it in the "Trouble Shooting Clinic" at Elmhurst, as described in Chapter 16. As a matter of fact, the problem of recruiting qualified psychoanalysts was a fairly difficult one, as many of those approached doubted that controlled research could be successful in so short a time. It is gratifying to report that the initial doubts of the participants were apparently successfully dispelled.

L. Small served as therapist in one case, I in another. During those times, neither of us participated in research activities which could have contaminated

---

[2] The raters of this study group consisted of members of the New York Psychoanalytic Institute (L. Bellak, M. H. Hurwitz, M. Malev, and H. H. Schlossman), a classically psychoanalyzed, psychoanalytic psychotherapist and psychologist (L. Small, Ph.D.), a training candidate at the Psychoanalytic Institute of New York Downstate Medical Center (M. Brzostovski, M.D.), and a W. A. White trained, but mostly classically oriented psychologist and psychotherapist (A. Antonovski, Ph.D.). In addition, L. Small and T. Dineen made valuable contributions to the research design.

our functioning. There is a question whether the therapist himself should predict. Arguing for it is the fact that it may sharpen his thinking and that, after all, he is the best-informed. However, he may be tempted to act on his predictions and proceed to bring about the predicted outcome (self-fulfilling prediction).

PROCEDURE

The two patients whose sessions were to be taped for experimental study were selected by the research staff. It was desirable that they be likely to be suitable for dynamic psychotherapy and likely to stay through five sessions. In that sense these patients do not constitute a random selection. On the other hand, they were not specially selected for treatability. No other patients were started on treatment for this specific purpose and given up. No other patients were taped and rejected for the sake of preferring these patients. Unless the research staff is credited with a truly uncanny ability to select two patients who would be models of treatability, these patients must be considered fairly representative of those judged to be amenable to dynamic psychotherapy.

On the other hand, even if these patients had been selected out of hundreds of available ones for special suitability, it would not alter the fact that they were live human beings. If their problems could be understood in dynamic terms by several independent judges and predictors, including the therapist, and if all of these could agree in a methodologically carefully controlled, statistically significant way, then a lawfulness to those hypotheses underlying the propositions concerning the study and treatment must be assumed.

The patients were informed that the interviews would be taped and gave their written permission for taping and study. As soon as an interview was taped it was transcribed and made available to each rater. Only after he had rated a protocol was the next one made available. In the second case, predictors and judges were selected by lot.

METHOD OF ANALYSIS OF DATA

Two methods of analysis were employed. Method I uses a set of rating scales whose items are based upon a psychoanalytic model of personality functioning. Method II was designed to permit, in addition, the analysis of specific content material which was drawn from the patient under study. In contrast to the theoretically derived variables which were used in Method I, these were derived from the actual case material by members of the research team not directly involved in therapy, rating, or prediction, after all five interviews were transcribed.

METHOD I

(1) DERIVATION OF THE RATING SCALES

Three areas of therapeutic endeavor were selected for study: appraisal of the patient's illness, treatment plan, and patient status in each session.

Dynamic Appraisal (Scales 1 and 2). Following a paradigm which had been found useful in brief psychotherapy, a scale (No. 2) was devised to permit objective ratings which would adequately describe the source of the patient's current illness in dynamic terms. On the assumption that psychological distress is often the result of (a) a precipitating event which (b) arouses certain impulses which (c) result in certain impulse, ego, and superego modifications which constitute the patient's symptomatology, a set of subscales was developed to permit objective ratings of these three facets of psychiatric illness.

The subscale consisted of the following elements:

Primary Impulses
Drives as Defenses
Affects and Feelings
Ego Defenses
Superego Reactions
Ego Functions

Each of these subscales was in turn comprised of a number of relevant items: for example, under Ego Defenses the most common defense mechanisms were listed. The raters were instructed to indicate first the primary impulses which were aroused in the patient by the precipitating event and to indicate their intensity on a 7-point scale. They then proceeded to indicate the subsequent personality reorganizations which took place, by assigning numerical values, ranging from −3 through 0 to +3, to the other items. The complete scale is presented on p. 135.

Treatment Plan (Scales 3 and 4). Because of its limited time span, brief psychotherapy must be highly focused; its goals need to be very carefully specified. Accordingly, a scale was designed which would permit objective description of those aspects of personality functioning which need to be altered to help the patient achieve a more satisfactory way of living. One set of variables was concerned with the goals of treatment and another set of ratings involved the areas to be chosen for intervention and the types of intervention to be chosen.

Each scale consisted of the following subscales and is quite similar to the Dynamic Appraisal:

Impulses
Affects and Feelings
Ego Defenses
Superego Reactions
Ego Functions

SCALE 1

PRESENTING PROBLEM AND PRECIPITATING EVENT

1. Chief complaint, as described by patient:

2. Problem(s) selected for therapeutic attention:

3. Problem(s) to be avoided and reason(s) for their avoidance:

4. Precipitating event(s):

Patient_____Rater_____Date_____Int. #_____
                        Therapist   Judge
                        (circle one)

SCALE 2

DYNAMIC APPRAISAL

Primary Impulses Aroused		Intensity of Manifest Secondary Reactions

Passivity	0 1 2 3	*Drives as defenses*	
		passivity	-3 -2 -1 0 $+1$ $+2$ $+3$
Activity	0 1 2 3	activity	-3 -2 -1 0 $+1$ $+2$ $+3$
		homosexuality	-3 -2 -1 0 $+1$ $+2$ $+3$
Homosexuality	0 1 2 3	heterosexuality	-3 -2 -1 0 $+1$ $+2$ $+3$
		aggress-hostility	-3 -2 -1 0 $+1$ $+2$ $+3$
Heterosexuality	0 1 2 3	sadism	-3 -2 -1 0 $+1$ $+2$ $+3$
		masochism	-3 -2 -1 0 $+1$ $+2$ $+3$
Aggress-hostility	0 1 2 3	_____	-3 -2 -1 0 $+1$ $+2$ $+3$
		_____	-3 -2 -1 0 $+1$ $+2$ $+3$
Sadism	0 1 2 3	*Affects and feelings*	
		anxiety, fear	-3 -2 -1 0 $+1$ $+2$ $+3$
Masochism	0 1 2 3	elation	-3 -2 -1 0 $+1$ $+2$ $+3$
		depression	-3 -2 -1 0 $+1$ $+2$ $+3$

RATING SCALES

Primary Impulses Aroused

self-esteem -3 -2 -1 0 $+1$ $+2$ $+3$
guilt, shame -3 -2 -1 0 $+1$ $+2$ $+3$
anger, rage -3 -2 -1 0 $+1$ $+2$ $+3$

0 not aroused   _____ -3 -2 -1 0 $+1$ $+2$ $+3$
1 slight arousal   _____ -3 -2 -1 0 $+1$ $+2$ $+3$
2 moderate arousal   _____ -3 -2 -1 0 $+1$ $+2$ $+3$
3 strong arousal

Ego defenses
repress-denial -3 -2 -1 0 $+1$ $+2$ $+3$
projection -3 -2 -1 0 $+1$ $+2$ $+3$

Intensity of Manifest
Secondary Reactions

rational-intell. -3 -2 -1 0 $+1$ $+2$ $+3$
displacement -3 -2 -1 0 $+1$ $+2$ $+3$
isolation -3 -2 -1 0 $+1$ $+2$ $+3$
-3 strong decrease   reaction form. -3 -2 -1 0 $+1$ $+2$ $+3$
-2 moderate decrease   ident. w. agg. -3 -2 -1 0 $+1$ $+2$ $+3$
-1 slight decrease   _____ -3 -2 -1 0 $+1$ $+2$ $+3$
   0 no change   _____ -3 -2 -1 0 $+1$ $+2$ $+3$
$+1$ slight increase   _____ -3 -2 -1 0 $+1$ $+2$ $+3$
$+2$ moderate increase
$+3$ strong increase   *Superego reactions*
intensity -3 -2 -1 0 $+1$ $+2$ $+3$
consistency -3 -2 -1 0 $+1$ $+2$ $+3$

Strength of Ego Functions

_____ -3 -2 -1 0 $+1$ $+2$ $+3$
_____ -3 -2 -1 0 $+1$ $+2$ $+3$
_____ -3 -2 -1 0 $+1$ $+2$ $+3$
-3 strong impairment
-2 moderate impairment   *Ego functions*
-1 slight impairment   reality testing -3 -2 -1 0 $+1$ $+2$ $+3$
   0 no change   object relations -3 -2 -1 0 $+1$ $+2$ $+3$
$+1$ slight improvement   thinking -3 -2 -1 0 $+1$ $+2$ $+3$
$+2$ moderate improvement   impulse control -3 -2 -1 0 $+1$ $+2$ $+3$
$+3$ strong improvement   synthesizing -3 -2 -1 0 $+1$ $+2$ $+3$ U
autonomous -3 -2 -1 0 $+1$ $+2$ $+3$ U
_____ -3 -2 -1 0 $+1$ $+2$ $+3$
_____ -3 -2 -1 0 $+1$ $+2$ $+3$
_____ -3 -2 -1 0 $+1$ $+2$ $+3$

Patient_____Rater_____Date_____Int. # _____
           Therapist   Judge
            (circle one)

SCALE 3

Treatment Plan—Goals of Treatment

Impulses

passivity	−3	−2	−1	0	+1	+2	+3
activity	−3	−2	−1	0	+1	+2	+3
homosexuality	−3	−2	−1	0	+1	+2	+3
heterosexuality	−3	−2	−1	0	+1	+2	+3
aggression-hostility	−3	−2	−1	0	+1	+2	+3
sadism	−3	−2	−1	0	+1	+2	+3
masochism	−3	−2	−1	0	+1	+2	+3
————————	−3	−2	−1	0	+1	+2	+3
————————	−3	−2	−1	0	+1	+2	+3
————————	−3	−2	−1	0	+1	+2	+3

Affects and feelings

anxiety	−3	−2	−1	0	+1	+2	+3
elation	−3	−2	−1	0	+1	+2	+3
depression	−3	−2	−1	0	+1	+2	+3
self-esteem	−3	−2	−1	0	+1	+2	+3
guilt, shame	−3	−2	−1	0	+1	+2	+3
anger, rage	−3	−2	−1	0	+1	+2	+3
————————	−3	−2	−1	0	+1	+2	+3
————————	−3	−2	−1	0	+1	+2	+3
————————	−3	−2	−1	0	+1	+2	+3

Ego defenses

repression-denial	−3	−2	−1	0	+1	+2	+3
projection	−3	−2	−1	0	+1	+2	+3
rational-intellect.	−3	−2	−1	0	+1	+2	+3
displacement	−3	−2	−1	0	+1	+2	+3
isolation	−3	−2	−1	0	+1	+2	+3
reaction formation	−3	−2	−1	0	+1	+2	+3
identif. w. aggress.	−3	−2	−1	0	+1	+2	+3
————————	−3	−2	−1	0	+1	+2	+3
————————	−3	−2	−1	0	+1	+2	+3
————————	−3	−2	−1	0	+1	+2	+3

Superego reactions

intensity	−3	−2	−1	0	+1	+2	+3
consistency	−3	−2	−1	0	+1	+2	+3
————————	−3	−2	−1	0	+1	+2	+3
————————	−3	−2	−1	0	+1	+2	+3
————————	−3	−2	−1	0	+1	+2	+3

Ego functions

reality testing	−3	−2	−1	0	+1	+2	+3
object relations	−3	−2	−1	0	+1	+2	+3
thinking	−3	−2	−1	0	+1	+2	+3
impulse control	−3	−2	−1	0	+1	+2	+3
synthesizing	−3	−2	−1	0	+1	+2	+3
autonomous	−3	−2	−1	0	+1	+2	+3
————————	−3	−2	−1	0	+1	+2	+3
————————	−3	−2	−1	0	+1	+2	+3
————————	−3	−2	−1	0	+1	+2	+3

Patient_____Rater_____Date_____Int. #_____

Therapist   Judge

(circle one)

Scales: −3 strong decrease, −2 moderate decrease, −1 slight decrease, 0 no change, +1 slight increase, +2 moderate increase, +3 strong increase.

SCALE 4

TREATMENT PLAN: AREAS AND METHODS OF INTERVENTION

Area of Intervention	Rank Cluster		Methods of Intervention	Rank Cluster
Impulses				
passivity___			Catharsis___	
activity___				
homosexuality ___			Mediate Catharsis___	
heterosexuality___				
aggress-hostility___			Understanding-Interpreting___	
sadism___				
masochism___			Sensitization___	
			Repression and Restraint___	
Affects and feelings			Making Something Ego Alien___	
anxiety, fear___				
elation___			Support___	
depression___				
self-esteem___			Intellectualization___	
guilt, shame___				
anger, rage___			Counseling & Advising___	
			Direct Environmental	
			Manipulation___	
Ego defenses				
repress-denial___				
projection___				
ration-intell.___				
displacement___				
isolation___				
react form.___				
ident. w. aggress.___				
Superego reactions				
intensity___				
consistency___				
Ego functions				
reality testing___				
object relations___				
thinking___				
impulse control___				
synthesizing___				
autonomous___				

Patient___ Rater___ Date___ Int. # ___

Therapist   Judge

(circle one)

Each of these subscales was composed of a number of items, as previously described. The raters were instructed to describe the changes which needed to occur in the patient to achieve a reduction of her discomfort. This was done by rating each item on a scale ranging from −3 through 0 to +3. The complete scales are given on pages 136-137.

Session Observation (Scales 5 and 6). In order to permit objective ratings of the session-to-session changes in the patient, a scale was developed which was identical with that used for the Treatment Plan, with the addition of items which described the patient's behavior in the interview. The raters were instructed to rate the behavior of the patient as she appeared in each particular session (p. 140). A similar scale judged the therapist (p. 139).

(2) TRAINING SESSIONS

Before the scales could be applied under controlled conditions, it was necessary, first, to acquaint the clinicians who were to serve as raters with the use of objective rating methods in research, to familiarize them with the particular scales that were employed, and to reduce whatever negative attitudes they might have had toward the possibility of producing dynamic changes in brief psychotherapy.

A number of training sessions were held in which all the participants applied the scales to transcripts of interviews with patients who were then currently in treatment in the Trouble Shooting Clinic. Independent ratings were followed by group discussions in which differences in conceptualization were resolved, errors in rating techniques were rectified, and common definitions of the variables were agreed upon. Where necessary, minor changes were made in the rating scales and in the Manual of Directions (available upon written request).

As stated before, a considerable amount of skepticism was initially expressed by the participants concerning the possibility of therapeutic change within such a short period of time. However, these attitudes were revised as the participants were able to see similarities between the practice of brief psychotherapy and the methods they themselves commonly employed in handling crises in their own practice.

(3) PATIENTS

Of the two patients who served as subjects, Patient A was a housewife who complained of depression and suicidal fears; Patient B was an unmarried graduate student with complaints of anxiety and indecision in regard to social relationships. Each patient received five interviews at the Trouble Shooting Clinic which were tape-recorded with their consent.

(4) APPLICATION OF THE RATING SCALES

Following the training sessions, the rating scales were independently applied by five of the participants to Patient A according to the procedure described earlier.

After the ratings of Patient A were completed, a general meeting was held to explore any difficulties which might have arisen and to compare reactions to the procedure. This was followed by application of the rating scales to Patient

SCALE 5

SESSION OBSERVATION: THERAPIST

Area of Intervention	Rank Cluster	Methods of Intervention	Rank Cluster
Impulses		Catharsis	
passivity			
activity		Mediate Catharsis	
homosexuality			
heterosexuality		Understanding-Interpreting	
aggress-hostility			
sadism		Sensitization	
masochism			
		Repression & Restraint	
		Making Something Ego Alien	
Affects and feelings			
anxiety, fear		Support	
elation			
depression		Intellectualization	
self-esteem			
guilt, shame		Counseling & Advising	
anger, rage			
		Direct Environmental	
		Manipulation	
Ego defenses			
repress-denial			
projection			
ration-intell.			
displacement			
react form.			
ident. w. aggress.			
Superego reactions			
intensity			
consistency			
Ego functions			
reality testing			
object relations			
thinking			
impulse control			
synthesizing			
autonomous			

Patient_____Rater_____Date_____Int. #_____
                    Therapist   Judge
                    (circle one)

SCALE 6

SESSION OBSERVATION: PATIENT

Impulses	
passivity	
activity	
homosexuality	
heterosexuality	
aggression-hostility	
sadism	
masochism	

Affects and feelings	
anxiety, fear	
elation	
depression	
self-esteem	
guilt, shame	
anger, rage	

Ego defenses	
repression-denial	
projection	
rational-intellect.	
displacement	
isolation	
reaction formation	
ident. w. aggressor	

Superego reactions	
intensity	
consistency	

Ego functions	
reality testing	
object relations	
thinking	
impulse control	
synthesizing	
autonomous	

Relationship to Therapist	
cooperative	
submissive-dep.	
active re probs.	
hostile	
suspicious	
demanding	
seductive	
aloof	
intellectual	
open to interp.	
anxious	

Rating Scale

3 strong
2 moderate
1 slight
0 absent
X no basis for rating

Patient_____ Rater_____ Date_____ Int. #_____
       Therapist Judge 1st Half 2nd Half
       (circle one)   (circle one)

B. In rating this patient, the six participants were divided into three judges and three predictors. Both judges and predictors rated the patient on Scale 2 and Scale 4 for interviews 1 and 2.

The Session Observation scale was applied by the judges to all the sessions, with the instructions to rate the patient as they judged her to be in each session. The predictors were asked to *predict* the status of the patient in the succeeding session; that is, after having listened to the recording and read the transcript for interview 2, for example, they were to rate the status of the patient as they anticipated she would appear in interview 3. Each of the specific items under each subheading was rated on a five-point scale.

RESULTS: METHOD I

(1) LEVEL OF AGREEMENT

(a) *Dynamic Appraisal.* In attempting to formulate their understanding of the dynamics of the patient's illness, the judges and the predictors were able to agree at high levels among themselves. The mean reliability coefficient for the combined ratings of Dynamic Appraisal for both patients for all raters was .80 (Table 1).

It needs to be stressed that this coefficient does not refer to any relationship between prediction and judgment. With this rating scale, predictors and judges, acting as judges, expressed their conceptualizations of the psychiatric problems of the patients, and, as the results indicate, were able to do so with a high level of interjudge and interpredictor agreement. Insofar as the reliability of such ratings is an index of their "accuracy," the findings also indicate that all the raters were of equal proficiency in their ratings (judges $r_{xx} = .81$; predictors $r_{xx} = .78$).

There appears to be some slight improvement in the reliability of ratings with the second patient, suggesting the influence of increased familiarity of the raters with the rating procedures. However, it should be noted that no such change occurred with respect to ratings of Treatment Plan and Session Observation.

A careful evaluation of the dynamics of a patient's illness has been held to be of extreme importance in brief psychotherapy because of its highly limited, focused nature (see Chapter 8). The present findings indicate that it is in fact possible to arrive at highly reliable estimates of the psychodynamics of the patient within one or two interviews, as is required for the successful practice of brief psychotherapy.

TABLE 1

DYNAMIC APPRAISAL

Patient	A			B			A & B
Interview	1	2	1 & 2	1	2	1 & 2	1 & 2
Judges	74	75	75	84	91	87	81
Predictors (as Judges)	—	—	—	72	84	78	78
Judges and Predictors	74	75	75	78	87	83	80

Mean reliability coefficients, obtained by means of Tryon's Variance Form, of ratings of Dynamic Appraisal by judges and by predictors serving as judges. (Decimals omitted.)

It is also important to note that the obtained reliability coefficients of these ratings, which were based upon the fairly abstract conceptualizations of psychoanalytic theory, compare favorably with ratings based upon scales whose items are of a much more concrete and molecular nature.

Table 2 reveals that the ratings of the subvariables which comprise the Dynamic Appraisal scale were all above .70. It would appear from inspection of these data that measurement of the structural aspects of behavior (ego functions, defense mechanisms, superego reactions) is more reliable than is the assessment of motivational strivings (drives, impulses, affects, feelings).

(b) *Treatment Plan.* Ratings of judges[3] in formulating a plan of brief psychotherapeutic treatment were as reliable as were their formulations of the dynamics of the patient's illness. The mean reliability coefficients for ratings by judges of the Treatment Plan for both patients in the two interviews in which this rating was made was .77 (Table 3).

(c) *Session Observation.* In evaluating the current psychodynamic status of the patients in each of their interviews, the over-all mean reliability coefficient of the ratings obtained from all the participants with both patients in all the interviews was .78 (Table 4).

Comparison of the relative reliabilities of judges and predictors is best made with reference to Patient B in which both sets of ratings were made for all interviews except the last. (It will be recalled that a division of the raters into judges and predictors was done with Patient A in interviews 3 and 4 only.) The data in this respect indicate that there was greater agreement among the judges

TABLE 2

DYNAMIC APPRAISAL

Variables	Mean r_{xx}
Primary Impulses	78
Drives as Defenses	71
Affects and Feelings	75
Ego Defenses	91
Superego Reactions	91
Strength of Ego Functions	85
Mean	80

Mean reliability coefficients (Tryon's Variance Form) for ratings of each of the conceptual variables for each of the patients, by both judges and predictors (as judges) in both interviews. (Decimals omitted.)

TABLE 3

TREATMENT PLAN

Patient	A			B			A & B
Interview	1	2	1 & 2	1	2	1 & 2	1 & 2
Mean reliability	86	82	84	63	75	70	77

Mean reliability coefficients (Tryon's Variance Form) of ratings of Treatment Plan by judges. (Decimals omitted.)

[3] Predictors did not formulate the *Treatment Plan.*

than there was among the predictors, suggesting that the process of prediction is less reliable than that of judgment.

There appear to be some indications of change in reliability of judgment over the five interviews. In both cases, the reliability of judges' ratings was below their mean in the first interview, rose above the mean in interviews 2, 3, and 4, and then declined slightly in the last session. The reliability of predictions remained at approximately the same level during the first three interviews, then rose sharply in the fourth.

(2) ACCURACY OF PREDICTION

The "accuracy" with which the predictors were able to predict session-to-session changes in the psychodynamic status of the patient was assessed by obtaining correlation coefficients between the ratings of judges on Session Observation and the predictions of predictors on Session Observation for each interview. That is, the *actual* ratings for the variables in interview 2, for example, were correlated with the *predicted* ratings for interview 2, which had been made by the predictors on the basis of interview 1.

The mean of correlation coefficients thus obtained for all four interviews was .62, significant at the .01 level of confidence. Correlations between prediction and judgment remained fairly consistent throughout the four interviews, with the exception of a slight decline in interview 4 (Table 5).

METHOD II

(1) DERIVATION OF THE RATING SCALES

Following the application of Method I to the interviews with Patient A, it was decided to devise a method of analysis which would assess the ability of trained clinicians to predict the effects of *specific* psychotherapeutic interventions upon

TABLE 4

SESSION OBSERVATION

Interview	1	2	3	4	5
Judges, Patient A	48	81	89	90	79
Predictors, Patient A	—	—	82	68	—
Judges, Patient B	81	84	94	84	80
Predictors, Patient B	66	67	63	84	—

Mean reliability coefficients (Tryon's Variance Form) of ratings of Session Observation. (Decimals omitted.)

TABLE 5

ACCURACY OF PREDICTION AND INTERVIEW

Interview No.	2	3	4	5	N
Mean rho	64*	65*	57*	62*	38

* Significant at the 5% level.
Mean coefficients of correlation (rho) between judgments and predictions. (Decimals omitted.)

the patient's functioning, as well as the effects of what transpired in an interview taken in its entirety.

In addition, it was also felt desirable to devise a method which would take into account some of the actual problem areas and dynamics of the particular patient. Instead of being only theoretically derived, some variables to be employed in Method II would be based on concrete case material. Accordingly, a scale was devised which would meet these objectives.

The five interview transcripts of the completed second case (Patient B) were carefully examined and all the interventions of the therapist which were more than simple questions or reformulations of the patient's statements were extracted. Broadly speaking, these interventions might be classified as interpretations, suggestions, advice, etc. These statements were presented to the treating therapist who was asked to record his intentions in making each intervention: i.e., what effect did he expect the given intervention to have on the patient?

Nineteen such therapist interventions were selected; for instance, with reference to interview 1:

Context
   Patient is talking of her concern about whether or not people like her and of wanting to be able to accept herself.
Intervention
   "You are so concerned with what they think because you have doubts about yourself."

The expected effects of these interventions as stated by the therapist numbered forty-three. These forty-three variables were recast in the form of dimensions of behavior and combined into a questionnaire subdivided into four categories:

(A) *Insight Variables*. Twenty-seven items consisted of statements about the patient's degree of *insight* into a number of variables. The predictors were asked: How much awareness will the patient have at the end of five sessions about:

   Examples: 1. Her fear of not being loved leading her to be exhibitionistic.
              27. Her need for affection being related to feeling rejected by her mother.

(B) *Problem Areas*. Seven items were concerned with the patient's major problem areas. Here the predictors were asked: What do you predict the magnitude of change in the following variables will be in the patient by the end of the fifth session?

   Examples: 30. Her concern and fear about sexual acting out.
             34. Her degree of feminine identification.

(C) *Therapy Behavior*. Five items described the patient's behavior in the therapy sessions.

   Examples: 35. Her willingness to work on dream material.
             38. Her willingness to work on problems around exhibitionism.

(D) *Other*. Four items were included for purposes not relevant to this research.

(2) APPLICATION OF THE SCALES

Since the participants had been familiarized with the use of rating methods through their experience with using Method I with Patient A, and because of the relative simplicity of the rating scale, no training sessions were held. In addition to application of Method I with Patient B, the participants were asked to include Method II also.

The judges were provided with the above scales and, using a scale of values ranging from 0 to 4, were asked to rate the patient's current degree of *insight* into dynamic themes (Insight Variables); the current status of her difficulties (Problem Areas); and her relationship to the therapist (Therapy Behavior). This was done for each session.

The predictors were given a more complex task. They were provided with the nineteen specific interventions that had originally been given to the treating therapist (there were four such interventions for each interview, except one interview in which three were given). With *each* intervention, they were given the rating scale and asked to predict the effects of that specific intervention upon the list of forty-three variables; these are referred to as Specific Predictions. In addition, they were also asked to predict the effects of the session as a whole; these are referred to as General Predictions. The predictors thus completed twenty-four rating scales.

RESULTS: METHOD II

(1) LEVEL OF AGREEMENT

Both the judges and the predictors achieved satisfactorily high levels of agreement among themselves using the method previously described. Mean reliability coefficients among judges, and among predictors making specific predictions and predictors making general predictions, ranged from .75 to .76. No differences of significance between predictors and judges or between the specific predictions and the general predictions of the predictors were observed, as can be seen from Table 6. It can therefore be concluded that psychoanalytically trained raters can agree satisfactorily among themselves about the presence and intensity of specific personality variables as they manifest themselves in brief psychotherapy.

Table 6 and Table 7 present reliability coefficients of judgments, specific predictions, and general predictions in relation to interview and variables. The

TABLE 6

LEVEL OF AGREEMENT

Interview No.	1	2	3	4	5	Mean
Judgments	65	90	86	69	68	76
General Predictions	64	79	80	76	—	75
Specific Predictions	75	82	65	81	—	76
Mean, all Predictions	70	81	72	79	—	75
Mean, all Ratings	68	84	77	75	68	75

Extent of agreement among raters as measured by Tryon's Variance Form. (Decimals omitted.)

TABLE 7

LEVEL OF AGREEMENT

	Insight	Problem Areas	Therapy Variables	Mean
Judgments	63	91	88	81
General Predictions	61	85	76	74
Specific Predictions	60	74	95	76
Mean	61	83	86	77

Extent of agreement among raters as measured by means of Tryon's Variance Form. (Decimals omitted.)

main conclusions to be drawn from these data are that (a) there is a slight rise in agreement at the second interview; (b) there is less reliability in judgments and predictions concerning Insight Variables than in judgment and predictions about Problem Areas and Therapy Variables. It is not clear why there was disagreement. From a strictly conceptual standpoint, this area is certainly much less important than the area of dynamic appraisal, treatment plan, and therapy variables. It might well be that in order to appraise insight, the face-to-face situation with the patient may be more important than for other judgments, i.e., smiling, puzzlement, a show of comprehension might remain unverbalized. Therefore, electrical recording and transcripts alone may have to be supplemented by filming of the interview to avoid this difficulty. Nevertheless, it remains very questionable whether this particular advantage might not be outweighed by the disadvantage of such a procedure from both the dynamic and the economic points of view.

(2) ACCURACY OF PREDICTION OF CHANGE

The degree of accuracy with which the predictors were able to predict changes in the forty-three content variables was assessed by first determining the "actual" direction of change in the variables which occurred during the five interviews. This was done by obtaining the mean numerical rating given to each variable by the three judges in each interview and comparing it with the mean numerical rating given to each variable in the fifth interview. This permitted each variable to be described as increasing, decreasing, or not changing over the five interviews.

A similar procedure was followed with the predictions. For each variable, the three predictions were averaged to yield a mean predicted directional change.

To assess the accuracy of prediction, a simple percentage of correct predictions was derived for each of the five General Predictions and the nineteen Specific Predictions. This was done by comparing the mean predicted directional change for each of the predictions and the actual mean change which took place between the interview in which the prediction was made and the final (fifth) interview.

Fifty-one per cent of the General Predictions and forty-six per cent of the Specific Predictions were "correct" in that they agreed with the actual direction of change as rated by the judges.

These percentages, shown in Table 8, are significant at the 5% level of confidence, as determined by a chi-square test of the significance of the difference between the obtained proportions of "correct" predictions against the theoretically expected proportions of one third correct. It can therefore be concluded that, when making predictions of *direction of change* in personality variables (increase, decrease, or no change) in brief psychotherapy, psychoanalytically trained judges will be correct to a significantly greater extent than chance.

This ability to predict change is lower, however, than the ability to agree on the simple presence or absence of a variable. This is quite understandable, as prediction of direction of change involves more complex propositions. Though there is plenty of room for improvement, the present data indicate that prediction of direction of change in a statistically significant way is possible.

Table 8 also presents percentages of correct predictions in relation to interview and variables, respectively. In general, accuracy of prediction does not seem to be significantly related to the position of the interview in the series of five. Therapy Variables are not predicted as accurately as are the other variables.

Prediction as a tool of research in psychotherapy is extensively discussed in Chapter 7. In summary, the aims of prediction can be formulated as follows[4]:

(1) To demonstrate the fact that something useful is happening.

(2) To illuminate the process involved and to validate or reject hypotheses and to devise "recipes" of logical sequence, e.g.,

if condition A exists,
condition B will follow.

if, however, intervention C is made,
condition B will be modified.

TABLE 8

ACCURACY OF PREDICTION

By Interview	1	2	3	4	Total
General Predictions	56	58	53	49	51
Specific Predictions	53	54	36	38	46

By Variable	Insight	Problem Areas	Therapy Variables	Other	Total
General Predictions	55	54	13	55	51
Specific Predictions	46	58	17	49	46

Accuracy of prediction as measured by the percentage of correct predictions. The level of significance was determined by a chi-square test of the difference between observed proportions and the theoretically expected proportions (expected = 33% correct by chance).

---

[4] I am indebted to Dr. Peter Knapp, Professor of Psychiatry, Boston University Medical School, for a stimulating interchange on the problems of prediction.

Various types of prediction can be distinguished:

(1) *Persistency Prediction*

A symptom or syndrome is present now, and it is predicted that the same symptom or constellation will continue to be present.

(2) *Trend Prediction*

There is a trend toward a specific syndrome. This trend will remain as in 1, above, will diminish, will increase.

(3) *Cyclic Prediction*

Involves the prediction of cyclical trends.

(4) *Logical Prediction on Probability Theory (Nagel, 1939)*

Since A is present, B will probably follow;

Since A is present, B, C, D, as *collaterals* must also be present.

IO

METHODOLOGY AND RESEARCH IN THE
PSYCHOTHERAPY OF PSYCHOSES

As this section makes clear, the methodology of psychotherapy and the methodology of research have much in common. Basic to both is a systematic inventory of all aspects of the patient's illness, conceptualized according to a general theoretical scheme. If treatment is in order, the techniques chosen will be determined by the main characteristics of the illness. Research is seen as a further step, and, as described here, would represent a systematic attempt to assess the outcome of treatment. Perhaps the most telling suggestion made in this chapter is that therapeutic techniques should be closely coupled to diagnostic impressions, with the therapist conversant with a wide range of procedures and sufficiently flexible to use them all.

THE BASIC PREMISE OF THIS CHAPTER is that *psychotherapy* may be briefly defined as "a verbal or otherwise symbolic interaction of a therapist with a patient, for the latter's benefit, guided by an orderly and integrated series of concepts with regard to effecting beneficial change." It is hoped that this definition, inadequate as it is, will exclude treatment by "instinct," "intuition," (except as a preconscious form of conceptual thinking), psychotherapy as art, faith healing, general philanthropic strivings, etc., and will set the frame of reference for an orderly methodology. However, an integral part is the inclusion of a number of procedures which are not part of psychotherapy proper, but rather operations subsidiary to, or extensions of, psychotherapy. Among the former belongs the use of psychotropic drugs to facilitate psychotherapy; to the latter belong milieu changes, e.g., to ensure the lasting effects of psychotherapy in a less pathogenic setting.

As psychotherapy remains central and the additional procedures would be useless without it, we include these auxiliary measures under the heading of psychotherapy. An argument could be made for calling the total approach discussed here "the psychodynamic approach to the therapy of psychoses."

The meaning of *research* will be restricted in this paper to systematic investigations, with methodological safeguards for the soundness of conclusions: this presupposes a search carried on by more than one person, in order to have a chance for controlled comparisons of independent judgment and work done in such a way that the primary data are repeatable and publicly demonstrable (e.g., by tape recording).

These strictures are established as a matter of practicality: undoubtedly, research in the sense of a systematic search can and has been carried on fruitfully by individuals without any of the limitations mentioned above. Very likely, all

NOTE: From *American Psychiatric Association Research Report,* No. 17, November, 1963. Reprinted by permission of the publishers.

great basic insights and hunches have been obtained by individuals working alone, not by teams. However, psychodynamic theory and psychotherapy abound in creative hunches and have a dearth of verified data. Controlled teamwork seems primarily necessary now to check our wealth of hunches.

To proceed with the discussion of methodology and research in psychotherapy, it is necessary to state some basic propositions concerning personality, diagnoses, and treatment.

(1) *Personality* is the complex aggregate of personal experiences of a unique organism in a lifetime: the experiencing is obviously a function of the experiencing organism *and* the experienced data. Some variables of the organism, as well as the ever-increasing apperceptive mass, continuously structure the impact of new experiences. In recent years, both psychoanalysis and academic psychology have found it useful to speak of perception in relation to personality and its development. Among psychoanalysts, Kurt Eissler (1953a) put it most succinctly when he said that "experience becomes structure" in talking of the vagaries of ego development. For a psychoanalyst, the libido theory as discussed in Chapter 1, with its implicit propositions concerning the acquisition of learning, affective charge, variants of drive related to the developmental timetable (as well as the proposition concerning transformation of energy and the concepts of autonomous functions) complements the essential field of forces.

(2) In the sense of the above statements, *diagnosis* consists of establishing precisely the relationship between the person we meet and the events that went into forming him at different times in relation to different people and different events, including cultural settings (one might say that the purpose of taking a psychiatric history is to establish the *present status* of the *past*); of course we stay ever mindful of the organismic equipment as much as it can be discerned, as well as of the stages of development at which a person had different experiences. It complicates matters that not only individual events have to be evaluated, but also the effect of event C in relation to the fact that A and B preceded it: that is, the loss of a mother in childhood might be brought in relation to the earlier advent of a younger sibling and the previous prolonged absence of the father from the parental scene. What's more, not all personality factors can be related even in a complex matrix of one-to-one relationships; separately experienced events not only affect subsequent events, but a variety of experiences may assume Gestalten (configurations), which are in terms of Gestalt psychology more than the sum of the parts, are newly emergent wholes, and have an effect as such on later experiences. Our task is not made easier by the reflection that we can no longer think in the terms of the rigid determinism of the nineteenth century, but can only expect our hypotheses to provide a guide to the most probable effects to expect in terms of statistical probability theory. Nevertheless, I believe that current psychoanalytic theory provides us with a good enough framework to be able to do quite a useful and creditable job, if used rationally and systematically.

As clinicians, we are usually concerned with diagnoses as an appraisal of disturbances. For that purpose, the nature of the disturbance needs to be *described,* aside from being brought into relationship to the acquisition of variables in question. My own suggestion has been to use a *detailed survey of ego functions* and of the individual patterns of disturbances as a basis for a profile of a descriptive and qualitative-quantitative assessment of the nature of disturbances. Psychoses as a group share the common denominator of relatively more severely disturbed ego functions, or of more ego functions affected, than in the neuroses or in the normal range. Relatively circumscribed profiles of disturbance constitute the different nosologic groups, including the organic ones. Psychoanalytic dynamics provide us with an excellent set of propositions to understand intermediary states and the changes from one clinical group into another, since it permits us to speak of fields of forces which in some, under some circumstances, may become stabilized in the classically known disease pictures, while remaining fluid in others.

METHODOLOGY OF PSYCHOTHERAPY

Psychotherapy is concerned with the restructuration of the personality. Since this original structure was acquired by learning, new learning experiences are needed for changes in the structure. To be sure, when I speak of therapy as problems of learning, I use learning in the broad sense of American psychology as subsuming all acquisition of experience (not only the kind that is acquired in school or as the products of a directed teaching process): the child in a disturbed home "learns" that anything might happen, and "learns" that inconsistency is the rule.

One can probably formulate some general principles of psychotherapy of psychoses: they might be comparable to the general principles of other medical or surgical management. I would count here patience on the part of the therapist, willingness to listen, and ability to establish a relationship. However, general preliminary principles of psychotherapy will not be enough for more than the most superficial temporary success in some instances. Eissler (1952) has justifiably spoken of these original steps as dealing merely with the acute phase, while the difficulties of stable therapeutic change, according to him, come in the clinically "mute" phase. Surely all psychotics share a certain common denominator, if our definition is to be useful at all: namely, some extreme of disturbances in one ego function or another and usually in several; severe anxiety, latent or manifest, and some disturbances in the firm establishment of the secondary process are also the rule. Beyond these generalizations, each psychotic is a unique person with unique patterns of disturbances and unique forms of an "intact residue" (Katan, 1953) and a unique personal history. Therefore, general principles cannot be mistaken for the whole of psychotherapy, as has quite often been done. Each psychotherapy must consist of different problems of learning, that is, of learning and relearning, and the therapy has to be tailor-made to fit the particular patient as understood diagnostically. It follows, perforce, that I consider treatment methods not painstakingly anchored to extensive diagnoses and specifically planned prescriptions of therapy as inadequate. A general prescription of relationship therapy, communications therapy, work therapy, family therapy, group therapy, or psychoanalysis of any persuasion is insufficient if not accompanied by specific sets of propositions diagnostically, dynamically, and therapeutically.

Having defined problems of therapy as matters of learning makes it possible now to proceed schematically and, for the purpose of this review, briefly, to the proposition that the rational approach to optimal psychotherapy must be tied to the explicit question: How will this patient best unlearn, learn, or relearn, or learn differently what he needs to learn, specifically to lose certain symptoms, acquire certain functions, and change the structure of his personality?

What sort of patient do we have? What sort of therapeutic learning procedures are available to us?

The broadest conception of learning has been the idea of learning by insight. Psychoanalysis and dynamic psychotherapy seem primarily based on insight.

If we have an ambulatory psychotic amenable to treatment in the office, a variety of psychoanalysis is frequently employed, especially faithful to the original model (though in Kleinian theory), for instance by Rosenfeld (1947) and in psychotherapy by Bychowski (1952). In an orthodox approach, I would say that analysis actually means reduction of apperceptive distortions into their genetic components, with the expectation that in the light of adult intelligence and with the help of the therapist's reality testing, etc., a new and better realignment of apperceptions will take place. Perceiving the common denominator of distortions in an "aha" experience is supposed to lead automatically to a new configuration in free association.

The learning by insight is supplemented by learning by "working through" genetic, contemporary, and transference experiences. Particularly with regard to the two latter forms of working through, *learning by conditioning* plays a role: reward of correct behavior and "punishment" of wrong (neurotic) behavior by anxiety and other forms of neurotic pain play a prominent, though generally not explicit, role in Freudian theory. A third factor, part of the transference relationship, involves *learning by identification* (by making the analyst a new introject). Indeed, in a more or less classical analysis, the personality is restructured to a large extent by learning in relation to the therapist. If we accept Eissler's (1953a) brief dictum that "percept becomes structure," one could say that orthodox analysis relies heavily on perceptual restructuration by analysis of the components and facilitations of new configurations.

A clear-cut point of departure for variations of psychotherapeutic strategy and tactics with psychotics can be made from their inability to utilize sufficiently the one or the other of these basic steps of more or less classical psychoanalysis.

Insight may be impossible for some patients because they do not have the logical equipment for the syllogistic thinking involved. This may be due to a failure to acquire enough of the secondary process and the hierarchical relationships of cause and effect, time, place, and person. Arieti (1962) is among those who have particularly addressed themselves to dealing therapeutically with such logical problems. Concreteness of thinking is another problem, comparable to the concreteness of thinking described by Piaget in children. Verbal therapy and the use of insight may be impossible in some such instances, though Arieti has suggested ways of dealing with this problem.

In other instances, a more concrete learning situation may nevertheless enable the patient to have some insight: conjoint psychotherapy, as Jackson and Weakland (1961) have described it, or "conjoint consultation and confrontation," as I would rather say, may accomplish this step; if the patient is actually seen together with the mother, the actual behavior of the mother with the therapist and vice versa may give the patient insight that was impossible in a strictly abstract situation.

Working through in the ordinary psychoanalytic situation may also not at all suffice in some psychotics. The relearning may again have to be supplemented by or attained altogether in more concrete, more often repeated experiences of a certain kind: group psychotherapy with actual learning of the consequences of "wrong" behavior and reward by the group of "right" behaviors may build impulse control, and other restructurations unattainable by verbal abstractions in the very best individual therapy. Habilitation, or rehabilitation, such as that described in Chapter 17, as going on in the sheltered workshop at Altro, also belongs here.

Learning by identification with the analyst or learning indeed by interaction with the analyst "as the corrective therapeutic experience" which Neo-Freudians stress (over genetic propositions) may indeed play a useful role, though not as much, I suspect, as Neo-Freudians would have it and not enough in many psychotics.

Such learning by carefully employed strategy and tactics in the management of the transference situation has been especially valuably described for manic-depressives by Jacobson (1954).

It may be most expeditious to design schematically a *catalog of therapeutic techniques* corresponding to the scheme of ego functions and their disturbance enumerated in Chapter 13.

(1) *Disturbances in adaptation to reality* is a very large category, needing much subdividing. To pick out just a few: inappropriateness needs reality testing, analysis of the apperceptive distortions. Insight therapy and restructuring of the apperceptive mass is basic here. Disturbances in the sense of reality, such as feelings of unreality, need not only insight, but often also drug treatment of the anxiety and aggression immediately precipitating the disturbances of body image and body boundaries: sometimes excessive anxiety alone produces over-breathing and an alkalosis with changes in muscle tone, etc., which by itself causes feelings of unreality-depersonalization and can be allayed by teaching a breathing technique, by drugs to allay anxiety, *etc.*

To give one other small example of a specific problem and a way to meet it, let me refer to a disjointed walk and generally poor coordination as a symptom of a poor body image, as well as of conflicts and lack of automatization of muscular functioning (because of the failure to neutralize aggressive and sexual drives). Sometimes I have found it useful to send such patients for a kind of muscle re-education which follows the school of Gindler (Meyer, 1961) and helps patients develop, first, awareness of proprioceptive stimuli and, later, automatization of muscular functioning. When the impulse charge is generally too high in a patient, vigorous exercise may be a temporary help and therapeutic adjunct.

(2) *The disturbance of the regulation of drives* leads to difficulties with detour behavior, shows itself as a lack of frustration tolerance, and may result either in psychotic acting out, or catatonic stupor, or depressive or manic behavior, depending on the rest of the constellation of the personality.

Psychotherapeutically, teaching the patient to recognize "internal signals" of anger and anxiety (in order to act on them), is extremely valuable (Eissler, 1953a).

The use of energizers and tranquilizers for the control of drives within a psychoanalytic framework has been particularly described by Ostow (1959). While it is not necessary to subscribe to his own very specific conceptualization of the effect of these drugs, there is little doubt that his empirical observations are very valuable.

For the acquisition of frustration tolerance required in the ordinary social process, I know of no better means than the sort of rehabilitation (or habilitation) program now taking place at Altro workshops (described in Chapter 17). It amounts to acquiring impulse control and learning object relations much as I have described by the use of the Schopenhauer parable of the porcupines on a cold winter day (they were cold but when they huddled they stung each other until, moving back and forth, they found the optimal distance at which they gave each other some warmth without too much discomfort). Group therapy also may prove a training ground for learning socialization and drive control.

(3) *Disturbances of object relations,* such as narcissistic overinvestment of the self, symbiotic and excessively anaclitic relations, are best treated via the transference relationship and interpretation of the defense nature of secondary narcissism, if it is involved. In the very severe disturbances treated by Sechehaye (1951b), her implicitly "phase-specific" way of establishing object relations is admirable: for example, in her treatment of a young girl she first made contact with her feet. In another way, John Rosen's direct analysis (1953) has provided another means of establishing object relations in the very withdrawn. The "motherhouses" Schwing (1954) has suggested are concerned with another way of learning or relearning object relations poorly formed in childhood or infancy. A setting like the Altro workshops is yet another useful milieu of learning object relations.

(4) *Disturbance of the thought processes* with their contaminations (in Rorschach language) and other evidences of primary process thinking can be extremely difficult to treat. If the disturbances of thinking are relatively circumscribed, as in an intelligent, otherwise intact paranoid, the problem may be relatively easily handled in a psychoanalytic type of psychotherapy. If we deal with infantilism and an essential lack of having learned the necessary hierarchy of cause and effect, time and place, etc., the task of helping the patient acquire a secondary process can be very tedious and long-drawn-out.

If a secondary process was acquired, but is flooded by the primary process, Alpert has devised an ingenious technique (for children) of simply not responding to primary-process types of communications and responding favorably to secondary types of responses (personal communication). In effect, a reward and punishment system leads to a reinforcement of the secondary-process forms of thinking.

Arieti's (1962) attention to the distortions of logic in his patients, the efforts of the semantically inclined, and the work of Bateson et al. (1956) with regard to the double bind and the ensuing confusion are very valuable in different instances.

In some patients, an extensive paranoid system or even a hebephrenic condition has led to a stable symptom formation unapproachable by psychotherapy. In such instances, sensory deprivation or LSD may well serve to prepare the patient for psychotherapy by loosening the apperceptive distortions.

(5) *Disturbances of repression and other defensive functions* can be successfully treated by psychotherapy. The therapist must provide for an integrated superego, seeing to it that it be not too strict (to be tolerable) in some areas and not too lenient in others—as is usually the case. Judicious firmness and permissiveness at different times in relation to different sets of problems is indicated.

Secondary measures of manipulation of the environment to decrease the pressure of stimuli that need defensive functioning are often essential. Drugs, brief hospitalization, changes in vocation, habitation, and living habits may be necessary. It is essential that the therapist conceptualize well and not hesitate to insist on drastic changes (rather than indulging in analytic aloofness from decisions involving reality).

(6) *Strengthening of disturbed autonomous functions,* such as language and motor performance, is essential in some cases—say of an immigrant in the first instance, and a poorly coordinated adolescent in the second instance.

Very often the autonomous functions are part of the "instant residue," and must be drawn upon heavily in reconstructing the disturbed areas of the personality. A firmly established work habit, a high intelligence, may be invaluable assets in an otherwise severely disturbed psychotic.

(7) *The synthetic function* is usually only strengthened as a result of the improvement of the other ego functions by various means. However, the psychotropic drugs, e.g., of the phenothiazin variety, seem to counteract dissociation directly, thus having a synthesizing and integrative effect. It may be that they accomplish this feat indirectly by drive control, or by some more direct effect on the organic substratum.

These are the directions I think psychotherapy of the psychoses has to take: appraisal of the disturbance (in terms of ego functions) and prescription of treatment to help restructuration.

A certain amount of psychoanalytic insight-psychotherapy plays a dominant role in the majority of instances. I tried to illustrate that this therapy itself must be greatly varied, and supplemented with a wide variety of other measures, particularly in the more regressed patients. At times, it is mostly the psychoanalytic knowledge of the therapist that is useful, the interventions themselves being only to a small extent verbal or symbolic, but rather manipulative and directive. There is no scarcity of suggested procedures in the literature. The problem has been so far that each investigator has touted one particular approach as good for all psychotics: what is necessary is to use the most appropriate procedure or set of procedures in a given case.

It may also be useful to state clearly again that both unlearning and relearning are necessary to psychotherapy, and that the methods for unlearning may have to be quite different from those of relearning. Insightful psychoanalytic psychotherapy may often be best for unlearning apperceptive distortions. Group therapy and a great number of other methods may be necessary to provide the essential relearning.

The psychotropic drugs have permitted us to carry on the process of learning by insight, by trial and error, under something akin to carrying on a surgical intervention with the benefit of anesthesia and physiological support. Where ordinarily frustration, excessive impulse, or anxiety would make the therapeutic process unbearable, these drugs have helped to go through with the learning process until the new structure is well-enough established and hopefully automatized and integrated enough not to need the drugs any more.

The psychotropic drugs resemble the aid which supportive physiological measures give during a surgical intervention, in the sense that they seem to be able to increase the synthetic functioning of the ego. Dissociation seems decreased and learning possible, when without them the primary process would abound to the extent of not permitting secondary-process activity.

Some psychotherapeutic learning has been barely effective or much slower than necessary because *formal aspects* of learning have been neglected. One of the long-established principles of learning theory is the principle of spacing or *dispersal of training*. Periods of learning interrupted by pauses are often more effective than a continuous effort. Some demands made by psychotherapy, the regressive effect of the therapy itself, and the secondary gains from the dependence might be minimized by spacing, aside from allowing for better silent integration and working through during the interval. The experience of the plateau typical for every learning experience often has a retarding effect on the psychotherapeutic process, if not an altogether disrupting one for both patient and therapist.

In all psychotherapeutic interventions, *economy of interpretation* must be related to the profound understanding of the total field of forces. One is reminded of the anecdote of the time Hitler's car was supposed to have broken down in a small Polish village and all the assembled Nazi bigwigs and engineers could not make it move again. Finally, a Polish mechanic was brought up, took one look, hit one part of the machinery hard, and the motor sprang to life. When the amazed Hitler asked how much he owed him, the man demanded 1,000 zloti. "One thousand zloti for one whack?" Hitler asked in astonishment. "No," the mechanic shook his head, "only ten zloti for the whack—990 *for knowing where to whack."* A sophisticated type of economic psychotherapeutic intervention has much in common with the point of this story.

This story of economy of action brings us to another matter in the consideration of formal principles of learning in psychotherapy: that is, that to communicate a fact to be learned is a formal problem in itself. As far as verbal communication is concerned, the apt illustration is an excellent means. One of the best features of Viennese psychoanalysis was a large stock of stories and jokes; it is not a bad idea to have a certain number of stories and examples in stock for conveying certain learning experiences.

Another formal aspect of learning methodology, briefly to be mentioned, is the fact that *active learning* is more effective than passive learning. This should mean not only that the patient should discover as many of the necessary insights as possible himself, but that one may sometimes have to use certain artifacts with psychotics to encourage active learning, namely asking the patient to formulate certain propositions, to repeat them, and to integrate them in various facets under consideration. Furthermore, acting out must be understood as the repetition of wrong responses; therefore, it must be avoided as much as possible so as not to interfere with the learning of "right responses."

Finally, a further consideration of the therapeutic learning process shared again with all learning: *how to make it stick!* Clinically, we speak of avoiding relapses; specifically, to keep in mind regression as part of terminating psychotherapy, aside from other possible vicissitudes in the course of often prolonged learning experiences. I have suggested elsewhere (Chapter 17) that the patient be left with a carefully cultivated positive transference and a clear understanding that he is welcome to return, though it would be much better if he did not need to do so. For work in institutions, I have suggested that a shift from the original therapist or follow-up worker in carefully conceptualized steps should be provided. Sometimes an auxiliary therapist may be interpolated as protection against disruption during the process of therapy by illness of the therapist or other vicissitudes. Such an auxiliary therapist may also serve as a diluter of transference or countertransference at critical times. At certain times, he may be a useful intermediary in a process of developing independence from the therapist, in some cases interpolated between the therapist and the very little known follow-up worker. In essence, by such a process, the gradual weaning from the therapist may take place, not so unlike the gradual resolution of the bonds between children and parents in the normal maturational process. By maintaining a positive transference toward the therapist, and by avoiding a fear of rejection in the terminating process, one accomplishes various purposes: retention of the therapist as a benign, introjected figure with its effect on the whole personality and maintenance of motivation to do well for the sake of the therapist; these forces are similar to children's renunciation of primitive modes of behavior predicated upon the love and approbation of the parents as motivating factors until autonomy takes over.

RESEARCH

Questions of research in psychotherapy resolve themselves clearly into attempting to formulate the following:

(a) A precise statement of the individual problems of the patient

(b) A precise prescription to meet these problems

(c) An attempt to assess the success of the prescribed program.

To speak usefully of research nowadays, it must be insisted that all formulations be made in a way that can be checked by methodologically acceptable means.

(A) A PRECISE STATEMENT OF THE INDIVIDUAL PROBLEMS OF THE PATIENT

It is basic for the solution of any problem that there be, first, agreement on the definition of the problem. Therefore, research in psychotherapy of psychoses should address itself first to attempts to come to methodologically acceptable forms of agreement on the nature of the disorder of a patient.

My recommendation is that a statistically useful number of patients be each "diagnosed" by a number of independent judges with regard to the nature of their personality and personality difficulties. Needless to say, these judges need a common language and common concepts to be able to speak to each other, and must be able to compare and agree or meaningfully disagree. Therefore, each group of studies should initially be confined within one "school of thought."

Later, if there is agreement within a certain school, one might attempt inter-school comparisons.

My own preference runs toward a "profile" based on ego psychology, establishing detailed patterns of functioning for every ego function, as I have outlined elsewhere.

(B) A Precise Prescription to Meet These Problems

If several judges show high correlations in their rating of a patient's personality and disturbances, it would then be time to see if the same team can agree independently and correlate highly on the procedure to be followed to do the necessary unlearning and relearning.

Again, if psychotherapy is to be more than rule of thumb or guesswork and be teachable beyond the anecdotal method, it must be possible to formulate detailed specific rules for individual treatment of each patient; roughly, equally well-trained and experienced therapists must arrive either at the same set of steps and formulations to be followed or at a small number of acceptable variations, in a statistically satisfactory way.

(C) An Attempt to Assess the Success of the Prescribed Program

Only after independent judges are able to correlate highly on formulations concerning "diagnosis" and "treatment" is it reasonable to enter upon the sea of difficulties contained in the appraisal of the effectiveness of treatment.

There are, of course, several hundred papers concerned with many different approaches to the problem of assessing psychotherapy by a large number of criteria and methods, e.g., of the process type, of the outcome type, a combination of these two, by experimental analogues, and many others. A general review of criteria of mental health has been provided by Jahoda (1958). My own suggestions (see Chapter 8) have been concerned with repeated short-range and long-range predictions.

A number of forms of content analysis have been used for the appraisal of the psychotherapeutic process (Lennard and Bernstein, 1960). The Bales interaction system, considering psychotherapy a dyad, has played an outstanding role (Hare et al., 1960; Fink, Jaffe, and Kahn, 1959). Electronic high-speed computers have been used for accumulating data on the process of psychotherapy. Needless to say, electronics will not be of any help if the concepts are not sound. A combination of prediction on the basis of clearly stated hypotheses and content analysis may be especially useful.

A possible approach to the study of the effect of psychotherapy might center around the "primary-process index." The primary-process index was initially developed by Holt for study of the Rorschach (1956). In essence, a computation of the primary-process index of the content of psychotherapeutic interviews in psychoses is a special type of content analysis. The same method can be applied to the study of psychotherapeutic interviews and was used in an exploratory way by me and Chassan to study the effect of drugs on the process of psychotherapy (described in Chapter 12). Primarily, this study concerned itself with the statistical design of single-case psychotherapeutic research.

I I

THE CONCEPT OF PROJECTION:
AN EXPERIMENTAL STUDY

The defense of projection, as classically conceived, may be said to have two basic features. Oversimplifying to an extreme, we can say that in projection, ego-alien features are (1) assigned to another person in order that (2) they do not come into consciousness. To study this defense systematically, Bellak designed another ground-breaking experiment in which college students were criticized as they were giving TAT stories. The findings from two samples show that aggression in the stories (by definition, projected aggression) increased after criticism. What is more, projection is adaptive, as shown by the fact that aggression was attributed primarily to the more aggressive stimuli. Worth underlining is the fact that the subjects told the stories while lying on the couch and the clarity of the findings may be due to the deeper regression induced by this procedure. The deeper the regression, it might be argued, the "purer" the specimen of fantasy that is obtained.

Data pertaining to the second part of the definition are less definitive. For projection to operate as a defense in this situation, it should prevent aggressive feelings toward the experimenter from coming into awareness, and on this point further research is needed. After being the butt of such remarks as, "These stories are about the worst I ever heard," etc., the subject would ordinarily feel angry; if the theory is correct, his angry feelings should decrease to the extent that they are projected onto the TAT cards. Thus, the subject who projected a larger amount of aggression should feel less anger than the subject who projected less. In fact, we do not know precisely how they felt. The positive findings on projection of anger in the present study lay the groundwork for a further study by Bellak of changes in the awareness of anger as a result of projection hypnotically induced (see Crafts et al., 1950, pp. 440-457).

The experiment is an illustration of sensitive clinical research in which the experimental manipulation is not only effective, but also makes good clinical sense as well. Criticism from the experimenter, because it is appropriate to the situation (and therefore believable), is a much more powerful stress than some other threat (such as shock); perhaps for that reason, the results are nicely in keeping with the main hypothesis which stems from the *clinical* theory of psychoanalysis.

The key ideas presented in this chapter have been subsequently elaborated in later papers (Bellak 1950, 1954a and 1954b).

PROJECTION IS A TERM very much in use in present-day psychiatry and in clinical, dynamic, and social psychology. Frank (1939) suggests that it is one of the many concepts which are typical of a general trend toward a dynamic and holistic approach in recent psychological science, as well as science generally

NOTE: From *Psychiatry,* 1944, 4, 353-370. Reprinted by permission of the publishers.

speaking. He likens projective techniques, in this context, to the position of spectral analysis in physical science.

Projection is one of those dynamisms, originally described by Freud, which impress one as products of excellent clinical intuition, which never yet has been sufficiently verified to satisfy the man of rigorous science.

This is of course not an isolated case. Throughout all science progress is found to have been made on the one hand by bold advances of empiricists, only much later corroborated by experimental science, and on the other hand by originally theoretical work which later finds important practical application.

It is believed that science *does not* deal with truth in a philosophical sense, but only with hypotheses as approximations to "truth." A psychological concept is judged as useful if it allows one to understand, to predict, and to control behavior (see Allport, 1942). It is the purpose of this paper to examine the concept of projection in this light.

The term "projection" was introduced by Freud as early as 1895, in his paper on the "anxiety neurosis," in which he said: "The psyche . . . finds itself in the *neurosis* of anxiety if it notices that it is unable to even out the (sexual) excitation originating *from within*—that is to say, *it behaves as though it were projecting that excitation outwards*" (Freud, 1895a, p. 112).

Further elaboration of the concept took place in his paper on the case of Schreber in connection with, and as the chief *modus operandi* of, paranoia (Freud, 1911). Briefly, the paranoiac has certain homosexual tendencies, which he transforms under the pressure of his superego from "I love him" to "I hate him"—reaction formation. This hatred he then projects onto, or ascribes to, the former love object, who now becomes the persecutor. The ascription of hatred presumably takes place because entrance into consciousness and realization of the hatred is prohibited by both the superego and the ego—conflict with mores and reality—and because the externalized danger is easier dealt with. To be more specific, the superego inhibits expression of the hatred because it morally disapproves of it and fears retribution, and the ego resists because of the reality danger involved in such disruptive action. *Projection, therefore, is the ascription of feelings and qualities of one's own to other people as a defensive process, and without being aware of these phenomena.*

Healy, Bronner, and Bowers (1930) define projection similarly as "A defensive process under the sway of the pleasure principle whereby the ego thrusts forth on the external world unconscious wishes and ideas which, if allowed to penetrate into consciousness, would be painful to the ego."

While projection thus originated in connection with psychosis and neurosis, it was later applied to other forms of behavior, for example, as the main mechanism in the formation of religious beliefs, as set forth in *The Future of an Illusion* (Freud, 1927). While originally repression was the sole defense mechanism, at present at least ten of them will be considered, and projection is firmly established as one of the most important. Yet relatively little work has been done on projection. Sears (1943) says: "Probably the most inadequately defined term in all psychoanalytic theory is projection."[1] There is, indeed a long list of papers on projection, particularly clinical-psychoanalytic ones, and some

---

[1] The concept was further discussed in Bellak (1950).

academic ones (see de Saussure, 1929; Frank, 1939; Feigenbaum, 1936; Hoffmann, 1935; Kaufman, 1934; Posner, 1940; Rado, 1919; Sears, 1936, 1937; Sears, Hovland, and Miller, 1940; Weiss, 1932; Wright, 1941; and Young, 1927).

Recently the concept of projection has been used in a good many tests or so-called projective techniques. Among them are the Rorschach and William Stern's Cloud Pictures as senior partners, but also the Thematic Apperception Test, Tautophon, Gamma Inkblots, Sentence-Completion Tests, finger painting, dramatic production, and doll play.

More will be said about these techniques later. While they have contributed little to the clarification of the problems so far, they make an investigation and clear definition of projection particularly urgent because of their widespread use as clinical instruments of considerable importance.

While there is a large number of experiments involving projection in one way or another, few claim to investigate projection as such. Starr (1935) asked subjects to gaze into a glass ball and describe what they saw. He concluded that since the subjects were "seeing" things which were not objectively there, they were projecting. Sears and Posner (Sears, 1936, 1937; Posner, 1940) studied projection as a social phenomenon, asking subjects to rate themselves and their friends on certain character traits, finding essentially that one tends to ascribe certain undesirable characteristics which one has oneself to other people. Sears says of his and Posner's study that "The confirmation is exceedingly indirect" (Sears, 1943).

Murray (1933) presented portraits to children and asked for judgments of "goodness" and "badness" of the people before and after telling them terrifying stories; he found an increase in "badness" judgments afterwards. Sanford (1936) withheld food from subjects, and then presented them with various stimuli and found that reference to food increased with the amount of time food was withheld. Neither Murray nor Sanford refers explicitly to or mentions the term projection, however.

Wright (1941) produced conflict in children placed in a situation requiring a generous or selfish selection of toys, and reports that this conflict was revealed in projective stories told by the children. A significant correction was found between the intensity of the conflict and the degree to which themes of destruction, punishment, and self-justification were elaborated.

Rodnick and Klebanoff (1942) had a group of known to be well-adjusted and a group of known to be badly-adjusted subjects that they frustrated by controlling their scores in a game involving motor coordination. The subjects were given a modified Thematic Apperception Test before and after the frustration. Among other things it was shown that the poorly adjusted men had a decrease of themes of superiority. The projective technique was used more as a means to measure frustration than was the experiment used to demonstrate projection.

EXPERIMENTAL STUDIES

For the present experiment on projection, the Thematic Apperception Test was chosen as a medium because of prior familiarity with it.

The Thematic Apperception Test, originated by Morgan and Murray (1935), consists of a series of pictures, ten of which are usually presented to subjects at each of two sittings. Before being shown the first picture, the subject receives instructions in a standard form, mentioned later, to tell a story about the pictures.

These pictures usually represent certain social situations. The test is "based upon the well-recognized fact that when a person interprets an ambiguous social situation, he is apt to expose his own personality as much as the phenomenon to which he is attending" (Morgan and Murray, 1935). Previous attempts at validation of this thesis had been made by Morgan and Murray, who reported on a patient whose thematic apperceptions "adumbrated all the chief trends which five months of analysis were able to reveal." Other validational work is reported by Harrison (1940), who says that "biographical and personality information, including interests, attitudes, traits, problems, and conflicts were analytically deducible from the stories of psychiatric patients with a high degree of validity (83%) when hospital case records were used as the validating criterion." The work of Balken and Masserman (1940), who found characteristic differences among the productions of patients consistent with the psychodynamics of their illness, and the work of Sanford, previously quoted, point in the same direction.

For the present study, interest is not in showing the existence of projection by establishing a correlation between factual data concerning the subjects and similar data deducible from their response to the pictures, but rather in creating ad hoc a variation in their sentiments, the appearance of which in the stories should be predictable if the concept of projection is valid.

For the present investigation, projection is defined very much according to the earlier formulations of Freud as the ascribing of wishes, needs, thoughts, and sentiments which one has oneself, to subjects or objects of the external world without realizing that one does.

A theoretical examination of the phenomenon and an attempt at redefinition of the concept follows.

FIRST EXPERIMENT

The following procedure was employed to *test the existence* of the hypothetical process of projection: ten pictures of the Morgan-Murray Thematic Apperception Test (Murray and staff, 1943) were given to seven subjects. The subjects were students of Harvard University and members of the R.O.T.C. Naturally they were uninformed of the purpose of the experiment. As a matter of fact, they were not seen primarily for the reason of this experiment, but rather in connection with an examination of their general personality make-up. The ten pictures were divided into two sets, A and B, five pictures in each set. Three subjects were given pictures 6 to 10, set A, first; four subjects were given pictures 1 to 5, set B, first. The selection of the students for the order of procedure was random. After having been given the customary instructions, the experimenter made no comments while listening to the first five stories of the pictures. After the fifth picture, however, sharp criticism was expressed of the stories told, and the criticism was repeated in modified form after each story from then on. The form of criticism was kept practically identical for all subjects.

The *underlying assumption* was that the subjects would resent the criticism, would not be able to express their resentment directly, since the experimenter was considered an authoritative person, and would, therefore, project their aggression by introducing more aggression into the stories after criticism than into those told without criticism. The pictures used were from the 1942 set of the TAT: set A—pictures 6 to 10—consisted of the following: 6—an operation, a young man in the foreground; 7—a man on a couch, another bent over him—hypnosis; 8—cowboys at rest; 9—man with raised fist; 10—two boys standing in archway. Set B—pictures 1 to 5—consisted of the following: 1—mother and son; 2—a boy on a couch with a pistol on the floor; 3—a nude man and a nude woman, faced by a draped woman holding a baby—Picasso; 4—an older, gray-haired man facing a younger man; 5—a man gripped from the rear, only several arms visible.

Each subject was interviewed in the same room, and was asked to lie down on a couch. The experimenter was seated in the rear. Standard instructions were:

"This is an opportunity for free imagination. I want you to make up a story. Tell me what has led up to the situation shown in the picture, describe what the characters are feeling and thinking, and tell me what the outcome will be. Speak your thoughts out loud as they come to your mind. Use your imagination freely, and make up anything you please."

After these instructions the subject was given the first picture, and the following one whenever he completed the story and returned the picture. When a subject asked whether he should stop or carry on, he was informed explicitly that this was always for him to decide. Whenever he felt that he had said all he wanted, he handed back the picture.

As already mentioned, after each subject's fifth story, sharp criticism was expressed by the experimenter, by content and tone of voice. The criticism was kept general and unsuggestive, on the one hand to avoid suggesting any content, and on the other hand to increase by its very generality the subject's resentment. The criticism was standardized and given as follows:

After story five: "These stories are about the worst I ever heard. They are illogical and unstructured. Could you try to get some better ones?" After six: "There are still no ideas in it, no life—nothing. Could you try some more?" After seven: "This is some of the damnedest stuff I have ever got. Try this one." After eight: "You are pretty hopeless. See what you can do with this one." After nine: "Well, this is your last chance to show if you have anything in you. Go ahead!"

The experimenter attempted to make this sound as spontaneous as possible. The conditions were the same for all subjects. All were seen in the same room, on the same couch. The walls of the room were bare. A microphone concealed in a table lamp transferred the spoken word in most cases to a recording device on a lower floor, or in some cases was taken down directly by a stenographer on the next floor. The text was later taken down in shorthand and typed.

The typewritten stories were later analyzed, for the number of aggressive words, by the author and two psychologists not informed about the procedure.[2] No particular attempt at an exact definition of an "aggressive" word was made,

[2] I am indebted for this service to Dr. Silvan Tomkins and Mr. Donald Fiske.

but the three judges discussed some examples. All aggressive words were counted in the stories. The three counts differed very little; the average was taken and the statistical analysis made of them. At the same time the judges rated the stories for aggression on a five-point scale; the results agreed closely with the results obtained by counting words, and only the tabulations of counted words are presented herewith.

ANALYSIS OF THE RESULTS

Table 1 shows that if Set A was given without criticism and Set B with criticism, 6.40 times as many aggressive words appeared in the stories to Set B than to Set A.

Table 2 shows that if Set B was given without criticism and Set A with criticism, Set B still produced 1.46 times as much aggression as Set A with criticism. However, as will be seen in Table 3, and as can be seen by comparing Tables 1 and 2, Set B without criticism produced much less aggression than Set B with criticism, and Set A with criticism produced much more aggression than without criticism. One can, at this point, arrive at the conclusion that Set B, by its very nature, elicits more aggression than Set A, although an increase according to the hypothesis takes place.

Table 3 then shows explicitly that Set A produces less aggression than Set B, even if it is accompanied by criticism, but does produce twice as much aggression under this condition as if it were not accompanied by criticism. It suggests that projection works there just as well, only not strongly enough to make up for the margin Set B has by its very nature of suggesting aggression. Also, Table 3 shows that Set B with criticism produced almost twice as much aggression as Set B without criticism, and that even if A plus B are compared under conditions of criticism with those without, there is about twice as much aggression produced under the influence of criticism.

TABLE 1

NUMBER OF AGGRESSIVE WORDS IN STORIES TO TAT PICTURES;
SET A WITHOUT AND SET B WITH CRITICISM

	Subjects				
	MA	FR	AM	Sum	Ratio
Picture Set A—without criticism—6 to 10	0	3	2	5 ⎫	
Picture Set B—with criticism—1 to 5	12	11	9	32 ⎭	6.40

TABLE 2

NUMBER OF AGGRESSIVE WORDS IN STORIES TO TAT PICTURES;
SET A WITH AND SET B WITHOUT CRITICISM

	Subjects				
	MC	HA	GO	DE	Sum	Ratio
Picture Set B—without criticism—1 to 5	8	4	3	4	19 ⎫	
Picture Set A—with criticism—6 to 10	6	1	2	4	13 ⎭	1.46

In order to satisfy minds demanding more sophisticated statistics than simple ratios, an analysis of variance was made of the same data. Employing much greater statistical rigor, it shows essentially the same facts, and assures the significance of the obtained differences.

Table 4 shows that if one compares the over-all difference between stories related to Set A plus the stories related to Set B without criticism to stories related to Set A plus Set B with criticism, the difference in amount of aggression is very significant in the direction of the hypothesis.

Table 4 also confirms the finding that there is an essential difference between Set A and Set B in their ability to elicit aggression. Although the finding is significant only at the seven percent level, one may say that in general Set B is more likely to elicit aggression than Set A. This is also shown in Table 5. If both sets are given with criticism, this difference in the ability to elicit aggression is further enlarged.

One may assume, then, that not only is there an increase in aggression in the stories told to either set, under criticism, due to projection of the subject's own aggressive feelings as reaction to the criticism; it may also be concluded that these aggressive feelings are more readily projected into material which lends itself more easily to such an interpretation of aggressive character by its original nature than others which do not have this quality.

TABLE 3

NUMBER OF AGGRESSIVE WORDS IN STORIES TO TAT PICTURES;
SET A AND SET B WITH AND WITHOUT CRITICISM

	Without criticism	With criticism	Ratio of means
Set A and B—1 to 10	25.50	53.00	2.09
Set A—6 to 10	6.25	13.00	2.09
Set B—1 to 5	19.00	32.00	2.10

TABLE 4

SIGNIFICANCE OF DIFFERENCE IN NUMBER OF AGGRESSIVE WORDS IN STORIES
WITH AND WITHOUT CRITICISM TO SET A AND SET B AND SIGNIFICANCE OF
SET A AND SET B TO ELICIT AGGRESSION

Source of variation	Degrees of Freedom	Sum of Squares	Mean Square	F	p
Total	13	180.93	13.92	—	
Error	10	38.84	3.88	—	
Difference between A and B without criticism	1	16.29	16.29	4.20	.07
Difference between A and B with criticism	1	94.29	94.29	24.30	Beyond .001 (very significant)
Over-all difference between A and B with and without criticism	1	31.50	31.50	8.19	Beyond .05 (significant)

Table 5 shows that although the difference in amount of aggression elicited by Set A with and without criticism is in the direction of the hypothesis, it is not really significant. However, the difference in amount of aggression under the same conditions for Set B is significant beyond the one per cent level. It also shows that the over-all differences between A with criticism plus B without criticism is significant, confirming the points found in Tables 3 and 5.

In view of the few subjects employed, it was desirable to support the results by other means. It seemed particularly important to show that the subjects giving stories to Set B were not persons who, by their very nature, were less aggressive and gave less aggressive stories than the average subject might; it was also desirable to show that, on the other hand, the subjects giving more stories to Set B under criticism gave, actually, more aggression than the average subject gives.

For this reason, an analysis was made of the stories told to the same pictures by 25 other Harvard students, for another purpose, but under standard TAT conditions.

The means of the number of aggressive words used by this control group was computed, and a test made on the difference of their mean with the ones of the present experimental group. Table 6 and Table 7 show that, on the one hand, there was no significant difference in the number of aggressive words found in the stories told to the pictures of Set B by the present subjects, without criticism, and the control group. On the other hand, it was found that a significant difference existed between the number of aggressive words produced by these 25 control subjects and the subjects who had the same pictures with criticism.

DISCUSSION OF FIRST EXPERIMENT

The obtained data seem to permit the conclusion that the existence of projection as defined may be considered as a fact. However, additional experiments seem necessary to investigate why there was no significant difference in amount of aggression in stories 6 to 10 with and without criticism. As was mentioned

TABLE 5

SIGNIFICANCE OF DIFFERENCE OF NUMBER OF AGGRESSIVE WORDS TO SET A WITH AND WITHOUT CRITICISM AND SET B WITH AND WITHOUT CRITICISM

Source of variation	Degrees of Freedom	Sum of Squares	Mean Square	F	p
Error	10	38.84	3.88	—	
Difference in A—with and without criticism	1	4.29	4.29	1.11	n. s.
Difference in B—with and without criticism	1	60.01	60.01	15.49	Beyond .01 (significant)
Over-all difference between A with and without criticism and B with and without criticism	1	77.79	77.79	20.05	Beyond .01 (significant)

before, this might well be because these pictures by their very nature do not easily lead to interpretation of aggressive acts, and it may be that projection of certain sentiments needs a stimulus at least somewhat likely to be projected upon. After all, even the early paranoiac projects only on *certain* people, and only with the progress of the disease are indiscriminate ideas of persecution found.

To test this hypothesis it is necessary to take a series of ten pictures, all of which could *equally* invite an interpretation of aggression by their nature, and then give 1 to 5 to a certain number of subjects without criticism, and 6 to 10 with criticism, and again reverse the arrangement for an equal number of subjects. Then it would be expected that there might be significant differences either way. To test this assumption, the second experiment was carried out.

Obviously, aggression need not only call forth aggression in another person. Clinically speaking, there was good reason to assume that some of the subjects might respond with themes of submissiveness in their stories, and others with plain despair. It seemed very difficult to demonstrate this quantitatively, but several people trained in the interpretation of the TAT agreed on this independently. While this fact shows the possible use of this technique for other variables in personality, it may explain why the results of this experiment were not more clear-cut. These latent differences in reaction were, of course, paralleled by manifest differences: while one subject said he was so discouraged that he almost quit, other subjects denied that they were much concerned. A few subjects showed marked blanching, blushing, and tremor of the hands. One subject, who stuttered, stuttered twice as much under criticism. Two subjects aired their aggression directly by blaming the poor quality of the pictures, and one blamed the experimenter for unprecise instructions and criticism.

TABLE 6

NUMBER OF AGGRESSIVE WORDS IN STORIES TO TAT PICTURES 1 TO 5—SET B— WITHOUT CRITICISM; THE MEAN VALUE OF 25 COMPARED WITH THE MEAN VALUE OF 4 EXPERIMENTAL SUBJECTS

Mean of 25 control subjects	Mean of 4 experimental subjects	p
3.92	4.75	t is 0.49 n.s.

TABLE 7

NUMBER OF AGGRESSIVE WORDS IN STORIES TO TAT PICTURES 1 TO 5—SET B; THE MEAN VALUE OF 25 CONTROL SUBJECTS WITHOUT CRITICISM COMPARED TO THE MEAN VALUE OF 3 EXPERIMENTAL SUBJECTS WITH CRITICISM

Mean of 25 control subjects without criticism	Mean of 3 experimental subjects with criticism	p
3.92	10.66	t is 3.7 (significant beyond .01)

It may also be mentioned here that projection of the immediate sentiments did not interfere with projection of deeper-lying determinants. This seems to be a very important point, since it has often been asked if one does not simply project the fragments of the immediate past into the TAT. On the basis of the material, it was felt that even though the immediate aggression was projected, the underlying personality was equally revealed.

For instance, the two halves of the experiment lead to the same conclusion about relative morbidity of the themes related. That is to say, if somebody pursued neurotic themes without criticism, the neuroticism also appeared in the five stories under criticism although usually accentuated by the added tension. And if somebody seemed not neurotic in the first five stories, the added aggression did not essentially change this picture. It seems as if the less stable subjects transformed aggression into aggression befalling the hero, that is, accepted aggression passively, while the more sturdy subjects identified themselves with increasingly active aggressive heroes. One subject reported equally autobiographically in both halves, while another one managed to turn all the unpleasant, dangerous or undesirable features of the stories, as somewhat suggested by the pictures, into pleasant, innocuous themes.

SECOND EXPERIMENT

To follow the indication suggested by the first experiment, namely that projection is in part a function of the stimulus, the second experiment was devised. Fundamentally, it is similar to the first one. Ten subjects were employed, students of Harvard University, who were sent by the Student Employment Office, and were paid for their services. The only specifications given to the Employment Office were that the students should not have studied psychology.

Again the TAT was employed as a vehicle of projection. However, this time the picture sets were matched in such a way as to be equally strong stimuli for aggression. That is, ten pictures were employed, divided five into Set A and five into Set B. Each of the five in Set A was so selected as to match one in Set B for suggestion of aggression in each character. The judgment of aggressiveness suggested in a picture was based on data derived from experience with these pictures on about 50 subjects in other investigations.

These pictures, from the 1942 set of the TAT, were in part identical with the first experiment, but reshuffled. Set A consisted of the following pictures in the order given: A1—man with upraised arm and open mouth; A2—a rural scene; A3—a man gripped from the rear; A4—an operation; A5—a man shaking his fist. Set B consisted of: B1—a young woman clutching a young man; B2—a man's silhouette against a window; B3—a boy on the couch with a pistol on the floor; B4—two boys standing in an archway; B5—an older, gray-haired man facing a younger man.

Subjects 1, 2, 4, 5, and 9 had Set A first; the rest had B first. This order was determined by drawing lots. The procedure from this point on followed that of Experiment 1: After the fifth picture story the experimenter began to criticize the subject and the criticism became increasingly stronger until the end of the series.[3]

RESULTS

The complete analysis of variance of these data is presented in Table 8.[4]. The results may be summarized as follows:

First, the effect of the criticism is to increase the number of aggressive words used in the stories. The mean number of aggressive words per subject before criticism is 12.6; after criticism, 23.7—a mean increase of 11.1 words, this increase being significant at the five per cent level.

Second, the two groups of pictures are approximately equal in their capacity to evoke aggressive responses, since the mean square for this comparison is only slightly greater than the mean square for "error"—$F = 1.32$.

Third, the differential effect of criticism on the two groups of pictures—interaction of pictures and criticism—is also negligible—$F = 1.32$. It may be concluded, therefore, that the *a priori* equating of the two groups of pictures was successful in eliminating both the over-all effect of the pictures and the interaction of pictures and criticism as an important source of variation.

Fourth, differences between subjects who were exposed to identical conditions are significant at the two per cent level. In other words, some subjects use more aggressive words than others, and this occurs to a degree greater than that accounted for by the stimulus conditions. Since individual differences of this nature were not significant in the earlier experiment, the result suggests that this group is somewhat more heterogeneous than the earlier group with respect to its projection of aggression as a reaction to criticism.

Fifth, the remaining degrees of freedom which measure "discrepance" or the effect of uncontrolled or unspecified factors provides a suitably sensitive "estimate of error" with which the effect of the controlled or specified factors may be compared.

In addition to the results summarized in Table 8, there were two other findings which are worth noting. First, both the mean and the standard deviation of the number of aggressive words for this group of subjects are significantly greater than for the earlier group. This appears, however, to have been an artifact of the scoring technique, for in the second experiment a much broader meaning was given to "aggressive" words, by including words which sometimes have an aggressive meaning even though they did not have an obviously aggressive meaning in their present context. The second additional finding is that not only does the mean number of aggressive words used in stories increase as a result of criticism, but the variability among the subjects increases as well. The standard deviation of the ten scores before criticism is 9.81; after criticism it increases to 22.20—a difference significant beyond the five per cent level.

Criticism, then, results in an increase in the number of aggressive words and also increases the differences among individual persons. A re-examination of the earlier experiment suggests that a similar, although less marked, result occurred then, but was obscured by the striking differential capacity of the two groups of pictures to elicit aggressive responses. When this latter source of variation is eliminated, the increase in variability among subjects in Experiment 2 is a clear

---

[3] I am indebted for the scoring of the series gathered with this procedure to Miss Shirley Mitchell and Miss Ruth Markman.

[4] I am indebted to Dr. Daniel Horn for aid with all the statistical problems.

consequence of the criticism. This latter finding is very important since it shows that even though a recent event may change the nature of fantasy material related in a definite direction, the amount of such change is subject to significant individual variations which would allow diagnostic differentiation.

Moreover, the fact that the two sets used evoked about the same amount of aggression supports the theory that aggression was projected in accordance with the specific aptness of a stimulus to be interpreted as aggressive, or more generally speaking, that such stimuli are primarily projected upon in a certain way as to lend themselves by their very nature to such an interpretation. This also explains the discrepancy in the result of the earlier experiment in which no care was taken to select the pictures from this standpoint.

AN EXAMINATION OF THE CONCEPT OF PROJECTION

One might speak of the first experiment principally as an attempt to verify the *predictive power* of the concept of projection. Similarly, one could say that the second experiment endeavored to show both the ability *to predict and to control* behavior by means of this hypothesis. It now remains to try to understand the process of projection.

By understanding *projection* something *subjective* is meant in distinction to the objectivity of prediction and control, possibly the subjective *experience of closure*. More accurately, it means the ability to see the *sequential nature and causal relationship of events* in terms of previously established concepts.

The investigation was begun with projection defined as ascription of needs and sentiments which one has oneself to the external world as a defensive process of which one is not aware.

Subjects were presented with pictures of the TAT and it was found that aggression could be induced in subjects and that this aggression was projected into their stories in accordance with the hypothesis.

Furthermore, it was found that some pictures are more often responded to with stories of aggression, even in normal circumstances, if the experimenter does nothing but simply ask the subject to tell a story about them. Also, it was found that those same pictures lend themselves much more to projection of aggression than others not suggesting aggression by their actual character.

TABLE 8

THE ANALYSIS OF FACTORS CONTRIBUTING TO THE TOTAL VARIANCE OF AGGRESSIVE WORD SCORES BEFORE AND AFTER CRITICISM; THE SUBJECTS ARE 10 HARVARD UNDERGRADUATES OBTAINED THROUGH THE COLLEGE EMPLOYMENT OFFICE

Source of variation	Degrees of Freedom	Sum of Squares	Mean Square	F	p
Total	19	6506.55	—	—	—
Due to criticism	1	616.05	616.05	5.40	.05
Due to pictures	1	151.25	151.25	1.32	—
Due to order of pictures—interaction of pictures and criticism	1	151.25	151.25	1.32	—
Between subjects under same conditions	8	4675.80	584.47	5.13	.02
Interaction of subjects, criticism, and pictures—used as estimate of error	8	912.20	114.02	—	—

It is believed that the first fact—that a picture showing a huddled figure and a pistol, for instance, is more suggestive of aggression than one of a peaceful country scene—is nothing but what common sense would lead one to expect. In psychological language this simply means that the response is in part a function of the stimulus. Allport has spoken of this behavior as *adaptive* behavior; it needs to be considered with and distinguished from expressive and projective aspects of behavior.

By adaptive behavior is meant those aspects of an artist's work which are determined by the material with which he works, whether it is clay, marble, oil paints, aquarelle, English, or German. Furthermore, it is determined by the nature of the stimulus, whether he is depicting a bullfight or a coronation or a mountain scene. As I shall mention later, it is also determined by his task.

Summarizing, I could say his creation has to adapt itself to certain external conditions.

By *expressive* aspects I mean that if a number of artists were exposed to the same conditions, the same product would not be expected. There would be individual differences in the way they make their strokes, with the brush or chisel; there would be differences in the colors they prefer and differences in arrangement and distribution of space. In other words, certain predominantly myoneural characteristics, as Mira (1940) calls it, would determine some features of their product. They would differ in *how* they adapt themselves.

Finally, returning to projection; given the same external conditions to which to adapt, different people would differ in the conception of the theme. A scene one person apperceives as the brute aggression of a cruel sadist another one may see as the gallant triumph of mind over matter; or a mountain scene which calls forth in one person associations of the helpful spirits of fairies, another may see as the playground of sinister agents of the devil.

In other words, one would be inclined to say that they also project their sentiments or attitudes into their work. It seems quite possible, then, to separate these three aspects of behavior, namely adaptive, expressive, and projective, insofar as the amount of each can be varied independently of the other two.

The amount of adaptive behavior will vary conversely with the degree of exactness of definition of a stimulus, and will also depend on the task or set or Aufgabe. For example, if one of the pictures of the Stanford-Binet Test (revised Form L) depicting a fight between a white man and Indians (*Frontier Days*) is presented and what seems funny about the picture is asked, the situation is well enough defined to elicit the same response from the majority of children at the ages of 10 to 12. On the one hand, it is the clearness of the picture and on the other hand the definiteness of the task that determine the verbal behavior. Additional examples may clarify this. Presented with a statue and asked to copy it in marble, an artist would exhibit mainly adaptive behavior. Or, for instance, hearing an air-raid siren after having received definite instructions about what to do in such a case, one exhibits adaptive behavior.

Projection will vary in amount inversely with the clearness of the stimulus and also inversely with the exactness of the instructions concerning the task. If one takes another picture of the Stanford-Binet (revised Form D, 12-3), the messenger boy whose bicycle has broken down, and asks the subject to describe what is going on, one deals with a more complex situation, and the instructions are less definite—"Look at the picture and tell me all about it"—therefore, the response is less uniform and may present potentially more features of projection. Of course the importance of the third determinant of behavior, namely the characteristics of the individual subject, is obvious in this instance. On the one hand, the intelligence of the person is important, and on the other hand, other facets of his personality are significant, as will be pointed out later.

Concepts of the Gestalt School permit one to express this situation rather well. One may say in those terms that the less structured the field is originally, the more structuration will be done by the ego and vice versa. In an ambiguous picture, personality variables will determine mainly what becomes figure and what becomes ground. This cognitive function is greatly influenced by a tendency toward tension reduction.

To stay with the previous examples, if an artist now were simply given a block of marble and asked to produce something, and stimulus and task were only slightly defined, his projective behavior would be at a height. Furthermore, if the air-raid siren sounded and the subject were not acquainted with its nature and meaning, and did not have any instructions about it, he might interpret it as anything from the howling spirits of hell to the announcement of dinnertime, in accordance with his present personality make-up and his previous experiences, whether he felt guilty or hungry.

The experiments herewith reported have shown that projection may in part be influenced by the *nature* of the stimulus. While it holds true that there is more projection—and less adaptation—if the stimulus is not well defined and the task is not well defined, a stimulus more suggestive of aggression will allow it to be projected more easily than one not suggestive of aggression at all. To be more exact, given two pictures of the same clarity of definition, schematically speaking, and given the same task, the nature of the picture will have an influence on the kind of drives projected.

Levine, Chein, and Murphy (1942) have added evidence for another interesting fact. Their findings suggest that when a need is more and more increased, in their instance by frustration, not only increased projection of this need is found, but at the same time increased adaptive ability. Hungry subjects not only projected ideas pertaining to food, but were also able to perceive objects actually pertaining to food and presented so as to be perceived only with difficulty more often when hungry than when not hungry.

Dynamically this phenomenon can be understood very well. Under adverse conditions the adaptive or problem-solving functions of the ego are increased. At the same time, as long as this still fails to bring satisfaction, fantasy gratification in the form of projection is achieved as the next best thing.

So far the variable in which psychologists are most interested, namely the personality structure of the subject, has been neglected. When projective tests are used clinically, the basic assumption is usually that definition and character of the stimulus and of the task are given and that responses to them have been established by a number of subjects. The second assumption is that the individual variations in the content of the responses are functions of experience and projection of the dynamic structure of the personality of each subject. This was shown by various investigations (See Harrison, 1940; Rotter, 1940; Sanford et al., 1943).

Practically, the task of finding projective trends in someone's responses is not very difficult, and is more convincing than any theoretical discussion could ever be. If a psychologist is presented with 50 people's responses to the same 20 pictures, nearly everyone will appreciate the individual differences, the intrapersonal consistency of certain trends, and the meaningfulness of these trends in terms of the personality of these subjects, if one can compare it with objective data about them.

It was Sanford (Sanford et al., 1943) who suggested recently that projection of needs and sentiments into fantasy material is not only a function of the presence and over-all strength of these needs and sentiments, but also depends on the degree of possibility of manifest expression of such a need. In other words, sex needs may be projected more frequently and extensively into fantasies if the manifest expression of sex need has to be inhibited. In other words, projection is a function of the character of the stimulus and the dynamic characteristics of personality and of the environment, and the amount of projection varies inversely with the clarity of definition of stimulus and task.

Expressive behavior, finally, seems to be of a nature somewhat different from both adaptation and projection. Given a fixed ratio of adaptation and projection in someone's responses to either Stanford-Binet picture, people may vary in their style, in their organization. One may use long sentences, many adjectives; someone else may use short sentences, pregnant phrases of strictly logical sequence. If they write their responses, they may vary in upper length and lower length, in spacing. If they speak, they differ in speed, pitch, or volume, all these being personal characteristics long considered stable characteristics of every person.

Similarly, in the case of my second example, the artist may chisel in small detail and with precision, or choose a less exacting form. He may arrange things symmetrically or off center. And again, in response to the air-raid signal, somebody may run, crouch, jump, walk, talk—all in his own typical way.

In other words, expressive features reveal themselves in how one does something, projection and adaptation in what one does. While the amount of adaptiveness and projectivity of a response may vary with the exactness of definition of the stimulus and the task, and adaptation and projection may be said to vary inversely with each other, it seems practically impossible to have only the one or the other without some admixture.

If, then, adaptation and projection determine *what one does* and expression *how one does it,* it is needless to emphasize that one can always ask *how one does what one does.* Adaptive, projective, and expressive aspects of behavior are always coexistent.

In the case of well-known artists, for instance, and various of their products, the ratio of adaptive versus projective material and the expressive characteristics may vary, of course. It might be said, for instance, that Goethe's *Werther* was highly projective, while *Faust* was partly written by projection and partly shows Goethe's dealing with the problem of human happiness which is more or less adaptive and is a recognition of an objective situation eliciting problem-solving behavior. Also, he varied his expressive mode. Furthermore, one could contrast both Goethe and Schiller, as poets who projected a good deal of their own personality into their figures, with Shakespeare or Dickens who did so relatively rarely.

Such a distinction between the various aspects of any creative work may avoid many of the current arguments about whether some work is to be understood as only a projection of an artist's neurotic tendencies or if he is dealing rationally, adaptively, with an existing problem. Usually both aspects are to be dealt with. The same holds true for projective tests. In the Rorschach, for instance, the material for adaptive expressive, purposeful behavior is inkblots. By their very unstructuredness, they are supposed to define the condition as little as possible, allowing the subject to structure the field, thereby revealing his expressive and projective characteristics. The expressive qualities are later examined in a standard fashion, for the percentage of whole responses versus detail responses, or the color responses versus form or movement concepts, and such a ratio has permitted a differentiation of various groups. At times the Rorschach will show a story of a bear following a smaller animal, or a chameleon poised for its prey, and the interpreter will draw certain conclusions for such dynamic scenes if they occur several times and so deal with some "projective" material. But on the whole, most Rorschach experts pay rather little attention to that, and I am inclined to say that the *Rorschach is hardly a projective test by the criteria advanced so far;* rather, *it is an expressive technique.* There are even more purely expressive techniques, such as Mira's Myokinetic Psychodiagnosis (Mira, 1940) or possibly graphological analysis.

Professor Mira's new technique for detecting conative trends of personality is based on the assumption that every mental attitude in the human subject implies a corresponding muscular attitude, in which the movements leading to the realization of the purpose contained in the mental attitude are to be facilitated and those opposite to it are to be rendered difficult. He thus developed a technique of detecting the involuntary expressions of the predominant attitude of reaction, evaluated as a function of the shiftings observed during blind execution of linear movements in the fundamental directions of space. Mira called his method Myokinetic Psychodiagnosis because he believes that it is through myokinesis that one gets an understanding of the fundamentals of the psyche. His technique constitutes as purely an expressive approach as one can find.

Many tests are on the projective level. The TAT, for instance, doubtless has all three features—adaptive, expressive, and projective—but a heavier emphasis on the projective ones because of the dynamic individual interpretation of ambiguous situations. The adaptive aspects here are also greater than in the Rorschach: that is, there are persons and objects depicted, which are usually commonly recognized as such—an older man, a younger man, or a couch.

As indicated before, there is no doubt that a great deal of material in the stories directly results from the very nature of the picture. With normal subjects it is to be expected that the stimulus will be adequately recognized and responded to, even though every once in a while one finds, even there, obvious misrepresentations. Thus, for instance, a male figure was perceived as a woman by two of about 50 college students, and something that was practically always described as a pistol was described as a hole in the floor by one subject. But aside from this, one can safely assume that the stimulus plays an important part in the related material, as my experiments showed. That the stories told have certain expressive features which may be used diagnostically has been particularly shown by Balken and Masserman (1940), who analyzed the verb-noun

ratio and other linguistic criteria, and found significant characteristics for different clinical syndromes. On the subjective side, one subject makes the older man
in a picture a father who loves his son very much and does all he can for him,
while somebody else makes him a hostile father, or perhaps a lawyer, or an old
criminal, or the King of England, or a famous surgeon, and the stories built
around them vary just as much. That is, the stimulus is perceived, but perceived and interpreted differently, in such a way that one seems again justified
in assuming that one is dealing with projection.

It was found in the first experiment that the subjects tended to ascribe excessive aggression to the persons in the pictures particularly if the adaptive
aspects of the picture were somewhat suggestive of aggression or at least could
relatively easily be so interpreted. The second experiment corroborated the impression that, other conditions being equal, one is likely to project a given sentiment on a stimulus that by its very nature lends itself to such an interpretation.

It was this finding in its very obviousness that led to further thought on the
subject. For one thing, it seems rather easy to show that this is a condition
equally met in everyday life or clinical experience. Neurotics will project their
attitudes on a selected group, where it is relatively rational to expect such attitudes. Even the paranoiac, in the initial stages projects on only a small number
of people motives which are often not entirely absurd; only with the progress of
his disease does he usually become less differentiating of the stimuli he projects
on, and finally believes the whole world is persecuting him. One school of
thought would describe this progressive development as a generalization of a
conditioned response; or, it might be better to say that there is an increasing
readiness to react in a certain way to given stimuli, or a readiness which ren-
ders many different stimuli functionally equivalent.

One wonders, then, if one could not reduce the process of projection as described in the experiment in the following manner: The experimenter criticizes
the subject; such criticism makes the subject angry and aggressive; because he
accepts certain cultural standards or has learned to react in specific ways, he
does not express his aggression overtly, but maintains this readiness for aggression which in turn leads him to interpret any situation at all likely to be so interpreted, or at a certain point *any* situation, as one of aggression.

How such a readiness is expressed, or what the mechanics of it is, could be
perceived in several ways. One could conceive of it in purely associational terms,
that is, that every forthcoming stimulus calls forth associations of aggression.
Or one could conceive of it as a conditioning process or choose to express it in
terms of the Gestalt School as the best configuration at the time given. It is
believed that the conditioned-response concept will be most helpful, and it has
been chosen for later discussion.

That the readiness is maintained and that final execution is mandatory could
easily be conceptualized in neural terms, such as underlie Murray's need concept (see Murray, et al., 1938), and is only one manifestation of a biological
need for tension reduction.

In the case of the experiment, and for that matter, in the case of any projective test, it may be fairly easy to see that behavior is guided by such as just
described: in the case of a subject who projects his fear of a dominant father
into the stories, it might simply be said that he has learned to experience his

father as dominant, has a readiness or set to perceive his father and figures more
or less resembling his as dominant, and that any figure suggestive of a father in
the TAT sets off such responses—conceptualized in any or all of the "lingoes."

Of course it is true that any recent experience may possibly cause such a response. As far as clinical interpretation is concerned, one will consider the response as truly dynamically significant only if a similar theme recurs several
times in forms which cannot all be due to some recent experience, as for instance
a movie. A story dealing with a cruel father putting his son into jail because of
disobedience may be due to a recent "superficial" experience. If, however, other
stories are told in which a male teacher punishes a boy for breaking a rule by
keeping him confined in a dark room, and later a story is told of a little animal
that ran away from the parental nest and was promptly devoured by the big bad
wolf, and all this in the face of the fact that altogether different stories are being
told to these stimuli by other subjects, it seems justified to assume a deeper
significance.

Furthermore, it seems correct to assume that if one specific response from
recent experience is given to a picture that often elicits completely different
responses from other subjects, one again seems justified in assuming that the
response could only or mostly become dominant in the welter of all recent experiences because it happened to fit a pre-existing pattern.

The range of stimuli so interpreted would almost be an index of the rigidity of
the subject, which is one of the most important aspects of neurotic behavior.

It is only fair, though, to see if such a process would really also have explanatory power in the case of the paranoiac. After all, I have talked only about test
behavior so far. Accepting Freud's formulation, I believe that the paranoiac
first has homosexual affection for some people. Reaction formation transforms
this into aggression, and now he "projects" this aggression on the former love
object. It seems quite possible to conceive of these stages in the way described;
one would find it further very helpful to retain psychoanalytic terminology, and
say that the homosexual desires may be conceived of as part of the id, a hypothetical locus of drives. These impulses are inhibited by the power of the ego
and superego—hypothetical locis of adequate social behavior—and reaction
formation into hatred takes place. Aggression is unacceptable to the ego and
superego; the readiness for aggression is maintained and other normally inadequate stimuli perceived as aggressive. The complexity of the processes may be
of any order without essentially changing the state of affairs. Phenomena lying
between the extremes of test behavior on the one side and paranoia on the other
side may be similarly conceived. It seems necessary to indicate, though, that
one would speak of projection in the strict sense only if the cycle consists of at
least:

The presence of a certain attitude, sentiment or thought.

Its inhibition by the ego and superego—exclusion from activation or consciousness.

The maintenance of readiness—set—to act according to the thought, attitude, or
sentiment.

The perception of an ordinarily inadequate stimulus as adequate for eliciting the
specific attitude or sentiment or thought.

The inhibition of such action by the ego and superego because of its moral and
realistic implications and inhibition of recognition of one's own attitude.

An increased readiness to perceive any stimulus as related to the specific sentiment or thought or attitude, and its generalization to such a degree that nearly any
stimulus calls forth the associations of the inhibited sentiment.

Closely allied to the concept of projection is the concept of displacement; in
fact, projection could be called the dynamic basis of displacement, as used by
Freud. That is, a sentiment existing for one object is displaced onto another.
For instance, the child who is angry at the mother may go into the yard and
kick the dog. In my conceptualization, there is first the presence of a certain
need, sentiment, or attitude, namely to hurt somebody; second, its inhibition by
the superego and the ego—it is immoral to kick one's mother, and it is unwise
since she is stronger; third, the maintenance of readiness—set—to act according
to this sentiment, to kick somebody; and fourth, the perception of an ordinarily
inadequate stimulus as adequate for the eliciting of the specific sentiment of
aggression when there is little or no interference from ego or superego, that is,
if the dog is known not to bite, and hurting an animal is relatively less repre-
hensible.

This concept is widely misconceived as projection.[5] Most so-called projective
techniques in children deal with displacement rather than projection. If a child
plays with dolls who represent the family and dismembers them as an expression
of aggression, this is displacement and not projection. Similarly, it is displacement rather than projection with which L. J. Stone deals in his game of balloons.

In the TAT one deals with projection, since the subject does not displace his
aggressive feelings from the father toward the father figure by tearing the cards
or sticking pins into the paternal picture, a behavior which one encounters in
play therapies, but ascribes his feelings to the son image in the picture and
denies that they are his own toward his father.

Similarly, in the reported experiment, one would be dealing with displacement
if the subjects were physically aggressive toward the figures representing the
experimenter. But what they actually do is to ascribe aggression to figures whom
they fail or refuse to recognize consciously as themselves or the experimenter.

Sears (1943) feels that one is dealing with a different concept of projection in
"projective tests." He conceives of Murray's and Sanford's experiment only as
evidence that organizational and motivational properties of a person influence
the perceptual and judgmental processes, and thinks that such a usage must be
separated from the defensive meaning given the term in paranoia. In paranoia,
he feels, the outstanding thing is the defense against anxiety-arousing impulses.
On the other hand, I believe that in Murray's, Sanford's, and my own experiments, essentially the same process as in paranoia is being considered; the mere
fact that the impulses are ascribed to the outside world and that one fails to
recognize one's own subjective part in the judgments made is evidence of defensive processes against the painful insight that one is afraid, hungry, or angry
without being able to do something about it.

Projection in the case of the paranoiac could be differentiated from that in the
neurotic and the normal person by the *extensiveness* of the use of this mechanism: while the normal person projects only occasionally, the neurotic is likely

---

[5] I am indebted to the late Dr. Ernst Kris for this suggestion.

to meet a good many situations with this mechanism, and the psychotic has managed to make an admirably consistent system of it.

One could also speak of *intensity* of projection as a differential criterion. By this is meant that there are varying degrees of awareness or potential awareness of this process. If something is said to be unconscious, as is the projective mechanism, one is well aware of the fact that there may be more or less of an inhibition of the becoming conscious of unconscious material. The self-observation of the normal may soon tell him that he is probably distorting his perceptions, or he will be amenable to interpretation. This will be much less true for the neurotic, for whom it is much more important to keep the powerful disruptive tendencies from consciousness, and interpretation will find much resistance. Finally, a fully developed psychotic will find it completely impossible to become aware of the subjective nature of his world.

I believe that transference is a phenomenon closely allied to projection and displacement, or probably only a combination of the two, amenable to the same breakdown into various steps.

In transference to the analyst, for instance, one "transfers" feelings which one once had for the parents and which have now become directed to the analyst. This means that attitudes and needs are aroused which cannot be gratified in relation to the original stimulus—the parents and the readiness to react in such a way is maintained and discharged upon this—rationally—inadequate stimulus. Thus, it seems, transference is only a special case of displacement. However, projection may enter in, since one may not only feel love or hate for the analyst, but also assume that he loves or hates one.

It remains to be seen if other psychoanalytic mechanisms can be similarly broken down to such terms as inhibition, maintained readiness, generalization of stimuli, and final response. One may hope that such a breakdown will further bridge the cleft between clinical concepts and experimental verification.

AN APPROACH TO THE EVALUATION
OF DRUG EFFECT DURING PSYCHOTHERAPY:
A DOUBLE-BLIND STUDY OF A SINGLE CASE

Patients are clearly people, but when they become subjects in research they all too quickly become numbers—faceless and interchangeable. For a while it was thought the more subjects the better, further increasing the anonymity of the individual; to rest a study on a single case was long considered a violation of good statistical practice, flying in the face of the law of large numbers upon which probability theory is so largely based. As this chapter makes clear, individual cases can be treated statistically in a responsible manner, and even the lack of independent observations may not invalidate the use of such standard procedures as the t-test. This observation is in keeping with the current idea that the parametric procedures are surprisingly robust and will tolerate the violation of many basic assumptions.

Because the findings in single-case studies are based on the individual patient, they are directly applicable to the further treatment of that patient; as the concluding section makes clear, the *statistical* conclusion—that the drug makes for improvement—was later borne out in practice. Of course, the counter-argument could be made that the results, because they are so closely tied to this particular case, do not have general significance and, therefore, do not represent a useful contribution to knowledge. This conclusion is partly true; we need to know more in a general sense about the diagnostic status of the patient before the findings can be fully appreciated.

IT IS A WELL-KNOWN PARADOX that convincing experiences of clinicians are derived from intensive clinical work with individual patients, while research data are usually obtained from extensive statistical studies of rather large populations of patients and are often rather superficial.

The evaluation of psychotropic drugs shares many problems with the evaluation of psychotherapy: the problem of valid and reliable judgments, the effect of time, and the problem of understanding and demonstrating the process of the therapeutic effect, rather than a mere evaluation of the result. Not the least among these difficulties derive from the procedure of testing various hypotheses by comparing groups of patients in terms of the relative efficacy of two or more medications. The inability to specify particular patient parameters in relation to the statistical results of such studies, the unknown characteristics of the pop-

NOTE: From the *Journal of Nervous and Mental Disease*, 1964, 139, 20-30. Reprinted by permission of the publisher and J. B. Chassan, co-author, whose collaboration is gratefully acknowledged. This paper also appeared under the title "An Introduction to Intensive Design in the Evaluation of Drug Efficacy During Psychotherapy" in *Methods of Research in Psychotherapy*, edited by Louis A. Gottschalk and Arthur H. Auerbach. Copyright © 1966 by Meredith Publishing Company. Reprinted by permission of Appleton-Century-Crofts.

ulation of patients from which the research subjects are presumably considered as a random sample, and the consequent poverty of operational implications of the results of such studies are among the many difficulties one encounters in what has been called the extensive model of clinical research design.[1]

From another point of view, the use of the extensive model has the effect of exaggerating some of the differences in orientation between clinical research and clinical practice with a consequent feeling of alienation from research on the part of many clinicians who might otherwise be strongly motivated toward it. Research in which statistical comparisons are limited to tests between groups of patients ignores what is happening to the individual patient, to the ebb and flow of his symptoms, to their interpretation within a dynamic framework so important to an understanding of individual psychopathology, and to a more definitive understanding of differential drug effects. There has long been abroad in the land of clinical research the notion that comparisons between groups of patients is the *sine qua non* of statistically valid scientific clinical research, and that the study of the individual case must be relegated at best to a status of intuition and the clinical hunch, not capable of statistical testing and validation. For reasons that have been discussed in some detail (Chassan, 1960, 1961), this view is seen to lack validity in its own right. It has unfortunately tended to perpetuate a basically superficial methodology as a unique prototype for science in clinical research with mental patients.

What we are stating here is not that the extensive model itself is necessarily unscientific nor that when properly and appropriately performed cannot be viewed as a statistically valid approach to clinical investigation; but rather that it is quite limiting, and that the clinical-statistical study of the individual case (i.e., the intensive design) is, at the very least, a much-needed complementary approach. A previous attempt to bridge the difficulties between the clinical and the experimental statistically useful approach by the method of repeated short-range predictions and judgments by independent observers after interaction in psychoanalytic interviews has been made as outlined in Chapter 8. This study involved not only one psychoanalyst as a clinician but three psychoanalysts working as predictors and three as judges in a complex experimental setting. The controlled sequence of multidimensional observations was thus made in the framework of testing various hypotheses relevant to the population implicitly defined by the parameters of the single case under study.

The purpose of the present report is to demonstrate a method (and its feasibility) for the evaluation of drug efficacy within the context of the single case and particularly within a framework of the process and practice of psychotherapy by one therapist. A recognition of the possible advantages of the use of drugs as an adjunct to analytically oriented psychotherapy antedates the present age of ataractics (see Bellak, 1949a), although very little, if any, formal research using the double-blind technique seems to have been done in this area.

Although this study is based on data from only one case, it is not intended to convey the impression that intensive research designs should necessarily be limited to a single case. The essential property of the intensive design is that

---

[1] An analysis of the difficulties of the extensive model from a clinical as well as a statistical point of view will be found in Chassan (1960, 1961), as well as a discussion of some of the advantages of the alternative approach in the use of *intensive* design.

each patient in a study is observed periodically over some time span, and that statistical inferences including tests of hypotheses concerning treatment effects are made basically, *within* the data of each case separately, so that if there were, say, six patients in a study, it would be as though one were gathering and analyzing the data from six separate studies. An incidental advantage of having several patients in an intensive design, apart from the larger number of within-patient hypotheses one can then test, is that one can, upon failing to obtain within-patient significance, and depending upon the over-all design of the experiment, pool the data in a manner which may still yield a valid, statistically significant result, although the particular hypothesis tested in this way will then approach the type of hypothesis tested in an extensive design.

LIMITATIONS

This investigation was set up mainly as a short, preliminary study to determine whether some of the procedures (such as those described below) necessary to establish a tight double-blind study for the evaluation of the efficacy of a drug such as chlordiazepoxide (Librium)[2] by the use of an intensive design, and during a segment of psychotherapy, are feasible. Since this was the primary goal rather than that of testing hypotheses concerning the efficacy of the medication by this method at this time, no attempt was made to provide an adequate time span for the patient under study to provide a reasonable probability of obtaining statistically significant effects. For the purpose of determining feasibility it was thus estimated that a sequence of ten weekly interviews would be adequate. Contrary to expectations, we did obtain at least borderline significance in a number of the eight variables which were observed at each interview, favoring the active medication over the proverbial identical-appearing placebo, and in each of the remaining variables the averages on chlordiazepoxide showed less psychopathology than the corresponding averages on placebo.

Despite these particular results, however, the short time span, and concomitantly, the small number of observations such as were made in this study would in general have to be regarded as a serious limitation on the chance of securing sufficient data to obtain statistically significant differences toward the detection of true effects. This is, of course, a widely recognized limitation of a very small sample, whether the sample size is based on the number of patients in an extensive design, or on the number of observations along the time axis of the individual case in the intensive design.

There is also a second danger, usually not explicitly stated, and perhaps not generally recognized, but nevertheless implicit in the use of very small samples. This can arise even when an apparently statistically significant result *does* occur, in both the intensive design when a too-small time sample of the single case is taken and in the extensive design when too few patients are used. This second difficulty arises from the influence that one or two extremely biased observations, say, can have on a total, or on an average, based on a very small number of observations. The term, biased observations, in this context would apply as well to instances of cases that really do not belong in a study, or to the effect of extremely atypical events (as can be the case in a single-case study based on a small time sample) as well as to isolated instances of observer bias in both

---

[2] The chlordiazepoxide used in this study was supplied by Hoffmann-La Roche, Inc.

types of designs. In larger samples the influence of the singular atypical observation will obviously be less important.

ASPECTS OF THE DESIGN

Selection of Patient Variables and Description of the Patient

One of the advantages of intensive design is that, in focusing on the individual case, it encourages the use of items for rating and evaluating psychopathology which, at least in the view of the clinician who is treating and observing the patient, are specific *to* the patient. This is in contrast to the approach which is so often used in the extensive design when patients with diverse symptomatology and dynamic patterns are thrust, as it were, onto a single hyperdimensionalized rating sheet and in which statistical analyses take no account of highly relevant individual differences in the interpretability of the direction of a patient's movement along one or another particular scale item, or dimension.

The patient selected for this study was known to me through a previous course of treatment. The patient suffered from acute anxiety, feelings of depersonalization, and marked dissociation. From this previous contact, years before this study, together with observations made during an interview with her a week before the beginning of the study proper, I constructed a set of eight variables, as follows:

(1) Evidence of primary process thinking
(2) Anxiety
(3) Confusion
(4) Depression
(5) Hostility
(6) "Sexual flooding"
(7) Depersonalization
(8) Ability to communicate usefully

Each of these items was rated by the author at the end of each session of psychotherapy on a six-point scale. For each of the first seven items a zero rating indicated a complete absence of pathology and a rating of five represented the most severe level of pathology. For item 8, a zero represented the most pathological state, and a five the most favorable.

The rating scale used in this case was subjective in the following sense. The individual patient had already been well-known to the therapist from a previous course of treatment and was used as her own frame of reference. The previous experience with this patient was one of the reasons for using her in the present study. Previous work with scales involving approximately the same variables, under controlled circumstances (described in Chapter 7 and 13) had given the therapist a measure of confidence about judgment reliability. Definitions used in this previous work constituted the conceptual point of reference. Nevertheless, in the absence of independent observers this procedure remains crude and strictly an exploratory approach. There is no reason, however, why the same procedure using independent ratings of taped interview material cannot easily be made methodologically acceptable.

A few brief concrete examples may be useful. With regard to depersonalization, lack of any reported experiences of this nature (by this highly intelligent patient who has had experience with such feelings as well as an excellent verbal facility for describing them) was considered a reasonable basis for scoring depersonalization zero. A rating of five was given when the patient's report included such material as the following:

"I feel odd. I feel strange, as if I were drunk, in a daze. I took a walk and everything looked unreal and I began to feel quite sick. . . . I had very odd thoughts and the perspective of the ground was very strange. I felt, I am not sure whether I am there. I look in the mirror. I have the feeling of a stuffed head. Lights bother me, outdoors looks very strange. I feel as if I were someone else."

Intermediate ratings of depersonalization were made when the patient mentioned only some of these complaints; the ratings were based on the frequency of these phenomena since the previous interview and the degree of disturbance they caused. They were sometimes crippling, and at other times transitory and only mildly interfering.

With regard to the primary-process ratings, contamination (in the Rorschach sense), discontinuity in thought process, intrusion of illogical material, and the presence of incomprehensible autistic material were some of the features observed.

An example of the emergence of the primary process, an experience which was associated with feelings of unreality, can be found in the following:

"I had odd thoughts . . . concerning the house number (which I live at now) and where I used to live. . . . Something about not being sure and being confused as to past experiences (and present ones), past locations . . . when I was a child. . . ."

Unusual forgetfulness and many parapraxes were part of the disturbances by primary-process material. At times, associations were so "free" that it was very difficult to follow the story the patient meant to relate. The difficulty of following the patient's story seemed to lend itself particularly well to rating—an over-all view of just how much interference there was with communication in a particular hour.

Ratings of anxiety and depression leaned heavily upon the Elmhurst Scale used in a previous study of drug effects discussed in Chapter 13.

MEDICATION TREATMENT SCHEDULE AND ADMINISTRATION

At the end of the initial interview (just prior to the beginning of the study proper), the patient was given a bottle of capsules, instructed to take three capsules per day, and to return the bottle at the next interview. At the end of the subsequent meeting she was given a second bottle of identically appearing capsules with the same instructions. This procedure was repeated until a total of ten bottles were thus received and returned by the patient. Each capsule in a given bottle contained either chlordiazepoxide (10 mg. per capsule) or placebos, identical in appearance to those of the chlordiazepoxide. At the end of the study, the set of ratings pertaining to a given interview was related to the medication the patient was on during the week's period immediately preceding the interview, providing a basis for the comparison between effects on chlordiazepoxide and those on placebo. The actual sequence of medication corresponding to each psychotherapy session was as indicated in Table 1.

It should be noted that I was not aware of the medication the patient was on during a given week, nor did I know the points at which a change in medication was made.

DISTINGUISHING BETWEEN POSSIBLE EFFECTS OF PSYCHOTHERAPY AND DIFFERENCES IN EFFECT BETWEEN MEDICATIONS

The purpose of the method described in this paper is the evaluation, based on observations made during the course of psychotherapy, of the comparative efficacy of two medications. The purpose was, of course, not that of evaluating the effect of the psychotherapy itself. Nevertheless, in the analysis of the data one must take into consideration the possible effect of psychotherapy (confounded with the effect of time) as a factor in influencing levels of psychopathology as distinct from the influence of differential drug effects. For this reason one cannot, say, simply divide the time span into consecutive halves with one medication scheduled for the entire first half, and the other for the second. Such a procedure would obviously confound differential drug effects with those of psychotherapy and of time. In using the intensive design for the evaluation of differential effect between two medications, one must, therefore, utilize a design which allows for a number of alternations back and forth between the medications throughout the course of the study. An elementary statistical approach to the analysis of data thus obtained is suggested in Figure 1. Here, as an example, the sequence of evidence of primary-process ratings is plotted along the time axis (connecting consecutive points, and identifying each plotted point according to whether the observation to which it corresponds was made after a week of placebo or after a week on chlordiazepoxide). A next step is to fit a trend line to the data. Finally, we study and analyze the configuration of plotted points and their identifying medication in relation to their position with respect to the fitted trend line.

It may be of some interest to view the data plotted in Figure 1 from a descriptive point of view before presenting the results of any formal statistical analysis. First, it is noted that over the ten weeks of the combined administration of psychotherapy and medication (the latter in accordance with the sched-

TABLE 1

MEDICATION SEQUENCE

Session No.	Medication
0*	None
1	Placebo
2	Chlordiazepoxide
3	Chlordiazepoxide
4	Chlordiazepoxide
5	Placebo
6	Placebo
7	Placebo
8	Chlordiazepoxide
9	Chlordiazepoxide
10	Chlordiazepoxide

* The initial interview.

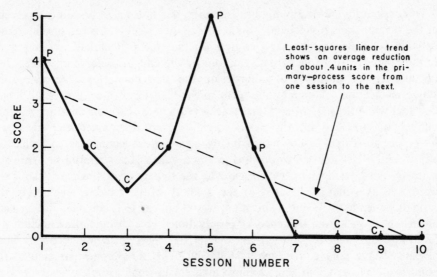

FIG. 1. Sequence of primary-process ratings.

ule given in Table 1) the fitted trend line describes an *average* decline in the primary-process pathology score of about .4 unit per week (i.e., from one session's rating to the next). We note further that three of the four observations which follow a week of placebo definitely lie above the trend line, indicating a worse-than-average score, while five of the six points relating to the use of chlordiazepoxide are below the trend line, indicating a better-than-average score. It should be noted that the single observation on chlordiazepoxide which lies above the trend line is the last in the series, and it has an actual primary-process pathology score of zero (which was also true of the last four observations). Thus its representation as worse than average, or rather, worse than trend, is in this case the result of having selected a straight-line trend for reasons of simplicity of exposition. A somewhat more complex trend fitted to the data could have eliminated this feature, perhaps adding slightly to the favorable comparison between active medication and placebo.

Table 2 presents a tabular analysis of the primary-process ratings, comparing averages on chlordiazepoxide with those on placebo. These comparisons are made using both the trend-adjusted scores and the raw scores. Averages over the entire run are compared between active medication and placebo, as well as averages based on subsequences of observations on the same medication. It is seen that the difference in the average scores favors the active medication over the placebo, and that in this particular set of data the use of the trend-adjusted score reduces the difference from that obtained by the corresponding raw score averages by a small fraction. We also note that in going from one subsequence to the next, on the two occasions when the alternation went from placebo to chlordiazepoxide, the average primary-process score dropped, while in the cases in which the direction was from chlordiazepoxide to placebo the average increased. Further, primary-process averages for each of the two subsequences on chlordiazepoxide are distinctly below each average on placebo in both the raw and trend-adjusted sequences.

In considering the data plotted in Figure 1, one notes a zero score on placebo at the seventh week followed by three consecutive weeks of zeros on chlordiazepoxide. One might raise the question whether the patient had not improved to the point of being free of the symptom by the end of the seventh week, thus invalidating for purposes of comparison the subsequent three zeros on the active medication. A counterargument might then be in the form of an assertion that while the patient first finally achieved a zero score on placebo, it is not unlikely that three consecutive weeks on chlordiazepoxide helped keep her there. Reference to Table 2 shows that taking trend into account has the effect of adjusting the last few scores upward in the manner of a compromise. An element of clinical judgment, with regard to the dynamics of the particular case, insofar as this may be related to the stability of so rapid a leveling in the rating independently of the medication, would appear to be unavoidable in such an instance. A longer sequence of observations which would have included a few more alternations between the active and inert medications might have obviated heavy reliance on such a judgment. This is, of course, related to the point made earlier about shortcomings inherent in small samples, whether dealing with a small time sample of the individual case in the intensive design, or with small numbers of patients in testing between groups in the more conventional extensive design.

SUMMARY OF RESULTS ON OTHER ITEMS

As was the case in the ratings on *evidence of primary process,* the weekly observations on each of the other variables, namely, *anxiety, confusion, hostility, "sexual flooding," depersonalization,* and *ability to communicate,* had more favorable averages on chlordiazepoxide than on placebo. Table 3 shows a comparison between effects, both within the raw scores and the trend-adjusted scores on each of the observed outcome variables.

TABLE 2

EVIDENCE OF PRIMARY PROCESS

Session No.	Medication	Raw Scores		Trend-Adjusted Scores	
		Session Score	Sequence Average	Session Score	Sequence Average
0	None	5	5.0	—	—
1	Placebo	4	4.0	2.2	2.2
2	Chlordiazepoxide	2		0.6	
3	Chlordiazepoxide	1	1.7	0.0	0.7
4	Chlordiazepoxide	2		1.4	
5	Placebo	5		4.8	
6	Placebo	2	2.3	2.2	2.5
7	Placebo	0		0.6	
8	Chlordiazepoxide	0		0.9	
9	Chlordiazepoxide	0	0.0	1.3	1.3
10	Chlordiazepoxide	0		1.7	
	Placebo mean	2.75		2.45	
	Chlordiazepoxide mean	0.83		0.98	

In discussing the primary-process ratings given in Table 2, it was noted that with respect to both the raw and the trend-adjusted scores, alternations from a subsequent of observations on placebo to a subsequence on chlordiazepoxide corresponded to an improvement in the average rating for a subsequence, while an alternation in the opposite direction (i.e., from chlordiazepoxide to placebo) resulted in a worsening, i.e., in an increase in corresponding average primary-process pathology. Among the other seven observed items of psychopathology similar fluctuations in subsequence averages occurred in *anxiety, confusion, depersonalization,* and *ability to communicate.* This did not hold for the trend-adjusted scores in *"sexual flooding"* nor for the raw scores in *hostility.* While this type of alternation in sequence averages also appeared in the raw scores on *depression,* very little significance can be attached to this because of the relatively small difference between placebo and chlordiazepoxide in the over-all average rating for *depression.* (See Table 3.)

STATISTICAL ANALYSIS AND QUESTIONS OF STATISTICAL SIGNIFICANCE

Given a set of results showing differences between two medications, it is no longer merely the avant-garde who has learned to ask the question: "Are the results statistically significant?" or "What is the level of significance in the difference between drug effects?" Anyone who has had the least exposure to clinical research is aware of the operation of the laws of chance, and of the problem of differentiating between true effects and chance effects. However, what is not always clearly understood is that there is no absolute or unambiguous answer to a question concerning an exact level of significance *without reference to some mathematical statistical model* which for purposes of statistical inference must be assumed to be correct if probability statements such as those concerning levels of significance are to remain credible. The normal distribution, and the mathematically related Student-t and the chi-square distributions, for example, are mathematical models whose absolute truth in relation to a set of data can never be demonstrated. They can only be assumed to be reasonable models of the reality (sometimes also assumed) to

TABLE 3

EFFECTS: RAW AND TREND-ADJUSTED SCORES

	Average Raw Scores		Average Trend-Adjusted Scores	
	Chlordiazepoxide	Placebo	Chlordiazepoxide	Placebo
Primary process	0.83	2.75	0.98	2.45
Anxiety	0.75	1.75	1.40	2.15
Confusion	0.67	2.00	1.37	2.40
Hostility	0.83	1.50	1.63	2.05
"Sexual flooding"	0.83	1.75	0.98	1.45
Depersonalization	0.67	2.75	1.45	3.32
Ability to communicate	0.50*	1.75*	0.35*	1.37*
Depression	1.00	1.25	†	†

* The lower the numerical score, the better the ability to communicate.

† Depression is the only item for which a decreasing trend was not at all evident from the data.

which they are applied. This is, of course, not intended in any way as an argument against the use of the normal and related distributions. There is certainly much empirical evidence to support its use in very many diverse areas, and the central limit theorem of statistics, better known to statisticians than to clinicians, adds a theoretical argument in favor of its use. Nevertheless it is, say, by no means always clear whether a given set of data ought to be analyzed by the use of tests based on an underlying assumption of normality, or whether a nonparametric approach should be used. The investigator who applies both types of tests to the same set of data will in general obtain two different levels of significance. Fortunately, in a great many cases, one such level serves as a fairly good approximation of the other. But when one test yields a level of .04 and the other a level .07, an obsession about reaching "the" .05 level can provide an unfortunate and objectively unnecessary degree of discomfort. The point may be a bit belabored here, but it is made to emphasize that there is generally speaking no single, simple, precise, and unambiguous answer to the question of statistical significance which can be taken as absolute. Judgment, statistical as well as clinical, often has to be invoked with an awareness of one's possible biases.

Another type of problem which relates to the question of how well a statistical model fits the reality of a given clinical design, and one which is often more difficult to handle than the question of parametric versus nonparametric approaches, is that of statistical independence. The question of choosing between a parametric and a nonparametric test is of relatively little consequence if in both cases statistical independence is assumed and the reality of the clinical setting is such that such an assumption may be tenable. It has been suggested (Chassan, 1960, 1961) that the assumption of statistical independence in the observation of individual patients on the same ward (as is generally implicit in statistical tests applied to groups of patients) was open to serious question and could consequently result in gross errors in statistical inference. Data subsequently presented (Kellam and Chassan, 1962) provide strong statistical evidence of such lack of statistical independence.

A statistical analysis of the data gathered in this study falls into the area of statistics known as time-series analysis. The question of statistical independence is a matter of concern in the analysis of data from a time series to the extent that a particular observation may be statistically dependent on the previous observation, or on a sequence of immediately preceding observations. Thus, the level of a patient's pathology during an observation period may be statistically dependent on his level during the previous period *in a given setting or context of observation*. The greater the statistical dependence on previous states, the less is there an immediate justification for, say, a standard application of the *t*-test to determine significant differences between time-series segments. However, unlike the situation in extensive designs in which tests between groups of patients are performed at only a single point in time, or even when an initial point is used as a covariate for adjusting end-point observations, the data from the time series itself provides information concerning the degree of dependence in the series. If this turns out to be quite small, then standard tests, such as the *t*-test, may be expected to provide reasonably valid significance levels. In fact, on the basis of some preliminary theoretical statistical analysis it appears that the standard *t*-test can be used with reasonable validity even within a highly auto-correlated, dependent series. Much technical statistical research remains to be performed in this area, but this does not counterindicate the use of the standard *t*-test as a reasonably accurate tool.

Applying a *t*-test to residuals from trend for each of the eight items, the largest *t*-value, 3.12, obtained for *depersonalization,* was significant at the .01 level. A *t*-value of 1.89 was obtained from the *evidence of primary-process* residuals, which is significant at the .05 level (one-tailed test). The corresponding *t*-values of each of the other six items were all smaller, and did not reach generally accepted levels of significance. Of these, the one closest to significance was *ability to communicate,* with a single-tailed level of .09. The smallest difference, as noted above, was that obtained for *depression.*

When a *t*-test was applied to the *raw* scores on the items found to be significant on the trend-adjusted scores, acceptable levels of significance were also found. The *t*-value for *evidence of primary process* remained practically unchanged (increasing slightly to 1.90) at the .05 level, while that for *depersonalization* declined from 3.12 to 2.15. The latter value, however, is still significant at a (one-tailed) level of about .03. A third and final test for drug effect applied to the *primary-process and depersonalization* ratings involved a covariance analysis in which time (i.e., research hour number) was taken as the covariate as a means of adjusting for trend. In this test, the significance level for both variables dropped somewhat, falling between .05 and .06.

The question which of the three procedures used in testing for true drug effect is the most valid can only be answered theoretically, and in terms of which of the corresponding statistical models is the most valid. This is not always a facile decision, particularly when so small a series of observations is involved. One might ask whether adjustment for trend is valid for this set of data, as the trend line itself was not particularly marked in relation to the variation of the data about the trend line. On the basis of so small a set of observations, this may still be a matter of judgment.

In the analysis of covariance as it has been applied here, the assumption was implicit that two parallel linear trends existed, one corresponding to the placebo and the other to chlordiazepoxide. The analysis of covariance then tested the null hypothesis that the lines are identical.

Analyzing the residuals from the single trend line (corresponding to Figure 1) as was first done does not necessarily test directly or make any direct assumption about two separate trends, but rather tests for a significant difference in departures from a common trend.

INTENSIVE DESIGN IN RELATION TO PLACEBO REACTION, FOLLOW-UP, AND SUBSEQUENT TREATMENT OF THE INDIVIDUAL CASE

A particularly valuable property of designs in which one tests *primarily* for significant effects within the individual patient rather than between patients is the specificity of the results—in terms of significance or nonsignificance—in relation to the patient himself. The procedure not only provides valid data for evaluating whether a treatment is effective, but incorporates the feature of identifying particular patient characteristics which may be relevant to the effect of the treatment in accordance with the results provided by the series of data from each patient in such a study. The comparatively large number of hypotheses which one can thus test by applying an intensive design in a relatively few well-selected (not necessarily randomly selected) patients with some variation in their characteristics, makes it possible to develop an organized program of clinical research with more clearly specified objectives than can possibly be achieved in a sequence of extensive designs in which hypotheses can only be tested for groups of patients taken as a whole. This can be achieved by a systematic selection of patients, chosen for similarities and dissimilarities in particular patient characteristics, and in relation to ongoing results provided by sets of intensive studies.

Apart from the rather broad implications for clinical research methodology as such, the use of the intensive design has, as a corollary, a particular use in the subsequent treatment of the individual-study patient himself.

First, consider such questions as, "Is patient A a placebo reactor?" or "Did A actually benefit from the active medication?" Questions such as these cannot be answered as a consequence of patient A's participation in a clinical research project in which hypotheses are tested between groups of patients. For example, in a study in which one group of patients is on an active medication and the other on placebo, if A belongs to the group selected for treatment on the active medication, and if, further, A should show an improved score, there would be no way of determining from the data of the study whether A improved because he was on an active medication or whether he merely reacted as he might have to a placebo. If A had instead been selected for treatment with placebo, then (1) a failure to improve would give no information concerning how effective treatment with the active medication would have been for him; or (2) if he showed improvement on placebo one still could not state whether improvement might not have been even greater on the active medication. Neither, incidentally, can one state definitively that the reaction would necessarily have been a true placebo effect. Such an effect (i.e., improvement without active medication) can logically result from a complex of circumstances which happen to coincide with the administration of the placebo, or with the point in time at which the placebo observation is made and may be entirely unrelated to it. It is this—at least apparently—random aspect of psychopathology levels within the individual patient along the time scale that has led to the development of the intensive model (Chassan, 1957, 1959).

Thus, with respect to the continuing treatment of the individual patient participating in the extensive model, the results of a particular study which may show a statistically significant greater improvement on active medication than on placebo will not, in general, or with any degree of confidence provide specific information about whether a *particular* patient benefited on the active medication and therefore might be benefited by its continued use beyond the study. In a very loose way (because of the wide range of various relevant characteristics of patients) all it does is to indicate that the active medication is a better bet than the placebo. Now, if the study involved one active drug against another (instead of against a placebo), even so gross an assessment would be difficult or perhaps more dangerously misleading, for presumably some of the patients who apparently improved on the drug which came out worse in the comparison might not have been helped by the "better" drug.

Although the use of a crossover within the framework of the extensive model may be a little more informative about the individual case, it would still not be anywhere near adequate from the point of view of statistical significance *within* the individual case. Several crossovers back and forth for each patient would, of course, provide data for intensive-model analysis.

In an intensive design, again apart from its broader implications for research, a statistically significant finding is significant, in particular, for a specific patient, and therefore may well indicate the course of further treatment for that patient. The small number of cases that one requires for an application of the intensive model, the minimum number actually being a single case (as in the present study), thus not only allows the practicing psychotherapist to engage in meaningful research to satisfy some of his own interests without requiring elaborate, and/or institutional settings, but also represents a use of research methodology in actual treatment and for the maximum benefit of the patient under treatment.

Clinically, the patient under observation in this study did well. Some months after termination of this series of therapeutic interviews, she had some recurrence of anxiety in response to reality difficulties, at which time a prescription for a short period of medication with chlordiazepoxide seemed efficacious.

13

THE EFFECTS OF DEPROL ON DEPRESSION:
A METHODOLOGICAL STUDY OF THE
PSYCHODYNAMIC EFFECTS OF
PSYCHOTROPIC DRUGS

This chapter provides a sampling of the problems faced in clinical research. Three attempts were made to assess the effect of the drug Deprol on depression. In the first, problems developed with the rating scale; in the second, only 20 percent of the patients completed the treatment; and in the third, although reliability had improved and dropout rate was sharply decreased, findings were nonsignificant. This study is sobering reading for anyone interested in clinical research, but despite its negative outcome, it provides certain object lessons. In the first place, it illustrates the need for a series of progressively refined studies in a specific area; in the second place, it makes an interesting contrast to Chapter 12. In this study a large number of patients in three successive studies provided no evidence that an antidepressant had any more effect than a placebo; in Chapter 12, *one* patient in *one* study showed a significant difference between drug and placebo. Nothing could more dramatically highlight the usefulness of the single-case approach.

THE EVALUATION OF TRANQUILIZERS and other psychotropic drugs shares the methodological difficulties of the evaluation of other therapies, especially psychotherapy. Outstanding among the difficulties in this latter field have been the criterion problem, the problems involved in the fact that there may be spontaneous changes over a period of time, and the impossibility of matching patients. The double-blind method of study of an experimental group and a control group has met some of these problems in what must be called "outcome" studies; in essence, they provide a chance to compare patients before and after, but such studies fail to clarify the essential nature of the changes in a given patient, the psychodynamic factors affected by the drug at the time of the changes.

In order to deal with these problems we designed a process study concerned with the psychodynamic effect of one particular drug, Deprol, recommended for the treatment of depressions.

The crux of our method is predicated upon the fact that we were not only interested in variables such as "degree of depression" but wanted to anchor our appraisals in specific psychoanalytic hypotheses with regard to depression, viz., that depression involves a great deal of orality, intra-aggression, a severe superego, narcissism, and low self-esteem (Bibring, 1953).

NOTE: From the *Journal of Nervous and Mental Disease,* 1961, 132, 531-538. Reprinted by permission of the publisher and L. Salk and D. Rosenhan, co-authors, whose collaboration is gratefully acknowledged.

The method of study emphasizes a multiplicity of ways of gauging the drug effect: on the conscious, preconscious, and unconscious level, by studying manifest behavior, projective data, and dreams; by methods of appraisal of different dimensions, namely clinical rating by clinical interviews and observation by nurses, as well as dynamic study of Thematic Apperception Test (TAT) materials and dreams, and also by study of TAT material by the semantic method of content analysis. The ratings deal mostly with the conscious level, the TAT with preconscious and some unconscious material and the dream with the unconscious level.

Aside from different levels and forms of study, it is an important feature of the design to attain measures not only before and after the drug, but to study the process of dynamic change by measurements in the course of treatment.

The advantages of most of the features mentioned above are, we submit, obvious. The advantage of gauging preconscious and unconscious changes aside from manifest ones may need a word of explanation: the theoretical interest in studying the relationship of the variables mentioned to depression, and the effect of the drug on the one or the other or all of them, is easy to see. Surprisingly, the practical importance of the dynamic appraisal of latent factors seems less apparent: that many a depressed patient may improve manifestly without doing so latently, and then commit suicide. The clinical dictum that depressed patients become most suicidal after some manifest improvement has some basis in the assumption that only when the worst lethargy has worn off are they "energetic" enough to harm themselves. (In a more sophisticated view, one might see a deep depression as a partially successful defense against aggression, which when interfered with may lead to intra-aggression.)

Most important in this context is the idea that certain drugs may well produce manifest improvement without a really dynamic change. Dexedrine and its derivatives may serve as an outstanding example of this possibility: very often a superficial elation is produced which may not stand at all in the way of a suicidal act. On the other hand, it is likely that if a drug can be shown to do away with the dynamic forces responsible for the depression, a more genuine and clinically safer result has been achieved. By tapping the preconscious as well as the unconscious level, we are in a better position to appraise "real" change as opposed to "superficial" change: we are in a better position to predict manifest behavior of the patient as the depression lifts.

With regard to both the process approach and its interrelation to specific psychodynamic hypotheses, this study is related to earlier explorations of the psychoanalytic process spoken of in Chapter 8.

In effect, we set out to test whether Deprol will, indeed, decrease depression and whether this decrease, if it occurs at all, will also manifest itself in any or all of the variables hypothetically related to depression. Because the two component drugs of Deprol are also considered anxiety-relieving ones, we included scales concerning this variable.

It was possible, then, that we might find that Deprol has no effect whatsoever on patients and cannot be significantly differentiated from the placebo—or it might turn out that the patients were clinically judged manifestly less depressed, or not depressed, but showed no changes in TAT or dreams. It might also develop that they would show changes in some of the variables and not in others, or show changes in their conscious and preconscious functioning as gauged by the TAT, but not show changes in their dreams.

It was also possible that the two drugs in Deprol might bring about a reduction of anxiety without showing any effect on any level with regard to depression. Ideally, however, one could postulate that an antidepressant would lead to changes observable clinically, as well as on the level of the TAT and that of dreams.

PROCEDURE

Subjects and Method

The subjects selected were patients who were either admitted as inpatients to the psychiatric wards or seen in the outpatient clinic at the City Hospital at Elmhurst. They were admitted to the study if they presented symptoms of depression regardless of their functional diagnosis, were between the ages of 21 and 65, showed no history of organic brain disorder, had not had ECT, were not alcoholics or drug addicts, and had not received tranquilizing medication for at least one month prior to the study.

The subjects selected were randomly assigned to either the experimental or control group. Once selected for the study, the patients were not given any other form of therapy.

Basic Procedure

The basic procedure involved the collection of three types of data:

(1) *Clinical ratings* based upon periodic interviews by psychiatric staff. For each interview two staff members were present, completing their rating scales independently. Each patient had the same two interviewers throughout the study. The rating scales were designed to yield data with respect to anxiety and depression.

(2) *TAT:* Immediately following the clinical rating the patient was given cards 1, 2, 3BM, 11, 12MF, 14, and 15 by the research psychologist. Each patient wrote his own responses on a form designed for this purpose. This procedure was based upon Eron and Ritter's (1951) findings that written TATs yield the same quality and amount of thematic content as orally administered TATs. My instructions for the TAT were used.

(3) *Dreams:* A special form was presented each morning by the nurse to the inpatients in the study on which to write their dreams. The outpatients were asked to write their dreams each morning and to bring them in when they came for their next interview and TAT.

Much experimentation and variation in time interval and frequency of rating and testing, as well as with the kinds of rating scales to be used, was conducted during two pilot studies before the final investigation was begun. These studies are briefly described below, together with the major problems encountered.

Study #1: The patients selected for this study were randomly divided into two groups. Over a period of six weeks, one group received Deprol (benactyzine and meprobamate, Wallace) 400 mg. four times a day, while the other group received a placebo on the same schedule. During this period each patient was interviewed and given the TAT, as previously described, once a week. Dreams were collected daily and an attempt was made to have the ward nurse fill in a rating scale daily on the behavior of each patient in the study. The scale used was provided by the Wallace Laboratories. In carrying out this study we found the patients to be very resistant to the TAT at such a short interval as one week and for six consecutive weeks. In addition, there was the problem of the patients' remembering their responses from week to week which, although it might occur in both the experimental and control groups, would tend to obliterate any changes that might be due to drug effect. We found that some patients reported dreams while others did not, leaving us with meager data in this area. Further, we found it impossible to get daily ratings from the nurses or to obtain satisfactory agreement among the nurses in their evaluations. Since the nurses were not on regular schedules we could not get the same nurses to rate the same patient throughout the study. Additional problems developed with the rating scale used by the interviewers: a low level of reliability was found. Early in this study we noted clinically that the effects of Deprol were very weak, and recognized the possibility that attempts to measure dynamic change in the patient would show little if any difference. But at the same time it was felt we might be prejudging Deprol if we did not continue to acquire a reasonable sample. I have had occasional good empirical results with Deprol on patients under close supervision. We attempted, therefore, to make changes in the second study to overcome the problems encountered in the first.

Study #2: The patients in this study were divided into two groups, as before, and given placebo or Deprol. They were interviewed and given the TAT in the manner described above, together with the daily collection of dreams. The nurses' behavior-rating scale was eliminated. The interviews and TAT were given at the outset, again after four weeks and, finally, after eight weeks.

During this study, data collection was begun with 32 patients, but completed with only six, giving us a dropout rate of more than 80 per cent. Some outpatients failed to keep appointments because of the long interval between meetings; some improved sufficiently to go back to work; some got worse and required hospitalization. Among the inpatients, some became agitated and required additional treatment which disqualified them; others were taken from the hospital by the family. Apart from this, some of the clinical staff felt strongly that a two-month period was too long to keep a patient on either Deprol or a placebo without any additional treatment.

Nothing could be done about the unevenness in reporting dreams. Reporting them in writing was clearly disadvantageous, but a lack of personnel made it impossible for this material to be collected orally, as we would have preferred. The clinical rating scale was modified and a number of training sessions were held with respect to its use; this yielded a higher degree of agreement.

The scoring system for the TAT was variously modified, and in each instance this resulted in low reliability between two scorers, requiring further development.

The third and final study constituted an additional attempt to refine our methods and procedures to overcome the problems described above.

Study #3: A group of patients was selected as described earlier and randomly placed in either an experimental group or a control group. These patients were interviewed, tested with the TAT, and checked daily for dreams as outlined before. The interviews and tests were given at the outset, two weeks later, and again after four weeks. During the first two weeks the patients in both groups were given the placebo, while in the second two-week period the patients in the experimental group were given Deprol and those in the control group continued on placebo. The purpose of starting all patients on placebo, rather than starting some on the drug and then changing to placebo, was to avoid a possible carry-over effect of the drug. This design was also selected so that each patient would serve as his own control.[1]

The dropout rate in this study decreased sharply (to 26 per cent) in comparison with the previous study, presumably as a result of the shorter interval. Further development of the TAT rating scale proved successful and, as a result, we achieved adequate reliability. (See Table 1.) The clinical ratings also proved acceptably reliable. (See Table 2.)

Because of the unevenness of the dream material collected we were not able to subject it to meaningful analysis.

RESULTS

Twenty-six patients, equally divided between experimental and control groups, completed the study. The data collected consisted of clinical and TAT ratings. Both collections of data were analyzed with respect to anxiety and depression.

Clinical ratings (Figure 1): In analyzing the clinical ratings with respect to change in anxiety level we find that the experimental group (solid line) seemed

TABLE 1

INTERJUDGE RELIABILITY BETWEEN FOUR JUDGES OF TAT PROTOCOLS
USING THE ELMHURST TAT RATING SCALE

Scale Category	W*	Level of Significance
Depression	.85	.01
Anxiety	.61	.05
Hostility	.86	.01
Superego	.63	.01
Passivity	.70	.01
Narcissism	.83	.01

* Kendall's W. (Siegel, 1956, pp. 229–239).

TABLE 2

RELIABILITY BETWEEN TWO JUDGES OF CLINICAL RATINGS OF PATIENT BEHAVIOR
USING THE ELMHURST CLINICAL RATING SCALE

Scale Category	Rho	Level of Significance
Depression*	.75	.01
Anxiety†	.73	.01

* This is item #6 on the scale, one rating of the global impression of feelings of depression.

† This is the sum total of items #1, 2, and 3 on the scale, which are concerned with manifest physical symptoms of anxiety, the patient's feelings of anxiety, and an inference of the existence of anxiety which the patient has not verbalized.

[1] Following a suggestion by Dr. J. Chassan (1960), then Chief, Statistical Service, St. Elizabeth's Hospital, Washington, D.C., consultant to our statistical and methodological problems. He also suggested a specific method of statistical analysis of one case as useful for the future.

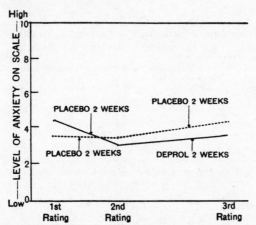

FIG. 1. Change in level of anxiety as measured by The Elmhurst Clinical Rating Scale. (Median anxiety level given for each group; ratings are on a ten-point scale.) Control group N=13; Experimental group N=13. See text.

to have a slightly higher level of anxiety at the outset than the control group (dotted line) and that during the first two-week period, when both groups were on placebo, the experimental group tended to show a drop in anxiety level while the control group remained the same. None of the differences, however, were significant (t-test).

Since subjects were randomly assigned, it is assumed that the difference between the two groups at the outset was a function of chance, as were their respective shifts on the second rating. Comparison of the change from the second to the third rating, when Deprol was used in the experimental group, shows no significant difference. Deprol, then, caused no change in anxiety at the clinical level.

The clinical ratings of change in level of depression (Figure 2) show that the groups were at the same level at the outset, had an insignificant drop at the

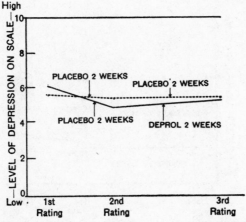

FIG. 2. Change in level of depression as measured by The Elmhurst Clinical Rating Scale. (Median depression level given for each group; ratings are on a ten-point scale.) Control group N=13; Experimental group N=13. See text.

TABLE 3

CHANGE IN ANXIETY FOR EACH SUBJECT AS MEASURED BY
THE ELMHURST CLINICAL RATING SCALE

	Experimental Group	Control Group	Total
Change from 1st to 2nd Clinical Interview (interval of 2 weeks)*			
Less anxiety	8	7	15
No change or more anxiety	5	6	11
Total	13	13	26
Change from 2nd to 3rd Clinical Interview (interval of 2 weeks)†			
Less anxiety	7	4	11
No change or more anxiety	6	9	15
Total	13	13	26

* Subjects in both groups received placebo during this interval.

† Subjects in experimental group received Deprol and those in control group received placebo during this interval.

second rating, and converged at the third rating. Deprol obviously did not cause a significant decrease in depression at the clinical level.

Another method of analysis of the clinical data was employed, to focus on intraindividual rather than median group change. For intraindividual change in anxiety level (Table 3) there is seen to be no significant difference between groups from the first to the second rating.

Table 4 shows no intraindividual change in depression at the clinical level.

TAT ratings: In analyzing the TAT, using our own TAT rating scale in relation to change in anxiety level (Figure 3), we find no significant decrease in anxiety. That is, the change from second to third rating for the experimental group (solid line) is not significantly different from the change that occurred in

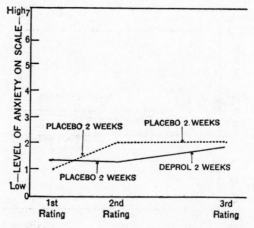

FIG. 3. Change in level of anxiety as measured by The Elmhurst TAT Rating Scale. (Median anxiety level given for each group; ratings are on a seven-point scale.) Control group N=13; Experimental group N=13. See text.

TABLE 4

CHANGE IN DEPRESSION FOR EACH SUBJECT AS MEASURED BY
THE ELMHURST CLINICAL RATING SCALE

	Experimental Group	Control Group	Total
Change from 1st to 2nd Clinical Interview (interval of 2 weeks)*			
Less depression	6	4	10
No change or more depression	7	9	16
Total	13	13	26
Change from 2nd to 3rd Clinical Interview (interval of 2 weeks)†			
Less depression	5	5	10
No change or more depression	8	8	16
Total	13	13	26

* Subjects in both groups received placebo during this interval.

† Subjects in experimental group received Deprol and those in control group received placebo during this interval.

the control group (dotted line.) This is also the case for level of depression (Figure 4).

The intraindividual change between the three ratings of the TAT material with reference to anxiety (Table 5) and with reference to depression (Table 6) also indicates that Deprol had no significant effect on anxiety and depression.

An analysis of intraindividual change between the three ratings of TAT material with reference to depression (Table 7) by yet another method, namely, a thematic content analysis (number of depressive themes per TAT protocol), indicates again that Deprol had no significant effect on depression. These data, analyzed in terms of both median group change and intraindividual change, and from the point of view of clinical behavior as well as at the psychodynamic level, show that Deprol had no significant effect on anxiety or depression.

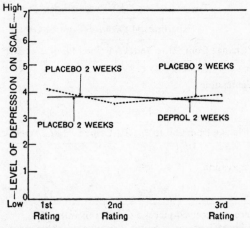

FIG. 4. Change in level of depression as measured by The Elmhurst TAT Rating Scale. (Median depression level given for each group; ratings are on a seven-point scale.) Control group N=13; Experimental group N=13. See text.

TABLE 5

CHANGE IN ANXIETY FOR EACH SUBJECT AS MEASURED BY
THE ELMHURST TAT RATING SCALE

	Experimental Group	Control Group	Total
Change from 1st to 2nd TAT (interval of 2 weeks)*			
Less anxiety	5	2	7
No change or more anxiety	8	11	19
Total	13	13	26
Change from 2nd to 3rd TAT (interval of 2 weeks)†			
Less anxiety	4	5	9
No change or more anxiety	9	8	17
Total	13	13	26

* Subjects in both groups received placebo during this interval.

† Subjects in experimental group received Deprol and those in control group received placebo during this interval.

A further TAT content analysis[2] was conducted, focusing upon manifest content of the theme only, with no effort to interpret latent content. A list of themes is presented in Table 8.

In this analysis, each answer to the following questions about each TAT card was categorized according to whether it contained a depressive theme:

    (1) What is happening now?
    (2) How did it begin?
    (3) How does it end?
    (4) How do the characters in the story feel?
    (5) What are they thinking about?

TABLE 6

CHANGE IN DEPRESSION FOR EACH SUBJECT AS MEASURED BY
THE ELMHURST TAT RATING SCALE

	Experimental Group	Control Group	Total
Change from 1st to 2nd TAT (interval of 2 weeks)*			
Less depression	5	5	10
No change or more depression	8	8	16
Total	13	13	26
Change from 2nd to 3rd TAT (interval of 2 weeks)†			
Less depression	8	9	17
No change or more depression	5	4	9
Total	13	13	26

* Subjects in both groups received placebo during this interval.

† Subjects in experimental group received Deprol and those in control group received placebo during this interval.

[2] Performed by Henry Lennard, Ph.D., of the Bureau of Applied Social Science, Columbia University, New York.

TABLE 7

CHANGE IN DEPRESSION FOR EACH SUBJECT AS MEASURED BY THEMATIC
CONTENT ANALYSIS OF SUBJECTS' TAT PROTOCOLS

	Experimental Group	Control Group	Total
Change from 1st to 2nd TAT (interval of 2 weeks)*			
Less depression	8	3	11
No change or more depression	4	9	13
Total	12	12	24
Change from 2nd to 3rd TAT (interval of 2 weeks)†			
Less depression	4	3	7
No change or more depression	8	9	17
Total	12	12	24

* Subjects in both groups received placebo during this interval.

† Subjects in experimental group received Deprol and those in control group received placebo during this interval.

If two depressive themes were referred to in answer to one question, only one (the first) was coded. If two or more themes were given in answer to one question and a distinctly hopeful theme followed the depressive one (e.g., "he felt very sad but now he feels very happy"), the depressive theme was not coded.

The results of this manifest content analysis show no significant difference between experimental and control groups.

DISCUSSION AND CONCLUSION

It would appear, from this analysis of the effects of Deprol and placebo by the double-blind method on a group of depressed patients, that Deprol had no measurable effect. With the use of clinical ratings and TAT protocols at three different times, as well as the content analysis of TAT protocols, there appeared to be no significant difference between the effects of the placebo and Deprol. In essence, the experimental findings were consistent with the clinical impression

TABLE 8

TAT THEMES OF DEPRESSION

alone	kill oneself (action or desire)
feeling bad	loneliness
crying	loss
death (including symbols of death such as grave, etc.)	rejection
	remorse
depression	resignation
destruction	sad (despondent, desolate, gloomy, sorrow, distraught)
disappointment	
grief	separation
guilt	shame
helplessness	unhappiness
hopelessness (despair)	unloved

—that Deprol did not seem effective in hospitalized patients or those coming to an outpatient clinic.

The possibility remains that Deprol may be effective on patients in private practice who are less severely disturbed than the group under study here. Furthermore, our method of study needs to be applied to forms of treatment where there has been stronger empirical evidence of changes, as for instance to patients receiving electroconvulsive treatment. Under such conditions, we expect that our approach will reflect changes consonant with clinical experience. A replication with a larger sample is indicated. In order to obtain dream material for rating and content analysis, more frequent and direct contact must be made with patients by psychologically trained personnel.

14

EFFECTS OF TWO ANTIDEPRESSANT DRUGS

ON DEPRESSION

A study of two further antidepressants is reported in this chapter. One (Nardil) works by activating the reticular system and increasing the flow of affective stimuli; the other (Tofranil) seems to do the opposite. Both are found to reduce depression in the clinical situation, and the question arises how such differently acting drugs can have the same effect on what is purported to be a single disease. This is the question studied in this chapter.

Comparisons with Chapter 13 are inevitable but difficult to make because different response measures were used in the two studies. The first set of studies relied on the TAT; the present experiment used the Rorschach, the Global Ego-Strength Scale, and other instruments—but *not* the TAT. The two chapters may indeed be making the same point but we cannot be sure. More often than we may realize, the same phenomena may be categorized in different boxes because they are expressed on different measuring instruments.

AMONG THE DRUGS currently in use in psychiatry, some of the most challenging have been the antidepressant varieties. The usual model employed in studying the effects of these drugs, whether double-blind or not, is the simple "before-after" experiment. For the most part, interest is centered on the outcome rather than the processes initiated in response to medication, particularly psychological processes.

I have described an attempt to assess the clinical usefulness of one antidepressant (Deprol) in Chapter 13 and the general psychodynamic effect of chlordiazepoxide (Librium) in Chapter 12. The present study[1] focused on the fact that, although it has become apparent that different drugs may have an antidepressant effect, specifically the MAO inhibitors, little has been done to study the differential psychological pathways through which these drugs may express their effect.

One of the few relevant neurological-psychological hypotheses expressed has been the one by Himwich (1960): namely, that drugs which activate the reticular system (e.g., MAO inhibitors, like Nardil [phenelzine dihydrogen sulphate]) increase the flow of affective stimuli to the C.N.S., giving them access to neural

NOTE: From *Psychosomatics*, 1966, 7, 106-114. Reprinted by permission of the publishers and S. Rosenberg, co-author, whose collaboration is gratefully acknowledged.

[1] At the time of the design and initiation of the study, Ann Neel, Ph.D., was associated with the senior author and Sidney Rosenberg, M.A., and made basic contributions which are gratefully acknowledged. Ruth Cooper, Ph.D., and Renate Safrin, Ph.D., as members of the Research Committee, played a continuous, active, and most constructive role in the progress of the research project. We are grateful also to Eva J. Meyer for her help as Grant Administrator. The study was supported by NIMH Research Grant MH-10994 (formerly MY-6257), to Leopold Bellak and Sidney Rosenberg.

channels which influence behavior. Drugs which inhibit the reticular system (e.g., Tofranil [imipramine hydrochloride]) filter out afferent (affective) stimuli, not allowing them access to neural channels which influence behavior.

Following this hypothesis, it would seem that the MAO inhibitors produce their effect by activating the depressed person, making him more subject to influence and direction from his emotions and impulses. The non-MAO inhibitor, Himwich's hypothesis seems to imply, reduces the influence of affect and impulse. In both cases, when drug therapy is successful, we observe a "lifting" of the depression. How can two drugs with opposing physiological effects produce the same clinical effect? Assuming the fact that this happens, how does it happen, and what can we learn from it about drug action and about the psychodynamic factors which are concomitant to it?

It was decided to study the possible psychological process of effect of two antidepressants, one an MAO inhibitor (Nardil) and the other not (Tofranil). There is a consensus (Mendelson, 1960) that depression is the dynamic result of fluctuations in self-esteem, feelings of deprivation and loss (and attempts at restitution), marked intrapunitiveness, marked severity of superego control and, finally, fluctuations in reality testing and other ego functions. Most specifically, we are here concerned with the hypothesis that in depression the poorly resolved conflict between aggressive (particularly oral-aggressive) drives on the one hand, and the ego and superego control of these drives on the other hand, is crucial.

If Nardil then should shift the dynamic forces by releasing more aggression and other drives, one could expect that the superego control will not inhibit the aggression to the point where it is made into intra-aggression. On the other hand, if Tofranil should strengthen the controlling functions further, it could be expected to decrease aggression to such an extent that the depressive responses will no longer be a necessary defense against it.

Assuming then the Himwich hypothesis that MAO inhibitors activate the reticular activating system and allow more access to affective stimuli, and that Tofranil inhibits the R.A.S. and blocks off affective stimuli, the psychological processes paralleling such drug-induced changes should manifest themselves differentially.

THE PRESENT STUDY

The present study involved three groups of 25 depressed patients each, who were in turn given Tofranil, Nardil, and a placebo. All the precautions necessary for a "double-blind" study were carefully observed. The manufacturer (Geigy Pharmaceuticals and Warner-Chilcott Company) were kind enough to provide us with the drugs and placebo capsules, indistinguishable from each other by color or shape.

The selection of the patient population was random to the extent that each new admission to the Department of Psychiatry of a large municipal general hospital (City Hospital Center at Elmhurst) was taken into the study and randomly assigned to one of the three experimental groups (Nardil group, Tofranil group, placebo group), provided that he or she met certain criteria, as follows:

(1) *Age:* Between 18 and 55 years.

(2) *Extent of depression:* Score between 20 and 40 on the Depth of Depression Inventory (DDI) (Beck, et al., 1961), indicating the presence of a moderately deep depression.

(3) No *ECT* within the preceding six months.

(4) No psychotropic *medication* within the preceding 30 days.

(5) *Manifest symptoms* of depression, regardless of what other diagnostic group might be involved, provided that physical illness was excluded.

(6) Ability to *read and write* in English.

Only patients who, in the normal course of events, would have received antidepressants as the first choice of treatment were to be included.

In the circumstances, understandably, we had to restrict ourselves to a rather small sample (over an 18-month period, only 75 patients were found suitable from a population of well over 1,000 consecutive admissions): a large number of patients coming for admission had already been on one or another kind of drug obtained from their family physician, private psychiatrist, or from the hospital staff itself while undergoing outpatient evaluation and treatment prior to admission.

In all cases where patients worsened clinically to such an extent that in the normal course of psychiatric practice a change in the therapeutic modality was warranted, the patient was removed from the study group and given other appropriate medication, psychotherapy or, when required, ECT.

PROCEDURE

Immediately upon admission, or at least within 24 hours, potential subjects were given the Depth of Depression Inventory in order to determine suitability for inclusion in the study. If this criterion was met, the patient's clinical chart was distinctively marked, alerting the attending psychiatrist and the nursing staff to this fact. As soon as possible thereafter, and *prior* to the initiation of drug therapy, a thorough psychological interview was held with the patient, followed by the administration of a battery of psychological tests. In addition, each patient selected for the study was interviewed by the clinical director of psychiatry,[2] and rated for both anxiety and depression on a specially constructed clinical rating scale, used in previous drug research (see Chapter 13). Patients were then assigned in random order to one of the two drug groups or to the placebo group. During the course of this double-blind study, the identity of the treatment modalities was unknown to the staff and to us until all scoring, ratings, and evaluations were completed. After a period of from three to five weeks of continued medication, and prior to discharge, each patient was re-examined and tested by the clinical director as well as by the psychologist.

INSTRUMENTS AND MEASURES

Following interviews with the clinical director of psychiatry and with the psychologist, a battery of tests was administered which was designed to evaluate changes in underlying dynamics, with particular emphasis upon ego func-

---

[2] I am indebted to Martin Dollin, M.D., then Clinical Director of Psychiatry, for his cooperation.

tions. Several scales of various sorts purport to measure aspects of ego functioning; three such scales were selected for this study.

(1) *The Barron Ego-Strength Scale* (Barron, 1953). This scale consists of 68 items culled from the MMPI and is conceived of as a rather global measure of the adequacy of ego adaptations. The items themselves suggest that the scale measures the extent to which a person is willing to acknowledge certain kinds of pathology, or areas of personal discomfort and concern, or to express preferences for a variety of activities.

(2) *Holt's (1960) Primary Process (Pripro) Scoring of the Rorschach.* This scoring technique is designed to derive measures relating to the amount and kind of impulse, the quality of thinking, and the extent of drive regulation as manifested in responses to the standard administration of Rorschach inkblots. Measures can therefore indicate the proportion of drive-related responses (aggressive, oral, libidinal), the degree of impulsive "push" (defense demand), and the adequacy with which such impulses are coordinated with the demands of reality (defense effectiveness). Other categories of responses can be scored with this system, but were not considered strictly relevant to the purpose of the present study.

(3) *The Id-Ego-Superego Test (IES)* (Dombrose and Slobin, 1958). This instrument consists of four subtests, each of which permits the quantification of impulsivity, superego pressures, and adequacy of reality testing (i.e., "ego strength"). The scores from each of the subtests are combined in an over-all profile, reflecting the distribution of energy of these three forces (id, ego, superego).

It was felt that the measures referred to above might provide data concerning the relationships between drives (id), regulative and integrative variables (ego), and social and moral prohibitions (superego) as they are modified in accordance with the hypotheses outlined by Himwich regarding the action of antidepressants. None of the above measures, however, was felt likely to provide the necessary specificity and subtlety of detail required for a comprehensive evaluation of the effects of these drugs upon various aspects of ego functioning. The steady advances in ego theory have produced a complex series of constructs which must be dealt with. These constructs have been formulated by me into a theory of seven interrelated functions ascribed to the ego:

> Reality testing
> Object relations
> Thinking
> Regulation and control of drives
> Defenses
> Synthetic functions
> Autonomous functions (perception, intention, object comprehension, thinking, language, productivity, and motor development).

In order to tap ego functions as conceived of in my theory, a specially constructed experimental rating scale was devised, the Global Ego-Strength Scale (GES) (see Appendix).

(4) *The Global Ego-Strength Scale (GES).*[3] The GES was designed for use following an extended interview. Over-all numerical ratings are provided for each ego function in accordance with my hypothesis, based upon a number of individual ratings of dynamic processes subsumed under each major function of the ego. Preliminary analysis of two-rater and five-rater reliability indicated sufficiently high agreement among a rather heterogeneous group of judges to warrant inclusion of this scale in the present study. All ratings were based upon interview material only.

(5) *The Wechsler Adult Intelligence Scale (WAIS).* In order to determine whether responses to, and ratings of responses to the interview/testing procedure were influenced in any way by the verbal ability or general level of intelligence of the patient sample, six subtests of the WAIS were administered to each subject (three verbal: Information, Comprehension, and Vocabulary; and three performance: Digit Symbol, Picture Completion, and Block Design). In addition, it was hoped that the prorated WAIS score would be sensitive to changes relating to the ego function of thinking and reality testing as a result of drug therapy.

RESULTS

Table 1 reports some of the basic data regarding the total sample utilized in the study. The typical patient was a young adult, of about average intelligence, with a modest amount of secondary education. At the time of admission, he or she was suffering from a depression of moderate dimensions, as measured by the DDI, and was retained in the study for a period of about one month. About 80% of all patients in the Psychiatry Department (of 150 beds in a 1,000-bed general hospital) were generally discharged as improved or recovered within

TABLE 1*

DESCRIPTION OF THE SAMPLE
(N = 75)

Variable	Mean
Age	33.4 years
Education	2.4 years H.S.
Duration of Medication	34.8 days
Prorated WAIS Score	97.7
Average DDI Score (Admission)	26.5
Average DDI Score (Termination)	23.8

* No significant differences were found between the three experimental groups (Nardil Group, Tofranil Group, and Placebo Group; N = 25 each) on any of the above variables.

---

[3] The Global Ego Strength Scale is largely superseded by a more sophisticated and detailed appraisal of ego functions, of which the Rating Scales for Scoring Ego Functions from the Clinical Interview is one part. This Rating Scale was developed as part of a research project entitled "Patterns of Ego Functions in Schizophrenia," carried out with the support of Grant Number 5RO1-MR11662 from the National Institute of Mental Health, Leopold Bellak, Principal Investigator. (This research involves rating of ego functions not only from interviews, but also from a Psychological Test Battery and a set of experimental laboratory procedures.) This Rating Scale is the result of collective work of the entire research team and specifically the contributions of Marvin Hurvich, Mark Silvan, Robert Beck, and Helen Gediman.

thirty days, as part of an intensive treatment program. All patients utilized in this study fell into this category. As mentioned, those who would have been changed to other treatment modalities in the course of their ordinary treatment program were so changed and dropped out of the project sample, generally within two weeks.

There were no significant differences with respect to these variables between any of the three groups studied. Women constituted about 55 per cent of the sample, men about 45 per cent. Although it was originally planned to study men and women in roughly equal proportions, it was found that men were harder to retain for a variety of reasons, particularly because of pressures for discharge and a return to the status of breadwinner.

Table 1 also shows that the average score on the DDI tended toward the lower (i.e., "less depressed") end of the scale. In practice we discovered that persons scoring much beyond 30 on this instrument tended to present a clinical picture requiring either a combination of various drugs or ECT, and so could not be included in our study. It is therefore important to note that the conclusions reached by the authors have reference to patients who were for the most part moderately depressed.

In order to determine whether significant differences occurred between the Nardil and Tofranil groups, and between each of these drug groups and the placebo group, a series of t-tests were performed relating to each test score employed in the study.

Table 2 summarizes the results. There were no differences among the three experimental groups on any of the paper-and-pencil tests employed as measures of ego function. Neither the Barron Ego-Strength Scale nor the IES test scores differentiated among the groups. It was also found that ratings by the clinical director of psychiatry on the Elmhurst Clinical Rating Scale did not differentiate among the three groups. This measure was meant to be used as a method for independently evaluating change, at least on a rather gross clinical level, and therefore constituted a criterion measure against which results were compared. These results indicate that on the manifest clinical level the amount of judged improvement between the two drugs and placebo was not significantly different.

It is with measures which demand more subtle evaluations, measures which tend to focus upon unconscious dynamisms, that some significant and rather revealing differences emerge.

RESULTS WITH RORSCHACH PRIPRO SCORING SYSTEM

The Rorschach, scored according to Holt's (1960) primary process (Pripro) scoring system, yielded significant differences which are in support of the basic hypotheses of the study. Table 2 indicates that the percentage of generally drive-related responses, the percentage of responses with specifically aggressive content, and the total number of responses to the Rorschach significantly increased in the group of patients who received the MAO inhibitor (Nardil), when compared to both the non-MAO inhibitor (Tofranil) and the placebo groups. Similar differences were not found between the Tofranil and placebo groups. This result is in conformity with the hypothesis that MAO inhibitors facilitate affective arousal.

TABLE 2*

SIGNIFICANCE OF DIFFERENCES BETWEEN IMPROVEMENT SCORES ON RORSCHACH, PRIPRO
SCORING, AND GLOBAL EGO-STRENGTH SCALE (GES) WITH THREE GROUPS OF PATIENTS
(NARDIL GROUP, TOFRANIL GROUP, AND PLACEBO GROUP); 25 IN EACH GROUP

Outcome	Measure	Construct	t	Level of Significance
Nardil > Tofranil	Rorschach: No. of Drive-related R	ID (Drive)	2.23	.05
	Rorschach: No. of "Aggressive" R	ID (Drive)	2.10	.05
	Rorschach: No. R	ID (Drive)	2.56	.02
	GES: Degree of Defensiveness	Defense	2.39	.05
Nardil > Placebo	Rorschach: No. of Drive-related R	ID (Drive)	2.66	.02
	Rorschach: No. of "Aggressive" R	ID (Drive)	2.81	.01
	Rorschach: No. R	ID (Drive)	2.11	.05
	Rorschach: Defense Effectiveness	Defense	2.39	.05
	GES: Defense	Defense	2.09	.05
Tofranil > Nardil	Rorschach: Defense Effectiveness	Defense	2.58	.02
	GES:	Object Relations: Quality	2.36	.05
	GES:	Control & Regulation of Drives	2.71	.02
	GES:	Synthetic Functions	2.19	.05
Tofranil > Placebo	Rorschach: Defense Effectiveness	Defense	2.60	.02
	GES:	Relation to Reality: Accuracy	2.22	.05
	GES:	Object Relations: Quality	2.41	.05
	GES:	Control & Regulation of Drives	2.13	.05
	GES:	Synthetic Functions	2.30	.05

* Out of a possible 75 comparisons, 57 failed to reach significance, including measures on
the IES Test, Age, Length of Hospitalization, the Barron Ego-Strength Scale, the WAIS,
Rorschach "Defense Demand" and number of "Libidinal" responses, Global Ego-Strength
Scale categories of "Thinking" and "Autonomy," and the Elmhurst Clinical Rating Scale. For
reasons of space, only the 18 significant differences are reported in the above table.

It was also found that both Tofranil and Nardil increased the ability to regulate and control impulses, if compared to the placebo group, as measured by
the "defense effectiveness" score on the Rorschach. Tofranil, however, was
apparently more effective in bringing about this more efficient regulation than
was Nardil. This result is consistent with the hypothesis that non-MAO inhibitors filter out afferent stimuli, and therefore inhibit affective arousal.

RESULTS WITH THE GLOBAL EGO-STRENGTH SCALE (GES)

A number of results (similar to those obtained with Holt's scale) were also obtained with respect to the measurement of change in ego functions, as rated on the Global Ego-Strength Scale. "Accuracy of attention," as a subfunction of "Relation to reality," was significantly improved among those patients treated with Tofranil, as compared to the Nardil and placebo groups. A likely inference is that "relation to reality" was improved in the sense of increased accuracy in interpersonal perception as a result of a decrease in affect. Tofranil was also of significant value in improving the quality of "object relations" and the capacity to control and regulate drives, when compared with the Nardil and placebo groups. Table 2 indicates that Tofranil has a significantly greater effect in improving the "synthetic functions" than did either Nardil or placebo. No significant differences were found with regard to the "autonomous functions" among the three experimental groups.

No differences among the three treatments were found in terms of the "adequacy of defenses"; however, Nardil was found to be significantly helpful in increasing the extent and intensity with which a variety of defenses were employed, as measured by the GES.

In five of the seven major ego functions assessed by the GES (Reality Testing, Object Relations, Regulation and Control of Drives, Defenses, and Synthetic Functions), differential effects were found which seem to be related to the type of medication used. No differences were found with the remaining two functions, i.e., "Thinking" and "Autonomous functions." Above all, in no case were placebo effects greater than those found for either of the two drug groups.

CONCLUSIONS

It can be concluded that, at least with respect to the internal dynamics of the patient as measured by the Rorschach and the GES: (a) antidepressants account for some significantly greater change in psychodynamics than does a placebo, and (b) the direction and kind of psychological change that does occur, occurs in different ways depending on choice of MAO or non-MAO inhibitor.

Further, the psychodynamic changes that were observed in the present sample were, in general, in accordance with the propositions of Himwich regarding the way in which these two classes of drugs affect the central nervous system: namely, that Nardil, an MAO inhibitor, activated the R.A.S., increasing affective stimuli to the central nervous system, and that Tofranil, a non-MAO inhibitor, filters out affective stimuli to the central nervous system by inhibiting R.A.S. activity.

The observed changes are also consistent with the psychoanalytic hypothesis that depression may be relieved either by a decrease of the control of aggression (and turning it, in that process, from intra-aggression to extra-aggression) or by a decrease of (oral) aggression either in a primary way or by an increase in control. In psychotherapy these ends are usually achieved by integration of unconscious aggression, making it conscious, and by a decrease of overt aggression by interpreting its manifest content and bringing it under better ego and superego control. The crucial change needs to be one between the force of aggression and the force of control; the two drugs under investigation seem to have affected primarily the one or the other.

It should not be overlooked, however, that the changes observed in dynamics failed to manifest themselves in gross overt behavior as measured by the criterion rating scale (i.e., the Elmhurst Clinical Rating Scale) either with regard to differences between the two drugs or between the two drugs and the placebo.

Our experience that monoamine oxidase inhibitors are no better than placebos parallels the conclusions of Jonathan Cole (1964) in his recent and most extensive review of the efficacy of antidepressant drugs. Our findings also parallel his conclusion that the imipraminelike drugs may be useful in a milder depression. While he reported that there was no criteria for predicting which patients will respond best to either one of the antidepressant drugs, our data suggest that imipramine may be more successful in those in whom the synthesizing functions of ego and increasing control of impulses are desirable, in contrast to those depressions where release of drives, especially aggression, might be desirable.

To generalize these findings with caution, our findings may suggest that imipramine, with its tendency to facilitate integration and control, would be especially useful in depressions with an underlying schizophrenic syndrome.

Cole (1964) also concludes that imipramine diminishes the likelihood of recurrence of depression, or may lengthen the time between attacks. This is important to keep in mind in view of the fact that, by purely clinical appraisal, the two drugs and the placebo seem to have been indistinguishable at the end of hospitalization.

The instruments found to be most useful in discriminating among the experimental groups in this study were the Global Ego-Strength Scale (GES) and the primary process scoring of the Rorschach (Pripro). In each case, sufficient reliability was established prior to the actual ratings of the experimental sample. A further reliability check carried out at a later stage in the research indicated that these reliabilities were maintained (Tables 3 and 4).

The question of validity has yet to be determined. The present results failed to provide conclusive evidence of *concurrent* validity in that the criterion measure of change (Elmhurst Clinical Rating Scale) did not distinguish among the three groups. Nevertheless, the finding that the results, in terms of these two instruments, were in general agreement with hypotheses based upon Himwich's propositions regarding the neuropsychological effects of MAO inhibitors and non-MAO inhibitors, provides a measure of *construct* validity worthy of further investigation.

The most clear-cut result seems to lie in the fact that Tofranil significantly increased the synthetic functioning of the ego, in accordance with the hypothesis that it would weaken the impulses and thereby permit the synthetic functions to increase. It may be that the drug counteracts dissociation directly, thus having a synthesizing and integrative effect, i.e., the increase in synthetic and integrative functions produces drive control. The change in synthetic function is of particular significance from the point of view of the over-all quality of ego functioning. The synthetic function is probably the aspect which overlaps most with

TABLE 3

FIVE-RATER PERCENTAGE OF AGREEMENT ON THE GLOBAL EGO-STRENGTH SCALE
(N = 5 Protocols)

| | % Agreement | |
Ego Function	Absolute	One-Point
Relation to Reality		
a—Accuracy of Perception	63	90
b—Span of Perception	59	83
Object Relations		
a—Quantity of Contacts	57	84
b—Quality of Contacts	68	90
Thinking	63	84
Control & Regulation of Drives	65	89
Defenses (Combined)	60	85
Synthetic Functions		
a—Manifest Level	61	90
b—Latent Level	66	88
Autonomous Functions		
a—Degree of Autonomy: Manifest	65	92
Degree of Autonomy: Latent	81	100
b—Areas of Autonomy	67	89

TABLE 4

TWO-RATER RELIABILITIES* FOR THE GLOBAL EGO-STRENGTH SCALE
(N = 15)

| | r_{xx} | |
Ego Function	Manifest	Latent
Relation to Reality		
a—Accuracy of Perception	.74	
b—Span of Perception	.72	
Object Relations		
a—Quantity of Contacts	.78	
b—Quality of Contacts	.80	.66
Thinking	.84	
Control and Regulation of Drives	.74	
Defenses		
a—Degree of Control	.78	
b—Adequacy of Control	.84	
c—Degree of Pathology of Defensive Syndrome	.92	
Synthetic Functions		
a—Present	.73	
b—Past	.54	
Autonomous Functions		
a—Degree of Autonomy	.72	.58
b—Areas of Autonomy	.79	
Mean Reliability (Manifest)	.76	
Mean Reliability (Manifest and Latent)	.74	

* Reliability computed on the basis of one-point rater agreement.

all other ego functions and is most highly correlated with the general concept of ego strength. The outstanding schizophrenic characteristic—looseness of association—relates to the low synthetic function of the ego. Although the size of the current sample precluded a test of significant differences between schizophrenic and nonschizophrenic depressives, our data indicate that the schizophrenic depressive tended to be rated lower with respect to synthetic function than the nonschizophrenic depressive. Should further investigation support this as a significant difference, a more rational basis for the selection of appropriate antidepressant medication would be provided.

The failure of the paper-and-pencil tests to differentiate among the three treatment groups, while certainly disappointing, is not surprising since a similar failure occurred with respect to the criterion measure. It must be kept in mind that in many other branches of medicine, e.g., those dealing with liver function, the subtle laboratory tests often have to be considered more reliable guidelines than manifest clinical judgment. It is felt that the most significant problem in the current research study is the fact that the criterion measure, based on clinical judgment, was probably not of sufficient range and subtlety.

Section III: Some Applications of Clinical Psychoanalysis

ONE TEST OF A THEORY is its ability to survive change, and the papers in this section describe some of the new pressures brought to bear on psychoanalytic concepts. The theory was originally developed in the family-centered world of Victorian Vienna with its appreciation of privacy and individuality. To what extent does it apply to modern society with its de-emphasis on the family and its technological advances that have reduced privacy to a severe degree? To what extent, furthermore, does modern society, with its new stresses, produce a new character type? This problem is discussed in Chapter 15. We could add the further question of whether the influence of society, because of its exponentially increasing demands, is not overbalancing the influence of the early formative period of development. To the degree that personality is *not* formed by age 5 and is still subject to later change because environmental pressures are so extreme, a different personality therapy, and therefore a different view of treatment, may be necessary. For example, if later influence is crucial, the importance of reconstructing early childhood experience may be lessened, with a greater emphasis being placed on reality problems.

A similar shift in treatment is forcibly brought about when psychoanalysis is applied to problems in the community. As Chapters 16, 17 and 18 make clear, treatment must be focused on reality factors. The role of the transference is played down in favor of a supportive, more realistic contact; regression is viewed as a defense rather than (as in classical analysis) a treatment aid; and therapy must be brief. Despite these changes in strategy of treatment, heavy use is made of psychoanalytic concepts. To take only one example, delayed recovery from tuberculosis can be viewed as a gratification of the patient's passive wishes to be taken care of, with a consequent temptation to remain feeling sick.

Whether changes in procedure are caused by the treatment situation, as in cases of rehabilitation, cardiac illness, and tuberculosis (see Chapters 17 and 18) or by technological changes that make the formative years less critical (see Chapter 15), the theory is still on trial. If it purports to be a theory of personality, it must provide for new findings and generate new modes of treatment to answer new demands. Psychoanalysis has been successfully adopted to the treatment of the borderline patient; it remains to be seen whether it can also handle the newer character types. For too long a time, the *method* of treatment has remained more or less fixed, without the necessary awareness that it implies a certain theory of illness. As the theory changes to take account of new data, methods must change as well.

15

PERSONALITY STRUCTURE IN A
CHANGING WORLD

Despite the changes produced by the atomic era and the information explosion, the American character, according to some observers, has remained surprisingly constant. Twenty years ago Kurt Lewin tried to describe it schematically as a small circle (the private self) surrounded by a larger circle (the public self). In this chapter Bellak shows how applicable this picture still is to the highly interacting modern world. The small inner core is still cut off, and perhaps one test of a successful analysis is the extent to which it implicates the inner self.

THOUGH PSYCHOANALYSIS traditionally focuses primarily on intrafamilial determinants of personality structure, some historical shifts in the clinical picture have generally been noted. This holds true not only for the perfectly obvious changes in manifest content, e.g., of delusional and hallucinatory material, from a possession by the devil to the influencing machine, to various electrical and radio effects, and, during the last war, to influence by radar; it has also been noted that there is an apparent change from the high frequency of gross hysterical manifestations in the time of Charcot, Janet, and the early years of Freud to an increase in relatively subtle character disorders. It is a moot point how much psychoanalytic sophistication itself, as well as the different modern socioeconomic factors, may have contributed to a change in mores that grossly permits greater personal freedom, produces less coarse repression, and engenders more complex solutions of conflict.

More important, I believe, is the fact that we are apparently in an era of some deep-going character changes which have not, as yet, been systematically recognized and discussed. These character changes are predicated upon changes in the process of identification in a world increasingly characterized by rapid mobility of socioeconomic, technological, and geographic frames of reference for identification.

At the same time, "energy" relocations affect the structure of personality. There is not only a decreased stability of internalized objects by virtue of greater mobility of all reference points, including parents; there is also a restructuration due to a greater input than ever before of all sensory stimuli due to the tremendous increase in media of communication. Not only does more assail the child and adult today by radio, TV, movies, more reading material, car, and jet plane, but it also comes from all over the world, from more people. Because of the technological advances and the population increase, and urbanization, the num-

NOTE: From the *Archives of General Psychiatry*, 1961, 5, 183-185. Reprinted by permission of the publishers.

ber of stimuli and interactions per hour in everybody's life is much greater than it used to be a year ago, 10 years ago, or 20 years ago.

"Outer directedness," as Riesman (1950) calls it, is probably largely an adaptive mode, and only secondarily used as a defense against anxiety and loneliness in our modern society.

Since there are now in everybody's life so many more "object relations," in the broadest sense, each one of them is less intensely cathected, briefer, shallower. Friendship in the old sense is said to be much rarer.

While the factors described hold more true for present American society than any other, they will hold increasingly true for all other societies as they increasingly partake in the socioeconomic and technological changes already existent in the United States.

The outstanding characteristic of American culture today is the impact of communication and change: television, radio, newspapers, magazines, and tons of professional literature bombard us constantly. The loss of identity of modern man is largely the result, I believe, of adaptation to a constant flow of changing stimuli; any event, indeed any individual, is merely a matter of the moment. There can no longer be a Dreyfus affair, a Sacco and Vanzetti trial to stir the world for years; the most stirring events are immediately superseded by other equally stirring events. Communication and travel have made this wide world very small, and in it we are constantly beset by new problems. The Second World War and the Nazi holocaust are old hat, Vietnam dimmed Korea, Sputnik outsparked atomic fission, the Cold War, Dulles, Sherman Adams, North Africa, Salk vaccine, the Congo—we can barely digest our breakfast news before more is in front of us. Add to this a tremendous social mobility, the fact that hardly anyone belongs today to the socioeconomic group to which his parents, or even he himself, belonged some years ago, and one has a dizzy world of great achievements, great problems, and no fixed place to belong.

The problem of loss of identification, of identity, and of self-boundaries is a most important one. Erich Fromm (1940) undoubtedly made a basic contribution to its understanding when he discussed the loosening of social structures as responsible for a lack of superego integration and a consequent "escape from freedom" into the social pathology of Nazism. Undoubtedly, the world-wide phenomenon of juvenile delinquency is related to a similar lack of integration of values and systems in a fast-changing world.

My own feeling is that the whole nature of "object relations" has been changing and will increasingly change in years to come. If this seems hard to accept, consider how different some of our object relations are today from what they were in the past. Romantic love, humane treatment of criminals, the Geneva Convention concerning prisoners of war, and the outlawing of slavery are all quite recent developments: People used to enjoy hangings, public amputations, and floggings. A great sense of identification, social consciousness, and humanism are relatively new.

It is unlikely that we will simply return to earlier forms of human relations. It is likely that under the impact of constant stimuli from all the means of communication—as well as the lack of identification because of great social and geographic mobility—the Angry Young Men and the Beatniks will be followed by a generation that does not protest any more; it will not be angry because it will not have the need for deep permanent relations. In other words, I believe that, increasingly, a character structure will develop which we used to consider a character *disorder:* one characterized by shallow, transitory object relations with little subjective feeling. One has seen such characters develop out of environments that did not permit strong identifications, such as in children reared in many different foster homes and in orphanages. This type of character has also been seen in people exposed to overwhelming experiences, such as in former inhabitants of concentration camps. They may appear to function well enough, but hardly anything seems to go more than skin deep; there is a strong armor that wards off all more intense feelings. Oriental impassivity may well be similarly a result of exposure to overwhelming experiences of helplessness.

Kurt Lewin, the great Gestalt psychologist, has expressed relevant ideas without giving them the particular context advanced here. He compared the European and American personality by drawing sets of two concentric circles to illustrate his point. In the case of the European, the inner concentric circle is only a little smaller than the outer, but has only moderately thick boundaries. He shares only a small area of his life with others; he lives behind closed doors and behind fences, does not announce his salary, sleeping habits, etc. But the few people whom he permits with ease into the inner sanctum become his best friends with whom all is shared. The American, in contrast, has a great deal of space between the inner and outer circles, but the smaller one is very strongly drawn. Almost anybody is admitted to a variety of intimacy; first names, political beliefs, divorces, salary, are all out in the open. But hardly anyone, if anyone at all, is permitted to share the real inner sanctum. Therefore follows the sense of loneliness, the lack of belongingness.

It is my guess that the way the world is developing will make the American type of spheric arrangement universal with an even smaller inner circle, if there is one at all.

The exterior, however, may well become more civilized, literally, more urbane. Greater interaction and interdependence alongside the probably still higher standard of living will probably make for manifestly more amiable relations. A kind of "cocktail party sociability" may prevail, a culture of the urbanely uninvolved.

Again, the American scene may serve as a guidepost for universal development. American social and professional relations are manifestly much less conflictual than European ones. If there is any doubt, compare the American's relations to his employer, policeman, bureaucrat, to the European counterpart. An inexperienced European may have to read an American letter of rejection three times over before realizing the rejection: it is blunter in Europe.

In summary, content and structure of personality always seem to change, in relation to and interactive with, among other things, technical and socio-economic changes in a culture.

In our present culture, since the First World War, and particularly since the Second, the tremendous mobility of social, economic, technical, and geographic factors combine with the great onslaught of communications media and our extended horizon to produce personalities with less firmly established identifications and less intense object relations. While the present middle-aged and some of the young adult generation react with a sense of loneliness and lack of identity, some others and probably the future generation may have a "shallow" character structure, though of greater cosmopolitan, urbane smoothness and no great sense of lack of belongingness. The "lonely crowd" may become the "uninvolved one."

16

PSYCHOANALYTIC THEORY AS THE BASIS FOR SHORT-TERM PSYCHOTHERAPEUTIC TECHNIQUES IN COMMUNITY PSYCHIATRY

This chapter attempts to place the problems of community psychiatry within the framework of psychoanalytic theory. Modifications are clearly in order; the original treatment model of long-term individualized treatment that generally de-emphasized reality problems in favor of learning about unconscious dynamics must be adapted to a program of brief psychotherapy with an emphasis on adjustment. Clearly, the psychoanalytic model cannot be applied; can psychoanalytic theory? This chapter provides an initial positive answer.

IT HAS OFTEN BEEN SAID that an effective community psychiatry program will encompass three types of service: prevention, treatment, and rehabilitation. Therapeutic techniques are involved at each of these levels, and, essentially, psychotherapy constitutes our basic tool in any framework. However, its scope, as well as its limitations, are determined by the unique perspectives of community psychiatry.

First and foremost, our efforts to organize therapeutic services in a community psychiatry program must be governed by a desire to make such services available to as many members of the community as possible, even if this means that only relatively limited help will be provided. To quote Leighton, "Action on behalf of one must be within the framework of calculations for the many" (1960).

On the basis of this orientation, the goal of therapy in a community program is necessarily restricted to providing the patient with enough help to enable him to "carry on" from there. In this context, the patient's ability to "carry on" may mean that he has attained at least minimal functioning, or that his functioning has improved, with decreased subjective difficulties; that he has acquired enough strength to avail himself of more extensive treatment facilities, e.g., the services of a psychotherapist in private practice, by virtue of his improved earning power or increased motivation; that he has been helped to move toward improvement or "cure" by a phenomenon well-known in all medical disciplines —whether conceptualized in Selye's terms or in the homeopath's optimistic concept of "vis medicatrix naturae." In any event, profound restructuring of the personality, through psychoanalysis or lengthy psychotherapeutic treatment, will be possible only rarely. Rather, the wide availability of our psychiatric facilities will depend on the judicious modification of established treatment techniques. Yet, at the same time, we believe that in order to be truly effective, these techniques must be based on a profound knowledge of psychoanalysis, and more

NOTE: From *Handbook of Community Psychiatry*, edited by L. Bellak, New York, 1964. Reprinted by permission of Grune & Stratton; present version somewhat revised.

particularly on the following basic propositions concerning personality, diagnosis, and treatment:

Personality is the complex aggregate of personal experiences of a unique organism in a lifetime: the experiencing is obviously a function of the experiencing organism *and* the experienced data. Variables of the organism, as well as the ever-increasing apperceptive mass, continuously structure the impact of new experiences. In recent years, both psychoanalysis and academic psychologists have found it useful to speak of perception in relation to personality and its development. "Experience becomes structure," to borrow Kurt Eissler's succinct statement (1953a). For psychoanalysts, the libido theory as discussed in Chapter 1, with its implicit propositions with regard to learning, affective charge, variants of drive in relation to the developmental timetable (as well as to propositions concerning the transformation of energy and the concept of autonomous ego functions, and other metapsychological considerations), complement the essential field of forces.

Diagnosis consists of establishing the precise relationship between the patient and the events which determined the course and nature of his ego development at different times, in terms of his relationships with persons in his environment, and situations, including cultural settings. Concurrently, we remain ever mindful of the patient's organismic equipment, to the degree that it can be discerned, as well as the specific stages of development at which significant experiences occurred. Our task is complicated, of course, by the fact that not only must we evaluate the effect of the isolated event, but also the effect of event C in relation to the fact that events A and B preceded it. Furthermore, not all personality factors can be related to even a complex matrix of one-to-one relationships. Not only do separate experiences affect subsequent experiences, but a variety of experiences may assume Gestalten (configurations), which in terms of Gestalt psychology are more than the sum of the parts, rather newly emergent wholes, and as such affect later experiences. Nor is our task made easier by the fact that we no longer think in terms of the rigid determinism of the nineteenth century; at best, we can only expect that our hypotheses will provide a guide to the most probable effects. Nevertheless, if it is applied rationally and systematically, I believe that current psychoanalytic theory provides us with an adequate framework in this area.

In its classic sense, psychotherapy is defined as the restructuration of the malfunctioning personality. This malfunctioning is conceptualized as the direct result of "bad" learning experiences which must be "unlearned." Thus new, corrective learning experiences are needed to produce changes in personality structure.

Customarily, in long-term psychotherapy of neuroses the therapist tends to place less emphasis on the patient's immediate day-to-day problems, and to direct his efforts to the analysis of transference and resistance phenomena, dreams and fantasies, all of which emerge in the course of the patient's free associations. This enables the patient to become gradually aware, on a conscious level, and then to "work through" previously repressed infantile wishes and conflicts. Obviously, however, sufficient time must be made available for the patient to acquire this awareness, to absorb this genetic, dynamic material, and to learn new ways of behaving. Nor will the therapist attempt to expedite this process.

Rather, his activities will focus upon reflection and interpretation, and may be characterized as generally expectant.

In contrast to the long-term goals of established psychotherapeutic procedure, the goals of psychotherapy in community psychiatry must understandably be restricted by the limitations imposed by short-term therapy. More specifically, as mentioned earlier, our primary aim is the alleviation of the patient's acute symptoms. We attempt to do this by helping him to mobilize his resources to deal with the immediate, pressing psychological difficulty. Our secondary objective is to enable the patient, once he has worked through this "emergency," to deal with future conflicts more effectively. Obviously, under optimal conditions, we would hope both to supply long-term psychotherapeutic treatment and to serve all applicants. Regrettably, however, realistic considerations, i.e., the long waiting lists which all community psychotherapy centers must cope with, require that we focus our attention on those therapeutic measures which will best enable us to meet the needs of a major portion of the population.

The model I have in mind is the kind of treatment situation we have tried to fashion at City Hospital in Elmhurst as part of our Comprehensive Community Psychiatric Program. The patient population at City Hospital may be categorized as follows: Those patients we believe can be helped with three to five therapeutic sessions are assigned to the "Trouble Shooting Clinic" of our outpatient department; those patients who require somewhat more prolonged therapy are assigned to our Mental Hygiene Clinic; finally, patients who require hospitalization are admitted to our inpatient service. All patients, regardless of diagnosis, are seen immediately at the Trouble Shooting Clinic, although they may be reassigned later.

The treatment program we have instituted in our outpatient department provides a good example of the application of the principles of brief psychotherapy within the framework of community psychiatry. In brief psychotherapy, it is essential that the therapist understand the "psychodynamic picture" as quickly as possible. In order to acquire such understanding, he must understand not only the nature of the patient's presenting complaint, but also the factors which precipitated this particular complaint. Concurrently, he must be able to relate these precipitating factors to the life history of the patient. As a result, brief therapy frequently presents many more difficulties than does long-term treatment. In long-term psychotherapy, one has an opportunity to investigate and carefully trace the configuration of the patient's behavior pattern. One has time to test the hypotheses which have been formed regarding the dynamics of the patient's pathology. By means of trial and error, and other learning methods on the part of both the patient and the therapist, the patient's behavior gradually changes. Conversely, in short term "emergency" therapy, time is of the essence because of the nature of the presenting problem or the frame of reference. Hence, this type of thorough approach to the problem is not feasible.

GENERAL PRINCIPLES OF BRIEF PSYCHOTHERAPY

As stated earlier, the purpose of brief psychotherapy is to relieve the patient's presenting symptoms as quickly as possible. Three general rules can be formulated which are designed to facilitate this procedure. First, the dynamics of the chief complaint, with regard to the relationship of the symptom to the previous personality structure and the current life situation, must be clearly understood. Second, the therapist must attempt to change those factors which lend themselves most efficiently to change. Third, the approach which he utilizes in effecting such change will be determined by the needs of the particular patient. Above all, however, the therapist's approach is a flexible one, and his decision about the technique to be employed with a particular patient will be determined solely by his treatment goal in this particular setting, that is, to restructure the patient's personality so as to enable some improvement in his total life situation in as brief a period of time as possible.

The first of these objectives may be achieved by taking an exhaustive history of the onset of the patient's complaint, as well as his developmental history. Indeed, these data are of primary importance, and well worth the investment of time necessary to accumulate them, for on the basis of this history the therapist should be able to gain a complete understanding of the factors which precipitated the patient's problem, of his contemporary life situation, and of his development within the framework of his family environment. The history taking can also be instrumental in establishing rapport with the patient: the patient interprets the therapist's lengthy interview as indicative of the therapist's interest in him. Its main function, however, is to bring about the therapist's thorough understanding of the patient's illness, in dynamic terms, that is, in relation to his total life situation. The purpose of history taking must be *to understand the present status of the past*.[1]

There are two major avenues of approach to the actual problem of alleviating the patient's symptoms, albeit these are often intertwined and can be separated only for purposes of argument. One method focuses primarily on producing environmental change, which, in turn, will produce psychological changes in the patient. The second focuses on attempting to change the patient's personality directly by psychological intervention.

ENVIRONMENTAL INTERVENTION

At times, a particular environmental factor may be most amenable to change and sufficient benefit may derive from efforts along such lines. The relatively simple case of the child who is brought to the psychiatrist because he has developed nightmares may serve to illustrate. We learn that the child's nightmares began when he was moved into his parents' bedroom to sleep, after an unemployed relative had arrived for a visit. The family sees no relationship between these events, but we know that the child's anxiety is due to the overstimulation and misconceptions aroused by proximity to his parents. Therefore, we must try to persuade the parents that it is better for the child to sleep on a relatively uncomfortable cot in the kitchen than in their far more comfortable double bed with them. If the child's nightmares are of recent origin, this sug-

---

[1] For a further detailed conceptualization, see Chapter 9 and Bellak and Small, 1965. A careful history becomes the main basis for dynamic conceptualization. Predicated upon this dynamic understanding, it is essential to formulate the area of intervention, the method of intervention, and the sequence of areas and methods of intervention. Whether intrapersonal or environmental changes are chosen, or which of the forms of intervention discussed here are used (cathartic intervention, etc.), must be part of a parsimonious and carefully thought out plan.

gested change in sleeping arrangements may suffice as a therapeutic measure and, incidentally, prevent even more severe pathology. If it is at all feasible, a simple explanation of the reasons for this recommendation should be given to the parents as well, in order to strengthen their resolve to institute this change, and in the hope that they may be able to generalize this information for application in other appropriate instances.

Other types of intervention have also been described by Bibring (1949), myself (Bellak, 1952b), and more recently and most ambitiously, by Caplan (1961), who suggests focusing on environmental conditions and their change or elimination if they cause emotional problems. This includes social conditions, as well as such factors as unnecessary separation of children from their parents, etc.

PSYCHOLOGICAL INTERVENTION

There are a number of psychological techniques which may be effectively employed in brief psychotherapy. I have found the following broad outline useful in this connection.

Cathartic Interpretation. A cathartic interpretation is concerned with the translation into consciousness of an unconscious drive or idea. However, this technique can be used advantageously only if the therapist is certain that the interpretation will not be too painful for the patient. Thus, he must take precautions to make it bearable, and utilize this means of treatment only after he has taken such precautions.

The implementation of this technique may take a variety of forms: For one, the therapist may choose to interpret the symbolic content of the primary disturbing sentiment directly, whether this sentiment derives from aggressive, exhibitionistic, sexual, or other impulses. Consider, for example, the panic-stricken adolescent whose panic started with the fear that he would have an epileptic attack. The idea of a seizure is realized as something aggressive and/or sexualized. He feels one loses control and does all sorts of wild things in a state of excitement and presumably this feeling became more acute the night prior to his coming to the psychiatrist—while he was out on a date. One might choose to interpret this by saying to the boy: "Look, you really must have felt some impulse of grabbing that girl and really letting yourself go. This must have frightened you, because you really don't know what you might do. You were afraid you might lose control (and behave like an epileptic) and hurt her, hurt yourself, and God knows what else." One might also have to couple that with other images, memories, and ideas that the boy has about sexuality, because he has never had a sexual experience and does not really know what happens.

When catharsis is the treatment of choice, it is often best to couple it with other techniques. A mildly depressed patient may profit by this approach. In such circumstances, an intra-aggressive impulse might be interpreted as follows: "You are so damned angry at your sister, you wish she would drop dead." This interpretation would then be followed immediately by some sort of reassuring statement: "This idea upsets you so much *because you're a very conscientious person who wouldn't harm a fly.* So instead of really telling her to 'drop dead,' you withdraw from her and sulk. You were really angry at yourself for having such a thought and that's why you became depressed."

In the preceding example, in addition to tempering the cathartic interpretation with reassurance (i.e., that the patient is ". . . a very conscientious person. . . ."), another maneuver was utilized which might be called *mediate psychotherapy*. The interpretation described the patient's feelings in a socially unacceptable way: i.e., "You are so *damned* angry . . ." This in itself has a certain cathartic effect on the patient. Thus, strong unacceptable thoughts were expressed, but the patient did not have to take the responsibility for their expression. In fact, the doctor was responsible for their expression, which made socially unacceptable impulses more acceptable to the patient's superego.

Drive Repression. This technique may be illustrated by citing the case of an 18-year-old girl who is panicky because of aroused sexuality. There is a great deal of petting going on among her group of friends, and she has indulged in this for competitive reasons: since the other girls pet heavily, she must do so too, in order to be popular. But she is experiencing a great deal of anxiety, because she comes from an environment which stresses that this is not the thing to do. She tries to settle the conflict between her severe superego and continuing to do what she is doing—out of competitive reasons, and perhaps because of some genuine sexual interest. The therapist helps her by supporting the superego and saying: "Don't do it now; you don't need to. It's quite understandable that you feel badly about it. You want to sort out your feelings first. You can go about it differently, more slowly, at a later time." And, again, while the therapist explains that she must understand more about what is happening, he can enlighten her tactfully and help dispel incorrect notions she may have about sex.

Intellectual Understanding (and utilizing intellectualization as a defense). The case of a patient whose panic is associated with a somatic condition can serve to illustrate this technique. This man's panic, with suicidal thoughts, was precipitated by a coronary occlusion. Since he is an intelligent man, it may be wise to try to alleviate his anxiety by discussing the physiopathology and pathology of the coronary with him in simple terms. Thus one might say, "What happens in an occlusion is that a blood vessel becomes stopped up. You were very sick at that time because your heart didn't get enough blood. Almost as soon as that happened, though, new capillaries were formed, collateral vessels started to form, and they can now carry on the circulation to the heart. In addition, instead of lying around at home because you feel that moving around may 'kill' you, you have to understand that physical exercise, within limits, will actually stimulate further production of collaterals." One can then compare this process to the repair of a fracture, emphasizing that the normal reparative processes come into play and are facilitated by moderate exercise.

In all probability, however, this technique will have to be supplemented. Presumably, such an illness has concomitant symbolic meanings for the patient which will play a part in the manifest picture. Encouraging him to be active, rather than to be passive, may help him to alleviate his panic.

Increasing the Patient's Self-Esteem. Almost invariably, and particularly in emergency situations, the therapist will attempt to strengthen the patient's ego by increasing his self-esteem. At the outset, he will attempt to cope with the trauma the patient has suffered as a result of the realization that he needs advice from a psychiatrist. Apart from his feelings of rejection, failure, etc., the patient is convinced that his need for psychiatric consultation means that he must be deficient, which further lowers his self-esteem. In addition, the patient's sense of oral deprivation, his projections, regressive and other pathological phenomena contribute to his self-depreciation. It is important that the therapist attack this problem early in treatment by pointing out the patient's positive achievements: he has accomplished something; he has been able to tolerate a good deal; and now, above all, he is willing to do something constructive to help himself. The therapist must also convince the patient that because he understands his situation, he will be able to help him.

It may be necessary to establish a fairly familiar relationship with the patient, contrary to usual psychotherapeutic practice, to achieve this objective. The therapist remains the authority, but at the same time the patient is made to feel that he is on the same level as the therapist, and that the therapist is not contemptuous of him. Furthermore, he is made to realize that his problem is not unique. It does not make him an inferior human being; nor is the therapist his superior. In brief, they can talk things over as equals.

Increasing the integration of the patient's superego, by creating controls or strengthening existing controls, may be useful strategy, particularly with those patients who tend to act out. Cultural factors or simple denial may make certain forms of behavior acceptable to persons with character disorders, despite the subjective and objective difficulties such behavior creates. A frank analysis of the patient's behavior by the therapist, with strong emphasis on the incorrectness, inconsistency, and self-destructive nature of specific patterns, may produce rapid changes in the patient's functioning.

Drug Therapy. Drugs may be used to facilitate communication in psychotherapy, or as an adjunct to psychotherapy. The large variety of psychotropic drugs available at present may, of course, be of great help. Even older drugs, such as those of the dexedrine or barbiturate family, may be used judiciously to reduce symptoms briefly, and thereby interfere with the secondary gains of psychiatric symptoms: for instance, a man who feels unable to take on a job after a period of illness with tuberculosis may be encouraged just enough, after some stimulant has been prescribed, to learn to prefer mature functioning to regression and passivity. In such a case, the drug can be withdrawn as soon as the adaptive healthy functioning is firmly established.

The possibility of unfavorable secondary effects in drug therapy is rarely mentioned; however, it merits consideration in this context. Patients with dissociative or self-observing tendencies are particularly likely to experience a "paradox" reaction of excessive anxiety and even panic to the changes in self-awareness and perception induced by such drugs. Thus, the therapist must alert the patient to the possibility of such transitory changes, reassure him when they do occur, and increase or decrease the dosage, as indicated; frequently, useful discussion of the meaning of the patient's fear of loss of control and related notions of insanity can be introduced at this point.

TREATMENT OF THE HOSPITALIZED PATIENT AND THE MORE SEVERELY DISTURBED PATIENT

Again, despite the modifications which are necessarily imposed in this setting, treatment techniques will derive from the psychoanalytic concepts of personality structure, diagnostic formulations, and treatment procedure.

As clinicians, we are primarily concerned with diagnosis as an appraisal of the patient's disturbance. Such an appraisal requires a description of the disturbance, apart from its relationship to the acquisition of specific personality variables. I have found it useful to apply a detailed survey of ego functioning and of patterns of individual disturbances as a basis for a profile of a descriptive, qualitative-quantitative assessment of the nature of the patient's disturbances (see Chapter 20). Psychotics as a group share a common denominator, namely their ego functions are more severely disturbed, or more of their ego functions are disturbed than is true of neurotics or of "normal" persons. Relatively circumscribed profiles of disturbance constitute the different nosologic groups, including the organic disorders. Psychoanalytic theory provides us with an excellent set of propositions to permit us to understand intermediary states and the changes from one clinical group to another.

One can probably formulate some general principles with regard to technique in psychotherapy of psychoses as well. Among these, I would include the therapist's ability to establish a relationship with the patient. As stated earlier, all psychotics share a common denominator, namely, severe disturbance of one ego function or another, and usually of several. In addition, severe anxiety, latent or manifest, and some disturbance in secondary-process thinking are usually the rule. Beyond these generalizations, each psychotic is a unique person, with unique patterns of disturbance, unique forms of what Katan (1953) has called an "intact residue," and a unique personal history. Therefore, each case will present different problems, and therapy must be tailor-made to fit the patient, in terms of his specific diagnosis. Obviously, given the many complex factors involved, in some instances the therapist's ability to establish a relationship with the patient will produce only the most superficial, temporary success. As Eissler (1952) has pointed out, while the therapist's ability to establish contact with the patient may be effective during the acute phase of the psychosis, stable therapeutic change is effected by more subtle techniques during the clinically "mute" phase.

For reasons outlined earlier, of necessity the Psychiatric Inpatient Service of City Hospital is designed to provide short-term, intensive care. Thus, the purpose of hospitalization is to deal with the acute phase of the psychosis, to mobilize the patient's resources, and to return him to the community as quickly as possible. At present, the average stay for adult inpatients is thirty days; adolescents and children are customarily hospitalized for approximately six weeks. Obviously, in these circumstances the patient and his family may require a good deal of support and direction immediately prior to and after his discharge, during what would be the equivalent of the "clinically mute" stage of his illness.

It may be useful to state again that, essentially, psychotherapy involves a process of unlearning and relearning. Within the framework of a community psychiatry program, therapy during hospitalization might be said to focus primarily on unlearning. Subsequently, when the patient is seen in the Day Care Center or Mental Hygiene Clinic of our outpatient department, or followed up by the Visiting Nurse Service, the therapeutic measures employed are oriented toward the process of relearning. In general, many of the tools which are employed in brief psychotherapy with our regular outpatient population may be utilized with inpatients as well, both during hospitalization and after discharge. In any event, in many instances, it will be impossible to state generally at what phase of treatment a specific technique will prove most effective.

It might be most efficient for our purposes to describe a catalog of therapeutic techniques which would correspond to specific disturbances in ego functions, as enumerated in Chapter 20.

(1) *Disturbance in the adaptation to reality.* Obviously, this classification would encompass a great many subdivisions. To mention just a few, inappropriate behavior may yield to direct analysis by the therapist of the incorrectness of the patient's acts. Drug treatment of the anxiety and aggression which precipitated disturbances in the patient's body image and ego boundaries may alleviate his feelings of unreality. Increased intellectual understanding may improve the patient's reality testing.

(2) *Disturbances in the regulation of drives,* manifested by a lack of frustration tolerance, may result in psychotic acting out, catatonic stupor, or depressive or manic behavior, depending on the individual personality constellation. The techniques of drive repression and cathartic interpretation may be helpful here; in fact, the therapist might permit himself more latitude in the use of cathartic interpretation with the hospitalized patient than would be true in an outpatient setting. At the same time, however, he must be prepared for the possibility that such interpretations may provoke agitated and violent reactions. Indeed, this technique may prove to be a double-edged sword, which can do a good deal of harm. To illustrate, a boy on a ward who jumped out of a running car (driven by his father) thinks he has destroyed the world. What he probably means is that he wanted to kill his father and he now feels that he had done so. A cathartic interpretation containing this conclusion may manifestly change that boy within a few hours, at least temporarily. Therefore, while he sits there, insisting that he should be killed because he has destroyed the world, the psychotherapist can say: "What I think is that you were angry and wanted to get rid of your father. Instead, you jumped out of the car because your conscience would not let you get rid of him." This may produce an immediate change in his behavior, but this change might not be a desirable one. For example, he may improve initially, so that he is no longer catatonic; but when he thinks about what the therapist has said, he may feel guilty enough to kill himself. Since it is possible to achieve such negative results, it is important to examine carefully every case in which cathartic interpretation is considered.

The use of energizers and tranquilizers for the control of drives has been described by Ostow (1959, 1962). While it is not necessary to subscribe to the author's very specific conceptualization of the effect of these drugs, there is little doubt that his empirical observations are quite acceptable.

For the acquisition of frustration tolerance required in the ordinary social process, I know of no better means than the sort of rehabilitation (or habilitation) program which has been initiated at the Altro workshops (see Chapter 17). The group therapy program we have instituted in the outpatient department at City Hospital may also prove a training ground for learning socialization and drive control.

(3) *Disturbances in object relations* are customarily treated via the transference relationship and interpretation in classical psychoanalysis. In the frame-

work of a hospital treatment setting, the therapist must attempt to cope with such disturbances, at least initially, by establishing a good relationship with the patient, and thereby increasing his relatedness. Group therapy and the Altro rehabilitation program may prove effective at a later point in therapy.

(4) *Disturbance of the thought processes,* with their contaminations (to use Rorschach's phrase), and other evidences of primary-process thinking pose great therapeutic problems. Some patients cannot attain insight into the nature of their problems because they do not have the logical equipment for the syllogistic thinking involved. This may be due to their failure to acquire enough of the secondary process to enable them to grasp the hierarchical relationships of cause and effect, time, place, and person. Arieti (1962), among others, has addressed himself to dealing therapeutically with such problems. Concreteness of thinking is another problem comparable to the phenomenon observed in children and described by Piaget.

Nevertheless, at times, a more concrete learning situation may enable the patient to acquire some insight. Conjoint psychotherapy, to use Jackson and Weakland's (1961) term, or conjoint consultation and confrontation, which I prefer to use, may accomplish this. To illustrate, if the patient is seen together with his mother, just observing the behavior of his mother toward the therapist, and vice versa, may be extremely meaningful for the patient, and produce insight which could not be attained in an abstract situation.

Again, the relearning process may have to be supplemented by, or acquired initially, in more concrete, frequently repeated experiences of a certain kind: group psychotherapy in which patients learn the consequences of "wrong" behavior, and are rewarded by the group for "right" behavior, may build impulse control and other restructurations which are unattainable by means of verbal abstractions, even given the very best individual therapy. The rehabilitation program at Altro would belong here as well.

Learning by identification with the therapist, or by interaction with the therapist as "the corrective therapeutic experience" which Neo-Freudians stress (over genetic propositions), may play a useful role, though not to the degree, I suspect, that Neo-Freudians would claim; moreover, for many psychotics it is not enough.

(5) The therapist can best treat *disturbances due to repression and other defensive functions* by providing for an integrated superego, that is, by seeing to it that it is not intolerably strict in some areas and not too lenient in others—as is usually the case. Judicious firmness and permissiveness at different times in relation to different sets of problems are indicated.

Manipulation of the environment to decrease the pressure of stimuli which require defensive functioning is often essential. Drug therapy, changes in vocation, habitation, and living habits may be necessary. It is essential that the therapist conceptualize well, and that he insist firmly on drastic changes (rather than indulge in analytic aloofness from decisions involving reality).

(6) *The strengthening of disturbed autonomous functions,* such as language and motor performance, is essential in some cases—of an immigrant, in the first instance, and a poorly coordinated adolescent in the second. In fact, very often, the autonomous functions are part of the patient's "intact residue" and

must be drawn upon heavily in attempts to reconstruct the disturbed areas of his personality.

Broadly speaking, it is necessary to appraise the patient's over-all ego functioning to assess the strength and weakness of individual functions, and then utilize those which appear to lend themselves to the achievement of therapeutic goals. If the patient has in the past evidenced a tendency to maintain his emotional stability by an obsessive-compulsive involvement with work, then this facet of his functioning must be encouraged. If the patient's reality testing can be improved because of his high level of intelligence, this asset will play a major role in therapeutic technique. If, despite the fact that the patient evidences extensive personality disorganization, his object relations are good, then his relationships with other persons should be encouraged just as relative isolation may be recommended in those cases where close interaction leads to paranoid ideation.

(7) Usually, *the synthetic function* is strengthened only after the other ego functions have been improved by various means. However, the psychotropic drugs, e.g., of the phenothiazin variety, seem to counteract dissociation directly, thereby producing a synthesizing and integrative effect. It may be that this can be accomplished indirectly by drive control, or by some more direct effect on the organic substratum.

In fact, on an empirical basis, supplemented experimentally by the pilot study (described in Chapter 12), I have little doubt that the psychotropic drugs are useful not only symptomatically, but as a constructive force in terms of the psychotherapeutic process. More precisely, the psychotropic drugs have permitted us to carry on the process of learning by insight, by trial and error, under something akin to a surgical intervention with the benefit of anesthesia and physiological support. Whereas, ordinarily, the patient's lack of frustration tolerance, of impulse control, and/or his extreme anxiety would make the therapeutic process unbearable, these drugs help him to "survive" the learning process until his new personality structure is well established and, hopefully, sufficiently automatized and integrated, so that he no longer needs the drugs.

GUIDELINES FOR THE FUTURE

Despite the limitations which are necessarily imposed on our therapeutic efforts in the framework of a community program, I believe that a systemized approach might be possible even for relatively unsophisticated therapists.

For example, research findings recently published by Hilgard and Newman (1961) have opened up a particularly fascinating vista in this connection. These authors found that a statistically highly significant number of women in a state hospital became ill within a year of the time that their own oldest child reached the age at which the patient herself had lost her mother. For preventive community psychiatry, this may mean that in the long run we will have available a variety of similar data which could be obtained by feeding the characteristics of a given population into an IBM machine—e.g., to find the likely candidates for such an anniversary psychosis! Even more important, these data might enable us to work out specific guidelines for the prevention and psychotherapy of the acute upset. Basic propositions, such as identification and envy, arousal of passive wishes, hostility, fear of loss, etc., might be expeditiously treated in such circumstances, provided the therapist has a thorough background in psycho-analytic dynamics.

The research project carried out at City Hospital was designed to contribute further to this systematic approach. More precisely, we included in this study a close and detailed survey of diagnostic procedures (including conceptualization of the patient's presenting problem, needs, preliminary treatment, and treatment goals), the nature of the therapeutic procedure utilized, and detailed follow-up information.

To this end, we engaged in an intensive analysis of cases treated in the Trouble Shooting Clinic of our outpatient department in order to determine the efficacy of specific treatment techniques (catharsis, support, direct interpretation, etc.) in short-term treatment, with very limited, specific goals.

(1) Discharged as improved (amelioration of symptoms).
(2) Referral to Mental Hygiene Clinic for long-term individual and/or group therapy.
(3) Referral to the Day Care Center for intensive, short-term, outpatient treatment.
(4) Long-term hospitalization.
(5) Short-term hospitalization.
(6) Termination by patient against advice.
(7) Other (death, change of residence, etc.)
(8) Repeated return to the clinic after discharge.

In addition, follow-up interviews were conducted three months, six months, and nine months after the termination of treatment to evaluate further the general outcome of treatment and the nature of the adjustment achieved by the patient.

The data thus accumulated gave us a picture of the relative effectiveness of treatment modalities, with respect to the special characteristics of the patient population served by City Hospital:

(1) The correlation among such variables as intelligence, socioeconomic status, age, diagnosis, and choice of treatment modality.
(2) The relationship among treatment modality, type of patient, and outcome of treatment.
(3) The relationship among treatment modality, diagnosis, and the outcome of treatment.

For a relatively small group of patients, the method of repeated short-range prediction and judgment was employed within different frameworks (see Chapters 7 and 8). Patient interviews were recorded, and observed through a one-way mirror as well; independent judges attempted to evaluate a number of variables, while independent predictors tried to predict the effects of interpretations on the course of treatment, from session to session. Unlike a previous experiment (described in Chapter 8), we included intrasession predictions, as well as judgments, to get a clearer picture of patient-therapist interaction, and at the same time to test our hypotheses concerning the effectiveness of various techniques used in brief psychotherapy.

Community psychiatry is, among other things, the historical result of the greater interdependence of human beings; there is a heightened awareness of the responsibility of society toward the individual and of the need to conduct individual behavior for the benefit of society as a whole; neither sentiment nor prejudice can minimize the importance of these considerations. These truisms have been clearly demonstrated; moreover, apparently, they are irreversible. Technological progress has brought with it the added interaction of individuals throughout the world; the increased likelihood that they will impinge upon one another; and, consequently, greater need for the regulation of such interaction. In the horse-and-buggy days, there was no need to impose speed limits or install stop lights. Before the world became one economic community, there was no reason for stringent tariffs. When people lived in rural areas, rather than crowded metropolitan centers, we could be less concerned with delinquency, vaccination, and sewage disposal. We can no longer afford such indifference in this atomic age when one person can pull the trigger which can destroy the whole world. Each person's action is, to a considerable extent, everybody's concern.

The conflict between the need to preserve the freedom of the individual and of private initiative versus the welfare state is one which we must face daily. Obviously, the mental patient's suffering is subjective; but it is equally obvious that the welfare of the entire nation is affected by the fact that approximately one half of the beds in hospitals throughout the United States are currently occupied by the mentally ill. Similarly, the entire population must bear the burden of criminal activity and political lunacy.

In the course of his everyday practice, the psychiatrist is frequently frustrated by his inability to utilize what professional tools he has, for lack of legislation to do so. Because the functioning of our courts is often antiquated and irrational, one severely disturbed youngster may be permitted to contaminate a whole neighborhood. There is little we can do to prevent disturbed parents from raising their children under psychological conditions which, in the judgment of *any* school of thought, are bound to produce disturbed adults. Yet those members of the community who need psychiatric care most in many instances refuse such treatment, and there are so far no ways of enforcing psychiatric care where it is most needed.

On the other hand, the community has long recognized the need for legal measures which will safeguard its physical health, and such measures have been instituted. Thus, once he has been identified, the person who has contracted a contagious disease must submit to appropriate treatment; moreover, he may be quarantined as well. As a further safeguard, the community requires its physicians to report the presence of a long list of diseases so that members of the community who have been exposed to the patient may be adequately protected against possible contamination. Other preventive measures have been instituted as well: children must be vaccinated against smallpox; public dining rooms must meet certain sanitary standards; the disposal of sewage and the by-products of industry are closely regulated. Certainly, similar legislation designed to protect the community against emotional contamination, to provide the necessary minimum protection for the many from the severe mental illness of the relatively few, would be equally appropriate.

Thus the enactment of legal measures which provide for the compulsory care of the public's physical health problems have established a precedent which may serve as a model for our efforts to diminish its psychiatric problems. If public

health workers have been successful in implementing legislation to make treatment of contagious diseases obligatory, the difficulties we encounter in the course
of our parallel efforts on behalf of enforced psychotherapy should not prove
insurmountable.

As we know, public health workers have met with a certain amount of resistance on the part of the community to measures which are designed to ensure
its physical well-being. We can expect an even greater resistance to our efforts
on behalf of its emotional well-being. After all, many of the patients we treat in
private practice entered treatment initially with little personal motivation, but
were forced by one reality situation or another: a spouse, a parent, fear of social
or legal consequences in the case of character disorders or perversions.

It has to be part of our armamentarium to make ego alien what was ego
syntonic, and to provide motivation where there was none to begin with. A
court order for psychotherapy might be as good a motivation for a start as any.
Legislated psychotherapy has a role to play.

An editorial in the *Journal of the American Medical Association* of July 7,
1962, on "the battered child syndrome," underscored the responsibility of the
physician to protect a child, for instance, from this crudest expression of psychopathology of parents in the form of physical violence. Indeed, the precept which
enjoins us to protect children against physical abuse is well integrated into our
code. I see no logical reason why this concept of protection of children against
physical harm should not be enlarged to the at least equally serious one of psychological harm. Society has every right to protect the child and itself. The
mistreated child of today may not only be the community burden of tomorrow,
but may also be the demagogue of tomorrow; he may be the delinquent, the
rabble rouser, part of the political lunatic fringe, and the one who presses the
button that could destroy us all.

An objection to public intervention concerning child rearing especially, and
psychiatric problems generally, is sometimes based on the notion that, after
all, we do not know enough about causation as yet and that there are great
divergencies in schools of thought. I think this is spurious reasoning and not in
accord with the facts. Of course, we have differences in opinions and our hypotheses will always be in flux as in any other science, but certain broad propositions
are quite generally agreed upon among all the basically informed. I have *not*
heard that abuse of children might not be harmful, nor have I heard that major
disturbances in the parents never result in marked emotional imbalance in the
children.

The influence of psychiatric concepts is not needed in the home alone. Long
ago, political folly had certain comic-opera aspects; and we might almost look
back on that era with some wistfulness. But in this atomic age, we can afford
neither an emotionally aroused, undisciplined rabble, nor political leaders who
do not possess sufficient intelligence, knowledge, or emotional balance for the
task before them. Because we tolerated the rise of Hitler and Nazism, six mil-
lion persons were murdered, and many more millions were casualties of war.
Were history to repeat itself today, the results could be even more disastrous.
The advent of Hitler has been attributed to the "closed mind," and concomitantly to what Rokeach (1960) has called the "closed belief system" which was
prevalent among Germans at the time. But the "closed mind" is not indigenous

to Germany; it may take root among the population of the Congo or in Mississippi as well—to endanger the survival of civilization once again.

A new executive arm of government which will concern itself with the everyday problems of child rearing as well as the emotional state of the community may have to be developed.

On a broader basis, psychiatric awareness will have to enter political considerations and the soundness of legislators and executives in a way that would be inappropriate to spell out on this occasion.

No doubt, though, that by a broad scope of activities, community psychiatry will increasingly have to be able to protect society as a whole, and simultaneously assure each individual as much chance for happiness as possible.

17

THE PSYCHODYNAMICS OF REHABILITATION

The process of rehabilitation starts long before the patient leaves the hospital. It can be carried on in a purely psychiatric setting or in a transitional setting, such as a rehabilitation workshop where specially trained personnel deal with both the job and with its psychological consequences. To go back to full employment the patient must give up the comforts of the treatment situation and the understanding of the treating physician, and frequently he prefers to remain sick in order to continue getting these benefits. These problems can sometimes be avoided by transferring him to a follow-up worker with whom he has a less intense relationship, thereby decreasing his temptation to remain a patient.

Preparation for rehabilitation has something of the same character as preparation for an operation or for a death in the family. It must be started well before the traumatic event takes place, and the more thorough the preparation, the better the chance of success.

EVERY PHYSICIAN AND THERAPIST would like to be able to treat pathological conditions etiologically and specifically. Moreover, the acute disorders, say, of an infectious nature, are the real pride and joy of every practitioner, if he happens to have the magic bullet to deal with them. This is heroic, dramatic, final, and gratifying.

Toilers in psychiatry, short of pushing the button on the ECT machine, are generally denied these easy pleasures. Workers in the field of rehabilitation of psychotics are the share-croppers of this domain. They get those psychotics who are too ill to recover in the way in which even most psychotics regain some health. Little drama, steadfast repair, a need for excellent frustration tolerance, and a willingness to take reasonable risks characterize this work.

Nevertheless, rehabilitation of psychotics is essential and presumably always will be, even if some magic bullet should be found for mental illness: a vast percentage of psychotics do not suffer so much from regression as from never having progressed sufficiently in reality testing, impulse control, object relations, and other ego functions (Bellak, 1958). Thus, they will always need a learning process which cannot be substituted for by medication.

We know that work and employment mean different things to different people: e.g., a livelihood, social status, prestige, and emotional satisfaction. It is obvious that these main factors often lead to increased frustration, especially in the mentally ill. However, professional workers know that, in spite of gainful employment with proper remuneration, many patients suffer frustrations that may be directly related to the work or to the working conditions themselves.

NOTE: From the *American Journal of Orthopsychiatry*, 1956, 26, 285-296, and the *American Journal of Orthopsychiatry*, 1960, 30, 346-355. Reprinted by permission of the publishers and B. Black, A. Lurie, and J. Miller, co-authors, whose collaboration is gratefully acknowledged.

Therefore, the problem is not only one of job skill, but of job attitude or work psychology (Bellak, 1958). The major task in rehabilitation is, then, the reconstruction of the patient's ego strength so that he can be made mentally fit and ready for work, and also able to cope with the emotional and interpersonal factors involved in starting and continuing on the job. Such an understanding and preparation of some mental patients for employment could not be accomplished in either the mental hospital or the vocational and employment service alone. The situation required an actual workshop environment which not only closely paralleled real working conditions, but also provided psychiatric, vocational and other rehabilitation services.

For many years Altro Health and Rehabilitation Services, Inc., has placed its rehabilitation center and its sheltered workshop at the disposal of postpsychotic patients, as well as providing rehabilitation for the two other exacerbating, relapsing types of chronic illness: tuberculosis and heart disease. It has evolved a program of rehabilitation centered in the services of the sheltered workshop, with a ring of protective professional services around the work setting. The "Altro," as the workshops have come to be known, is a garment-manufacturing factory, located in the Bronx in New York, employing some two hundred people and selling washable cotton apparel to hospitals, hotels, restaurants, and industrial plants throughout the country.

To the casual observer, the Altro looks, acts, and has "the feel" of a factory. There are two floors of modern, well-kept machinery, and a constant hum of productivity. Skilled, efficient foremen and management personnel keep the wheels turning, and appear to be attending only to the usual concerns of factory production. There are the expected time clocks for punching in and out, and bells clang at intervals, presumably announcing shift changes. The working floors are very well lighted, clean, and in cheerful colors—much better than one expects to find in most factories in the New York garment district. To the visitor in the know, however, the time clock represents the record by which the nursing and medical staff control the number of prescribed hours of work per day. The clanging bells signify rest periods at midmorning and midafternoon at which medically prescribed refreshments are served. The management person is just as likely to be one of the registered nurses, who is not in uniform but who nevertheless keeps in constant touch with the health of the patient. She has the power to decrease the working hours or to arrange for immediate medical attention for any patient, and can do this in spite of production requirements.

The major tool provided is the single-needle power sewing machine. Running this machine is sedentary work, demanding little physical energy output. It is possible for almost anyone with some manual dexterity and from dull normal intelligence up to learn the simplest sewing operations in a reasonably short time. Payment for work produced is on a piecework basis at the highest rates set for similar processes in unionized industry in New York City. As soon as the patient can sew a straight seam, he is given simple garments to work on, and he begins to earn wages.

Obviously, even if the new Altro employee were skilled at the sewing machine, his limited number of hours of work would mean a very small income. For most of the patients, their earnings for many weeks fall far below the income needed for themselves and their families. Therefore, the Altro Health and Rehabilitation Services subsidizes the earnings up to decent minimal budget requirements for the family. Where there is eligibility for public assistance, it is expected that this, too, will be drawn upon. Many patients reach a point of full self-sufficiency before they leave Altro Work Shops, earning as well as they may later do in the garment trade outside or in other occupations more suited to them.

No description of the Altro program would be complete without a word about the type of supervisory employees and foremen. As is true with any sheltered work setting, provision must be made for a certain number of key positions to be filled by nonclients. As the years have gone on and vacancies have occurred in these positions, applications have been received from ex-patients who have made good adjustments in the normal workaday world. Some of these workers were in the garment trade before coming to Altro Work Shops; some had their first training at Altro. These people bring to their supervisory responsibilities an understanding and awareness which is unique. They have demonstrated an ability to cope with behavior, symptoms, and adjustment problems superior to what one would find in skilled tradesmen of their kind who had had no personal experience with a relapsing illness or with a rehabilitation program.

The workshop may be seen as a world of topological relations. A topological concept of the world has been most lucidly compared to a map or diagram on a rubber sheet: the principal relationships are maintained, but the rubber sheet may be stretched and allows for some flexibility in the relationships. If a patient referred to Altro develops paranoid attitudes toward his fellow workers or foremen, and wants to quarrel about the work he has to do, he can have a conference with the social worker and the foremen for a discussion and a working out of the realistic nucleus of his complaints. If patients hypochondriacally stay home too often, they can discuss their fears of harming themselves by work, rather than being laid off. On the other hand, they are paid per piece, and the secondary gain in acting out decreases when the pay decreases.

In addition to nursing, medical, and supervisory personnel, each patient is assigned a caseworker; and the team of doctor, nurse, and social worker becomes responsible for planning and supporting the rehabilitation program for the Altro "employee." The basic aim of the Altro program is to return the client to as normal living conditions and working productivity as are possible in view of his capabilities and handicap. The stay at Altro can be looked upon as a form of industrial convalescence. The vast majority of the patients graduate from the Altro Workshops. When the client has reached the work capacity of seven or eight hours per day and is ready for graduation, the rehabilitation team, especially the social worker, helps him in the transition back to his former employment, to an occupation in the garment trade if that is warranted, or to further training in some other occupation.

The whole atmosphere is one of a reasonably positive transference, with rewards for maturation and with interpretations (frequently perceived as mild disapproval) for regressive behavior. The whole group structure is competitively oriented to achieving "health."

THE INITIATION OF REHABILITATION

In the more traditional hospital setting, it is essential that *rehabilitation be arranged for as early in the patient's stay in the hospital as possible*. Otherwise, one of the results is that many patients are discharged into the community only to relapse very soon. Experience has shown that most of the state hospitals' discharged patients are able to find employment on their own in the present labor market and that only the very sickest are usually interested in rehabilitation by such transitional employment as Altro offers. Many subsequent remarks have to be understood in the light of the fact that the Altro patients were usually the sickest—many of them having had several long periods of hospitalization and being without family or other resources. Aside from the hardship this places on the rehabilitation workers, the use of rehabilitation only for the sickest is probably not an optimum way of meeting the needs of the community. It is important to acquaint many patients with the need for supervised rehabilitation even if they are seemingly well enough to proceed on their own, and to plan rehabilitation early, when it seems indicated at all.

It is my belief that every hospital admissions conference on a patient should include a specific commitment on the prognosis, both short- and long-range. Such a statement (following the customary one of the diagnosis and not necessarily highly correlated with nosological entities) might, for instance, read: "Schizophrenia, acute, catatonic type. Fairly adequate premorbid personality, with difficulties in interpersonal relations, specifically in working situations: Expect prompt benefit from series of about 12 ECT; a relapse somewhere within a year of discharge of illness because of repeated acute conflict around sexual and aggressive problems. Thus, ECT should be supplemented with group therapy or group work while in hospital, and rehabilitation setting for some time after discharge. Social casework with family indicated to reduce conflict-producing atmosphere there."

Needless to say, every diagnosis and prognosis is but a working hypothesis and may turn out to be wrong. However, on the chance that a careful repeated conceptualization will give a better than 50:50 chance of being right, it is important that the patient and family be early motivated to rehabilitation even if the patient should manifestly appear to be in very good condition immediately after discharge. *Specific planning of the type of rehabilitation indicated* ("prescription for rehabilitation") is also important; preparation and planning are predicated upon the presence in the hospital, and at the initial conference and the discharge conference, of a rehabilitation psychiatrist and rehabilitation worker.

It has been our experience that such prognoses are rarely part of the hospital's evaluative armamentarium. In less rare instances, but still too infrequently, there is some provision for rehabilitation personnel in mental hospitals. The placing of a vocational counselor in juxtaposition to the psychiatric staff does not in itself ensure either an interest in rehabilitation for the patients or, what is more important, the development of rehabilitation prescriptions. Because it has been learned that such is the case, Altro has found it necessary to devote time and attention to the development of rehabilitation resources in the hospitals on which it depends for referrals. The most significant of these has been the establishment of a rehabilitation team at Rockland State Hospital under a grant from the National Institute of Mental Health. This team is composed of a psychiatrist, a social caseworker, a vocational counselor and a rehabilitation counselor from the the State Division of Vocational Rehabilitation. As a public-private cooperative enterprise, it has begun to stimulate the consideration of a "rehabilitation prescription" by members of the hospital psychiatric staff. It is used as much for rehabilitational evaluation (leading to such prescriptions) as it is as a resource for referral of patients ready for discharge and for whom rehabilitational planning is immediate.

From the time of initial consideration at intake, a specific formulation of assets and liabilities of the patient and his life situation is necessary. Such a dynamic study of the patient will permit one to predict the type of relationship he will develop to the worker and others, and to help formulate the steps in the rehabilitation leading to better object relations. At this time, too, it should be decided whether tranquilizers or other medication is indicated concomitantly, or whether provisional orders should be left in case of a crisis. Plans need to be made concerning the extent of the involvement of the family—whether foster home placement, additional psychotherapy, or other measures are necessary.

Psychological testing is an integral part of the planning too. Patients are given a battery of tests which usually includes the Wechsler-Bellevue Intelligence Scale, the Rorschach, a self-administered Thematic Apperception Test, the Horn-Tomkins Picture Arrangement Test (PAT), and other tests where indicated. The psychologist's appraisal of ego functioning, special liabilities and assets, vocational aptitude, and psychodynamic features is pooled with those of others of the rehabilitation team. Independent ratings of the patient's assets and liabilities by intake social worker, psychiatrist, psychologist, vocational counselor, and workshop staff are then interrelated for a total rehabilitation program for the patient.

An outstanding feature of rehabilitation of the type of psychotics in the community now referred for rehabilitation is the fact that one deals with patients who are so ill that it often seems they should have stayed in the hospital except that they would probably never get well enough there to be unequivocally ready to be discharged. We have therefore come to consider it essential that some means for easy rehospitalization remain open in case it should become necessary. An arrangement with the institution from which the patient comes, or some other hospital facility, so that the patient may be hospitalized quickly on request (but also discharged as promptly as seems necessary) is essential. This point should not be mistaken for the notion that the patient might best be rehabilitated institutionally in the first place: rehabilitation in the community is often a *sine qua non* for any rehabilitation on the part of the patient. The possibility for quick rehospitalization is simply a necessary administrative arrangement for work with this group of people. It is equally necessary that the arrangement permit continued contact by the rehabilitation personnel with the patient during a possible rehospitalization, to utilize this period for further working through and prompt return to the community when the crisis is over.

THE MIDDLE PHASE OF REHABILITATION

The caseload at Altro consists almost entirely of schizophrenics. Like other people, schizophrenics differ a great deal from one another and need quite different, and, in the last analysis, highly individual approaches to their rehabilitation. If an extremely weak ego is the common denominator of schizophrenics (Bellak, 1958) it must be remembered that different ego functions are involved to a differing degree in each case. The patient suffering from infantilism simpers, feigns helplessness, attracts attention, acts out impulsively, wishes to relate parasitically, symbiotically, or at best anaclitically; the intelligent, tense paranoid wants to maintain emotional isolation, is preoccupied with homosexual problems or more broadly with matters of activity and passivity, and is, so to say, explosively aloof. The schizophrenic with hysterical character formation experiences wide mood swings, is given to dramatic, ominous-appearing symptoms, and responds to "calls to order" as if magically transformed—for the moment. The schizophrenic with affective features will use excessive denial and be gay and apparently carefree, only to become suicidally depressed when the bubble bursts. Finally, there is the chronic "burnt-out" schizophrenic with many somatic delusions, quite bizarre symptom formation, apathy, but some remnant of a functioning ego.

Despite these many individual differences, these patients share some common features which support some generalizations about rehabilitation techniques. They all have some disturbances in object relations, the severity of which is bound to make unusual demands on whoever works with them in rehabilitation.

(1) When a patient is unusually passive to the point of inertia, or bristling with hostility or given to dramatic crises, it may be useful *to have two different people working with the same patient,* each seeing the patient alone. Generally, one can work on the transference problems of the other. Sometimes the caseworker will be the main carrier of psychodynamic intervention and a psychiatrist will play the episodic auxiliary role; other times it will be the reverse or two workers will collaborate. In some instances, the homosexual tension between a female caseworker and a female patient might become too much for both of them, and a male psychiatrist can be used to dilute this tension. Sometimes heterosexual problems need such intervention. Sometimes a patient may be in psychotherapy with a private psychiatrist who carries the main therapeutic responsibility, and the worker, though in close contact with the psychiatrist, may play a secondary role and help work through some transference problems.

(2) In cases where interpersonal tensions become too much to bear for rehabilitation worker as well as patient, two caseworkers should be used simultaneously, occasionally sharing a session with the patient. In the presence of some unusually taxing problems, they can give each other support; at the same time the patient often feels relieved from the implications of being intensely related to one person.

(3) The idea of having more than one person to relate to has relevance for the extramural management of these patients. Any therapist may become ill, take a vacation, or leave the agency. Such interruptions are likely to lead to marked repercussions in this group of patients; to have at least some acquaintance with another person in the agency may bridge the difficult time. It is there-

fore well to make certain that some *extra contact* with another professional rehabilitation worker is made, at least briefly, in the early course of the program.

Administratively speaking, the casework supervisor may be a good auxiliary contact person since she is more or less familiar with the case and may more easily be able to make time available on her schedule when the need arises. It keeps her in close contact with clinical problems and makes her higher skill available when there is most need for it. Workers with different personality features can be used to supplement each other—a permissive, slightly anxious one can be matched with a more authoritative and more controlled one. Above all, it is good to vary the caseload for each worker so that no one has only difficult patients.

(4) The *planning of the management of crisis* has to be a well-conceived part of a rehabilitation program for psychotics. The more clearly the psychodynamics of the patient are understood, and particularly the better the nature of the precipitating factors can be conceptualized, the easier it is to conduct the rehabilitative process and to anticipate or deal with crises.

The great flexibility of the service and the ability to marshal many resources are implicitly important features of a program like Altro's.

It became understood that a young woman had her original breakdown because the affection of a young man was too threatening to her relations to her mother. When, during rehabilitation, a young man wanted to become engaged to her and the mother became hostile and the daughter withdrew from the man and became more attached to the mother, and at ·the same time again produced paranoid delusions and hallucinations, only energetic measures were able to forestall a malignant regression. The patient's therapist had to increase her contacts with the patient. The mother had to be seen in intensive treatment. Since the mother in this case was also at least borderline, both mother and daughter were put on tranquilizers; the psychiatrist saw the patient too, to make some "cathartic" interpretations which had a better chance of being tolerated from him than from the caseworker.

During this time, great care was exercised to keep the patient on a stable work program at the Altro. Once the acute crisis was worked through, plans could be made for further and more farsighted steps. The malignant relationship between mother and daughter needed modification. It would have been ill-advised to try to place such a patient abruptly in a foster home or YWCA or similar setting. After the acute phase was over, the patient was encouraged to live with an aunt she had once spent time with before, as a sort of transitional weaning from the mother, to be followed by moving out to a women's hotel and further intensive psychodynamic work. During all of this there was no slackening in efforts toward preparation for her return to the working world.

As already mentioned, it is essential to have available the resource of rapid hospitalization of a patient, an opportunity to coordinate this with rehabilitation, and plan to release the patient from the hospital as soon as the crisis is resolved.

Another aspect of planning for crisis is the need to make provision for some responsible professional person in the normal life pattern of the patient who can take an active role in an emergency. Often there can be cooperation with the family doctor. If he has been contacted prior to the occurrence of crisis and has some knowledge of the rehabilitation process and of the patient, he can be very useful as the most immediately available professional in the patient's vicinity. He may be called upon to give an injection or take other emergency measures, often in counsel with the psychiatrist.

(5) The casework or psychotherapeutic approach per se is only one of the features of the Altro program. The *workshop* plays a very important part, particularly in the drawn-out middle or main phase of the rehabilitation process. There, the patient is exposed to a real world in which he has to play a real role. The difficulties in that area of functioning are not only brought home to the patient, but are also made known to the therapist by the workshop staff; this provides valuable interaction of realistic and therapeutic data not easily available in another setting.

Per se, the workshop permits the patient to learn object relations, to acquire frustration tolerance and anxiety tolerance in an environment that is realistic but flexible in its demands. Various other ego functions are given a chance to develop or be restored. Perceptual and motor skills help channelize unneutralized energy and indirectly strengthen impulse control, the self concept, and help restore the feeling of playing an acceptable social role.

Aside from the intrinsic role of the workshop as a "habilitation" or rehabilitation center, it plays the extrinsic role of keeping the patient under some responsible supervision, "out of trouble"; in that sense the workshop serves something of the function of a day hospital, releasing the patient for the evening and the night into the care of the family or family substitutes.

(6) Very often a family is not available, or the available one is not of the kind that can be considered to provide an atmosphere in which rehabilitation is even possible, let alone furthered. Work with the family is, of course, part of the program since this is the milieu in which the patient became ill, and it has to be modified if he is to avoid a relapse. But at times, the family milieu appears entirely unmodifiable—the pathological and pathogenic factors irreversible. When this holds true it is necessary to provide a foster home or some other facility. If the family setting is not "good enough" initially but may be modified to become bearable for the patient in time, a night hospital is often a desirable facility, a place where the patient can spend the time in the evening with some sociability and without the pathogenic influences of his family, when his ego strength may be at its daily ebb.

(7) Another major role in the rehabilitation program is undoubtedly played by *tranquilizers*. Curiously enough, for every psychiatrist who thinks little of psychotherapy there is at least one psychiatrist who has an antipathy for drugs. Frequently, a psychoanalytic orientation appears as a rationalization for a dislike of drug therapy; this attitude appears as a somewhat excessive denial of "pill magic." If chemotherapeutic means allow a strengthening of the ego by decreasing aggressive or sexual impulses and their ensuant complications and sequelae, and if such strengthening seems vitally necessary to avoid rehospitalization, drugs are obviously a good thing. There is no question, empirically speaking, that a good percentage of patients could not have been kept in the community without drugs.

Some of our patients had been put on tranquilizers by their hospitals and were maintained on the drug for a while after discharge; others were given drugs for the first time on entering the workshop, or were given them at periods of crisis.

All drugs are administered orally only, in tablet or capsule form, sometimes in combinations with methamphetamine or one of its relatives. By and large, Thorazine has proved most helpful in severe disturbances, and meprobamate in the lighter anxiety states. Deprol appeared experientially useful in depressive states (but see Chapter 13 for a cautionary finding).

PROBLEMS OF TERMINATION

Termination is likely to be beset by difficulties as soon as the specter of possible separation arises at all, before the really final phase of the relationship. Attainment of some marked progress and the possibility of independence and reasonably good functioning is often characterized by a sudden regression similar to the flare-up of transference neurosis in a psychoanalytic practice. The patient is likely to become acutely psychotic again, suicidal, or otherwise markedly disturbed. If this episode cannot be handled by casework, psychotherapy or chemotherapy, we have come to accept a brief hospitalization as a quite constructive step in the termination phase.

It seems as if the patient may not only be regressing under the impact of the threat of separation and of the moral masochism that makes any measure of happiness forbidden; he also seems to have a wish at times to test the therapist and his own attainment—a sort of testing of limits—as well as to be attempting a final assessment of the advantages of illness over the advantages of health. At this point, patients often request hospitalization, or arrange it by themselves. Typically, they soon decide, once in the hospital, that it was all a mistake and they want to be out again. It is useful in any case of hospitalization, whether instituted by the patient, his relatives, or the agency, to use this intramural episode for a final working through of the previously elaborated material and for an anchoring of the therapeutic attainments.

In this sense, brief hospitalization, usually for not more than a week or two, may be considered an integral part of the final working through of problems of rehabilitation with this group of patients.

After that episode, or its equivalent without hospitalization, and after the final regression has been worked through, another problem has to be faced. The main problem of termination is that there should not really be any: we are dealing with a group of patients of such severity of illness that they may usually not be expected to weather life entirely on their own. Practically, of course, it is not feasible to afford them support for life.

Luckily there is a means for a compromise: the patients do not need *actual* continued contact, but rather the feeling that they *can* have contact, that a parental figure is available to them. Analytically, this is, of course, simply the problem of leaving certain types of patients in a mild state of positive transference. Oberndorf (1953) has pointed out how in his experience this continued symbolic relationship may endure for decades, and beneficially so. In our own agency's experience with tuberculosis this fact has also been amply borne out and utilized.

The practical implementation of the change from an intense relationship to a specific therapeutic worker to a mildly positive and mostly symbolic relationship to the *agency* has led to the suggestion of a special arrangement. After termination has been discussed and worked through, another worker is introduced to the patient and a few sessions are held with both workers present with the patient. It is explained that the second worker will be available for follow-up help in the future. The original worker drops out and at least one meeting is held between patient and follow-up worker. By this means some transfer of feelings to the new worker is possible; the patient has somebody to fall back upon, and yet the secondary gains in the continued relationship and the tendency to relapse are markedly reduced. Administratively, it makes it possible to free each individual worker from the heavy drain of chronic continued dependence and to concentrate responsibility for all follow-up problems in one worker.

18

THE PSYCHOLOGY OF PHYSICAL ILLNESS:
A DISCUSSION OF THE PSYCHIATRIC
ASPECTS OF TUBERCULOSIS AND
CARDIAC ILLNESS

In the present chapter we arrive at a more concrete application of the principles discussed in Chapter 17. Although tuberculosis and heart disease are quite different, psychiatric treatment of the two is frequently similar, with an emphasis on educating the patient about how physical and emotional effects may substitute for one another. The treatment recommended here is relatively circumscribed and operates within a framework of psychoanalytic theory. It might be described as a short course in psychosomatic medicine in which the patient is both subject matter and student. He is taught by the use of such examples as blushing and hyperventilation how emotional causes may reflect themselves in physical changes; he is also taught to separate the emotional from the physical effects of illness. The general aim is to make the illness less gratifying by reducing the secondary gain, and less debilitating by keeping the physical symptoms distinct from the emotional response.

TUBERCULOSIS

The interrelationship and coexistence of psychiatric disorders and tuberculosis have long been of interest: a review of the literature revealed a paper on tuberculosis and insanity as early as 1863 (Clouston, 1863).

The present chapter deals in part with tuberculous patients seen for psychiatric consultation and treatment in a casework agency, the Committee for the Care of Jewish Tuberculous, now known as Altro Health and Rehabilitation Services, Inc. Only those tuberculous patients passing through the agency who were considered by the social-work staff to be significantly emotionally disturbed were seen. This sample constituted of about 10 per cent of the total caseload of the agency over about two and a half years.

Forty-six patients were seen by me for at least one diagnostic interview and the majority for a series of psychotherapeutic interviews. Those seen only once were followed in treatment conferences with workers who continued the contact with the patients. In addition to the 46 patients mentioned above, about 250 were known to me through casework and treatment conferences.

Of the 46 patients, 25 were males and 21 females. Their ages ranged from 17½ to 62 years, with 39 of the group falling between the ages of 25 and 45.

NOTE: From *The Psychology of Physical Illness,* edited by L. Bellak, New York, Grune & Stratton, 1952; *Social Casework,* 1950, 31, 183-189; *Social Casework,* 1950, 31, 292-298; and *Social Casework,* 1956, 37, 483-489. Reprinted by permission of the publishers and F. Haselkorn, co-author of the latter two papers, whose collaboration is gratefully acknowledged.

They fell into 17 different diagnostic categories, among which anxiety neurosis and hysteria were most frequent; four psychotics were also included.

The factors we observed in our patients nearly universally were: (1) traumatic effects of diagnosis; (2) increased secondary narcissism and changes in body image; (3) increased oral needs, with passivity; (4) problems of the return home (the same factors, in a general sense, as were mentioned in the preceding chapter).

TRAUMATIC EFFECTS OF DIAGNOSIS

The first response to being informed of the diagnosis was frequently an attempt at *denial,* the patient maintaining that it could not be so. Only in a very few patients was this denial pathologically prolonged. In the majority it was followed by a more or less pronounced *depression.* A *catastrophic reaction* was frequently based on some very primitive concept of tuberculosis, or occurred because it was seen in terms of the experience of another family member or an acquaintance. The most profoundly disturbing effects seemed to exist in those cases with a familial history, where the diagnosis led to identification with the previously affected family member. This was, of course, most traumatic in the case of men identifying with a previously ill mother, liberating more or less repressed anxieties. Acceptance of the illness often also brought about a profound *disturbance of the body image.* In the case of men with a great libidinal investment in their masculine prowess, this was particularly upsetting. (This observation, of course, also holds true for several other chronic diseases.)

A more specific response to the diagnosis of tuberculosis in some patients was observed as a *tendency to nausea and vomiting.* It was particularly marked in one young man who started this symptom the day of the diagnosis and maintained it for years. In another young man, who in early childhood had associated the idea of being ill with vomiting, this idea became reactivated on his being informed he had tuberculosis. In a third young man, the nausea was associated with anorexia, and he had to be hospitalized because of the danger of starvation. A parallel case of fear of tuberculosis manifesting itself as a fear of pregnancy was seen, in private practice, in a female patient. Her father had died of tuberculosis in her childhood, and an older sister died of the same illness during the patient's adolescence. She identified tuberculosis germs and sperms in an infantile fantasy of oral impregnation; all her symptoms were related to this fantasy—the fear of having holes made in her and bleeding to death. In the men, too, neurotic disturbances related to oral-passive wishes and defenses against them. (Apparently a certain amount of gastric disturbance may occur in pulmonary tuberculosis on a primarily somatic basis. Cohen [in Brown, 1933] points out that, as the tuberculosis progresses, there is a corresponding significant decrease of free acid in the gastric juices. In this series, 20.8 per cent of over 1,000 patients entering the sanatorium complained of gastrointestinal symptoms, which he considered a complication rather than a symptom of tuberculosis.)

There was absolutely no suggestion that a particular personality type appeared more frequently among the tuberculous patients than in the general population. Their responses to their illness could be clearly seen in relation to their pre-existing personalities, varying in basic dynamics as much as in any other group I have seen. Any similarity appeared to be a secondary change in response to this threatening disease and the chronic invalidism necessarily imposed for some years.

INCREASED SECONDARY NARCISSISM AND CHANGES IN BODY IMAGE

A painful organ or one known to be ill attracts attention. If the illness is chronic and of major importance, the ill portion is treated in a nearly anthropomorphized fashion, as a separate being. Special provisions are made for it and care provided, and a maternal attitude is established. This solicitous over-concern may, in varying degrees, be extended to the whole person and demanded from the outside world as well as tendered by the person toward himself. In the healthy person, a large emotional investment is made in a (developmentally changing) variety of figures; in the neurotic, an excessive investment in himself has been maintained. A physically ill person makes an increased investment in himself as a defensive measure against further harm. In the neurotic this reinvestment will be greater and there will be more reluctance to give it up when the crisis has passed than in relatively healthier people. This reinvestment we speak of as an increase of secondary narcissism.

The clinical manifestations of this increased narcissism and the disturbance of the body image are obvious and familiar: hypochondriacal concern, depression, and many bodily complaints that cannot be correlated with physical findings, persistent self-observation, and anxiety. The more manifestly observed increased oral needs and passivity also result.

INCREASED ORAL NEEDS AND PASSIVITY

The tubercular patient, then, becomes more narcissistic under the threat to his life. Sanatorium routine makes this almost inevitable. Rest is extremely important and all his needs are taken care of. A premium is put on his paying attention to his health, on his being passive, accepting all but spoon-feeding; he is generally forced to accept, for the time being, the image of almost being a baby. The current trend, fortunately, is to decrease the necessary passivity by permitting the patient as much self-direction as possible.

It is thus not very surprising that a good percentage of patients have a hard time giving up this attitude immediately upon being discharged from the sanatorium. They have seen other patients return with relapses, and they doubt, with justification, the doctor's criteria of health. The relatively psychologically healthy patients, or those who always had strong defenses against passivity and oral wishes (therefore probably "bad" sanatorium patients) will pass through this stage more or less easily. The more neurotic patients, or those who to begin with had a more infantile attitude or strong oral wishes, will hold onto the regressed position.

In clinical practice these tendencies manifest themselves in difficulty of rehabilitation. In the sheltered workshop these patients progress poorly and when it comes to looking for outside employment they somehow cannot find jobs. Careful examination will reveal either that they do not look very hard or that they unconsciously discourage prospective employers by some subtle means. This sort of patient expects things to fall into his lap. He expects the agency to continue to take care of all his needs, or he may transfer this attitude to public welfare institutions. The ambivalence ordinarily expressed toward the parents may be expressed toward the agency and the worker who represents it, and a more or less painful weaning process sets in.

At this point Freud's concept of the secondary gain of illness becomes useful: since he is an invalid, the patient is unconsciously set to enjoy all the advantages of this state while being taken care of.

PROBLEMS OF THE RETURN TO FAMILY

The patient who has been away from home for a period of from one to three years may have varying problems when he returns. As a father, he may have to adjust to the fact that he is not the head of the family any more, at least for the time being, if he is unable to provide for his family as before. Problems of status become a frequent cause for reactive depressions due to the repressed aggression they engender. That sexual problems exist is obvious. One woman's main problems and reactive depression centered around the fact that her 5-year-old daughter had become estranged from her over the past three years and had become attached to the foster parents.

In our experience, by far the most clear-cut problems occur in the return home of the adolescent or postadolescent patient. The boy or girl may have left home at, say, 17, and finally returned at 20. Many youngsters came from traditionally overprotected or patriarchally structured families. In the sanatorium they lived under altogether different conditions, in a sexually mixed group of all ages, and were exposed to many ideas. These circumstances, superimposed on the already autonomously revolutionary changes of adolescence, result in tremendous difficulties on returning home. While the average family has the opportunity to adjust to adolescent changes in small doses and with the normal amount of friction, our patients are confronted with sudden changes and violent clashes. These may lead to forceful regression with neurotic symptoms, or, if unattended, to a premature separation, with hardships and guilt feelings on both sides. Awareness of the need for special attention to the adolescent tubercular and their families therefore seems one of the most clear-cut results of our experience.

In summarizing, it can be said that about 10 per cent of the patients passing through this agency for the tuberculous appeared psychiatrically disturbed more than the "average" person. Psychiatric study of this sample revealed no specific character type or neurosis. A certain common denominator appeared in the psychological responses to the problem of tuberculosis; these patterns of reaction conform to expectations on the basis of psychoanalytic hypotheses concerning the effect of severe chronic bodily disease. Further factors are added only insofar as oral fantasies are more specifically stimulated by tubercular illness (oral contagion) and the particularly severe incapacitation.

The general approach to the patients' problems was that of brief psychoanalytically oriented psychotherapy within a casework setting. This connotes not so much an actual procedure as a frame of reference. In taking the patient's history an attempt is made to understand how the person has learned to perceive his environment through early and later experience, how he views the present situation in terms of his past experience; his chief complaints and symptoms must be understood as a compromise between his wishes and the way he perceives the environment, and attempts to help him are made by integrating physical and environmental changes.

If we are able to understand the dynamics of the patient in his present situation we must decide how to go about helping him. We are entirely in agreement with the excellent presentation of Grete Bibring (1949):

We do not use the term "manipulation," as it sometimes is used in casework, to describe the undesirable attempt of the worker to force his concepts and plans on the client. We use the term in a more positive sense. After listening to and observing the client we may use our understanding of his personality structure, his patterns, his needs and conflicts, and his defenses in order to "manipulate" him in various ways. We may make suggestions as to what steps may or may not help this individual to cope better with his problems; we may plan with him as to his emotional, professional, and recreational activities; we may give appropriate advice to members of his environment; we may modify our attitude and approach to his problems; or we may purposely activate relevant emotional attitudes in the client for the sake of adjustive change. It is in this specific sense that we use the term "manipulation."

For that matter, psychotherapy in general need not always use insight therapy, but may often find manipulation, abreaction, or clarification more profitable. This viewpoint needs emphasis, since, unjustifiably, a feeling seems to have developed in many conscientious caseworkers that nothing short of a complete psychoanalysis is of any value and that any symptom-directed approach is little more than quackery. We believe, on the contrary, that the full understanding that psychoanalysis gives us should be used to assess the available assets and liabilities in the patient and in the situation, and change those aspects in ways most profitable to the patient. We speak of brief psychotherapy in this instance, since circumstances did not permit a great time investment in an individual patient; thus, this time limitation became part of the therapeutic program, one of the factors considered in planning the optimal approach. It is true that this approach may not be suitable for every patient, and recourse must occasionally be made to lengthier psychotherapy.

The procedure used in the agency was as follows: the social worker worked with the patient, requesting a case discussion with the psychiatrist at the worker's discretion. In such an interview an attempt was made to arrive at a diagnosis, to discuss the psychodynamics, to plan further treatment steps, and to arrange a follow-up interview. If necessary, the psychiatrist saw the patient himself for diagnosis—if a differential diagnosis was difficult to arrive at or if the question of psychosis or suicidal risk was involved. If the case was not suitable for treatment by the social worker, the psychiatrist took the patient on or referred the case to an outside source.

The general frame of reference was that psychiatry is to a caseworker a basic science, as anatomy and physiology are to a doctor. Psychiatric principles enable the worker to understand the patient's psychodynamic structure and his clinical casework training equips him to help the patient. His casework training can be compared with the clinical training of the general practitioner, whose knowledge of anatomy and physiology does not give him the special knowledge and skill of the surgeon; similarly, the social worker does not have the equipment to undertake major psychiatric operations. He should have an understanding of them and, possibly, proceed with them under supervision after extensive experience.

This view, I believe, acknowledges the special skill and independent function of the social worker; like the general practitioner, the worker can handle many problems more competently than the specialist, since he is specially trained in casework techniques and generally has a broad view of the problems involved, including the social aspects, knowledge of the family and the social setting, and command of the community resources. Thus, we must see the worker both in juxtaposition and subordination to the psychiatrist for maximal usefulness.

Dealing with the Reality Problem. The tubercular psychiatric patient differs from the more usual psychotherapeutic patient in that he actually has a difficult reality situation to deal with: his illness or the danger of relapse, lack of earning power, as well as the other features mentioned above. The seriousness of these reality problems should never be forgotten or underestimated. A busy professional person working all day with such serious problems cannot afford to identify too much. At the same time there is a definite danger of not appreciating the actual difficulty of the situation and hiding behind a screen of professional jargon. To overlook the casework aspects of the reality situation is just as bad as to overemphasize them.

The Altro Health and Rehabilitation Services' Workshop provides an opportunity for graded rehabilitation by means of the needle trades, as described in Chapter 17. Here the patient may harden himself physically, improve his financial status, and, with the help of the caseworker, gradually take over ordinary responsibilities.

The patient with reality difficulties will, of course, blame all his neurotic problems on the reality situation. The way to deal with this problem is *to acknowledge fully his actual troubles, and then carefully to isolate them from the neurotic superstructure,* and to point out the irrational aspects of his reactions. An example I frequently use is the following: If there were ten people in a subway car and you performed the experiment of stepping on the left foot of each one, you would get widely differing reactions; some would give you an angry look, some would smile or ignore it, others would howl, still others would kick back, and some would actually feel guilty themselves. All these people were exposed to the same situation of, say, 180 pounds descending on their left foot. Why does each react to the particular situation the way he does?

We must also attempt to relate the existing reaction to characteristics that existed in the patient *before* his tubercular illness, and point out to him his propensity for this particular type of reaction—anxiety, depression, and so on. The attitude of the patient toward his problems has to be made *ego alien,* that is, unacceptable, instead of permitting it to remain ego syntonic. For that purpose it must be isolated, extrapolated, and held up as something pernicious in itself and independent of the reality situation, however difficult.

Dealing with the Transference Problem. What has been said about increased narcissism, oral needs, and passivity makes it evident that the emotional relationship of the patient to the worker is a particularly intense and conflictual one. Ordinarily I like to reserve the term "transference" for the relationship between patient and psychoanalyst; it is characterized by the fact that the analyst does not enter responsively into the situation, and that the patient must gradually relinquish his defense mechanisms in dealing with the analyst, permitting regression and freeing anxiety. This is a condition not ordinarily fulfilled in casework, but it is closely approximated in dealing with the tubercular patient; more than any other patient he has been reduced to a defenseless, nearly infantile pattern in the sanatorium, and he displays attitudes toward people otherwise found primarily in the psychoanalytic situation.

Because of the great psychosomatic lability of the tubercular, I believe that the transference situation, if we may call it that, needs to be considered with the greatest care. It is best to maintain a primarily positive relationship. I am not interested in creating a maximum of independence in the patient nor in severing the transference situation completely, much less abruptly. I leave the patient with the statement that I believe he is well but that I should always be glad to hear from him, whether he has problems or not. The tubercular patient is frequently, and justifiably, afraid of relapse and is being threatened by a catastrophic crippling of the ego. He is therefore entitled to a more supporting attitude than many ambitious workers are willing to give. In this connection it is interesting to point out that the incidence of relapse was very small under a regime that was only benignly supportive without any psychotherapy or even any specifically psychiatrically oriented approach. It would be unfortunate indeed if a too-active psychotherapeutic approach would increase the rate of relapse; the ideal goal is to improve the individual patient's adjustment and experiences by psychotherapy without overextending his assets.

Dealing with Orality and Passivity. It requires a great deal of tact to discuss with patients their oral and passive wishes. It is necessary first for the patient to accept such tendencies before it is possible to show their existence in him and to deal with them. An example I frequently use is the following: I discuss the feeling nearly everyone has on certain mornings, particularly if it is rainy or cold, when one has to get up to go to work: one feels one ought to go to work, even wants to go, and yet one wishes one could stay in bed. This very human feeling demonstrates the need for passivity in everyone, the wish to be taken care of instead of having to fend for oneself. A similar feeling may persist when one has become accustomed to the protected situation of the tubercular. We show the patient that it is perfectly reasonable to feel that way but that this attitude is a stumbling block. We may have to illustrate, by careful, detailed analysis of concrete situations, how the patient actually let slip some chance for improvement of his job situation. Limitations of agency funds may constitute the external compelling factor in decreasing the secondary gain of illness, if properly manipulated.

Anorexia and Other Psychosomatic Problems. In dealing with psychosomatic disorders, one of the main problems is to get the patient to accept the fact that emotional disturbances can cause bodily changes. The example of blushing is useful in this connection—embarrassment leading to a dilation of the blood vessels, the skin reddened by the blood shining through. A contraction of the blood vessels may lead to nutritional deficiencies and the ever-present germs may give rise to all sorts of eczemas and boils. One can explain that some people blush with the skin of their gut and get diarrhea or stomach ulcers. Many symptoms can be demonstrated to the patient as the result of fast breathing (hyperventilation) when anxious—dizziness, weakness, and so on.

Anorexia and nausea, as has been mentioned, are usually related to unconscious pregnancy fantasies or oral wishes. One can deal with them simply by explaining to the patient that he acts as if he were afraid of swallowing some-thing bad—perhaps germs—and in the case of anorexia tries to avoid it, or he regurgitates them in the case of nausea. Small doses of insulin to produce appe-tite are used by some physicians with great success, starting with 10 units and increasing by 5 units up to 25 units, two and one-half hours before meals, if the consulting lung specialist does not consider that the increased metabolism may be harmful and if the patient can be watched to avoid coma. In one of our severe cases, as previously mentioned, hospitalization was necessary to prevent physical collapse.

Depression. The tubercular patient is often depressed. He is in a difficult reality situation, facing oral deprivation on his return from the sanatorium and harboring much latent aggression against the world in general and against family members to whom he is supposed to be grateful, although he often has much reason to feel resentment against them. Demonstrating the aggression and re-leasing it, by pointing out how emotionally "reasonable" this reaction is, usually proves very successful. In a few more difficult cases a mixture of nembutal and desoxyn or methedrine has proved useful and harmless when used in consulta-tion with the tuberculosis specialist.

The Return of the Adolescent. The adolescent who returns to his family after years of absence has changed a great deal in his behavior and in his reac-tions to his family's behavior. As with all adolescents, we must gain his con-fidence, be on his side, and yet represent a parental figure who is not too per-missive, lest we increase his guilt feelings. If the disturbance is not too severe, a discussion of the typical problems of the adolescent—his growing up and the family's reluctance to acknowledge it, his ambivalence toward his parents, prob-lems of sex and of occupation inherent in this period—may help a good deal. It is almost always advisable to see the family or to have someone else see them to try to work out their difficulties. Only if the family is markedly pathological and no change can be effected is it advisable to help the youngster toward inde-pendent living quarters and a break with the family.

The Patient Who Acts Out. A fair number of tubercular patients react to their anxiety and passive wishes with a denial of illness, ignoring all precautions against overwork, colds, and so on. This holds true particularly for adolescents but also for adults with masochistic character disorders, or for male patients who have to deny their castration fears by exhibiting their toughness. If the acting out is mild it may be simpler and more advantageous not to disturb this pattern of adjustment. If there is actual physical danger, however, it may be necessary to analyze this defense precipitating anxiety if possible, which, together with an overcautious attitude, can be dealt with more easily. As in all intra-aggressive, self-harming behavior—and it may have to be designated as such—it is im-portant to identify the object of the original aggressive impulse; the patient may want to punish his mother or someone else by making himself ill again.

HEART DISEASE

Encouraged by the success of its multiple-service approach to tuberculars, the Committee for the Care of the Jewish Tuberculous then attempted to adapt its agency experience to the rehabilitation of cardiacs. There was little or no existing professional experience or tested knowledge to guide us. We had to find direction, at times gropingly, in a relatively unexplored field of endeavor.

Our purpose, broadly stated, was the rehabilitation of the cardiac, physically, emotionally, and socially. Objectives were defined in terms of maintaining health where this was possible and, in all cases, helping toward optimum adjustment in terms of use of work capacity and social functioning. The enabling services were Altro's sheltered workshop, described in detail in Chapter 17, which provided medical supervision of activity, casework, and psychotherapy.

To a great extent, cardiacs present the same social and emotional problems that arise out of tuberculosis. The crushing incapacitating effects of the diagnosis, the heightened insecurity, the exaggerated feelings of uselessness, the shattered interpersonal relationships due to ill health, are common to both cardiacs and the tubercular. These patients experience environmental frustrations and internal pressures which threaten self-esteem and engender attitudes more crippling than the disease itself. If generalizations can be made, cardiac sufferers are prone to even greater emotional reverberations because of the progressive nature of the disease.

Heart disease has certain unique sequelae that have special significance in the rehabilitation process. It is experienced as a severe threat to life, associated as it is with sudden death. Misconception about the diagnosis itself—for example, confusion of rheumatic heart disease with coronary disease—can result in inappropriate fear. More frequently, however, intrapsychic factors that have their dynamic roots in repressed fears of powerlessness, abandonment, and castration, now reawakened, account for the incapacitating fear of death.

The *fear of impairment by the process of rehabilitation itself* constitutes a particular obstacle in the treatment of the cardiac patient which is not usually encountered in other groups of disabled persons. The amputee, for example, does not often think of work as impairing his health. The cardiac patient frequently focuses on work as a hazard. His overwhelming fear that any exertion may shorten his life poses a special problem in his rehabilitation. On the other hand, the cardiac patient with a defensive need to deny his illness may be self-destructive; for example, the coronary patient who needs to push a piano around.

By the very nature of the organ it involves, cardiac illness poses another unique problem. The heart is the symbol of basic human emotions—love, affection, and hatred—and therefore holds a position of primacy among all body organs. The cardiovascular system is a special participant in affect syndromes. Arrhythmia, tachycardia, dyspnea are somatic equivalents of anxiety and need not be referable to heart disease. Psychosomatic studies have shown that the cardiovascular system can respond to stress situations with increased heart rate, rise in systolic blood pressure, and increase in cardiac output. Physiological changes and disturbances in autonomic rhythm can in turn create anxiety and apprehension, and set in motion a psychic-somatic circuit that challenges the most perceptive medical and psychiatric diagnostic skills. With anxiety manifestations that simulate cardiac symptoms, and with chronic tension states that affect internal physiological responses, the diagnostic problem created understandably furnishes added nourishment for the hypochrondriacal concerns of the cardiac patient.

Another factor that contributes to the disproportionate disability of some cardiac patients is what has come to be known as the *iatrogenic factor*. Doctors are likely to contribute more to the invalidism of the cardiac patient than to that of any other type of patient. This is probably related to the fact that, as a group, doctors are more likely than the general population to develop heart disease and tend, on the whole, to be extremely apprehensive about having a coronary episode. They are apt to project onto their patients their own anxieties according to their own psychological needs and to advise their patients to be unnecessarily restrained.

Mention might be made of the question of personality specificity for coronary artery disease, since certain dynamic constellations seem to recur. From our study material, however, there was no evidence that specific emotional constellations are significantly correlated with the development of coronary disease. Patients with a premorbid history of overcompensatory, competitive, aggressive behavior (used as a denial against excessive underlying passivity) appear most emotionally threatened by coronary disease, and therefore constitute a large number of those observed in rehabilitation programs. For these patients, outlets for discharge of anxiety in excessive activity are now denied. The resulting psychic conflict contributes further to the somatopsychological problem and poses a provocative problem for rehabilitation.

A self-employed electrical contractor operated a successful business until his cardiac insult at the age of 53. His pattern had been one of carrying an unnecessarily excessive burden and being unable to delegate responsibility to his employees. He appeared to get considerable gratification from his success in his work. Following the coronary episode, he immediately sold his business, and was still idle two and a half years later. It became obvious that, prior to his illness, he had used excessive activity successfully in combating tension and latent passivity. When the coronary accident made it impossible to overwork, he could not resolve his conflict between activity and passivity. His former sense of adequacy was replaced by anxiety, tension, apprehensiveness, and depression. He claimed to be confused by opposing admonitions—"Take it easy, learn to slow down"; "Why did you give up your business?"; "Don't let your fears get the best of you, it's all in your mind." He was unable to resume work, although the nature of his business would have lent itself to his assuming reduced responsibility. He considered his relatives overrestrictive and projected onto them his own anxiety which stemmed from the underlying conflict over his unconscious wishes to be passive.

A patient seen at intake is usually depressed, preoccupied with self, and in overt or disguised ways manifests a pattern of anxiety which invades all areas of his life. The external maladjustment is most often the problem presented, but the emotional component is only thinly masked. That the problems are interrelated is often recognizable even to the patient. He frequently has demonstrable evidence in that his attacks of pain seem more related to emotional strains and stress than to exertion. That fear is the major disability was seen in the number of patients who had had from one to ten years of unemployment, due not to physical handicap but to incapacitating fear and disabling panic and anxiety. Too often, by the time the patient had reached the agency, his attitudes had become fairly crystallized and he was less amenable to change. The restoration of capacities challenged all the skills at our command.

The extent of psychological invalidism among our patients was a compelling finding. It resulted in a change of emphasis in the program and a partial redefinition of objectives. Originally, the program had been geared to physical restoration and to determination of work tolerance. Our workshop physicians found that judgment of work tolerance pragmatically arrived at is more accurate than judgment arrived at by the physician clinically. It was anticipated that we would be serving patients who, for cardiological reasons, had limited work capacity but presented a potential for increasing activity under a carefully supervised regimen. Instead, the bulk of applicants were found physically able to work an eight-hour day, within certain limitations. A large proportion of these were unable psychologically to accept this fact, or else had complaints that were subjectively felt to be of cardiac origin, but upon medical examination were not found to be referable to organic disease. It was thus necessary to apply eligibility criteria with elasticity and to accept for service not only organic cardiacs but, as it turned out, those in whom the diseased heart was not the disabling factor.

Psychopathology was seen both as contributory to and derivative of the cardiac condition. Frequently the impact of the illness brought to the surface emotional disturbances that had been latent. Here illness did not create but rather exacerbated deep-seated problems formerly handled by successful adaptive defenses. Disease invariably tends to mobilize and bring to the fore all the psychic deviations, the repressed emotional conflicts in the development of the personality. For treatment purposes, psychodynamic understanding of the illness is important. Again, dynamic social histories are of inestimable help in determining whether the emotional imbalance is due primarily to the factor of illness or merely coexistent with and related to more deep-seated roots.

The psychological configuration most often seen is not the well-defined organized neurosis, but rather diffuse complaints of headache, fatigue, nervousness, irritability, insomnia, depression, and interpersonal difficulties. Anxiety formerly repressed or successfully channelized is unleashed, with the failure of the integrative function of the personality. To complicate the problem, anxiety is known to be associated with body and visceral changes such as tachycardia, dyspnea, arrhythmia, and so on, thus fusing psychic and somatic factors further. Fatigue and depression are both psychic and physiological processes. When the physician found no organic basis, when symptoms did not yield to medical treatment but lessened when attention was directed to underlying disturbances, when patients emphasized complaints not related to the organic picture, we could feel reasonably confident that we were dealing with emotional conflicts that had found expression in physical ways or subjective feelings of uneasiness. We tried constantly to guard ourselves, however, against schematized classifications of psychogenic or organic, but attempted always to focus on interaction and interrelationship.

Our multidisciplinary approach was based on the recognition of the interdependence of the emotional and physical processes. Based on this concept of organismic unity, the allied disciplines of medicine, social casework, and psychiatry were used, with the sheltered workshop as the operational setting for help.

Since a teamwork approach is now common to many welfare programs, I wish to emphasize only how it operated in this particular program of rehabilitation. The caseworker, in addition to his unique and generic function, played an integrative role, making the various services available in accordance with the foci of individual needs, and was responsible for their harmonious coordination. All patients attended the Altro Workshop, a special garment-manufacturing factory.

Self-help, inherent in the workshop philosophy, is an essential ingredient in recovery. The patient is an active participant in the rehabilitation process and not a passive recipient of help. The sense of usefulness, of achievement, of again belonging, is an important therapeutic by-product of the experience. Many of the cardiacs have come from shut-in, isolated existences. With the admission to Altro, the process of resocialization is begun.

The security and support of the group in itself serves in many cases to dissolve fears and restore feelings of adequacy and self-esteem. The fact of a common denominator within the group has meaning to the patient. Self-confidence is gradually regained as the patient tests his capacity in an actual concrete work situation. Too frequently, treatment is impeded by the absence of a favorable life situation in which to test the gains made. Altro provides a good reality framework, and an opportunity for diagnostic observation by the worker of the patient's adaptive patterns.

Work and activity are universal outlets for aggression. Many patients, as evidenced by their social histories, had apparently been able successfully to channelize aggressive drives in work. Idleness and inactivity following illness had created a psychological bottleneck for these drives. Once again, the patient is given the opportunity to work out his feelings in a releasing way.

One of the lesser, but by no means insignificant, values in the workshop, as a tool of help, is the avoidance of treatment consciousness. By and large, the applicant coming for admission to the workshop subjectively experiences less threat to his ego, less feeling of stigma. Patients who might otherwise never become known to casework agencies are able to accept Altro and, from that as a starting point, move on to accept help in other areas.

There is discussion of the interesting group psychodynamics that inhere in such a situation as obtains at the workshop in Chapter 17. I should like here to comment briefly only on one particular psychological aspect of the situation. I refer to the way in which the agency or the workshop becomes psychologically invested with all that the patient's problem or illness means to him. Patients naturally displace onto Altro their resentments, fears, and frustrations. All the pent-up aggressive impulses, all the infantile attitudes toward authority, are conveniently directed to the workshop. Fortunately, the shop personnel has gained sufficient knowledge of the more common manifestations of projection and displacement so as not to be threatened or to react vengefully. Insofar as possible, the workshop has been adapted to the patients' needs; where this is not feasible, it is perhaps not wholly unfortunate, since adaptation to reality is a primary goal to which the workshop is geared.

When the patient's behavior reflects any degree of personality disorder, it then becomes the appropriate area of the caseworker, the psychiatrist, or both. To date, our experience has revealed that there is a small proportion of patients who recover spontaneously as somatic illness improves or at least as the *status quo* is maintained. Frequently, the workshop has been able to carry a relatively well-adjusted patient over a period of severe stress caused by the trauma of illness, without appreciable use of auxiliary services. For the remainder, where the adjustment is blocked by either external or internal pressures, the caseworker is available on an intensive basis.

Since all patients come originally with the request for admission to the workshop, casework help is obviously not the service directly sought. Very soon, however, the patient begins to use the worker in meeting the problems of adjustment to the workshop. In some instances, the relationship is confined here. More frequently, the problems that emerge in relation to this adjustment serve as a springboard to help with the patient's social and psychological needs and their complex interplay.

The agency is fortunate in the availability of multiple services within its own structure to aid in the administration of its central function. Financial assistance is one of the concrete services available when more than straight maintenance is required. When the patient's income falls below agency budget standards, supplementation can be considered. Money is administered with understanding of the various meanings it can have for the patient, and of its dynamic quality in the helping process. Financial assistance is used to meet such needs as convalescence, vacations, housekeeping service, and so on, depending on the need and treatment plan. The worker is careful not to foster the desire for dependency and the wish to be cared for, both of which come with chronic illness, to the detriment of opposing impulses to prove oneself and to struggle toward independence. As with all environmental help, relief-giving is guided by sound sociopsychological understanding. We hope we have become sufficiently professionally mature that we do not minimize the inestimable value of practical help.

The worker needs to be alert, however, to recognize when the external maladjustment stems from internal conflict. When social adjustment is blocked by emotional difficulties that are not amenable to superficial help, use of relationship, interpretation, and insight treatment is considered. Elaboration here does not seem indicated in view of the abundance of the literature on treatment techniques. The helping process and skills involved are conventional casework methods. Treatment principles and tools differ only in the degree to which they can be adapted to this particular group, where the focus is on physical illness. The cardiac diagnosis, by its very nature, imposes certain limitations on treatment. Overloading the psychic capacities may adversely affect the somatic process. Cardiovascular dysfunction and physiological disturbance can result from psychic stimuli. Intensive therapy poses definite physical hazards for the cardiac patient. He characteristically discharges mental conflicts through physical pathways and thus any approach geared to uncovering deeper psychic layers may well produce intensification of somatic symptoms. Interpretations limited to the day-to-day manifestations of feeling and attitude seem, in most cases, all that can be comfortably tolerated. Goals must necessarily be modestly formulated with a recognition that there may be no basic resolution of problems. It might be said that treatment is symptomatically rather than generically directed.

Supportive relationships, with relatively little emphasis on the phenomenon of transference, are effectively utilized with cardiac patients. Given a supportive emotional environment, where ventilation of complaints, doubts, and fears is permitted, the patient can be helped to feel more comfortable. An experience in which his dependency (unless pathologically overwhelming) is accepted and recognized as the regressive pattern of illness where the latent infantile wishes are mobilized can be used to strengthen capacities rather than aggravate weaknesses.

There is usually no ambitious goal for giving the client insight, but he may be enabled to see in his emotional state some connection between his main conflicts and his symptoms, so that the incapacity in his personality is not disproportionate to the degree of physical incapacity. Somatic complaints of functional origin are not precipitously attacked or taken from the patient but are seen as purposefully generated by the psychic economy. Where behavior dynamics are understood in relation to symptoms, attempts can be made to bring personality tendencies into conscious relationship with symptoms. This is often demonstrable to the patient himself when physical distress is felt following an outburst of rage or aggression at some specific life situation. In short, the caseworker's goal is to help the patient utilize his psychic energy more effectively in facing his environment, though the worker may be acutely aware that fundamental difficulties are not eliminated.

The patient's intrafamilial relationships are so linked with his illness as to make family-oriented help frequently imperative. The focus on illness and its concomitant problems, however, is sharply retained.

Because this is a nonpsychiatric setting, the staff psychiatrist, who gives one afternoon a week, is used primarily in a consultative capacity. The worker prepares a summary for him around which a conference is held fairly early in the patient's contact with the agency. A tentative diagnostic formulation is made and treatment plans evolved. Emphasis is placed on dynamic understanding of current behavior, illuminating the background of the difficulty. When the patient's unique personality pattern does not come through clearly in the worker's report, or when difficult questions of differential diagnoses are involved, the psychiatrist may see the patient for diagnostic evaluation. The worker then proceeds with periodic psychiatric conferences scheduled for re-evaluation. Psychotherapy is handled by the psychiatrist when severe depression is prominent, or during very critical periods in the patient's situation. In some instances, when it has been jointly felt that the therapeutic process could be hastened, the psychiatrist has seen the patient four to eight times and has then sent the patient back to the caseworker. On the whole, there is extensive use of the conference method and a joint approach between the worker and psychiatrist.

Simultaneously, the worker has regular conferences with the cardiologist and is thus prepared to bring to the psychiatric conference some understanding of the somatic process, so that the patient is seen from both physical and psychical points of view.

The success of rehabilitation is, of course, related to many variables. The patient's potential for rehabilitation is determined by a total assessment of the medical, social, and psychological factors present. A research-oriented investigator would be able to elaborate an accurate rating scale and to arrive at a *rehabilitation index*. On a descriptive level, the following have proved helpful as criteria for determining the possibilities for rehabilitation: The *extent of physical disability* is obviously a strong determinant, although there are occasional exceptions. The *socioeconomic situation* is another important reality factor. To a great extent, however, the success of rehabilitative efforts will depend on whether or not destructive *emotional attitudes* can be reversed. The nature of the patient's premorbid personality adaptations is therefore a valid index for predicting success or failure in rehabilitating him. The premorbid personality can be evaluated in the following significant areas: general level of emotional maturity, degree of ego strength, extent of pre-existing hypochondriasis and anxiety, previous work history, and the nature of the defenses.

The level of maturity as manifested in the quality of the patient's interpersonal relationships is another indicator of success or failure. A careful anamnesis may disclose infantile attitudes which are not regressive consequences of illness, but rather are due to faulty development.

The patient's ego and its integrative capacities must also be assessed. Ego strength is reflected in: the nature of the self-image, the quality of reality testing and adaptation, the capacity to cope with life stresses, the patterns of control and frustration tolerance, and the nature of interpersonal relations. Some patients, despite weakened egos, can respond favorably to rehabilitation efforts because they have masochistic personality structures with a high degree of frustration tolerance. On the whole, however, when ego organization is weak, there is likely to be more regression and dependency, and less successful rehabilitation results can be expected.

The degree to which undue anxiety can be modified is related to the extent of hypochondriasis prior to the illness. When hypochondriasis has been present before the illness, it readily becomes channelized into the disability and often does not yield to the briefer forms of psychotherapy. Thus, in general, the existence of hypochondriasis adversely affects the prognosis for rehabilitation.

The past work history of the patient is of central concern since the usual goal is to have the patient return to work. The dynamic psychology of work has received considerable theoretical consideration. The ability to work is often unimpaired in persons who are otherwise extremely ill emotionally. Therefore, the work history is a better criterion for predicting the patient's future work adaptation than is an over-all psychodynamic assessment of him. With some persons, the work habit is a firmly established pattern and a relatively conflict-free area of the ego. It is important, therefore, to know the degree of work stability, the extent to which work has been a predominantly satisfying experience, and the emotional factors that have operated both in the patient's concept of work and in his self-concept as a worker.

We have suggested that the nature of the ego defenses is of great interest in any therapeutic or rehabilitation approach. A review of some characteristic defenses as they pertain to rehabilitation may be pertinent.

Defenses have been psychodynamically characterized as pathogenic and nonpathogenic. From the viewpoint of rehabilitation, it is useful to divide the defenses into those that are likely to facilitate rehabilitation and those that tend to impede it. For lack of more precise terminology, one may refer to those defenses that lead to rehabilitation, particularly in terms of work and reality adaptation, as "centripetal defenses"; "centrifugal defenses" are those that direct the patient's energies away from rehabilitation. In ordinary circumstances, denial and isolation are considered to be pathogenic defenses. For the rehabilitation process, however, these particular defenses may be positive factors. Provided the denial mechanism is not excessive (excessive denial leaves the way open to serious depression), it can permit a patient to cope with his disease and its concomitants in a seemingly realistic way which otherwise would not be possible for him. Isolation, by itself an unhealthy mechanism, similarly permits a person to take some measure of distance from his problems and allows him to function. The defense of overcompensation has been frequently described as a socially constructive one; for example, Demosthenes, a stutterer, achieved heights as an orator and Theodore Roosevelt, physically handicapped, became a Rough Rider.

On the other hand, there is a cluster of ego defenses that seem to militate against the patient's rehabilitation. Centrifugal defenses such as projection, rationalization, and displacement may become the pathways through which emotional conflicts of deeper origin are discharged. These defenses against anxiety are sometimes organized as an almost impregnable bulwark against rehabilitation.

PSYCHOTHERAPEUTIC ASPECTS OF CARDIAC REHABILITATION

We should like to consider here some practical techniques to be applied in the psychotherapeutic management of cardiac patients in rehabilitation programs. Obviously, suggestions about the use of techniques carry risk because of the personality variables involved in specific situations. Basic to any treatment plan is the individualized psychodynamic formulation referred to earlier. Only with full understanding of the patient's personality and the meaning of the illness for him is it possible for the therapist to use wisely some of the following manipulative and modified psychoanalytic techniques.

The patient's fear of sudden death and the possibility that his functioning may be impaired through the rehabilitative process have certain common aspects. The extent to which the underlying genetic basis for the patient's fears is dealt with by the therapist needs to be carefully circumscribed since interviews that are charged with emotional tension must be avoided and the patient's anxiety should not be mobilized. One should not minimize the usefulness of an instructive and *educational approach* in at least reducing the anxiety that stems from misinformation and ignorance. Drawing diagrams of the heart anatomy, explaining the particular disorder in mechanical terms with analogies familiar to the patient, can be corrective both informationally and emotionally. By explaining the relationship of vascularization to physical activity, the therapist can help the patient to alter his conception of the damage caused by work; one can point out to him that the heart is a muscle like the biceps and thus benefits from appropriate exercise. For obvious reasons, these techniques are most effectively applied by medical personnel.

The problem of the heart's special participation in all affective experiences, and the opportunity thus provided for increased hypochondriacal concern, may yield only to a psychoanalytically oriented approach. As with the tubercular patient, however, one should not overlook the effectiveness of a *graphic demonstration* to the patient of the *interaction of mind and body;* for example, in the production of palpitations. One might suggest that the patient visualize some anxiety-producing situation such as the moment prior to his being struck by a taxi. The effect on his heart beat and rhythm, and the respiratory irregularities that are likely to accompany anxiety, are readily recognizable to him. Simple demonstrations of the effects on the heartbeat of holding his breath can give him a conception of the somatic responses to anxiety. Hyperventilation is also likely to be responsible for some of the symptoms commonly attributed to cardiac problems. The acid base changes in connection with the excessive imbalance of oxygen and carbon dioxide in the blood are likely to produce dizziness and may produce chest pressure. Intercostal spasms and paresthesia in the hand are sometimes misinterpreted even by doctors as referable to heart disease, and thus understandably may confuse the patient. Helping the patient to see his illness in functional terms may have a therapeutic effect, since so frequently his own concept of it is much worse than the actuality.

It is suggested by the foregoing discussion that it is not sufficient to tell the patient that there are emotional factors operating in his disability. This type of statement implies to some people that they are being accused of malingering. A physical ailment sometimes serves as a psychologically protective disguise, and the suggestion of emotional causation may arouse considerable protest and reinforce defensiveness. However, imparting physical facts supplemented by graphic illustrations of the interrelationship of psychic and somatic factors will often allay any apprehension or anxiety that is not deeply rooted.

Psychotherapy in cardiac rehabilitation is emotional re-education and reorientation based on psychodynamic understanding. The goals are limited. The therapist addresses himself not to the total reorganization of the personality, but to a restoration of the patient's functioning on the level of premorbid adaptation. Psychological changes resulting from the illness can often be made reversible by this type of adjunctive psychotherapeutic manipulation, which is only minimally concerned with insight. The use of uncovering therapy to produce permanent character change is impractical. One should use such corrective tools of therapy as giving accurate information and reconstructing the patient's selfimage and body image. Treatment is concerned with making ego alien what has become ego syntonic—that is, changing the patient's concept of himself as a cripple and invalid by making unacceptable his various rationalizations.

The therapist needs to subject to examination the patient's premorbid difficulties that have been channelized into his heart disease. The patient needs to be helped to see how many of his anxieties pre-existed his illness and have simply taken on different identification tags. His projection of all difficulties onto his cardiac disease must be exposed, if the trend toward hanging onto his illness is to be reversed. It is, of course, important to acknowledge any actual physical limitations, and for some patients, these need to be stressed. The patient needs help, however, in seeing that these limitations do not interfere with his functioning in every area of his life. Whenever possible, defenses should be utilized constructively by helping the patient find ways of bearing his passivity more comfortably. He can find outlets for a need to control, for example, by being given increased responsibility in self-management in either his family or work situation.

Mention should be made of the role of drug therapy as an aid in the psychological rehabilitation of cardiacs. Sedatives, stimulants, and tranquilizers, properly administered, can be of strategic value in overcoming the patient's initial anxiety, reducing the secondary gain, and thus enabling him to experience a sense of well-being and health. Once the shift from capitalizing on suffering in a masochistic way to enjoying activity is accomplished, the drugs can be withdrawn.

The fact that the patient exists in the context of a family environment needs to be underscored. Even if superficial, sensitive examination of family relationships frequently discloses clues to unsound familial attitudes toward the patient and his illness, which exacerbate the patient's own invalidizing attitudes. Satisfying, cohesive, and supportive relationships that do not play into or mobilize the patient's unconscious desire for dependency and passivity are factors strongly influencing his successful rehabilitation.

The fact that work has profound psychological as well as social value needs no elaborate exposition. The sublimation of aggressive and libidinal drives, and the repression of anxiety through work, can frequently exert greater influence on the patient's recovery than psychotherapeutic intervention. The increased self-esteem that accrues through the dignity of being productive, the rewards and satisfactions inherent in achievement, and the opportunity for gratifying social relationships make work itself a primary technique in the restoration of the patient. It goes without saying that the particular work situation must be consonant with the patient's physical limitations and not in conflict with his emotional needs. For the patient who cannot work out his own adjustment, a sheltered workshop can often provide a therapeutic milieu in which he can regain his confidence and test out his work capacity in a transition between the acute phase of his illness and his return to employment.

Section IV: Studies of Schizophrenia

RESEARCH IN SCHIZOPHRENIA poses one problem that looms over all the rest. To be true to a theory which assumes that a psychiatric illness is multiply determined, the research design must handle a large number of variables simultaneously and be responsive to their interactions. The usual procedures for testing large numbers of variables require many subjects, the number of subjects hopefully exceeding the number of variables. In clinical research, however, the number of variables frequently exceeds the number of subjects. Some adaptation of the single-case method may provide a partial solution, but, whatever the solution, the old single-variable approach, as Chapter 20 in this section makes clear, is out of date.

The need for new methods and new answers points up the basic dilemma—the demand for knowledge far outruns the state of the art. Clinical psychiatry in general, and schizophrenia in particular, confront the researcher with problems that far exceed his methods or his understanding. The problems would ordinarily not be attacked at this state of the science because they do not grow out of past work; they confront us only because they are imposed by pressures from without. They do not come from the mainstream of theory and experiment as it develops in the laboratory, and therefore are notably difficult to categorize and find approaches to. The pressure for their solution puts the researcher in a dilemma because, in all likelihood, no solution is really possible and the desperation implicit in the search for an answer produces an explosion of methods which further clutter up the field.

In this domain, the fewer methods the better. The use of different response measures greatly interferes with a meaningful integration of findings of different studies; the contemporary confusion echoes the plea of Chapter 19 for some kind of over-all planning. A simple standardization of projective instruments would make possible transfer of findings from one study to the next, and we may soon be in a position to make such a decision. A similar decision on method would take longer to arrive at but would represent a similar advance. However, as argued below, such changes are difficult to legislate; they must come from the floor, as it were, and not be imposed from the rostrum.

Two further problems should be mentioned. First, there is still no certainty that a psychiatric illness is a disease in the usual medical sense, and schizophrenia is particularly open to this query. Our research has been largely based on an illness-drug-cure model, and we treat the disappearance of the symptom as one of the signs of cure. But if psychiatric illness is highly responsive to social factors, the drug may be less important than the doctor-patient interaction. In turn, the therapy—which is a social condition—may be less important than the fact that the patient is participating in a research and has thus become, for once perhaps, a highly valued member of society. The *fact* of the research may be more important than the treatment (drug, therapy, or whatever), and any research thus carries with it a built-in artifact which stands in the way of understanding the disease and treatment process. A meaningful study of this problem is long overdue. More important, however, is the fact that the medical model determines both treatment strategy and research design, and interpersonal factors are underemphasized, if not ignored.

The second problem stems from the fact that research, to be useful, must be based on theory, but applied research is under such pressure from without that it cannot wait. Each experimenter follows his own favorite conception of the disease, and the difference among theories breeds an even greater difference among research procedures and study outcomes. Furthermore, it is doubtful that a theory will be "validated" by research in the immediate future; thus we are without even the usual checks of theory and experiment. A satisfactory theory is long overdue; even more urgently needed is a single theory. Chapter 20 offers one possibility.

19

IS SCHIZOPHRENIA NECESSARY?

The quantity of research in schizophrenia is almost as staggering as the problem itself, and this chapter proposes a solution: the establishment of a National Institute of Schizophrenia Research, to be part of the National Institute of Mental Health. The Institute would be responsible for coordinating all studies in the area and for planning long-range goals; it might also make a start toward adopting a standard language and a standard set of research procedures. Similar planning is needed in almost every clinical area; research in psychotherapy is another example.

Although no one would quarrel with the diagnosis (the scattering of effort and the lack of coordination in schizophrenia research are readily apparent), one could argue that this state of affairs is not necessarily bad and that a certain amount should be allowed to continue. Some degree of thrashing about is necessary in science, particularly in its early stages of growth, and to cut it short might stifle the good along with the bad. Therefore, a coordinating committee must tread carefully and allow individual investigators maximum freedom; it might suggest policy but it should be lenient in its execution.

As this book goes to press, the National Institute of Mental Health has announced the founding of a coordinating center for research in schizophrenia —18 years after the suggestion was first made by Bellak (see his editorial in *Medical Tribune,* Oct. 6, 1965, p. 15, for a review of the problem and his attempts to organize a central agency). The contributions of this new center will be keenly awaited.

THE SCOPE OF THE PROBLEM

DESPITE TREMENDOUS ADVANCES in the understanding and treatment of emotional disorders, schizophrenia maintains its unchallenged position as the most prevalent and recalcitrant of man's mental ills. Its importance to the afflicted, to their immediate relations, and to the community as a whole cannot be overstated.

It is generally accepted that one-half the hospital beds in the United States are occupied by psychiatric patients and that about one-half of these patients are schizophrenics. The numbers themselves are staggering, but figures neither tell the whole story nor describe meaningfully that part of the story to which they refer. One could be falsely encouraged by the fact that psychotropic drugs and other methods of management have decreased the number of hospitalized patients by about ten per cent over the last decade. This decrease, however, must be viewed against the fact that in any given year twice as many people are hospitalized as were ten years ago. One must also remember that while drugs, better treatment, and changes of public attitude towards the ex-patient have all contributed to this decrease, the decrease itself does not represent either the cure of the disorder or a meaningful reduction of the problem.

NOTE: From a paper delivered at the occasion of receiving the Annual Merit Award of the New York Society of Clinical Psychologists, May 23, 1964.

The scope of the problem must also be seen in terms of its incidence outside the hospital. It has been estimated (Lemkau, 1958) that schizophrenia affects about 290 people per 100,000 of the general population. Of these, slightly over half ultimately require hospitalization. It is clear, on the basis of these figures, that there are almost as many persons who suffer the more subtle and latent forms of this disorder as there are those manifestly ill enough to require removal from the community.

One must also realize, when considering the incidence and seriousness of schizophrenia, that this is an illness which strikes most frequently in early adulthood. In this sense it is economically and sociologically more devastating than, for example, the malignancies which occur most often in the middle or later years.

These considerations—the tremendous number of persons affected, the increasing though shorter duration of hospitalization required, and the age at which this illness strikes, make an organized attack on the problem imperative.

OVERVIEW OF THE CONCEPTIONS OF THE ETIOLOGY AND PATHOGENESIS OF SCHIZOPHRENIA

In view of the great importance of schizophrenia•from a public health point of view, it is particularly distressing to note that conceptions concerning its etiology and pathogenesis are still in great disagreement. Furthermore, research in this direction is entirely without direction or integration. This is especially regrettable because it is well within our present ability to arrive at definitive data in these areas and to verify such propositions by integrated and focused research. As one example of the multitude of unintegrated factors currently under study, consider the contents relating to schizophrenia in one single issue of *The Archives of General Psychiatry* (April, 1964): "EEG and Behavioral Changes in Schizophrenia" by A. A. Sugerman et al.; "Perceptual Evidence of CNS Dysfunction in Schizophrenia" by I. Belmont et al.; "Blood Factors in Schizophrenia" by F. C. Brown; "The Bone Marrow in Schizophrenia" by M. Hirata-Hibi and W. J. Fessel; "Schizophrenia: 6-Hydroxyskatole and Environment" by F. C. Dohan et al.; and a paper on "Interrelated Schizophrenic Psychosis in Fraternal Twins" by D. C. Smith and T. Lidz. In 1948 I counted more than fifty different etiological factors claimed to be responsible for schizophrenia. The problem is that investigators are usually committed to think in black-and-white, all-or-none, single-factor terms instead of considering that different factors might be responsible for schizophrenia in different people or that a variety of factors might interrelate to produce it in any one individual.

Assuming that some investigators are aware of the possibility of multiple causation, they apparently forget it the moment they engage in research. Somehow their methodology forces them into narrow channels. "Cleanness of design" seems to sacrifice all relation to reality. A great variety of studies have reportedly found supposedly specific factors responsible for schizophrenia. But these studies, so cleanly designed, are rarely adequately controlled. They are rarely compared to a population sharing the *schizophrenic way of life*. The so-called etiologic factors all too often prove to be mere artifacts, true, at best, for one small group, at one particular moment, and in one particular environment.

Almost any example of current research will demonstrate this point. Consider a study of "Abnormal Leukocytes in Schizophrenia" by Fessel and Hirata-Hibi (1963) in which the authors purport to find that abnormal leukocytes of three types were present in the peripheral blood of almost all the schizophrenic patients studied. The point is that these cellular changes might indicate genetic, infectious, endocrine, or reticular endothelial abnormalities implicated in the etiology and pathogenesis of schizophrenia. While the experimental group was compared with *normal* personnel, it was not compared with people living the same schizophrenic way of life.

The importance of the way of life was illustrated in a study of some years ago (Bellak and Holt, 1948) in which Holt and I found that somatotypes among schizophrenics did not conform to Sheldon's hypothesis. We did find a positive correlation between ectomorphy and length of hospitalization, but it was a correlation that held true not only for schizophrenics *but for a control group of paretics* hospitalized for about the same length of time. A subsequent study by an anthropologist (Lasker, 1947) using volunteers on a starvation diet supported our findings. With regard to the supposedly characteristic carbohydrate metabolism of schizophrenics, nothing has happened to change Hoskins's (1946) summary that the only consistent correlation exists between the degree of tension and abnormal glucose tolerance tests, as Kety also points out. The need to provide the same environmental and living conditions for control groups was underlined by Kety's (1961) complex studies. He and his colleagues illustrated that the widely acclaimed etiological and pathogenic factors related to taraxein, ceruloplasmin, and the variations of serotonin were all artifacts, some of them definitely correlating with the dietary peculiarities to which the hospitalized schizophrenics were exposed.

I recently had occasion to respond to an editorial in the *Journal of the American Medical Association* (Bellak, 1964b) that addressed itself to the etiology of schizophrenia. The discussion implied that an increase of macroglobulins might play an etiological role in schizophrenia despite the fact that it was apparent that the same increase appeared in prisoners under the emotional strain of reporting to a parole board. It seems obvious that the change in macroglobulins is probably a secondary result of the *stress*. The reason I felt impelled to reply to the JAMA editorial is that all too frequently artifacts are widely hailed in the press without concomitant emphasis on the lack of breadth of the conception under consideration. Continuing and inappropriate attention by the lay and professional press to poorly controlled, narrow-slice experiments only serves to encourage similarly poorly conceived studies and consequently inhibit the development of more productively designed research.

Unfortunately it is not only the physiological studies of schizophrenic etiology and pathogenesis which are conceived in overly simple and confined terms. The sociological "double-bind" theory, other theories singling out semantic confusion, the postulate of specific psychodynamic factors within a family constellation— all of which purport to have been found to be *the* cause of schizophrenia—suffer from the same narrow overgeneralization and oversimplification, as for instance the work of Singer and Opler (1956) and of Sanua (unpublished) points out.

THE UNIFIED THEORY OF PERSONALITY

It is my opinion then that progress in dealing with schizophrenia has been hampered by the attempts to find *single* etiological factors common to *all* schizophrenics. Over the course of the past two decades I have formulated increasingly comprehensive hypotheses to attempt to deal with these shortcomings (see Chapter 20). In 1948, I thought in terms of distinguishing between primarily psychogenic and somatogenic schizophrenias. In 1949 (1949b), in 1952 (1952a), and in 1955 (1955a) the multiple factor psychosomatic theory of schizophrenia emerged, and still later (see Chapter 20) I proposed a unified theory of schizophrenia. Today I feel certain that schizophrenia can be included in an even broader set of hypotheses, within a unified theory of psychoses itself subsumed under a unified theory of personality.

This point of view is neither revolutionary nor even strikingly novel.[1] A small claim in this direction might be made for the fact that I propose to insist that each individual we describe be categorized systematically and routinely in terms of a whole *personality-gram* which would include, on the etiologic side, *all* levels of interaction. Borrowing from the excellent terms of S. Cobb (1943), I would state that the *genogenic, histogenic, chemogenic,* and *psychogenic* factors of each individual be appraised. *Sociogenic* factors must also be included. In this classification, genogenic refers to heredity as well as to congenital *Anlagen* with regard to stimulus barrier and activity type. Histogenic factors include both congenital and acquired tissue characteristics, ranging from electroencephalographic indices to signs of gross tissue change. The effect of bacterial or viral invasions might be included under the chemical aspects, as in the case of toxic disturbances, or under histogenic aspects as in the case of paresis or the rheumatic endarteritis Bruetsch (1940) has so long championed. Psychogenic and sociogenic factors obviously correlate closely; the specific experiential aspects relevant for the development of every person are merely put under different headings for convenience of labeling, they can be psychological if one is primarily concerned with intrapersonal or interpersonal dynamics, or sociological or anthropological if one focuses primarily on the consequences of membership in a particular social group.

I suggest that no person be discussed without these headings in mind, that no research in schizophrenia be designed without attention to each of these levels. I would hope to see this scheme parallel the basic framework of psychoanalytic metapsychology—the insistence upon viewing every unit of experience in terms of its adaptive, genetic, topographic, economic, and structural components. If one adds to this framework a study and description in terms of ego functions and their disturbances (see Chapter 20; Bellak, 1960), one has three interlocking sets of variables and hypotheses which hopefully will permit us to transcend the narrow and oversimplified work we so often have to contend with.

In discussing schizophrenia specifically, let me repeat that this syndrome is not a single disease entity, but rather a syndrome of severe ego disturbance. Severe ego impairment may be the result of any number of somatic or experi-

---

[1] As far back as 1942, I said something similar in a joint paper with Eliot Jacques on the dynamic conceptualization of case studies (Bellak and Jacques, 1942). Others have worked in the same direction.

ential factors in various combinations. The somewhat variable syndrome generally associated with this diagnostic label must be understood as the final common path of a number of conditions that lead to a severe disturbance of the ego. It is because so many etiological factors may lead to the final path that we speak of a *multiple-factor* theory, and it is because certain psychogenic and somatic aspects are probably present in varying degrees that we speak of a *psychosomatic* theory.

The unified theory of schizophrenia has gained some acceptance because it seems to resolve a number of problems and to provide an integrative answer. Yet a theory is no better than its verification by experimental procedure. During the last fifteen years I have designed a number of experiments and projects that attempt to verify, modify, or reject some of the fundamental hypotheses of this theory. One project centers around an attempt to define ego functions operationally; to establish definitions for good and poor functioning, to develop tests for each, and to arrive at ten crucial subtests organized much like those of the Wechsler-Bellevue. Weights would be given to each of these ego functions, and an attempt made to develop a *profile of ego functions*. These tests would be standardized on a scale that ranges from normal to the very disturbed functioning of schizophrenia. The ability of the tests to discriminate blindly would have to be ascertained.[2]

It is my main contention that in general schizophrenics would have a low ego strength, but that their individual profiles would vary greatly. I hypothesize that the *synthetic* function of the ego would, like vocabulary in the Wechsler-Bellevue, correlate most significantly with over-all ego strength and would be the function most fundamentally impaired. It is my hope that different patterns of ego disturbances would lend themselves to the establishment of different etiological factors relating to them. Since the scale would take cognizance of historical and physiological, as well as psychological and sociological, variables, I would hope that such an investigation would permit one to demonstrate the contribution of different etiological factors to the final common path.

Such a study would, however, be an academic exercise if it did not relate to prevention and treatment. Some plans were therefore developed to test the ego-profile theory as described and also to attempt to verify it by the method of prediction and the method of therapeutic and preventive test (see footnote 2 above).

The first purpose of this project is to make predictions at age ten of the occurrence of psychiatric disorders at age thirteen. Its second purpose is to evaluate the effectiveness of brief psychotherapy on those children predicted to become ill.

The project involves three steps: (1) testing and interviewing of children at age ten; (2) making predictions about their psychiatric status on reaching age

---

[2] While I developed the first designs for the project myself (Bellak, 1952a; Chapter 20 this volume), I later had the invaluable help of Renate Safrin, Ph.D., and Max Prola, as well as the help of Ruth Cooper, Ph.D., Sidney Rosenberg, and others who have worked painstakingly on the development of an ego-function scale that would lend itself to the evaluation of verbal interaction as well as other behavior in terms of quality and quantity of ego functioning. The projects described have so far not gone beyond the planning stage for extrinsic reasons.

thirteen; and (3) a follow-up examination at age thirteen. To this purpose, a large group of ten-year-old school children would be evaluated by a test battery designed to measure ego functions. Using the data obtained, raters would indicate the psychiatric status and disorder, if any, that each child would be expected to manifest three years later. Of those children predicted to fall ill, half would be offered some form of psychiatric treatment. A specific treatment plan for each child would be formulated after a careful analysis of the positive and negative features of the life situation. The plan would consist of a very specific prescription for brief, focused treatment, and might involve either direct contact with the child, alteration of his environment through contact with the significant persons in his life, or some combination of the two. It is hoped that these data, when checked three years later, would help to measure the degree of accuracy of predictions based on an evaluation of ego functions directed toward the early diagnosis and prevention of schizophrenia and other psychiatric disorders.

A third project would attempt to evaluate the effect of preventive child psychiatry on the incidence of psychiatric disorders in general and on schizophrenia in particular. Beginning with a prenatal history, a large sample of children would be examined annually. The parents of half these children would be chosen to participate in a program called "The School for Parents." This project was conceived as a practical approach to the problems of community psychiatry—one which would offer a realistically available modicum of preventive and therapeutic action. It is hoped that such a seminar would offer the possibilities of didactic as well as a variety of therapeutic group processes among the participants.

The object would be to see whether, by this very simple, inexpensive, widely applicable technique, a significant difference could be demonstrated in the incidence of psychiatric disorders generally and schizophrenia specifically between the experimental and control groups. It is also hoped to demonstrate that a significant percentage of such psychopathology might be prevented with a minimum of intervention.

There is hardly any question that a large part of the answer to the problem of schizophrenia lies in community psychiatry programs. To whatever etiology one subscribes, even in the current state of confusion, few psychiatrists doubt that unfortunate environmental conditions precipitate or aggravate any liability toward schizophrenic disorder, even the supposedly inherited tendencies. I have had occasion to discuss several community psychiatric measures before (Bellak, 1964a), and have made suggestions for necessary social legislation to safeguard the community's health.

THE NEED FOR A NATIONAL INSTITUTE FOR SCHIZOPHRENIA RESEARCH

There is yet another vantage from which to view the problem of schizophrenia. Although the National Institute of Mental Health awards many research grants for study in this area, the work has been unintegrated and often poorly conceived. Its paucity of results, its repetition of the same errors, its oversimplified and single-variable approach have already been discussed. Let me state firmly that I believe much of the lack of progress in schizophrenia research must be ascribed to a lack of central direction and integration.*

The administrators of research grants who are basically responsible for inviting members to the study groups and review committees have few, if any, clinicians on their working staff and rarely consult with active clinicians.† Those who are thought to be such often have had no more connection with the clinic than the gathering of the statistics of test development or the administration of institutions. The result is that the administrators and those they invite to study and review grant applications heavily favor the academic, administrative, and statistical points of view. It is an interesting note that the few experienced clinicians who have found their way into this sacrosanct company have been curiously ineffectual or positively overawed. One could speculate about the reception they receive as the minority party. By and large, these groups of administrators are likely to insist on "cleanness of design" above all else, and cleanness of design has usually implied single-variable, narrowly sliced studies which were not so much clean as sterile.

I have expressed these and similar sentiments on the policies governing research grants in print (Bellak, 1961) and in testimony before a Congressional Sub-Committee on Appropriations (Bellak, 1962). I restate it again because I feel it imperative to broaden the base in the fight for greater representation of clinicians and the clinical and creative point of view among those who award research grants in this area. In my opinion little can be expected from the many studies of schizophrenia supported by grants because of the inherent bias towards rigid and restricted design. Even if this situation were to improve, it would still be difficult to carry on the broad-scaled, controlled, multivariable research essential to the solution of the problem.

The kind of program I envision requires a combination of clinical experience, acquaintance with research methods, and broad familiarity with the available literature and current work. This is hard to come by in any one person or under any one currently existing roof. The answer will not be found merely by dispensing more grants to more people to study more groups of schizophrenics. *I firmly believe that what is needed is a mapping out of the areas that must be attacked, a parceling out of research projects that are internally related to each other, and a repeated testing of the hypotheses involved in an orderly, interlocking, and integrated way.* This can be achieved only by a central body functioning as a coordinator of all the research that would be conducted in various hospitals and communities across the nation. Furthermore, this coordinating board would function more effectively if located in an institute solely dedicated to research in schizophrenia and specifically charged with the interrelation of work going on in all other institutions and with the validation of their reported findings. A National Institute of Schizophrenia Research seems essential.

In summary then, I believe that schizophrenia can be understood in the terms of a multiple-factor theory. I believe that well-integrated research can, beyond a reasonable doubt, establish the multiple etiological factors that terminate in the

---

* In October 1966, a center for the study of schizophrenia was established at the National Institute of Mental Health, thus obviating my former critique.

† This does not hold true any longer, since the reorganization of NIMH in 1967.

final common path of ego disturbance that we label schizophrenia. I believe that our society cannot temporize any longer in implementing the necessary studies for definitively ascertaining the nature of this disorder.

In answer to the question posed by the title of this chapter, let me say that I do *not* believe schizophrenia is necessary. We know that in the process of growing up, the human condition carries with it inevitable traumas. We, in the mental health professions, are dedicated to the goal of reducing these traumas to a realistic minimum. Once the etiology and pathogenesis of schizophrenia is established, the extent of traumatization on a variety of levels that lead to this extreme of the "human condition" may be expected to diminish nearly to the point of disappearance.

20

A UNIFIED THEORY OF SCHIZOPHRENIA:
IMPLICATIONS FOR DIAGNOSIS,
TREATMENT, PROGNOSIS, AND RESEARCH

Schizophrenia, to a distressingly large extent, is a linguistic convention rather than a disease entity. The large category of symptoms associated with that disease, and the even larger range of etiological contributors, are all subsumed under a single word. Our language habits have led us to assume that one name must mean one disease; our respect for language has forced us to take an overly simplistic view of the phenomenon, and the consequences of this simplicity are still felt. Research on schizophrenia—one word—is believed to be about one problem, whereas there are almost as many problems as patients; treatment of schizophrenia—one word—is believed to deal with a single disease, and this belief, as the present chapter makes clear, is palpably untrue. The single label for the disease has kept alive hope for a single cure long past the time when such a hope should have been forgotten. We are the victims of an old-fashioned and inappropriate labeling system, and while the mischief caused by an out-of-date nosological system is widespread in psychiatry, it is perhaps felt most keenly with respect to schizophrenia.

To break down this simplistic view is the task of the moment; the enormous size of the task is represented by the length of this chapter. Schizophrenia is broadly conceptualized here as a disturbance of ego functions; the list of such functions (as shown in Table 1) ranges from disturbances in relation to reality, to disturbances in thought processes, to disturbances of the synthetic function. Seven main categories are listed, and each is subdivided into as many as eight smaller units. We have to deal, in short, with the whole field of ego psychology, and although we know a great deal about particular functions and their pathology, a theory of schizophrenia demands much more. It requires that we understand the relation of each function to every other function, so that, for example, we can describe how a thought disturbance will interact with a drive disturbance, how a thought disturbance can be exacerbated by inadequate reality testing, and so on. To the extent that there is no single cure, no single precipitating factor, and no single pattern of symptoms, the study of schizophrenia faces us with the study of life itself; it poses a philosophical problem for which it (ungratefully) requires a precise solution. It is partly to avoid such complexities that we adopt the oversimplifying single word, "schizophrenia."

As the idea of a final, common path is developed in the present chapter, a variety of contributing factors eventually merge to form the syndrome of schizophrenia. Time may show that this concept is a transitional one from the obviously simplistic idea of a single disease to a complex picture of many separate forms of ego disturbance which have very little in common. The

NOTE: From *Schizophrenia*: *A Review of the Syndrome,* edited by L. Bellak, New York, Grune & Stratton, 1958; the *Journal of Nervous and Mental Disease*, 1955, 121, 60-66, and 1960, 131, 39-46. Reprinted by permission of the publishers.

common variance shared by parts of the schizophrenia syndrome may, in time, be seen as specious—as our diagnostic procedures are sharpened and as our sensitivity to clinical details is increased. But these refinements lie in the future, and for the present the concepts developed here seem respectably parsimonious.

IN VIRTUALLY ALL SCIENCE the value of a hypothesis is measured by its ability to explain certain events (in their relationship to each other) and to predict and control future events. Although in certain circumstances—in geology, archaeology, or psychodynamics, for example—we may deal primarily with "postdiction" (the term originated by G. W. Allport) rather than prediction, the direction of the process need not make any difference. For that matter, prediction is also involved in these sciences: geologic or other constructive findings serve as useful inferences for future events in other places.

Psychiatric diagnosis, like all diagnosis, is, in essence, hypothesis. In a given case, the tentative diagnosis is a hypothesis of a lower level of probability than is the final diagnosis. The series of diagnostic procedures represents a sequence of tests of the validity and coherence of that hypothesis. Just as in medical diagnoses certain nosological entities are more or less firmly circumscribed hypotheses, psychiatric hypotheses, too, must be judged on the basis of their contribution to understanding, prediction, and control. In determining the value of a hypothesis, we must also consider the extent of its applicability, the width of phenomena it encompasses. A hypothesis which may be applied to only a single case is of little value. It is essential that hypotheses attain a high level of generalization.

On the basis of these criteria, the various hypotheses regarding schizophrenia which have been advanced over the past decades must be considered of very limited usefulness. It is indeed curious that even those authors who freely acknowledge this fact, and who, furthermore, seem agreed on the nonspecific nature of the syndrome, persist in their efforts to delineate specific etiological factors. In addition to those authors who are committed to purely psychogenic causes, or who subscribe to one kind of toxification or another, genetic defect, enzymatic or synaptic abnormality, others subscribe, more sophisticatedly, to an organismic factor. But even the adherents of this last theory are prone to search for one fact, or at least one level of functioning, rather than a variety of causative events, capable of leading to the same final common pathway. And closely related to this search for one single causative factor are the unproductive quests for one successful therapy, and the failure to formulate definitive diagnostic and prognostic criteria.

The present task, then, is to arrive at a comprehensive theory (with careful definition) of schizophrenia on the basis of the available data, which is consistent with understanding of the variety of symptoms, course, etc., control of the syndrome (therapy), and prediction (prognosis).

I have made previous attempts to formulate such a theory (1949b, 1955a). My concept of the nature of schizophrenia may be summarized as follows:

Schizophrenia or dementia praecox is a psychiatric syndrome, not a single disease. The somewhat variable symptoms generally associated with this diagnostic label must be understood as the final common path of a number of conditions which may lead to and manifest themselves in a severe disturbance of the ego. These conditions may range from a relatively purely psychogenic weakness of the ego to afflictions of ego functioning by disturbances brought about by infections, arteriosclerotic, enzymatic, toxic, or traumatic, constitutional, or genetic factors: in short, by any number of chemogenic, histogenic, genogenic, or psychogenic factors, or by any combination thereof.

While an outstanding somatic factor may be present, usually this must be accompanied by some psychological predisposition (in terms of ego patterns) to produce the schizophrenic syndrome.[1] Conversely, certain somatic factors are probably inseparably joined with the psychogenic etiology of schizophrenia, at least for those cases of early onset and severe outcome.

In brief, the multiple-factor, psychosomatic theory of schizophrenia permits one to understand schizophrenia as the common result of a variety of individually differing etiological factors. It enables one to make a prognosis on the basis of a careful study of the specific etiological causes involved in a specific case, and permits optimal therapeutic control of the highly individual constellation of forces resulting in the manifestly common path of the syndrome, by directly or indirectly, somatically, psychologically, or environmentally, producing better ego functioning.

The symptoms of schizophrenia show considerable individual variation, and show variability over the course of time. Thus, on a continuum of "psychiatric health" schizophrenia would cover a range, not a point. This range would start from the lowest point of health and would irregularly overlap with manic-depressive psychosis and severe psychoneurosis.

The symptoms of schizophrenia are manifested in various forms of poor ego functioning such as the emergence of primary-process thinking; poor control of drives; a poor relation to reality, adaptively and libidinally; poor defenses; impairment of some autonomous functions; and a low synthetic function of the ego. The characteristics of severe ego disturbance are identical with the formal signs and symptoms of schizophrenia as described by Kraepelin and Bleuler. The extreme disturbances of thought, motility, and perception found in catatonia, paranoia, hebephrenia, and schizophrenia simplex can be dynamically conceptualized as disturbances of the ego.

The interaction between theory and clinical practice is a special version of the problems of the relation of thought and action. The correlation between the psychoanalytic theory of schizophrenia and its treatment shows the customary phenomena related to learning; sometimes action is ahead of explicit formulation, presumably because preconscious cognition of the task was more accurate than conscious conceptualization; at other times, concept formation helps toward more successful intervention in reality.

---

[1] It has often been said that the only hypothesis in psychiatry of which we can be certain is that general paresis is caused by syphilis. However, the fact is that we do not yet know why the spirochetes will primarily attack the cardiovascular system in one person and the central nervous system in another. Furthermore, we do not know why an invasion of the central nervous system will produce schizophrenic-like psychotic manifestations in certain cases and not in others. It would be worth while to investigate whether patients with a premorbid tendency to dissociation and a disturbed life situation are more apt to respond to central nervous-system invasion with psychotic symptoms which, at times, are difficult or impossible to differentiate from schizophrenia.

In discussing the psychoanalytic concept of the ego and schizophrenia, we must state from the start that while there is nothing sacrosanct about Freud's tripartite model of ego, superego, and id, it has proved the most useful and most encompassing working construct advanced to date for the understanding, prediction, and control of behavior. In terms of this model, the ego subsumes the acquisition, possession, and execution of the specific functions discussed below. Freud's model was predicated upon the fact that discontinuous behavioral phenomena could be seen as part of a continuum if one inferred that some links were, or had become, unconscious. It followed that psychoanalytic theory had to concern itself with hunches about the nature of the unconscious data, with the processes by which they became and/or remained unconscious, and with the processes of making them conscious. This basic theoretical framework applied as much to the treatment of schizophrenia as it did to that of the neuroses.

The concept (or construct) of the ego can best be defined and described by its development and its functions. Furthermore, its qualitative pattern is the result of the quantitative degree of efficiency with which a variety of ego functions are performed, the totality of which may be referred to as ego strength.

The following codification of ego functions and their disturbances must be regarded as sketchy, rudimentary, and in many respects, superficial. Further-

TABLE 1

CONDENSED AND ABBREVIATED SCHEMA OF SOME GROUPS OF EGO FUNCTIONS
AND SOME OF THEIR DISTURBANCES

Ego Functions	Disturbances
1. Relation to Reality	1. Disturbances in Relation to Reality
A. Adaptation to reality	A. Disturbances in adaptive capacity
(1) Differentiation of figure and ground	(1) Inappropriate behavior with subjective or objective difficulties
(2) Role playing	(2) Inability to cope with deviations in normal routine
(3) Spontaneity and creativeness; regression in the service of the ego	(3) Failure in social adaptation; rigidity
B. Reality Testing	B. Disturbances in reality testing
(1) Accuracy of perception	(1) Projection, rationalization, denial, and the distortion of reality by hallucinations and delusions
(2) Soundness of judgment	
(3) Orientation in time, place, person	
C. Sense of Reality	C. Disturbances in sense of reality
(1) Good "self-boundaries"	(1) Feelings of estrangement and lack of spontaneity
(2) Unobtrusiveness of ordinary functioning	(2) Excessive feelings of *déjà vu*
	(3) Oneirophrenia
	(4) Cosmic delusions
	(5) Confused body images
	(6) Intrusion of self as subject or object
	(7) Physiological manifestations
2. Regulation and Control of Drives	2. Disturbances in Drive Control
A. Ability to engage in detour behavior	A. Conduct and habit disorders (tantrums, nail biting, etc.)
B. Frustration tolerance (neutralization of drive energy)	B. Accident proneness

TABLE 1 (*Continued*)

Ego Functions	Disturbances
C. Anxiety tolerance D. Integrated motility E. Tolerance of ambiguity F. Sublimation	C. Excessive impulsivity D. Tension states E. Catatonic and manic excitement F. Psychomotor slow-up of catatonia and depression G. Lack of or incomplete acquisition of control of excretory functions H. Physiological manifestations
3. Object Relations A. Capacity to form satisfactory object relations B. Object constancy	3. Disturbances in Object Relations A. Psychotoxic and psychic deficiency diseases (in infancy) B. Narcissism, autism C. Symbiotic relationships D. Anaclitic relationships E. Hypercathexis of the self; ambivalence, fear of incorporation, sadomasochism
4. Thought Processes A. Selective scanning B. Ability to avoid contamination by inappropriate material or drives C. Good memory D. Sustained ability to concentrate E. Abstracting ability	4. Disturbances in Thought Processes A. Thinking organized and compelled by drives B. Preoccupation with instinctual aims C. Autistic logic D. Loose and "nonsensical" types of associative links E. Distortion of reality F. Lack of referents in time and place, anthropomorphism, concretism, symbolism, syncretism, etc. G. Magical thinking
5. Defensive Functions A. Repression (as a barrier against external and internal stimuli) B. Sublimation, reaction formation C. Projection D. Denial, withdrawal, and other defenses	5. Disturbance in Defensive Functions A. Emergence of primary thought processes B. Overreaction to stimuli C. *Déjà vu* experiences D. Lack of drive control E. Frightening hypnagogic phenomena F. Increase in parapraxes G. Impairment in emotional control
6. Autonomous Functions A. Perception B. Intention C. Intelligence D. Thinking E. Language F. Productivity G. Motor development	6. Disturbance in Autonomous Functions A. Corresponding impairment of these ego functions
7. Synthetic Function A. To unite, organize, bind and create—the ego's ability to form Gestalten B. Neutralization C. Sublimation D. Somatic "homeostasis"	7. Disturbance in Synthetic Function A. Tendency to dissociation B. Inability to tolerate change or trauma C. Inability to "bind" psychic energy

more, any discussion of the ego as a single construct is likely to neglect the interrelation between the ego and all other aspects of psychoanalytic psychodynamics. Nevertheless, despite their drawbacks, isolation and codification are of practical value. The present formulation may serve as a frame of reference for diagnostic purposes. As a check list, it may serve as the basis for the future development of a quantitative scheme for rating purposes.

In any investigation of ego functioning, it is, of course, necessary to explore both contemporary and historical levels of performance. An assessment of congenital status is as essential as an appraisal of environmental influences. The final diagnostic impression of patterns and degrees of ego functioning will be obtained by comparing contemporary with developmental data. Ordinarily, we would expect the contemporary level of functioning to be consonant with the developmental history. If that expectation is not borne out, we must conclude that our data may be incomplete and thus will require verification. If, however, this deficiency has been ruled out and if, in the light of the data available, the patient is more disturbed than his developmental history would warrant, a latent organic disease must be considered as a possibility. If, by the same token, the patient has been more disturbed from infancy or early childhood than might be justified by environmental factors, congenital defect must be considered.

In the following headings of groups of ego functions, we are guided by the list of categories formulated by David Beres (1956);[2] the content of the discussion is based on general psychoanalytic formulations and a few relatively original propositions. In view of the familiarity of much of the material, some emphasis has been placed on those comparatively obscure aspects of ego functioning which are not prominent in standard texts on the subject. Furthermore, I would point out, once again, that the ego's functions are best seen as global; there is therefore a good deal of interrelationship and interdependence of the various functions discussed. Finally, the reader is reminded that any analysis of ego functioning will also ultimately involve an assessment of quantitative factors.

1.   RELATION TO REALITY

In accordance with Beres' conceptualization, our discussion will deal with three components of the relation to reality: adaptation to reality, reality testing, and a sense of reality.

---

[2] More recently (1966), the major propositions of this chapter have become the basis for an ongoing research project titled "Patterns of Ego Functions in Schizophrenia," supported by NIMH grant MH-5 RO1 11662. In the planning of this study, the list of ego functions has been enlarged to include the following ten categories: reality testing, sense of reality, regulation and control of drives, object relations, thought processes, * adaptive regression in the service of the ego, defensive functions, * stimulus barrier, autonomous functioning, and * synthetic functions (new categories are starred). The study will attempt to assay ego functions in 100 schizophrenics, 30 neurotics, and 30 normals, all matched on the Hollingshead Index. Each subject will be given a clinical interview, psychological tests, a battery of experimental procedures, and a battery of physiological measures. It is hoped to demonstrate that not only can one differentiate schizophrenics from neurotics and normals by means of different ego-function patterns and over-all ego strength, but that one can also differentiate intra-group patterns among the schizophrenics. If some clearcut patterns can be uncovered, it may be possible to formulate hypotheses with regard to primary etiologic factors.

ADAPTATION TO REALITY

Any attempt at a concise definition of adaptation to reality must necessarily be hampered by the very breadth of this aspect of ego functioning. In a general sense, our concepts of adaptation to reality and the synthetic function of the ego may be said to overlap. More specifically, adaptation to reality is particularly related to the autonomous functions of perception, thinking, and motor execution. Furthermore, adaptation to reality also involves the adequate control of drives and the employment of suitable defenses. Selye uses the term "adaptation" in its broadest organismic sense; certainly the ego is involved in this process of attempting to attain a degree of equilibrium—to maintain homeostasis or "stable states," to use von Bertalanffy's (1955) term. Nevertheless, it may prove useful to differentiate the adaptive functions of the ego from those functions which may be termed nonadaptive: this distinction applies, for instance, to the use of projective techniques where it may be useful to distinguish adaptive responses from those which are expressive (relating to style or form) or projective.

In some ways, as an aspect of ego functioning, the term adaptation is related to "adjustment" in its popular sense—with regard to getting along in the world in relation to family, school, employment, marriage, war, etc. It is useful, then, to relate adaptation to the cultural matrix; this would include "role playing"—a concept of social psychology not sufficiently applied in psychiatry. Role playing is an integral part of appropriateness of behavior and thus an important aspect of every psychiatric appraisal. The interview situation, as well as the psychiatric history, might be good indicators of adaptive functioning; the "stress interview" is certainly predicated on this assumption.

REALITY TESTING

Reality testing and the sense of reality are subsidiaries rather than coordinates of adaptation to reality. Reality testing is an intricate part of role playing and involves accuracy of perception and soundness of judgment. While autonomous functions such as intelligence are involved, most frequently successful reality testing concerns a differentiation of external data from internal determinants. The Rorschach is, of course, a particularly useful indicator of the accuracy of perception; items of the Wechsler-Bellevue have been used for appraisal of the soundness of judgment. The presence of some "popular" responses in the Rorschach and the level of form perception are two of the factors which permit appraisal of reality testing. The psychiatric interview's gauging of orientation in time, place, and person provides a gross indication of the patient's ability to test reality.

SENSE OF REALITY

In recent years outstanding contributions have been made to our understanding of the relationship of the infant to reality. Spitz (1957b), particularly, has studied this aspect of ego functioning in terms of the development of object relations. Quite briefly, psychoanalytic propositions maintain that the infant must differentiate himself from the rest of the world, and then, slowly, make finer differentiations of the self in relation to the time-honored variables of the psychiatric interview, mentioned earlier, of time, place, and person. Federn (1952) has made an outstanding contribution to our understanding of the problem of the self as an object in time and place. A good sense of reality—a clear differentiation of the self from the rest of the world—is largely predicated upon good "ego boundaries," to use Federn's term. (However, self-boundaries might be more accurate to avoid confusion of the self with the ego construct.) When self-boundaries are disturbed, perceptual distortion ensues and the sense of reality is correspondingly disturbed. In normal circumstances there is no conscious awareness of the self—just as there is no awareness of all other well-functioning and healthy parts of the individual. A good sense of reality is virtually predicated upon the lack of intrusion of the self as subject or object. Thus we resemble the centipede who functions well only as long as he moves automatically. When he must stop to wonder which leg to move next he is likely to become a very disturbed centipede. Whenever the immediacy of the relationship of the self to reality is interrupted we are dealing with a major or minor disturbance in the sense of reality.

DISTURBANCES IN THE RELATION TO REALITY

Disturbances in the Adaptive Capacity. Such disturbances lead to "maladjustment" to the people and tasks in one's life, and are manifested by varying degrees of inappropriate behavior with subjective and objective difficulties. More specifically, any deviation from normal routine will throw the patient with a markedly decreased adaptive capacity out of gear. Each new task or situation has a disorganizing effect. Frequently, such people create a way of life for themselves which permits virtual "splinting"—almost as one might favor a broken limb; they retire to an activity which requires fewer of their resources and to a routine which enables them to get along with a minimum of available energy. Such splinting periods occur frequently in the histories of schizophrenics. A frequent change of jobs is often an indication of a lack of adaptive ability, often with paranoid features. Failure in social adaptation is considered an outstanding feature of schizophrenic life history.

Disturbance in reality testing. The schizophrenic projects, rationalizes, denies, and distorts reality to serve his own needs. In lesser disturbances, reality testing may be "too good," devoid of all emotion: good object relationships involve a transcendence of immediate personal welfare. Narcissistic, basically depressed and isolated people, such as Schopenhauer, may be completely unable, and unwilling, to effect such relationships. They speculate quite logically about the value of life; looking for a means to an end, they are unable to enjoy the means, the object relationships themselves. (One could interpret Goethe's Faust as a search for happiness in "ends," only to find its source in the means.) Depressed patients have especially good form perception on the Rorschach (form perception is one aspect of reality testing), probably because of their lack of affective involvement with objects. Furthermore, excessively good reality testing of the immediate issue may lead to poor over-all relations to reality and may have a detrimental effect on the other ego functions. A person who is always right, one who is emotionally isolated, cannot be creative because of a lack of regression in the service of the ego. Thus persons with obsessive character disorders are likely to be best at the testing of objective reality at the cost of other functions. The presence of anxiety may enforce constant testing of reality to the point where the regression of perceptual acuity in the service of the ego, as postulated by Kris (1952), may be impossible, and insomnia, obsessive watchfulness, and lack of spontaneity or creativeness may result. Very poor judgment, hallucinations, and delusions are the most dramatic manifestations of disturbance in the sphere of reality testing.

Disturbances in the Sense of Reality. Disturbances in the sense of reality are probably among the most frightening human experiences and frequently provide the impetus for psychiatric consultation. There are, of course, many physiological disturbances of the sense of reality. Hypnagogic phenomena often occur on becoming very sleepy, on waking from a deep or drugged sleep, or on falling asleep. Feelings of lightheadedness experienced in severe fatigue or due to hyperventilation are generally mild forms of feeling of unreality. Mildly pathological forms of disturbance in the sense of reality occur with emotional isolation; a person who removes himself from the scene and becomes solely a spectator, who thinks out consciously (in an obsessive way) what to say next, will generally experience feelings of loss or lack of spontaneity and estrangement. *Déjà vu* occurs in normal people in stressful situations but is excessive in schizophrenics to whom everybody and everything seems familiar. Oneirophrenia, as a symptom or syndrome, is characterized by a dreamlike feeling about the world. Generally, feelings of unreality and depersonalization are related to the generating of unconscious hostile feelings.

Cosmic delusions—of being one with the world, part of the trees, of being able to know what the birds are talking about, of professing to experience the feelings of others—are frequent schizophrenic disturbances of the sense of reality. Outstanding are the symptoms of varying forms and degrees of depersonalization. The body image and its disturbances are obviously involved in the loss of a sense of reality. An extension of the body image, with loss of ego boundaries, as postulated by Federn, is basic to many ideas of reference, such as being constantly influenced by machines, rays, or various unrelated events.

2. REGULATION AND CONTROL OF DRIVES

The development of the regulation of instinctual drives involves the interaction of maturational phases of drive increase and drive decrease, and control, and a hierarchy of learned patterns of behavior frequently subsumed under the heading of socialization of the child.

There may be congenital differences in drive endowment; certainly environmental factors may activate or dull drives. The control of drives depends on both the strength of the drive push and on acquired means of dealing with drives. While we cannot enter into a discussion of the relative role of superego and ego in control of drives, it may suffice to say that the outstanding characteristic of disturbances in superego control is that one is usually dealing with an *unintegrated* superego, too weak in certain respects, too rigid in others, rather than an overstrict or too lenient superego.

It is the ego's task to engage in *detour behavior*—to postpone an immediate gratification for a delayed but greater one, and the more complex the society, the more hierarchies of detour behavior. *Frustration tolerance* and *anxiety tolerance* are important factors in the control of behavior, as is the tolerance of ambiguity in social situations, e.g., in the democratic way of life.

The concept of sublimation, and later the concept of the neutralization of drive energy (Hartmann, 1955; Kris, 1955), were formulated to describe the transformation of raw drive energy into forces in the service of the ego's adaptive functions. Libidinization of anxiety (a term coined by Kris [1941] to denote a situation wherein anxiety-arousing activity becomes pleasurable as long as the anxiety does not rise to an intolerable level) may be another means of dealing fairly successfully with some sexual and aggressive components. This is a device frequently employed by mountain climbers, test pilots, hunters, certain creative people, etc.

DISTURBANCE IN THE REGULATION AND CONTROL OF DRIVES

There may be a history of the lack of or an incomplete acquisition of control of excretory functions as primary models, and this may carry over later to other forms of behavior. Or we may encounter incomplete acquisition or loss of previously acquired control of more complex behavior. The identification figures and their responses to the child will be of paramount importance in this connection.

Conduct and habit disorders (in the official nomenclature) are early evidence of disturbance of control: tantrums, bedwetting, tics, nailbiting, etc. Neurosis, character disorders, and psychosis are their later equivalents.

Here, again, there are physiological manifestations of disturbances in drive control, in fatigue, for instance, and sometimes during adolescence, or menses, and at other times of marked physiological changes.

Slips of the tongue and other parapraxes are small everyday examples of lack of control of drives. Accident proneness, impulsivity, and tension states are other instances. "Acting out" may be a way of life in certain subcultures, such as the artistic world. Ultimately, there are, of course, the psychotic mannerisms, catatonic and manic excitement, the psychomotor slow-up of depression, and the rigidity of catatonia.

Tests designed to gauge expressive characteristics, such as figure drawing, especially Mira's Myokinetic Psychodiagnostic test (1958), and handwriting may reveal disturbances in drive control. Plot sequences of Thematic Apperception Test stories may reveal problems of drive regulations; Rorschach responses are, of course, of great value in this connection.

The clinical prodromata of manifest schizophrenia are often marked by episodes of loss of drive control: people who were formerly quiet and withdrawn suddenly become overactive, loud, and boisterous (without even the seeming happiness of manics) and then, rapidly, become hallucinated and deluded. Others who had been very inhibited sexually suddenly become promiscuous; those who were passive and compliant become aggressive.

In the acute schizophrenias of military personnel, the removal of external social restraints by virtue of a changed environment often seems related to the sudden loss of control: when a girl from a small town who had always lived close to her family is transported halfway across the world with her graces at a premium in a frustrated male population, she will require greater ego control than before to maintain equilibrium. By the same token, the sudden loss of privacy in military life deprives many a soldier of those protective, phobic, or obsessive-compulsive devices that previously enabled him to maintain control. The homosexual environment frequently adds intolerable strains to a person with barely controlled homoerotic strivings.

In schizophrenic pathology, both the nature of the drive and the attempt at control are frequently revealed in the content and form of delusion, hallucination, and motor behavior, which may be viewed as compromise formations between the struggling forces.

3.   OBJECT RELATIONS

The "ego" develops with the organism's increasing ability for perceptual differentiation. In this sense, the ego has been compared to an end organ; be that as it may, object relationship (as conceptualized in the libido theory) is an essential function of the ego. The primary function of the ego is to serve as a contact with reality and its objects.

Object relations have often been characterized by qualifying adjectives or trait names of analytic psychology, such as oral, anal (sadistic, masochistic), phallic, voyeuristic, exhibitionistic. In pathological terms, object relations are sometimes referred to as phobic, obsessive, hysterical, schizoid, or by such modifying terms as ambivalent, hostile, etc.

Curiously enough, all of these terms refer to the qualitative aspects of object relations. Little is found in psychoanalytic literature concerning the intensity of object relations. Yet this concept is important and dynamically useful. Schopenhauer's parable of the porcupines who on a cold winter day moved together to warm each other only to move apart because they hurt each other with their quills pertains here. They moved back and forth until they found the optimal distance at which they could give each other some warmth without inflicting too much discomfort. Thus we might speak of the "porcupine index" as the *distance in object relationships* which the person finds most comfortable. There are some who, at best, can only live in juxtaposition to each other, like Piaget's children at the stage of the collective monologue; there are those who need dramatic and complete closeness—who must virtually sit in each other's lap emotionally. Marital partners often control the intensity of their object relationships by limiting the frequency of contact; the husband may travel a great deal for business, the wife may be absorbed in community affairs. Sociometry has concerned itself with certain aspects of frequency (extent of contact) and intensity of object relations.

Psychoanalysts have found, of course, that the manifest aspects of object relationships is not a reliable guide to their actual nature, unless supplemented by dream and fantasy: what may appear to be a heterosexual relationship may turn out to be homosexual or narcissistic on closer inspection. Masturbation fantasies are probably the best single clue to the understanding of object relationships.

DISTURBANCES IN OBJECT RELATIONSHIPS

Such disturbances take many forms, and indeed constitute the main subject matter of all psychodynamics. Curiously enough, however, a one-to-one relationship does not necessarily obtain between the degree of disturbance in object relationships and the manifest pathology.

Most authorities would probably agree that many patients with character disorders must be considered more narcissistic than a good many schizophrenics, without the accompanying schizophrenic symptoms in the past or present or likely to appear in the foreseeable future. By the same token, there are schizophrenic patients who either had, or still have, good object relations even at the oedipal stage, or who, at least, have object relationships which are as good as those of a mere neurotic. Therefore, while the presence of narcissistic object relationships may be a further confirmatory sign of a psychosis, its presence or absence cannot serve as a diagnostic criterion, as earlier proponents of the libido theory would have it. This proposition is an important departure from the essentially libidinal consideration of psychosis of earlier decades toward the consideration of the total ego functioning as a diagnostic criterion.

Hartmann (1953), however, makes an important point when he differentiates narcissistic overinvestment of the self from narcissistic overinvestment of the ego. Self and ego (the latter defined as the totality of ego functions) can be fairly well differentiated, and it might well be that narcissistic character disorders are primarily distinguished by an overcathexis of the self. Schizophrenics, on the other hand, may be characterized by less investment in the self and more libidinization, that is, more libidinal overcathexis of various ego functions.

It therefore becomes important to define our frame of reference: to understand whether we are speaking of excessive narcissistic cathexis of the self or of narcissistic cathexis of the ego. (For the sake of clarity and accuracy it would be better to speak of narcissistic cathexis of a particular ego function rather than of the total ego; rarely are all of the ego functions narcissistically cathected.) To be more specific, a narcissistic cathexis of the thought processes would consist of a reification of thought, of the endowment of one's own thought with omnipotence, of an equation of one's thoughts with action, and with an ever-present awareness of the thought processes. Thought, in this sense, has lost its "trial action" aspect (Freud), has lost its object directedness, has lost its (semantic) symbolism, and has become overvalued as a thing unto itself. The economic viewpoint regarding characteristics of this phenomenon is, of course, only one of many; one could study it from the standpoint of developmental characteristics, formal aspects, etc.

On the other hand, hypercathexis of the self may well lead one to overvalue one's own importance, although even in the extreme this does not necessarily imply the existence of a psychosis. In true megalomania, of course, both narcissism of the self and narcissism of the ego function of thinking obtain and are interdependent.

Disturbances in the ego's relations to objects are, of course, manifold. Spitz (1945a, 1946a, 1951a) has described the psychotoxic and psychic deficiency diseases of infancy as early disturbances of the object relationship. Kanner, Mahler, and others have described the "objectless" autistic child; Mahler (1952) has described the specific lack of separation of the self from mother as an object in the symbiotic psychoses. Symbiotic object relations with the mother or mother surrogates are frequent and typical in adult schizophrenics; in the treatment situation they really want to merge with the therapist. More than just being orally dependent, they cannot conceive of the other person as having an existence except in relationship to themselves and vice versa. Excessive clinging, the expectation that their thoughts can be read, their needs divined, are manifest in these patients. Such object relations are often characterized by emotional storms of great intensity.

Very often the intensity of personal relations is accompanied by a fear of closeness, indeed a fear of "being swallowed up" and such relationships must be broken by the patient, frequently with great violence, as Eissler has described in great dynamic detail. When an attempt was made to rehabilitate hospital discharged schizophrenics by transitory employment in a workshop (Bellak, et al., 1956a), those patients with the type of emotional make-up described above proved a great deal more difficult to treat than the type of schizophrenic whose object relations are tangential, withdrawn, and whose capacity for interaction is at a minimum. Indeed, such a program of rehabilitation of schizophrenics could be conceived of as training in the tolerance for object relationships.

Finally, I would point out that what is frequently considered extraversion and sociability in a patient may occur, at best, at the anaclitic level and may have an erratic and superficial quality. The cocktail party is an excellent vehicle for what might be called "anaclitic sociability." Anaclitic object relations, in brief, are characterized by interactions where the other person is merely a source of (unilateral) direct drive gratification and is easily exchanged for any other object—in distinction to object constancy in the case of sublimated drives. Needless to say, a patient who, by virtue of having been class president, or cheerleader, or clubman, or who boasts of a promiscuous sex life, may give the impression of extraversion, cannot necessarily be said to have healthy object relations. Thus the concepts of manifest "extraversion" or "introversion" are of little diagnostic value.

4.   THOUGHT PROCESSES

Surprisingly, a great deal of misunderstanding and confusion seem to exist concerning the essentials of the psychoanalytic theory of thought, specifically the nature of the primary and secondary processes.

Primary and secondary processes may be considered from a genetic standpoint and from a formal standpoint. Genetically, as mentioned earlier, the perceptions of the infant are at first diffuse. Slowly increasing differentiation takes place—visually, spatially, and temporally, as well as in all other sense organs. As long as the child has no clear articulation of time and space, it lives in the world of Alice in Wonderland. As clearer conceptualizations are formed, the secondary process is gradually established.

In other words, the secondary process develops out of the primary process, but not to the exclusion of the latter: the memory of the poorly defined perceptual mass remains and constitutes the underpinning of the more rational secondary process. In connection with projective tests, I have used Herbart's (see Runes, 1942) concept and conceived of contemporary apperception (and thinking) as a resultant of the adaptive response to present stimuli *and* the past apperceptive mass. What is often almost romantically and overdramatically referred to as the "unconscious" is largely this mass of past apperceptions which, in their extremes of poor form and misconception, enter the world of dreams and psychosis or "contaminate" the contemporary thinking or adaptive processes, as in the parapraxes. They often emerge from preconsciousness rather than unconsciousness.

DISTURBANCES OF THE THOUGHT PROCESS

Although not among the first to emerge, disturbances in the thought process are among the most sensitive indicators of serious ego disturbance. Anxiety in relation to loss of impulse control, and very labile, uncontrolled affectivity, generally occur earlier in (acute) schizophrenia than do the thought disorders.

The formal characteristics of the primary process (the emergence of which constitutes the thought disorder) were originally identified by Freud and have been variously described since, as by Holt (1956): "First: the more 'primary' the thinking, the more it is organized and compelled by drives. Second: primary thinking can be recognized not only from its preoccupation with instinctual aims. It also has certain peculiar formal characteristics. These include autistic logic instead of straight thinking, loose and nonsensical types of associative links, and distortion of reality in numerous ways." These formal characteristics are largely identical with those also observed in children by Piaget (1923, 1936, 1937): the lack of referents in time and place, anthropomorphism, concretism, syncretism; and such characteristics as described first by Freud in connection with dreams: condensation, displacement, turning into the opposite, identity of opposites, using *pars pro toto,* symbolism, etc. The formal characteristics of the secondary process, on the other hand, attain their highest form in pure logic.

In essence, the secondary process as an ego function implies the ego's ability to scan selectively and to avoid "contamination" by inappropriate material. As long as the ego is sound the structure of the secondary process reigns; when it fails, the content and form of the primary process re-emerge.

The Rorschach test has certainly superseded all classical clinical procedures for the discovery of thought disturbances. However, it must be remembered that the manifest presence of some occasional characteristic of the primary process is not by itself a sign of schizophrenia, or for that matter of any pathology at all. Holt's index of primary thinking may be very useful for the solving of this problem in the future. Adolescents, artists, people who have had experience with free associating are particularly likely to show occasional signs of primary-process thinking without its necessarily having any pathological significance.

Again, a measure of regression, of faulty judgment, may be in the service of the ego, as Kris (1952) and Hartmann (1939) have pointed out. Jones (1953, 1955, 1957), in his discussion of genius, has suggested that an outstanding characteristic of Freud was a mixture of credulity on some occasions and subsequent brilliant sharpness in his thinking. It seems to be a variation of regression in the service of the ego to permit a testing of limits in periods of seeming stupidity which then give rise to the formulation of some new conception or the particularly clear delineation of a problem. Indeed, it is probably on that wavering boundary line between primary and secondary processes that genius and mental illness meet (when there is any potential talent).

The formal characteristics of schizophrenic thinking are identical with the formal descriptive characteristics of the primary process.

5. DEFENSIVE FUNCTIONS OF THE EGO

Repression was the first defense mechanism described by Freud, and only later did the approximately one dozen more specifically labeled defenses come under consideration, notably by Anna Freud (1936). In essence, the defenses are the main aspects of the ego's service as a barrier against external and internal stimuli. More specifically, the defenses provide various means of selectively dealing with internal and external stimuli: repression has come to be accepted as an important, normally present aspect of the mind. It is involved in any directed thinking or action, in that selective scanning, focusing, and purposive behavior simultaneously involve the exclusion from awareness and action of a tremendous number of other possible responses.

A systematic statement of the concept of the defenses has not yet appeared in the literature; semantic problems, anthropomorphisms, lack of definitions abound. By virtue of the fact that repression is an integral part of psychic functioning, we may conclude that it is, of necessity, a component of every other defense mechanism (a point not usually explicitly stated in psychoanalytic literature). Thus all other defenses involve repression plus certain other features: reaction formation involves the repression of one drive and the exaggeration of the opposite drive—love and hate, activity and passivity, nurturance and succorance, etc. I have discussed the complexities of projection before (see Chapter 11). Academically and clinically, denial is easily one of the most interesting distortions— with a central scotoma and centrifugal associations, including the affective changes so well described by Lewin (1950).

There is certainly suggestive evidence that a relationship exists between individual types of defenses and general organismic factors. The work of Fries and Woolf (1953) suggests that congenital activity type may be one possible determinant of the type of defense employed, at least with regard to its being relatively more alloplastic or autoplastic in nature.

Clinically speaking, defenses have been considered most importantly from the related viewpoints of the time of their occurrence in ontogenesis and their relative pathogenicity. By and large, the earlier it emerges the more primitive a defense, and the more pathological in adult life. Extensive denial and very marked projection probably vie for first place with regard to seriousness of pathology, by virtue of their effect on the person's adaptation to reality.

DISTURBANCES OF DEFENSIVE FUNCTIONING

An appraisal of the patient's defensive functioning is, of course, of prime diagnostic importance. Jacobson's paper on "Denial and Repression" (1957) contains an excellent discussion of defenses in relation to schizophrenia. Aside from an assessment of the actual operation of defense mechanisms, it is necessary to examine the relative stability or lability of the defenses: the potential for change from one type of defense to another, and the relative likelihood of, for example, obsessive isolation or phobic withdrawal developing into depersonalization and projection in given circumstances are important criteria. These statements highlight the fact that the "defensive process" and the result of that process are generally treated as interchangeable, although this does not seem practical: strictly speaking, it might be preferable to view depersonalization as a subjective state arrived at by various defensive means rather than as a defense in itself.

In its broadest sense, the loss of defensive functions overlaps largely with the concept of the failure of the synthetic function of the ego: If repression fails, and the primary process emerges, the patient seems unable to "hold together"; there is inability to concentrate, the memory is impaired, general efficiency is greatly decreased. It seems as if so much energy is being used up just for the barrier function of the ego (countercathexis), that hardly any is left for adaptive, spontaneous functioning. In the rigid preschizophrenic most of the energy is used for "barrier" function. Once the psychosis has become manifest, the barrier itself has failed and efforts at psychotic restitution are made. Overreaction to any stimulus, with great lability of mood, is a frequent result and is characteristic of acute incipient schizophrenia. The failure of repression may result in *déjà vu* experiences, in an increase in parapraxes of all sorts, in minor impairment of control, a lack of control of drives. Overcontrol of affect, ideation, and motor functioning may constitute a last-ditch fight against the breakthrough; disturbing dreams of a relatively undisguised nature may be further evidence of the loss of repression, as may be the presence of frightening hypnagogic phenomena. A weakening of repression may manifest itself particularly at those times when the ego is normally weakened.

If one follows a number of patients in their development from relative health into greater illness and back to improvement of recovery, one may study the relative sameness of psychological *content* under varying forms of defenses. Principally, character traits may change into a neurotic form of defense and into psychotic phenomena such as delusions and hallucinations and back again: a reaction formation against hostility in terms of neurotic behavior may change into a religious delusion of being Christ (by means of a projection of that hostility on the environment) who saves the world from destruction, that is, the patient's own destructive impulses.

6. AUTONOMOUS FUNCTIONS OF THE EGO

It has become customary to link Freud's postulation of "primary, congenital ego variations" with Hartmann's (1950a) concept of autonomous ego functions (perception, intention, object comprehension, thinking, language, productivity) as functions of the conflict-free sphere of the ego to which also belong phases of motor development and other maturational processes related to the learning process. It would be well to state explicitly that primary ego variations are probably paralleled by primary libidinal variations—that is, primary differences in drive endowment, discussed earlier in this chapter. Such a consideration seems basic, for instance, to Mahler's concept of the "autistic" childhood psychosis (in distinction to symbiotic psychosis) where the motivational relationship to the outside world seems weak.

In connection, with primary variations, it may be well to remember that science too has its vogues, and that times of relative liberality of spirit, such as those which followed the destruction of time-honored symbols after the French Revolution and World War I, are likely to stress environmental causation and deny the direct influence of genes and parentage. Times of relative conservatism such as those which followed World War II are likely to emphasize genetic propositions. Thus the current upsurge of interest in congenital variations in psychoanalysis may well be part of a trend of the times, as is the increased interest in biological aspects of psychiatry in distinction to psychogenesis.

In their broadest sense, these autonomous ego functions constitute organismic aspects of the personality which are primary—of genetic, intrauterine, intrapartum, or possibly early postpartum etiology (in terms of Spitz's postulates). Since the term "constitutional" is varyingly used, one might more specifically consider anthropometric aspects (such as Sheldon's [Sheldon et al., 1940] somatotypes) as syndromes of primary ego variations. Hartmann has pointed out that these primary variables may, of course, become involved in secondary problems of ego activity, including conflictual behavior.

DISTURBANCE OF AUTONOMOUS FUNCTIONS

Diagnostic appraisal of the disturbance of autonomous functions is of great clinical significance. The lay public is always impressed by the fact that schizophrenics, "crazy" people, can be very intelligent or proficient in any number of skills: linguistic, artistic, mathematical, etc. That is, certain autonomous ego functions may be affected by the schizophrenic process while others are not. Mathematical ability, in particular, may develop in lieu of object relations of a less abstract nature and may be a substitute for contact by language (Rosen, 1953). Intelligence, or some other ego function such as motility (in dancers), may be particularly well developed in some schizophrenics because this ego function was particularly favored during early development, at the cost of the more even development of other ego functions.

The classical concept of dementia praecox implies that the process of the illness produces a deterioration of intelligence; Bleuler's formulations initiated the dynamic wedge into the static concept of dementia praecox. Long-standing schizophrenia may, by disuse of the secondary process, by progressively failing attempts to withstand conflict, lead to stages of regression which might be termed vegetative states (excellently described and discussed by Arieti [1955]); on the other hand, many schizophrenics, even without treatment, never do regress or deteriorate to any such marked extent or, for that matter, to any general extent, but merely show an impairment of certain ego functions in certain areas. Thus paranoids may be completely intact, even in their thinking process, except in the specific areas of projection which constitute their symptomatology. While this seems clinically true, it is one of the facts which will bear thorough investigation by future experimentation and psychological testing. The clear sensorium of schizophrenics is generally mentioned as a differential diagnostic criterion (from organic psychoses) in standard textbooks, although, admittedly, this may not hold true for incipient schizophrenics.

Adolescents may present particular diagnostic problems, not only because of their increased drive as a primary datum, but also because so many of the autonomous functions are placed at the service of these drives and the defenses against them. Frequently it is difficult to decide whether evidence of such impairment of ego function is deserving of the schizophrenic label, or whether a less serious diagnosis, and one which is more favorable prognostically, might be justified. An early life history of relative health may be one of the determining differential criteria.

7. SYNTHETIC FUNCTION OF THE EGO

Nunberg (1931) has spoken of the synthetic function of the ego "as its ability to unite, to bind, and to create." One might almost interpret this as the ego's ability to form Gestalten; wider, in a sense, than just the peripheral concept, this definition includes a "buffering" ability. In any event, the synthetic function is probably the aspect which overlaps most with all other ego functions and is most highly correlated with the general concept of ego strength, much the way in which vocabulary is correlated with general intelligence.

The synthetic function certainly involves energetic, quantitative propositions. One is reminded of the image of the housewife with a basket and too many parcels and articles, who tries to hold on to one article only to drop first it and then another, in an uneven struggle between carrying capacity and burden. Janet used the term "psychasthenia" in this context to connote the splitting off of certain activities or functions because of psychic "weakness." Bleuler's delineation of the outstanding schizophrenic characteristic—looseness of association—may be dynamically described as the emergence of features of the primary process; economically this symptom relates to the low synthetic function of the ego of the schizophrenic, characterized by the ease of regressing from the secondary process.

In a similar but somewhat less colorful way, Siipola (1950) has conceptualized disturbances in the Rorschach as a defect of the synthesizing function: when a schizophrenic is faced with form and color, his ego may be unable to form one coherent Gestalt and the result may be a contamination like the classical "green grassbear." The normal ego, on the other hand, may be able to synthesize these two aspects into a "chameleon." With regard to the example above, Hartmann's (1950a) term, "organizing" function of the ego, has much to recommend it. However, an over-all concept of the synthetic function of the ego seems useful for clinical purposes: the interchangeability of symptoms which may range from primarily psychological manifestations to those which are primarily somatic, supports a "G" like Spearman's "G," which stands for general intelligence, a synthetic variable. The low incidence of allergic disorders in psychotics, and the return of allergic complaints after improvement or recovery, is probably one of the best documented instances of such interchangeability predicated on some generalized inability to "bind" (in a chemical sense) the divergent valences of the schizophrenic organism.

In this broad sense, the concept of the synthetic function overlaps considerably with other areas of ego functioning. Nevertheless, it seems to have enough specificity to support its independent status.

Disturbances in the synthetic function of the ego have already been touched upon in the foregoing description of this function. The patient's difficulties in appreciating the hierarchical arrangement of cause and effect, in the differentiation of figure and ground, in the use of *pars pro toto,* are, of course, also manifested in many physiological states, such as the dream, and in organic disabilities, such as the aphasias.

In schizophrenia, the degree of sickness, the patient's inability "to take it" (underlying the poor frustration tolerance, poor control, etc.), is most usefully subsumed under the concept of failure of synthesis. It manifests itself in the frustrating struggle of the therapist who often feels that no sooner has he "plugged one hole" than another opens—the constant stream of emergencies, of precarious situations, dynamically and realistically, which can tire the most energetic and engender a feeling of hopelessness in patient and therapist. To borrow a term from Lois Murphy (1956), the "coping" ability of the schizophrenic seems slow, and troubles constantly spill over in one area of functioning or another.

DEVELOPMENT OF THE EGO FUNCTIONS AND SCHIZOPHRENIA

The theory of the development of the ego involves propositions concerning organismic maturation of congenitally varying *Anlagen,* propositions concerning the acquisition of responses (psychoanalytic learning theory) in interrelationship with the environment, and propositions concerning the interaction of maturational and learned factors (phase specificity).

It would be well to keep in mind that "the ego" does not come about overnight; it is not borne in toto like Pallas Athene from the head of Zeus. As far as maturational factors are concerned, we must assume that certain types of "Anlagen" are present on genogenic, intrauterine, congenital bases, and may possibly manifest themselves from the first cry on (or earlier) in such precursors of organized relation to reality as postulated by Fries and Woolf (1953) in the concept, mentioned earlier, of congenital activity types. Imprinting, however, as shown by Lorenz (1935) and Tinbergen (1951, 1953) in their studies of animals, may well take place so early that much that appears as congenital may be environmental after all. As far as development in response to stimuli (as well as maturation) is concerned, it might be well to remember Spitz's (1946b, 1957b) observation of precursors of object relationship and such early vaguely differentiated phenomena as the smiling response. Furthermore, Glover's (1955) concept of ego nuclei is useful in accounting for the fact that some functions subsumed under the concept of the ego may begin earlier and others develop later, and that the concept of the ego as a well-integrated organization of responses is appropriate only at varying chronological points.

There is some observational and some experimental evidence, and it seems likely on neurological and general developmental grounds, that there is little differentiation of psychic functions in the infant prior to six months, Melanie Klein notwithstanding.[3]

At first, probably, the infant's sensory impressions are hazy, figure and ground are not well differentiated, the infant is unable truly to separate his own body from the rest of the world, or differentiate the proprioceptive and other subjec-

---

[3] Melanie Klein (1932, 1948) and her students conceive of infant development differently. In essence, they postulate perceptual organization virtually from birth on. Early ego functions are concerned with imagery revolving around the "good breast" and the "bad breast" and complex introjections and projections thereof. The "paranoid position" occurs in the third to fourth month of life and the depressive position in the sixth month. Her school maintains that the schizophrenic syndrome is, in essence, predicated on these early ego-object disturbances. Without entering into a detailed discussion at this point, I must tentatively reject this hypothesis primarily because it is difficult for me to conceive of the organism being endowed so early with such sharp perceptual qualities and such complex mechanisms, or with innate ideas, as Klein proposes.

tive perceptions from reality per se. There is, in fact, some evidence that the body and mind are *one* at this stage in the sense that perceptual stimulation seems necessary for somatic development. Braceland (1951) recently pointed out that Magoun (1952) has uncovered a diffuse afferent mechanism, sensitive to the total amount of external stimulation—a mechanism involved in the regulation of sleep and wakefulness and in the facilitation or inhibition of every sort of organismic activity. He continued: "It is a mechanism which may well be responsible for the phenomena observed by Spitz and others, that the amount of total stimulation during early infancy has an important influence on normal development." Spitz (1945a, 1946a) speaks of the "somatopsyche" up to the sixth month and has described "hospitalism" and "anaclitic depression" as clinical syndromes related to this concept.

Only when the perceptions become well enough differentiated into figure and ground so that the child can separate the surface of his own body from the environment can he be expected to tell the difference between himself and the rest of the world. We may arbitrarily consider this point as the beginning of the "self," one aspect of which we find it useful to speak of as the "ego."

Starting thus with the body as a figure and the rest of the world as a ground, the infant acquires other differentiations: he reacts differently to a smiling face than to a scowling one; by eight months he is able to differentiate others from the mother figure. With the ability to discriminate comes the accumulation of experience and the need to separate one stimulus from another, and the present from the past. Thus, the ego is, at first, that aspect of mental functioning concerned with the ordering of reality into figure and ground with regard to contemporary stimuli and their relationship to past experiences. In the most severe disturbances of the mental functioning, notably schizophrenia, this differentiation of body and the rest of the world, and of past and present, breaks down again, at least in part.

This ability of the ego to differentiate between figure and ground has recently been interestingly related to the brain. Linn (1954) has studied perceptual functions in the brain injured and observed defenses as Freud described them. Subscribing to Pitts and McCulloch's (1947) concept of "scanning," Linn believes that the ego tests apperceptions (in a scanning operation) as long as it is intact, but that brain defects may interfere with the efficiency of that scanning. He does not say so, but one might surmise that this takes place in some nonlinear relation to Lashley's (1938) concept of mass action and relative equipotentiality of the brain. Linn leaves the relationship to "functional" ego defect open, though this seems unnecessary. The scanning function of the ego can easily be understood as interfered with if circumstances so strongly revive past apperceptions as to distort each contemporary apperception to a point where it may no longer be perceived clearly as figure and ground. The phenomena of *déjà vu* in normals (at times of anxiety in a new environment) or in certain schizophrenics, who feel that they have seen every person they meet before or that he resembles someone seen before, most clearly illustrates this point. Wilder Penfield's recent report on the eliciting of previously inaccessible discrete memories, inclusive of affect, upon electrical focal stimulation of the brain, supports the psychoanalytic theory of unconscious memory.

The *reality-testing* function can be considered a structural capacity of the ego, namely in its ability to keep the effect of all but a few selected pertinent past apperceptions upon the contemporary apperception to a minimum (scanning); that is, to apply only those past apperceptions which have proved useful in dealing with a reality situation. If inappropriate apperceptions gain access to the conscious perceptual and motor apparatus, feelings and behavior inappropriate to reality may result.

We speak of this reality-testing function as associated with a structural aspect of the ego for this reason: If the personal history is of such a nature that apperceptions were clearly articulated (good configurations), and if the child developed good object relations, then the structural organization of the apperceptions is a firm one and not easily disrupted by disturbing contemporary apperceptions or drives. The healthy ego, because of a "good" organization of the memory traces and past apperceptions, keeps a firm grip on reality even in adversity or in monotonous circumstances. The ego's function as a barrier against excessive external and internal stimuli is related to the reality-testing function.

Thus, in summary, the ego selects and organizes those apperceptions which are conscious or can easily become conscious and which are continuously part of the contemporary apperceptions in a way which permits one to differentiate (by experience) various figure and ground judgments, e.g., external versus internal, and permits one generally to exercise "good judgment" founded upon past experience (memory traces of past apperceptions) as to what is safe and what is not, what is probable and what is not.

Psychoanalysis speaks of the primary and secondary thought processes in this context. The primary-process type of thinking exists before there is good orientation and good perceptual articulation. The primary process is characterized by a poor concept or no concept of time and space and the logical relationship between cause and event. This world slowly evolves adaptively into the clearly perceived, logically related one of normal adult behavior.

Psychoanalytic theory maintains that the secondary process is a relatively thin layer superimposed upon the primary process and that in a variety of physiological situations (fatigue, sleep), maturational stages (adolescence, climacteric, senescence), and pathological conditions (intoxication, brain damage), the primary process emerges to a degree and manifests itself in irrational, uncontrolled, inappropriate, disoriented behavior. All the pathological phenomena observed in schizophrenia can be related to this re-emergence of the primary process. Each given case will then only require additional investigation of the type of thinking and related modes of behavior, of why the emergence of the primary process took place (for a variety of somatic and/or psychogenic reasons), why it took place at a particular moment, and why the pathology took one particular form rather than another: that is, why certain ego functions are more disturbed than others—why certain features of the primary process of thinking (and resultant action) are prominent and not others.

Psychoanalytic theory is also concerned with the answers to these particular questions. It involves hypotheses of possible primary ego variations concerning the synthetic function of the ego. It involves specific hypotheses concerning the acquisition of a well-integrated ego: consistent teaching by "good" identification figures of right and wrong, encouragement of, and noninterference with, curiosity, lack of excessive suppression and avoidance of excessive stimulation of drives, and provisions for sublimation and neutralization of a variety of drives. These are the processes involved in the creation of a healthy environment for a developing child.

In capsule form, Weil (1953) speaks of development as a transition from primary narcissism to object cathexis, from omnipotence and magical thinking to reality testing, from the pleasure principle to the reality principle. Quoting Bender, Kanner, Rank, and Geleerd, Weil provides an excellent discussion of disturbances in the ego development of preschizophrenic children. Such development is characterized by inadequate or uneven progression of the various ego functions. Clinically, she finds that this uneven progression may manifest itself in three types of problems: problems of social adaptation, manageability, and the presence of neurotic-like symptoms.

Of necessity, propositions concerning ego development are closely integrated with propositions concerning libidinal and superego development. Hartmann (1953), in a paper on the metapsychology of schizophrenia, speaks repeatedly of the need for a systematic theory interrelating libidinal and ego development. This condensed paper of Hartmann's is undoubtedly a most important and profound theoretical contribution on the development of schizophrenia. A monograph would be desirable which might serve as a parallel running commentary on the issues briefly touched upon and mentioned by implication, on the hypotheses which Hartmann puts forth in his own concentrated version of the private language of psychoanalysis. Furthermore, many worthwhile research projects might be initiated on the basis of many of Hartmann's propositions. Central to Hartmann's theme is the ability of the ego to "neutralize" drive energy and thus make it available for conflict-free functioning.

However, it is most practical for us at this time to depict further ego development and its disturbances by means of a systematic discussion of each of those ego functions, as delineated above, with comments on the contributions of Hartmann and others in their appropriate context.

1. DEVELOPMENT OF THE RELATIONSHIP TO REALITY

We have discussed *reality testing* and the *sense of reality* as basic components of the ego. The relationship to reality involves the entire perceptual development of differentiation into figure and ground, and the four-dimensional orientation (time and memory being included). The sense of reality is closely interrelated with the development of object relations. The sense of "self-ness" results from the differentiation of the self and other objects.

Anything that adds to confusion in a child's attempt to grasp reality—lying, vague information, e.g., about questions regarding sexual differences—is likely to lead to an impairment in the testing of reality and the sense of reality. (In this sense, concepts of schizophrenia derived from semantics and communication theory have a kernel of truth in them; however, they disregard many other significant aspects.) Bilinguality may lead to semantic confusion, just as the mixed cultural milieu in immigrant families may lead to confusion of standards of behavior, and, more important, to a lack of clear-cut identification figures. Inconsistent upbringing, alternating overpermissiveness with severely punitive outbursts, is likely to leave the child without any frame of reference for its be-havior, of a clear concept of what is right and what is wrong. To a certain ex-tent, propositions of conditioning psychology may be useful here in that con-fusion has been experimentally demonstrated in animals exposed to varying responses. However, most dynamic "learning" is primarily dependent on good object relationships wtih subsequent internalization of these objects. If such good identification figures are not available because the significant figures are either narcissistic, extremely inconsistent internally, or varying, as is the case in fre-quently shifted foster children, or those who are exposed to frequently changing governesses, the learning necessary for reality testing, for a sense of reality, will be absent.

The earliest development of the *adaptation* to reality has been studied by Spitz (1945b, 1946b), Escalona (1948), Mahler and Elkisch (1953), and others. Hartmann's statement that "the lability of neutralization, or its impair-ment, is a fundamental characteristic of the ego disorder in schizophrenia" (1953) is most relevent here. The problems in this area are closely related to the control and regulation of drives. One might also point out the effect of primary variations in drive endowment on adaptive capacity. The thin protec-tive barrier against stimuli in sensitive preschizophrenic or schizophrenic chil-dren, described by Bergman and Escalona (1949), can be a result of excessive stimulation of drives, or congenital weakness of the ego's synthetic function, or the poor psychological development of "learning," or a combination of all three factors. Obviously, organic conditions, such as epilepsy or postencephalitis, are outstanding examples of the manifestation of a "thin" barrier to stimuli predi-cated upon a disturbance of the integrative capacity of the brain.

2. DEVELOPMENT OF THE REGULATION AND CONTROL OF DRIVES

One aspect of the libido theory constitutes a timetable for the manifestations of the "partial" drives. Psychoanalytic pedagogy is in essence concerned with the best possible parental interaction with these forces in a way to produce minimal pathological conflict and maximal integration without crippling ex-pression. Contrary to some popular conceptions, healthy development does not mean maximal freedom of growing up but judicious phase-specific control: too much or too little regulation will result in difficulties. In controlling the drives of the growing child it is important neither to overstimulate nor to sup-press them. The concepts of the development of the superego are equally applicable here. Identification and introjection play central roles in learning to control drives.

The disturbances in the development of the control of drives have been most succinctly described by Spitz (1951a) in a paper on "Psychogenic Diseases in Infancy." He relates three-month colic to primary anxious overpermissiveness in the mother, infantile neurodermatitis to hostility covered by anxiety, hyper-motility of the infant to an oscillation of the mother's attitude between pamper-ing and hostility, aggressive hyperthymia to a conspicuously compensated hos-tility of the mother, and anaclitic depression and marasmus to partial or com-plete emotional deprivation, respectively. The relationship between these early variables and schizophrenia are discussed in detail below.

In somewhat later years, persistent overstimulation of sexual drives by nudity, sharing of bedrooms, etc., and the arousal of aggression and its frustration seem to play a major role in many histories of schizophrenics. The ego seemed unable to cope with the tremendous amount of drive aroused. Perspicacious upbringing of children provides no more drive stimulation than can be managed by the limited apparatus of the child's organism and its restricted possibilities for discharge. In the paper referred to above, Hartmann proposes a detailed study of the conditions under which neutralization of libidinal and aggressive drives seems feasible, or rather in what ways it is interfered with in preschizophrenic development. Even more pertinent is the investigation of what environmental conditions will lead to a "withdrawal" type of schizophrenia and which will result in psychopathic or sociopathic behavior. From some observations of pairs of children in the same family, it has seemed to me that unmasked hostility in the mother led to sociopathic schizophrenic manifestations in the one child, and compensated hostility and guilt in the mother led to a quasi-neurotic, manifestly drive-inhibited schizophrenia in the other. Excessive cathexis of pregenital and, seemingly, genital drives seems to account for the syndrome of infantilism, with primitive, stormy acting out of sexual and other behavior in some schizophrenics.

3. DEVELOPMENT OF OBJECT RELATIONS

The dynamic, structural, and economic aspects of metapsychology find their focus in the concept of the development of object relations. Vicissitudes of identification, and introjection particularly, stand at the center of psychoanalytic theory. The ego develops in relation to reality, to objects. The main aspects of the libido theory deal with the determinants of object relationships—maturational, environmental, and economic. All that has been said previously with regard to object perception, the development from narcissistic to symbiotic and anaclitic and constant object relations (where objects are not a means to an end but an end in themselves) is pertinent here. Spitz's observations and Mahler's differentiation between autistic and symbiotic psychosis are also relevant here.

Too frequently in analytic theory, single factors are considered critical for the development of successful object relations. There is no reason why the temperature sense (I. Hermann [1929] and, later, Bak [1939] have stressed a generally overlooked modality, the perception of temperature; more disturbed people respond more radically to temperature and temperature differences than do their better adjusted brethren) the visceral, proprioceptive, visual, or any other factor, should be decisive for such development or even of prime significance. There is every reason to believe that all of the sense modalities contribute to the differentiation of self and nonself—perhaps in varying order of appearance or in individually differing importance. Thus one may agree with Hartmann's (1956) comparison of ego development to a type of block-building.

Earlier in this chapter, we discussed the various types of object relationships, characterized by their respective trait names. We would mention again that distance, the "porcupine index," is a rarely considered aspect of object relations, and seems to have a developmental history of its own: children brought up in homes with detached, distant, weakly libidinal subcultures often grow up quite satisfied with maintaining that status in adult life. Character disorders, or more frequently schizophrenia simplex with its sociopathic features, result in extreme cases. As a character trait such distance is probably useful in people who must manipulate the fate of others with little personal involvement, as one frequently encounters in military life, the business world, politics, and other situations which sometimes call for a hard-bitten and unsympathetic approach.

We know that overattention to bodily functions, hypochondriasis of the mother, overstimulation, may cause excessive narcissism and by the same token, lessened object cathexis. The development of normal object cathexis, as described for the oedipal constellation, is precarious. Any disturbance of the significant objects in the child's life is likely to result in similar (or mirror-image) disturbances in the child. Thus one might logically expect that narcissistic, sadistic, poorly integrated parents will bring up schizophrenic offspring, even without the benefit of genetic transmission. When such children are not as deeply affected by these environmental factors as one might expect, their good fortune is usually attributable to certain substitute parental figures, such as siblings, aunts, neighbors, teachers, nurses, who can be thanked for the seeming recessiveness of the disorder. In this connection, Sechehaye's (1951a, 1951b, 1956) case histories provide the most detailed account of disturbances in object relations. Her therapeutic process consists, to a great extent, of the establishment, or re-establishment, of normal object relationships.

4. DEVELOPMENT OF THOUGHT PROCESSES

The development of the thought processes, as a basic component of early ego development, has already been discussed. The nature of the primary process, and its formal characteristics, has been described, as was its gradual evolution into forms of the secondary process. The absence of this change, or the reversal of the secondary to the primary thought process under psychogenic or physiological or somatically pathological conditions, constitutes the most constant symptom of schizophrenia.

5. DEVELOPMENT OF DEFENSIVE FUNCTIONS OF THE EGO

The development of the defensive functions of the ego is possibly genetically, or at any rate constitutionally, determined in part.

Repression, though undoubtedly an inherent organismic capacity for restructuring parts into a whole, is, to a large extent, learned in the course of childhood. "Training" often means training in first suppressing consciously—and later repressing—desires, tabooed perceptions, and in acquiring frustration tolerance, detour behavior. Far from representing a pathological process per se, a child must be permitted to repress material rather than being overstimulated beyond all reason, or unwisely enlightened by inappropriate interpretation.

The development of nonpathological, noncrippling defenses is one of the major tasks of child rearing. In essence, this means introducing modes of perception and expression which do not bring one into conflict with reality. The channeling of libidinal drives during latency into curiosity and the desire to acquire information seems a good example of change of drive direction, of aim and mode of expression. Obviously, a lack of excessive drive is important; the quality of autonomous function, particularly intelligence, is of paramount significance in the facilitation of this process. As mentioned earlier, the more inclusive concept of the neutralization of aggressive and libidinal energy requires exploration in this connection.

6. DEVELOPMENT OF THE AUTONOMOUS FUNCTIONS

The study of the development of the autonomous functions has largely belonged to the field of academic psychology, albeit with insufficient attention to dynamic details, but rather adequate accounting of the formal characteristics. Piaget (1923, 1936, 1937) is, of course, the outstanding contributor in this area. Psychoanalysts have contributed to our understanding of disturbances in the development of these functions, notably intelligence and pseudo-feeblemindedness (e.g., Rosen's [1953] analysis of a mathematician with strephosymbolia). Greenacre (1947) has by implication contributed to the problems of learning difficulties in connection with her study of vision, halo, and headache. However, the study of the development of motor characteristics has been neglected in both academic and psychoanalytic circles, with the exception of the Moro reflex, the startle pattern, and the observations of Fries and Woolf (1953) and Mittelmann (1954) and, to a certain extent, those of Spitz (1951b).

7. DEVELOPMENT OF THE SYNTHETIC FUNCTION OF THE EGO

Relatively little can be said about the development of this most important ego function. Synthetic function is, in essence, an abstraction and as such does not lend itself to specific tracing. There is no doubt that the ability to "bind," to organize and integrate into wholes, increases with age, and probably well into maturity. As mentioned earlier, the role of the synthetic function in relation to the ego may be compared to the role of Spearman's "G" for intelligence and, more than any other ego function, may be considered innate. Just as "G" may well be the final common path of many well-integrated specific functions, high synthetic function is correlated with performance, unruffled by external or internal storms. When synthetic function is poor, the child will show uneven performance, with possible excellence in one or another of the autonomous functions and poor motor performance, poor object relations, and a poorly developed secondary process. More than any other function, it can probably be said that "what is good for the development of a strong ego, is good for the synthetic function."

PATTERNS OF EGO FUNCTIONING: ASPECTS OF EGO STRENGTH AND EGO WEAKNESS

Psychoanalytic theory is predicated upon propositions concerned with the dynamic interaction of various forces—organismic, maturational, and congenital—with learned responses: the interaction of drives, the environment, and its internal representations.

In that sense, character and personality can be understood as patterns of compromise, as resultants of a field of diverse forces. Ego functioning, more specifically, must be described by its pattern: while it may be rather uneven— one ego function may be "better" than another—and the blend is likely to be unique ultimately, each given pattern may be classified roughly under diagnostic or descriptive headings.

Inasmuch as assessments of the degree of functioning are involved in descriptions of patterns of ego functioning, quantitative assumptions cannot be avoided. Psychoanalytic theory includes many quantitative statements, as might be expected in a theory in which forces and economy play a leading role. (The entire concept of libidinal cathexis in object relations and internal representations is, of course, a basically quantitative one.) However, psychoanalysts generally shy away from attempts at precise quantification, almost as though there were merit in vagueness per se. On the other hand, academic and experimental psychologists are inundated with more procedures for "accurate" measurement than one can reasonably make use of (or sense of). It must be possible realistically to adapt the methods of measurement to the raw data available.

Meaningful methods of measuring ego strength are possible if ego strength is defined as "the totality of the ego's capacity to perform its many functions." Such a formulation involves the Gestalt proposition that the whole may be more than the sum of the factors of which it is comprised, that qualitative variations exist (as postulated by Hegel's *"Umschlag von Quantität in Qualität"*). Also, ego strength must be viewed globally, very much like Wechsler's (1939) view of intelligence. However, the ego cannot be conceptualized as a perfect sphere, with each area of ego functioning constituting a radius, or even be compared in this context to the segments of an orange. The image that suggests itself is that of an uneven raspberry on which each surface point constitutes the terminus of one of the many ego functions. Furthermore, this protean raspberry might be made of stretchable rubber which would change its shape developmentally and be subject to momentary and daily variations, yet have some permanent characteristics.

1. ATTEMPTS AT EXPERIMENTAL VERIFICATION

Experimental investigation and attempts at operational definition of ego strength should consist of tests or scales, briefly outlined as follows, for each of the areas of ego functioning, namely:

(a) The *relation to reality* may be assayed by subtests which study *adaptive capacity* in original situations such as those used in the Office of Strategic Services (1948); physiologic tests of adaptiveness to autonomic drugs, to exercise and swirling in the Baranyi chair, studies of mental set under sodium amytal, etc. The Rorschach, etc. are good indicators of *reality testing*. The *sense of reality* may be tested by standard exposure to perceptual isolation.

(b) The *regulation and control of drives* may be assayed by expressive tests (Mira, 1958), by tests of frustration tolerance after Luria (1932) and others, and tests of anxiety tolerance, similar to those of Tomkins (1946) and Haggard (1946).

(c) Capacity to form *object relationships* may be tested by a modified Szondi (Deri, 1949; Szondi, 1952), by the use of the TAT, etc.

(d) Tests of *thought processes* primarily involve the use of the Rorschach, using Holt's index of primary-process activity and possibly the Kohs Block test, etc.

(e) The *defenses* may be assessed in stress interviews, in frustration experiments, on the Rorschach and the TAT, etc.

(f) Intelligence tests, ability tests, tests of deterioration provide an index of *autonomous functions*.

(g) The *synthetic function* may possibly be investigated by means of flicker-fusion tests, tests of concentration, tests of perceptual stability, physiological tests.

2. HISTORY

A standardized history should be taken, with weighted scores for definite items, including family history of illness, history of individual development, nature of object relations, etc.

3. PROBLEMS OF EVALUATION

All these test data must then be weighted, after empirical evaluation of their prognostic usefulness, so as to allow summation and conversion into what might be termed a "Diagnostic and Prognostic Index."

Furthermore, in order to construct the afore-mentioned tests and scales, the validity and reliability of each subtest must be clearly established; like the components of an intelligence test, each part must be validated for its ability to differentiate crucially. Each subtest must be administered to normals, neurotics, manic-depressives, patients with organic brain diseases, and schizophrenics in order to assess its ability to differentiate between those subjects who are more disturbed and those who are less. For this purpose, exchange and substitution of items will frequently be necessary.

All measurements refer to an ordinal scale. Thus, statements regarding a specific datum only concern its relative size in comparison to another datum, without an assumption of equidistance of quanta on this scale (that is, c may be three times bigger than b, while b is only twice as big as a). Such an ordinal scale permits rank ordering of data, a method which has been useful in a number of areas of psychological and other scientific investigations, for instance, the "hardness scale" in physics which recently, however, has been based on a mathematical foundation.

The principal problem involved in an over-all concept of ego strength is whether it is reasonable to consider degrees of ego functions as additive; or whether it is feasible to consider a person schizophrenic on the basis of the significant impairment of only *one* ego function (and not the others). While ego strength is related to the *total* performance capacity of the ego, every ego function must be individually appraised quantitatively (and qualitatively) on standard tasks. As on the Wechsler-Bellevue scale, the total score needs to be transformed into a meaningful over-all picture, but no clinician would study the latter without examining the pattern of subscores and the qualitative way in which they were obtained.

While psychoanalysts are likely to regard the quantitative assumptions involved in this conceptualization with misgivings, one must remember again that the whole analytic house is built on quantitative notions. We speak of more or less cathexis, stronger or weaker aggression, lessened or increased positive transference, etc. The fact that these quantitative statements are made loosely is not a virtue. The reason too little attention has been paid to attempts to quantify more precisely is probably related to the misconception held in clinical circles that all measurements involve metric measurement—which, as we mentioned, of course, they need not.

Quantification would, naturally, suffer from all the problems of any arbitrary definition. If, for instance, we should agree that a total ego strength (at present nebulous) from zero to 25 constitutes an ego strength consistent with the diagnosis of schizophrenia, there will be the problem of what to call an ego strength of 26. This would reasonably involve further elaboration of any given score.

One might question whether it is clinically and theoretically feasible for only one ego function to fall below a certain point of efficiency, and whether this constitutes cause for the diagnosis of schizophrenia. If, in a given case, all other functions are rated rather high, we are confronted with something like a reversed counterpart to the problems of idio-savants in the fields of intelligence. Such an enigma of seemingly apparent good function except in one area—as in paranoid states—is more likely to arise on gross clinical inspection than on close psychoanalytic examination of ego functions. It seems extremely unlikely that such a case could occur.

Once again it may be useful to compare our concept of ego strength to the models for intelligence. Originally, Stern (1913) conceived of intelligence as simply general abstracting ability (G). Thorndike, at the other extreme, conceived of intelligence as a series of discrete specific functions (s_1, s_2, s_3, etc.). It was left for Spearman to integrate these two concepts and speak of G plus s_1, s_2, etc. Probably the most frequently accepted notion today is that a general factor is usually highly correlated with certain specific functions and that factor analysis reveals clusters of varying functions. Present models of intelligence are likely to prove of value in the conceptualization of ego strength.

The ultimate goal is, of course, to establish accurate normative procedures for the diagnosis of ego strength and ego weakness and patterns of ego variation. Some ego functions may be more regularly or more crucially involved in schizophrenic disorders than others. The most widely agreed-upon criterion of diagnosis of schizophrenia is the presence of primary-process thinking, the factor most constantly associated with extreme ego weakness. Furthermore, thought disorder is not likely to appear in isolation and is certainly more reliably present than hallucinations or delusions (particularly in the early stages) or any particular libidinal constellation. However, assessment of the degree of thought disorder requires discussion and definition, particularly as investigated in projective techniques. Psychologists have often been too eager to make the diagnosis of schizophrenia because of some isolated contamination or bizarreness; each individual case must be carefully examined. As already mentioned, artists, psychoanalyzed subjects, and others are likely to have "looser" thought processes without a tendency to such looseness as might constitute the schizophrenic syndrome.

Functionally speaking, the concept of ego strength or weakness can be likened to physical structures. Just as stability constitutes ego strength, so does rigidity constitute an aspect of physical weakness, and flexibility an aspect of physical strength. One is reminded of the architecture of bridges, or even of steel and concrete skyscrapers, which are erected to allow a certain flexibility and thus fare much better than structures built as rigidly as possible. The rigid obsessive-compulsive patient sacrifices adaptability for the sake of some stability. The hysteric, with his fluctuating ego boundaries, stands at the opposite pole. In both cases, alcohol and other anesthetics, in their effect on brain function, may loosen the arrangement—"weaken the ego."

As mentioned earlier, a measure of flexibility is necessary for a number of normal functions. Creativity, artistic or scientific, can come about only if figure and ground relationships may change freely. This is most easily observable, of course, in the painter and photographer, but holds true even for such functions as telling stories in the TAT, or being able to free associate. Kris's (1952) concept of regression in the service of the ego, briefly referred to previously, is closely related to Hartmann's postulation of self-exclusion. While in both cases a measure of control is relinquished, this is interpreted as a measure of strength.

In free association, one must permit a poor definition of contemporary apperception, precisely in order that past images may emerge. In what this writer has previously termed the "oscillating function" of the ego, it is at the same time necessary that one be able to compare the past apperception with the contemporary apperception (in reality testing in analysis). Similarly, as Hartmann and Kris have pointed out, the ability of the ego to exclude itself, and regression in the service of the ego, permitting a "soft focusing" of the ego, as it were, are necessary for falling asleep, proper functioning in intercourse, and creativity.

In summary then:

(1) The psychoanalytic concept of the ego is best understood as the totality of ego functions.

(2) The ego's functioning is judged by the total integrated performance of its functions, of which we have singled out (following Beres):
  (a) the relation to reality
  (b) drive regulation
  (c) object relations
  (d) thought processes
  (e) defenses
  (f) autonomous functions
  (g) the synthetic function

(3) The ego will function well—will be strong—
  (a) If congenital, genetic, and constitutional equipment is "good." If hereditary factors are involved in the presence or absence of mental disease then it would seem that ego strength or its lack is what is inherited rather than a specific form of psychopathology. (Statistics by Pollock, Malzberg, and Fuller [1939] offer convincing proof that there is a greater incidence of varied psychiatric disorders rather than of particular ones in certain families.) It would also seem that actual libidinal and generally psychopathological constellations would be secondary to the primary inherited defect, or ego strength, in such instances.
  (b) If environmental circumstances permit consistent "learning."
  (c) If the id drives are not overwhelmingly intense because of primary endowment or as a result of secondary stimulation.
  (d) A fourth determinant of ego strength may be the so-called secondary factors of a physiological, pathological, and environmental nature. The most obvious effects on ego strength were, for example, discussed by Bychowski (1949) in a paper on the study of the brain wounded, and can be observed in lobotomies as well. I have already referred to the physiological variations encountered in sleep, dreams, hypnagogic phenomena (Silberer's [1909] functional phenomena), in exhaustion (Varendonck's [1921] preconscious fantasies), adolescence, pregnancy, climacteric, and senescence.

PSYCHOGENESIS AND SOMATOGENESIS OF SCHIZOPHRENIC EGO DISTURBANCE

Consistent with the foregoing propositions, it may now be stated that any event which is likely to lead to a primary developmental weakness of the ego or to a secondary weakening of the ego of "sufficient" severity (sufficient to produce disturbances of ego functions as discussed above) may lead to the schizophrenic syndrome. Since somatic illness may also cause these ego disturbances, we must separate those cases in which environmental factors are sufficiently traumatic to account for the lack of ego strength from early infancy on (or which may give rise to an ego weak enough to permit schizophrenic regressions after a relatively satisfactory progression has taken place) from those where they do not suffice, and which, therefore, necessitate postulation of genetic or somatic factors.

The higher mental phenomena are linked to cerebral and particularly to cortical functioning. Thus, any affliction of the cerebrum may express itself in changes in the mental processes. The precise correlations between these two factors have been searched for by such men as Francis Gall, Fleurens, Fritsch, Hitzig and Lashley, among others; Goldstein's (1936-37, 1948, 1949) and Lashley's (1938) experimental and clinical studies have shown how subtly brain damage may affect the learning mechanism and the perceptual and integrative apparatus in a broad sense. It is entirely conceivable that a considerable number of widespread afflictions of the cerebrum may so weaken the coordinating and integrating mechanisms (which are included in our over-all concept of the ego) as to bring about the disturbances encountered in schizophrenia. Some etiological studies have presented enough evidence to merit serious consideration. To this group belong cases ascribed to apparently proved organic brain disease, such as were described by Ferraro (1951), Roizin et al. (1945), and Polatin et al. (1944) which manifest the clinical symptom of classical dementia praecox. Every older psychiatrist knows of patients who were considered typical schizophrenics until the spinal Wassermann test proved them paretic. Such afflictions of the brain might be of a histological, chemical, metabolic, or genetic nature (histogenic, chemogenic, and genogenic, as Cobb calls them) aside from the psychogenic factors already mentioned. Sometimes senile changes, frequently attributed to nonexistent arteriosclerosis, and probably due to chemical alterations, may bring about a psychosis without memory defects which is clinically indistinguishable from a schizophrenia. (The induced toxic psychosis, which is also pertinent here, is discussed in detail below.)

SPECIFIC PSYCHOSOMATIC ASPECTS OF EARLY EGO DISTURBANCE

Certain undeniable clinically observable facts are partly responsible for the tenacious persistence of the "organic" and "psychogenic" schools of thought. There is no doubt that there is a group of schizophrenics often referred to as "typical cases of dementia praecox," "process type," "endogenous," etc., who were apparently always dull, never showed much promise or sparkle, were always peculiar, and who, sooner or later, rather quietly slip into a manifestly psychotic stage, albeit with little psychotic productivity, and an early almost vegetative state. Very often these poor people are markedly asthenic, have inadequate circulation, and seem generally underendowed.

These cases stand in dramatic contrast to the wide variety and great numbers of persons diagnosed as schizophrenic, particularly in the last decade, with the help of the Rorschach and psychoanalytic sophistication. Such patients are frequently labeled "latent," borderline, or incipient schizophrenics, and in their full-blown state are often encountered in military hospitals, private sanitaria, private practice (and, sometimes, of course, in state hospitals). Many of these persons have led relatively normal lives into adolescence or even adulthood, and were often, in fact, particularly talented. The onset of their psychosis is usually characterized by a dramatic acute episode, often with a good prognosis.

Thus, one might speak of the first group as schizophrenias characterized by a failure in "developmental" progression; the latter group may reach various levels of development (even the oedipal stage with real object relations). However, their toehold on "normality" is a precarious one; schizophrenic regression under various circumstances is an ever-present possibility.

To be sure, these two groups are by no means sharply differentiated. At best, one could speak of a bimodal curve of distribution, though the sharpness of the curve remains to be established. The qualitative differences between people diagnosed as schizophrenics vary very widely from the impulsive infantile to the vegetative, withdrawn patient, to the person who showed great promise in early life or those with social-psychopathic features; all have in common a poorly developed ego, combined with too much drive or too little drive, an overly severe superego or a weak superego, etc. Furthermore, even those patients with satisfactory progression up to a point may have a poor prognosis and become backward and vegetate in certain adverse circumstances, such as lack of therapy in the acute stage.

As mentioned earlier, the group characterized by a lack of progression provides the primary impulse for the concept of endogenous psychosis, of genetic or constitutional etiology. These two factors undoubtedly play a role in some instances, as illustrated by Mahler's (1952) concept of "autistic psychoses." While there is much doubt about Bender's (1947) specific theory of lack of fetal development, it is possible that early, unrecognized encephalitis or other infectious or toxic insults to the brain may result in a disturbance of ego functions which manifests itself in childhood schizophrenia.

Primarily, however, it is my belief that many early childhood schizophrenias and many of the later adult vegetative schizophrenias with somatic stigmata may be satisfactorily understood (prevented and treated to a certain extent) as the result of the effect of poor mother-child relationships on the development of psyche *and* soma.

In a number of papers, Spitz (1945a, 1946a, 1951a, 1957b) has described the importance of the early relationship of the child to the mother. He has discussed a number of psychogenic diseases of infancy referred to earlier in this chapter, and classified them essentially into psychotoxic disorders (in which the quality of the maternal relationship is involved) and emotional deficiency diseases (in which the quality of the emotional relationship of mother to child is the etiological factor). In this latter group, he has described the results of such early emotional deprivation as "anaclitic depression" or "hospitalism." Both he and Ribble (1941) have described marasmus and eventual death of infants deprived of maternal affection and care even in the presence of excellent physical and hygienic conditions. Spitz hypothesizes this syndrome by stating that, as mentioned earlier, there seems to be no differentiation between somatic and psychic organization for the early human organism. Thus, he speaks of the somatopsyche to indicate the real unity of soma and psyche in infancy.

What we might call psyche at this stage is so completely merged with the physical person that I would like to coin for it the term *somato-psyche*. Subsequently the psychic and somatic systems will be progressively delimited from each other. Step by step, in the course of the first six months, a psychological steering organization will be segregated from the somato-psyche. This steering organization serves the needs of defense and of mastery. It is characterized by its organization, its structure, and by the quality of consciousness. This organized, structured and conscious steering organization is the nucleus of what we call the ego, a body ego in the beginning. It is thus delimited from the remaining *unconscious* part of the somato-psyche, which we will designate as the id.

Spitz hypothesizes that sensory perception of a maternal figure is an essential for the growth and life of the infant, and that in its absence the infant may not develop and possibly fail to survive even in the presence of the best physical conditions. In a controlled study involving two hundred institutionalized infants, he found the mortality rate to be 37½ per cent. In those children in whom the emotional deprivation was not so severe or did not have such severe effects as to lead to marasmus and death, Spitz noted not only severe depression but also marked bodily changes, cachexia, and underdevelopment. One might conceive of this phenomenon as occurring in a period when the somatic development of the sensory and motor apparatus requires "polarization" toward and by external stimuli of a consistent nature (mother figure).[4]

Some work reported by Leider et al. (1957) offers some data relevant to our thesis: These investigators from the University of Washington School of Medicine studied the object relationships in thirteen children between the ages of two and four years. Nine of these children were actually studied over a one-year period.

The behavior and attitude of the mothers in interaction with their children were a significant part of the study; the relationship between the skin-temperature changes and maternal behavior was noted and the following results were observed:

The children had warm hands when their mothers were able to provide comfort, love, and security in situations where this would be the mother's normal behavior. Unusually warm hands were the rule when the child was angered or

---

[4] This hypothetical construct of "psychosomatic polarization" is based on the polarization concept of embryology. Braceland's reference, previously mentioned, to Magoun's discovery of a diffuse afferent mechanism which seems sensitive to the total amount of sensory input and affects the total organismic functions gives some neurological support to these contentions.

The experimental work on the effects of perceptual isolation gives some indirect, though strong support to the propositions concerning the importance of consistent early perceptual relationships.

threatened and unable to express himself. Cold hands were the expression of fear as a result of the mother's disapproval of the child's behavior or pressing demands for conformity against the child's resistance. Skin-temperature drops of greater degree occurred in those children who were uncertain about their mothers' feelings toward them than in those who felt secure. Separation resulted in consistent, sharp drops in temperature in most children.

Children in sound and secure familial and emotional climates showed normal skin temperatures with little variability; children with less adequate patterns of adjustment showed rapid, extensive changes in skin temperature.

Anticipation of inoculation, involving fear and anger, brought about sharp falls in skin temperature; the period after injection brought sharp increases in skin temperature to above-normal levels.

Results of the study lead to an interpretation of the relationship between skin-temperature changes and emotional states. Lowered skin temperatures come about from preparation of one's inner defense against fear or injury. High skin temperatures result from the suppression of this normal defensive response, either by external or internal controls. The normal, warm skin temperatures represent states of comfort and relaxation without the need for the mobilization of the child's energy.

It would be interesting to see such research performed on even younger children, and applied to the investigation of other functions as well. At any rate, the data reported by Leider et al. certainly suggest that other adaptive mechanisms of the organism may be similarly affected by environmental events of significant nature. The work of Leider and his associates adds significance to studies of the role of temperature for schizophrenics discussed earlier, as postulated by Bak.

The observed facts are that infants who have a very poor maternal object, and who do not die of the deficiency, do develop a variety of disorders: they are more susceptible to infectious diseases, their coordination is poor, and they have a generally lowered responsiveness to stimuli (as observed in adult schizophrenia by the Worcester group and others). It is not too fanciful to infer that their habitus might have a tendency toward the asthenic leptosome (ectomorph). One might further hypothesize that the earlier the damage from lack of maternal stimulation, and the longer the insult, the more severe, the earlier in onset, and the more somatized the subsequent psychotic disorder.

It is my contention that the early cases of childhood schizophrenia and the "nuclear" cases of dementia praecox in which one is so impressed by somatic defects of the whole adaptive mechanism as described by Bender (1947) may be the result of such early disturbances in the relationship of the infant to the mother figure.[5] Under the impact of severe emotional deprivation, those children who do not die of "hospitalism" develop, according to this hypothesis, severe disorders of the neuroendocrine system and possibly the other somatic systems as well. This may then also account for the general deficiency of chem-

_____

[5] Some authorities still hesitate to speak of childhood schizophrenia, and there are others who still question the continuity between childhood and adult schizophrenia. In my conceptualization, there is no longer any doubt that childhood schizophrenia exists and that there is a direct continuity from childhood schizophrenia to adult schizophrenia.

ical and sensory adaptive mechanisms reported in adult schizophrenics, insofar as these cannot be most economically and parsimoniously understood as secondary phenomena (namely, secondary to contemporary emotional problems, as are, presumably, disturbances of the carbohydrate mechanism).

It must be emphasized again that such an etiological hypothesis as advanced here does not exclude a number of other factors (constitution, early encephalitis, etc.) as being of possible etiological significance in other cases. Furthermore, it must be remembered that schizophrenia is a disorder of the ego and occurs in differing degrees of severity. This type of early and extremely severe effect upon the ego would probably result in the most severe cases of schizophrenia, corresponding to the original concept of dementia praecox. In cases in which the damage to the ego either occurred later in life or was less severe, we may find such disturbances of the ego as are consistent with our ambulatory schizophrenics, the borderline and latent cases, and the acute psychosis of adulthood which follows a relatively normal early life.

The clinical manifestations by which we subclassify schizophrenics, following Kraepelin, have been widely accepted as (often overlapping) forms of restitution of a more or less destructive nature. The paranoid can be understood in terms of projection and as having achieved salvation in a relatively stable system of delusions, as conceptualized by Sullivan. The oneirophrenic states of Meduna and the schizophrenoid psychosis of Langfeldt are the bridge from severe hysterical states of dissociation to the autism of catatonic withdrawal as a defensive maneuver. Similarly, the hebephrenic can be understood by his symbolic and defensive productions. The simple schizophrenic is probably most easily understood as a result of defective development in infancy. His utter lack of affect, absence of an integrated superego, and frequently almost vegetative appearance are probably the results of very early trauma to psyche and soma. Even the socially oriented Sullivan tended to think of such patients as organically disturbed. Again, however, I offer the hypothesis of early somatization of the mother-infant relationship as particularly explanatory of the entire group of schizophrenia simplex.

ATTEMPT TO INTEGRATE VARIOUS AVAILABLE DATA INTO THE MULTIPLE-FACTOR, PSYCHOSOMATIC THEORY OF SCHIZOPHRENIA

Undoubtedly, the most thought-provoking psychiatric events of the recent past have been the two manifestly diametrically opposite ways of artificially producing psychotic conditions: the various drug-induced psychoses and the psychosis-like changes brought about by perceptual isolation.

DRUG-INDUCED PSYCHOSES

Experimental, drug-induced psychoses are not new phenomena. Baruk (1949) and de Jong (1945), among others, investigated them extensively and reported on them more than twenty years ago; de Jong published a book on *Experimental Catatonia* in 1945. The drugs used most often were bulbocarpnine, mescaline, and others. Most recently, however, lysergic acid (either as lysergic acid diethylamide, known as LSD-25, or as lysergic acid monoethylamid, codified LAE) has attracted a great deal of attention. Serotonin has also been featured prominently as playing an important role in "schizophrenic" metabolism, as has taraxein. The degree of interest elicited by such research is not quite understandable unless one remembers that hope springs eternal that one specific somatic, preferably biochemical, etiology for schizophrenia will be found. The development of ataractic drugs was in part responsible for a resurgence of these hopes. Also, the war years brought such a vogue of psychological and specifically psychoanalytic orientation that the current biological renaissance must be seen as a reaction to the former.

The principal value of drug-induced psychosis is quite clear; it is hoped that analysis of such an experimental model psychosis will point the way toward finding *the* crucial metabolic substance responsible for the schizophrenic disorder. Once the etiological agent is identified, the therapeutic and preventive battle would be more than half won.

An excellent discussion of the main issues involved in such research was offered by Savage and Cholden (1956). These authors have conducted extensive research in connection with the characteristics of the model psychosis induced by LSD-25 as compared to the schizophrenic psychosis. Ten staff members and ten normal volunteers from a religious community received a dosage of 100 mg. of LSD, administered orally to the staff and intravenously to the volunteers. The groups did not differ significantly in their verbalizations or in their behavior. It was noted, however, that intravenous injections produced symptoms within five to fifteen minutes whereas the staff members who ingested the LSD orally manifested symptoms of the model psychosis within thirty to sixty minutes.

The following similarities were found to exist in the model psychosis and the schizophrenic psychosis: both conditions are frequently accompanied by anxiety. The perceptual disturbances, including an altered perception of time, were noted in the model psychosis and, of course, these are also symptoms of schizophrenia. The subjects tested manifested both elation and depression, sometimes alternately, a characteristic also reported in schizophrenic patients. Hyperactivity and restlessness, common in schizophrenia, were recorded in the model psychosis. Thought disturbances, ego disturbances, and delusion formation were found to exist in both conditions.

On the other hand, the model psychosis differed from the schizophrenic psychosis in that auditory hallucinations rarely occurred, assaultive behavior was unusual, and the subjects did not regress to the degree characteristic of schizophrenic patients.

The authors maintain that the similarity between the model psychosis and schizophrenia may be explained on the basis of one of the following hypotheses:

(1) LSD is related to the chemical factor involved in the genesis of naturally occurring schizophrenia.

(2) Schizophrenia may be caused by some psychologic disorganization but is maintained by a metabolic and chemical disturbance that can be mimicked by the administration of LSD or mescaline.

(3) The LSD-induced state symptomatically manifests behavioral and experimental responses similar to those in schizophrenia; however, their symptomatic similarities in no way reflect similarities in cause.

(4) A rarely considered possibility is that, in the remote and distant recesses of mental life, there is a region in which impaired reality testing, hallucinations, de-

lusions and misperceptions abound. Both LSD and a series of disease entities entitled schizophrenia activate or bring into consciousness this aspect of the psyche.

One might reword this last point by saying that ego impairment and resultant primary-process manifestations may be caused by LSD or any number of other factors. At any rate, the authors clearly illustrate that the drug-induced psychosis and schizophrenia have many characteristics in common, but that the nature of the relationship between the two conditions is subject to conjecture, as before.

Some very sophisticated research along these lines, methodologically speaking, has also been reported by Hoffer et al. (1954). These authors have investigated the theory that a physiological substance may be one of the etiological agents in schizophrenia. This so-called M substance, related to both mescaline and adrenalin, has the psychological properties of mescaline but is effective in even smaller amounts. Mescaline is known to produce psychological disturbances similar to those of schizophrenia, and it has been observed that if adrenalin could be deprived of its pressor qualities it might be a hallucinogen. Thus "pink adrenalin," containing adrenochrome, was shown to be related to every so-determined hallucinogen. Under stress, the quantity of adrenalin in the body increases. This might be turned to adrenochrome in the schizophrenic person. Experiments on humans with a synthetic adrenochrome consisting of LD_{50} of 137 mgm. per kgm. manifested psychological properties similar to those produced by mescaline and by lysergic acid. However, adrenochrome appeared to be more insidious and longer lasting than either of the latter. Furthermore, it has been shown to produce EEG changes and to inhibit aerobic and anaerobic respiration of brain tissue in Warburg apparatus.

By suggesting that subjects with a "bad family background, liver disease," etc., be excluded from experiments with adrenochrome, the authors imply that a genetic or psychogenic predisposition would interact with the toxic factor. One might speculate about whether the relationship between these variables could be quantified: whether there are minimal quantities of any of the three factors necessary to produce the final Gestalt of schizophrenia? Needless to say, in clinical practice one would expect a borderline patient to respond more promptly with a delirium or a toxic psychosis or a plainly schizophrenic psychosis, under the impact of eclampsia or peritonitis with toxemia, or a severe nephritis, etc. The authors' future task is, of course, to show that adrenochrome exists in the human body in greater quantities in schizophrenics than in normals, or only in schizophrenics, and finally that the prevention of adrenochrome production or its destruction in the body leads to a remission and cure. This, indeed, would be fulfilling something like Koch's postulates.

An even more theoretical approach than the above, and no less impressive, has been made by Fischer (1954). This author suggests the use of fibrous wool protein as an "analogue" of the structural surface of neural receptors for the study of the mechanism involved in producing a model psychosis by drugs. The author has studied the affinity for wool of various hallucinogens and concludes that the higher the affinity of the drug for wool, the lower the amount of the drug required to cause hallucinations. Stress and adrenergic blockage seem to be essential components for the precipitation of model psychosis. Possibly persistent stress causing first sympathetic and then parasympathetic stimulation and overactivity tends to decrease the dosage of the drug required to produce hallucinations. The author further speculates about the possible aggravation and amelioration and prevention of drug-produced model psychosis. Inasmuch as the author recognizes stress as well as adrenergic blockages as essential for the production of model psychoses, he delineates a psychosomatic theory of psychoses quite consonant with my own conceptions, with quantitative implications.

A long series of toxic substances has been claimed for schizophrenic serology, most recently taraxein and serotonin. Reportedly, animals and humans injected with these and other toxic substances derived from schizophrenic serum have developed basic behavioral alterations consistent with the description of primary schizophrenic symptomatology as set forth by Bleuler. Since I doubt very much that there is one principal cause for schizophrenia, I would expect that if these and other findings are ever substantiated (none of similar earlier claims have been confirmed) that they will relate to metabolic changes produced by stress, anxiety, poor respiration, etc. The faulty carbohydrate metabolism once claimed as characteristic for schizophrenics has rather generally been accepted as a secondary phenomenon, also to be found in experimental subjects subjected to severe stress (Hoskins, 1946). A variety of investigations of physiological processes, such as the eosinophil response, the response to autonomic drugs, impaired detoxification of benzoic acid, 17-ketosteroid excretion, glucose metabolism, etc., suggest that in all these instances we are dealing with an organismic adaptation of considerable variability, and one secondary to emotional stress, and possibly a variety of different etiological factors. I have discussed many of these on previous occasions (Bellak, 1948). One is tempted to step into the dangerous path of analogy and to compare schizophrenia to the diagnosis of "fever" at an earlier stage of development of medicine. Fever, like schizophrenia, is the final common path of infection: Surely the fevers have a good deal in common clinically, even if they are investigated biochemically, neurologically, hematologically, and even serologically, though in the presence of vastly different specific etiologies.

PERCEPTUAL ISOLATION

A powerful support for the multiple causation of psychotic and schizophrenia-like or schizophrenic psychoses is provided by the investigation of the effect of perceptual isolation on the mind. Experiments in this area have been conducted at McGill, at Bethesda, at Harvard, and at other institutions. The largest number of subjects, with the longest exposure to isolation, were experimented with at McGill under the direction of Donald Hebb (see Lilly, 1956). Attempts were made to reduce the patterning of stimuli to the lowest level by the following techniques: A subject was placed on a bed in an air-conditioned box, with arms and hands restrained by cardboard sleeves, and eyes completely covered with translucent ski goggles. An observer was constantly present to observe and test the subjects verbally in various ways through a communication set. The subjects were college students who were induced by payment to continue for as long a period as possible. General phenomena observed were that after a few hours it was difficult for the subject to carry on organized, directed thinking for a sustained period of time; a great desire for any kind of stimulus or action occurred. Suggestibility was greatly increased. The differentiation between waking and sleeping became confused. Most subjects left after twenty-four to seventy-two hours; delusions and hallucinations of various kinds appeared primarily in those who stayed for longer than two days. When visual hallucinations were full-blown the material produced was similar to dreams, with the time dimension between events erased. Some subjects doubled their body image; others developed transitory paranoid delusions; one subject had a seizurelike episode with no positive EEG findings for epilepsy. The development of visual hallucinations, incidentally, followed the stages of development observed with mescaline intoxication.

The Bethesda experiments, under Lilly (1956), consisted of suspending the subjects up to the top of the head in a tank containing slowly flowing water at a temperature of 35.5°C (94.5°F). The subjects wore a blacked-out mask for breathing and nothing else. Thus the subject felt only the tactile sensations of the support and the mask since the water temperature was neutral. Even the usual feeling of gravity was lacking and sound level was very low, consisting of the subject's breathing sounds and some water movements. Immediately after the experience the subject was asked to write a report. In essence, the same stimulus hunger developed as had been reported by the McGill subjects. Slowly, reveries and fantasies predominated and projection of visual imagery occurred. In hypnagogic states small, irregularly shaped objects appeared; time sensation was distorted even after the experiment was over. Lilly offers a stimulating discussion of the implications of his findings concerning the projection mechanisms and the effect of nondischarged body libido (energy) on the production of fantasy.

Raines, Zimmer, Rome et al. (see Lilly, 1956) added many interesting points in their discussion with regard to similar experiments at Princeton, and dealt also with survivors of long isolation in connection with disasters. Zimmer, in particular, referred to some interesting experiments performed in Montreal which suggest that the overt expression of aggression by subjects prevented depersonalization, and possibly also the production of hallucinations—quite in keeping with analytic theory.

An Integrative View

The implications of these experiments with drugs and perceptual isolation and the future possibilities for research are, of course, extensive. The most obvious is that the final common path of psychotic experiences can be produced by psychological experiences (resembling those of narcissistic withdrawal) as well as by toxic substances. Both avenues for model psychoses lend themselves to an examination of psychodynamic propositions, and eventually to therapeutic endeavors. For instance, one is inclined to think immediately of the fact that paranoid conditions are generally refractory to treatment of almost any kind because of the very stability of the symptomatology. Might it not be feasible then to expose paranoids to perceptual isolation in the hope of initiating a restructuration or an increase of fluidity when faced with a lack of referents?

Certainly it is hoped that secondary metabolic changes, in the isolation experiments, will be examined and compared to those which occur in schizophrenics. One would expect many parallels. The literature abounds with physiological findings in schizophrenics and while most of these are never substantiated by subsequent investigations, and a few even overlap, they cannot all be experimental artifacts; probably some of them are due to processes secondary to the schizophrenic way of life.

A stress theory, with interaction of chemical and psychological factors, is quite possible and, in a good percentage of cases, very likely (whatever the X factors in addition to the psychogenic ones may turn out to be in individual cases). It would be a mistake, however, to discard concepts of specific pathogenesis and etiology of diseases completely. The GAS of Selye is likely to constitute a sound and lasting contribution, but cannot obviate a certain role of specificity. True, some people do not catch syphilis when exposed to it, and some who catch it seem to have spontaneous cures, and the response to the treponema varies greatly, but the fact remains that generally suitable exposure to treponema is likely to produce some form of syphilis.

Similarly, any number of factors may be involved in the condition we call schizophrenia, but in a significant percentage of these cases the psychogenetic factor plays such a large role as to make a universally crucial contribution by one chemical factor extremely unlikely.

Investigators are likely to be frustrated because of indiscriminate research for a uniformly present chemical, or toxic, or psychogenic factor. If cases of schizophrenia were screened first for the possible hypothetical role of any of these factors, and if the group most likely to have a chemical factor in common (because of an abundance of toxic, somatic manifestations, or because of a set of symptoms in excess of what one might expect from the immediate premorbid psychological history, etc.) were then investigated, the likelihood of success in finding some single chemical factor for certain schizophrenics would be greater. The same might be said for any other main etiologic agent. Cases in which one finds more pathology from early infancy on than one can very well conceptualize in terms of the patient's personal history should lend themselves to finding a significantly higher incidence of hereditary or constitutional factors than in a random sample of schizophrenics. Cases selected for incidence of unexplained high fever in infancy or childhood might be easier to identify by a common EEG pattern than randomly selected schizophrenics. And so on. Once the main etiological factor has been identified in each case, one might then go on to examine the relationship to other contributing psychosomatic factors and thus arrive at different etiological classifications of schizophrenia and understand each individual case by the pattern of contributing factors.

IMPLICATIONS OF THE MULTIPLE-FACTOR THEORY FOR DIAGNOSIS AND DIFFERENTIAL DIAGNOSIS

THE DIAGNOSTIC CONTINUUM

The concept of the schizophrenias as disorders of many different etiologies but with a shared final common path of ego disturbance leads quite logically to the concept that the diagnosis of schizophrenia at present can best be made on the basis of the degree of ego disturbance in a given patient. It also follows that the degree of ego disturbance we are willing to term "schizophrenia" is based on an arbitrary decision. Quite understandably, the literature abounds with divergent opinions on diagnostic concepts.

Naturally, there are variations of ego functioning in every person—that is, healthy people exhibit certain ego functions which are of a very high quality and others which are less efficient. It is probably true that a surprising number of ego disturbances, sometimes of considerable severity, appear in a large number of people who are generally considered normal statistically and from the standpoint of lifelong functioning. These are still "normal" people, however, by virtue of the fact that the ego disturbance occurs in a relatively small segment of their personality or one which, in their particular setting, does not crucially interfere with functioning. A fear of deep water, for instance, is not likely to be a vital disturbance in an arid state such as Kansas. One may find, on taking a careful history, that there was some episode in ego disturbance which, though fairly severe, was self-limited and subsequently without consequence. Chance and luck are involved in such matters: a marked disturbance in military service may become a matter of troubling public record and later secondary pathology; some private disturbance may forever remain unknown and become a subject of amnesia.

Under conditions of extreme deprivation some delusions or hallucinations (of food, water, companions) must be virtually considered as adaptive functions of the ego which will promptly disappear with the emergency and may have definite survival value including, particularly, the irrational feeling that a special deity is guarding one and the certainty that all will be well (Lilly, 1956). Then there are, of course, the wide variety of neurotic ego disturbances, described and listed in all standard works in which they are discussed. All these facts will serve further to highlight the difficulties in forming a diagnosis on the basis of one specific syndrome.

It is to be remembered that from a theoretical viewpoint we postulate that schizophrenia is not one condition, not one point on a continuum of ego strength, but a range on a continuum: within cases diagnosed as schizophrenia one could doubtless classify those which are sicker and less sick, patients with more and less ego strength (also varying ego strength in different areas at different times). In this sense ego functioning is not only to be seen as a quantitative proposition, but must be viewed as three-dimensional (greater or lesser, in different areas, at different times).

It might be feasible to refer to the foregoing list of ego functions, and their many subfunctions, for a schematic appraisal of the degree of pathology. A simple rank-ordering scheme could easily be established on a strictly empirical basis, and eventually a standardized set of tests, such as those discussed earlier, might some day be formulated.

It is useful to remember that, in essence, the diagnosis of schizophrenia is a phenomenological diagnosis—predicated upon the observable failure of ego functions rather than on assumptions concerning dynamic structure or other criteria.

Schizophrenia lies at the low end of the continuum of ego strength and normality covers a range at the other end. Presumably, manic-depressive psychosis, obsessive-compulsive neurosis, severe character disorders, phobias, anxiety hysterias and anxiety neurosis, and hysterias lie approximately in that order, reading from left to right, between these two points. However, this traditional viewpoint is of little value, since each of these conditions is characterized only by the outstanding symptom picture as expressive of certain defensive compromise formations. Psychopathology is determined by both qualitative and quantitative factors. The libidinal structure of the personality constitutes the bulk of psychoanalytic theory and clinical findings. It determines the *content*, i.e., what the patient experiences, the oral, anal, and genital features as well as the content of dreams, symptoms, character formation, etc. The factor of ego strength, by and large, determines the *form* which the content assumes, *how* the content expresses itself—as in a dream, a neurotic symptom, a delusion, or a hallucination. I believe that the libidinal content may be hypothetically the same in two patients, but that with a difference in ego strength one patient may be a neurotic (with neurotic symptoms) and the other may be a psychotic (expressing the same content in delusions and hallucinations); a third person—a "normal"—may express the same content in dreams and in some character formation. Schneider's (1954) "Sosein" of a psychosis—the content—as well as the "Dasein"—its etiologic existence—can thus be seen as principally possible on a psychogenic basis, though the psychosis—its "Dasein"—might also be due to an organic affliction of ego functioning as outlined earlier. There can be no question that a severe hysteria may involve a weaker ego and be a condition relatively closer to schizophrenia (even if the oedipal stage has been reached) than a mild obsessive-compulsive disorder or a circumscribed phobia. From that standpoint much more work must be done to arrive at a meaningful diagnostic scheme of neurosis and associated pathological conditions.

Schizophrenia may sometimes be difficult to diagnose in its early stages because the clinical picture may involve a vast variety of patterns of ego functioning. Some of these disturbances may, of course, be present in neurosis, circumscribed organic psychosis, character disorders, psychopathic (sociopathic) personalities, perversions, and other disorders.

It is not our intention here to discuss in detail the clinical problems of differential diagnosis, but rather to attempt a conceptual clarification: The clinical diagnosis of early schizophrenia must be predicated upon the judgment that the degree of ego disturbance is so severe and the defenses so pathological (Jacobson, 1957) that one may expect a full-blown psychosis with delusions and hallucinations without skilled intervention.[6]

Just as there are many varieties of full-blown schizophrenics, so there are many forms of early schizophrenic symptomatology. Sociopathic irresponsibility is indicative of poor integration of the superego and poor frustration tolerance; poor reality testing and poor object relations (by the ego) may occur in a person previously conscientious, polite, and kind to children and animals. Thus tabloids frequently print lurid accounts of choir-singing offspring of pillars of the community who apparently become psychotic suddenly and commit criminal acts. Yet it is quite possible that signs of disturbance had been present for a long time. Seclusiveness, as well as sudden extreme "extraversion," may be first indicators of a schizophrenic break. Lability of mood often signifies impaired control.

---

[6] Exceptions exist; see following section on differential diagnosis of borderline disorders.

Nor are the specific manifestations of ego disturbance the only prodromal signs of schizophrenia: The preschizophrenic personality may be sociopathic, infantile (little control, many pregenital drives), brilliantly highstrung (artistic or intellectual achievement at the cost of other development), excessively religious (as a reaction formation to poorly controlled hostility), dull and apathetic (because of early disturbance of autonomous functions and object relations), or have poor achievement (because of preoccupation with fantasies, etc.) despite high intelligence.

A good report of the great variety of full-blown schizophrenias is yet to be written. In essence, one schizophrenic may differ from another almost as much as any one individual from another. There are those who never progressed, and those who regressed from the highest levels of achievement; those who are obviously bizarre and hard to empathize with and those whom one is likely to consider less disturbed than they actually are because of a good façade. Some schizophrenics are very kind; others are cold and sadistic. Some have a great deal of productivity and sensitivity; others are seemingly without drive or ability. Schizophrenics have been unjustly defiled and romantically overestimated as artists, intellectuals, or, as some would have it, revolutionaries which society secludes from necessity. It is easier to be categorical about schizophrenics if one does not have too much understanding and knowledge of them.

DIFFERENTIAL DIAGNOSTIC CONCEPTS OF BORDERLINE, LATENT, INCIPIENT, AND POTENTIAL SCHIZOPHRENIC PSYCHOSES

In the diagnosis of schizophrenia a number of diagnostic labels of secondary order are frequently used in confusing ways, probably quite unnecessarily so.

(a) *"Borderline schizophrenia"* can be quite accurately defined in our scheme as a condition of ego strength and personality functioning which lies on the continuum between schizophrenia and manic-depressive and/or neurotic conditions. In an appraisal of the ego strength of such a patient, one finds that thinking, affective control, perceptual reliability, object relations are all of questionable soundness without being disturbed enough to merit the diagnosis of schizophrenia.

The diagnosis of borderline schizophrenia is indicated if the condition described refers to an apparently *stable* condition of functioning, perhaps even of lifelong duration, and without signs of deterioration. In that sense, "borderline" is identical with the term *"schizoid character,"* as relating to a character formation with many unfortunate defensive traits that are likely to make a person appear quite peculiar (even though he may often be quite brilliant and useful in isolated areas), yet never develop a frank psychosis.

(b) *Incipient schizophrenia:* If this same picture of dubious functioning is present, but accompanied by signs of increasing lability of mood, progressive inability of impulse control, increasing emergence of the primary process, and increasing crumbling of defenses with *déjà vu* experiences, feelings of unreality, impaired sleeping, impaired appetite, and a rising anxiety level, then we are dealing with incipient schizophrenia and steps might be taken to avoid its further progress.

The above discussion implies quite clearly that in diagnosis it is not only important to judge the nature of functioning and the quality of the defense patterns but also the *stability* of the defensive patterns. Clinical experience permits little doubt that many people arrive at certain character formations—more or less pathological or normal—which they maintain all their life. Thus not only do some people remain "borderline" all their life; some schizophrenics remain stabilized at certain levels of illness and do not regress further; others do. Some schizophrenics, and for that matter, manic-depressives, have four or five or more episodes during their lives, which always take the same form and which show spontaneous resolution. And some people have character peculiarities—schizoid or otherwise—which are lifelong, without any progression or regression of note. Clinical experience suggests the hypothesis that each person has a certain amount of ego strength—or, more specifically, strength of the synthetic function of the ego, and this very often involves the stabilizing of a certain level of pathology below which a person does not go in ordinary or possibly even extraordinary life circumstances.

(c) *Potential schizophrenia* seems a useful diagnosis if one can observe poor ego functioning with defenses that could eventually lead to a schizophrenic psychosis. That is, one might note the same symptoms as occur in borderline conditions, but with less stability in the defensive pattern. The borderline schizoid usually has little drive push; part of the stable solution is predicated on that aspect, and the other part on a severe superego, and some area of gratification, albeit a queer one. In the potential schizophrenic one may note previous episodes of increasing precariousness of balance between drive and defense, with outstanding defenses being those of denial and projection, and signs of loss of perceptual and motor control. In other words, the diagnosis of potential schizophrenia may be useful to connote a condition ranging between "borderline" and "incipient," the picture being more labile than in the former and less labile than in the latter.

(d) The designation of *"latent schizophrenia"* might be employed when there is evidence of an existing schizophrenia which is, for practical purposes, covered up most of the time: i.e., one might see in psychotherapy somebody who is usually under the influence of primary-process thinking, and constantly beset by severe distortions of reality, but who manages to keep all these problems private by the use of intelligence and clever rationalizations. Such a person requires a favorable environment in order to continue to appear manifestly normal. Usually a forced change in environment or a change in living circumstances will suddenly disrupt the delicate arrangement; the patient will then surprise the

FIGURE 1

DIAGNOSTIC CONTINUUM (SCHEMATIC PRESENTATION)*

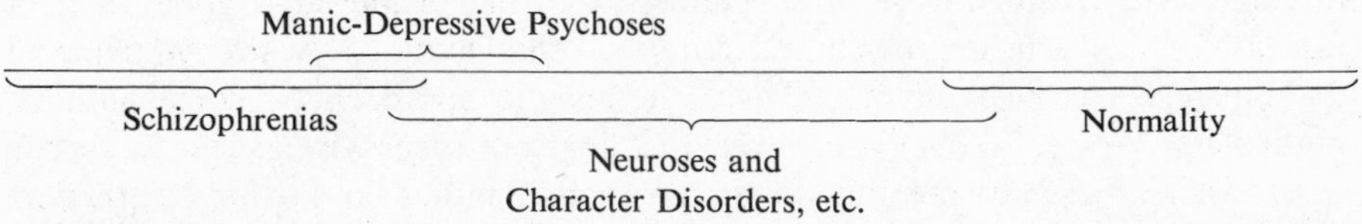

Manic-Depressive Psychoses

Schizophrenias   Normality

Neuroses and
Character Disorders, etc.

* This figure is a very oversimplified presentation of a diagnostic continuum and is without quantitative implications. For a more satisfactory representation a three-dimensional model of interacting forces would be desirable.

world with the emergence of full-blown delusions of obviously long standing. The latency in this concept then refers in essence to the social impression which this person makes—one which may maintain itself in ordinary clinical examination if the patient feels uncooperative, but which is extremely likely to appear in projective and other diagnostic testing, and in prolonged psychoanalytic interviews.

IMPLICATIONS FOR TREATMENT AND PROGNOSIS

THERAPEUTIC ASPECTS

If schizophrenia is a syndrome resulting from many etiologies, it is not likely that eventually there will be *one* rational treatment for the disturbance. This statement deserves some qualification, however. If, once again, schizophrenia may be compared to fever—in the sense in which "fever" was once used to connote a supposed entity, or even in its modern sense—one may speak of certain general therapeutic measures as useful, namely of certain supportive measures, of the reduction of the temperature if it reaches too high a level, and of the probable use of antibiotics, etc. The comparison of schizophrenia to the syndrome of nephritis may be more appropriate because of the relative specificity of the final common path and because in therapeutic procedures the general goal will be improvement of kidney function and interference with the causative factors, which may be toxic, infectious, mechanical, degenerative, etc.

Psychoanalytic theory, like physiological constructs, enables us to understand affliction of the ego. Since we conceive of the treatment of schizophrenia in terms of ego weakness, coexistent with great intensity of id impulses and a strong superego or a taxing reality situation, therapy would have to consist of either strengthening the ego directly, and/or weakening the id impulses and/or the superego directly, and/or decreasing the burdens of reality. Even in "primary psychogenic" schizophrenia the indicated treatment may take any of several forms.

As mentioned earlier, some schizophrenics do not suffer from a psychotic regression, but rather from a lack of progression. In those patients where the additional characterization might be called infantilism, we often deal with people who never went beyond an autistic or, at best, a symbiotic stage, whose ego never acquired frustration tolerance, who never achieved sharp separation of the secondary from the primary process, and who have a very rudimentary, unintegrated superego. Poorly integrated superego function, ranging from extreme severity at some times to extreme permissiveness at other times, will give rise to excessive conflict. Here the process indicated is one of education, of habilitation, in contrast to treatment for those patients who had achieved a good level of functioning, and who regressed and required rehabilitation. A strengthening of the superego has been suggested as a therapeutic approach by some authors, particularly Wexler (1951). However, this does not seem wise except in certain cases where the only possible hope for remission lies in further repression. Lobotomies have been known to decrease superego and id forces surgically, thus allowing the ego to form better compromises, provided that the ego itself, that is the integrative function of the frontal lobes, has not been damaged too severely. Since, however, lobotomies are very crude and irreparably damaging procedures of uncertain success, they hardly seem a method of choice.

An alternate indirect method of treatment would entail a weakening of the id forces. The psychogenic economy of some schizophrenics may be characterized by too strong an id push, due, perhaps, to early overstimulation or overcharging of the organism through parental seduction. Treatment for these patients will consist of building barriers on the one hand, and decreasing inhibitions, denial, and repression on the other. It will consist of supplying the means for better reality testing. Somatic means, such as tranquilizers, for decreasing the id push might be suggested. Thalamotomy—the procedure for destruction of thalamic cells by electrocautery under X-ray guidance—might be considered a direct attempt to decrease emotional impulses.

There has been and is an abundance of theories on the nature of the effectiveness of the major forms of shock treatment (Gordon [1948] has reported on fifty theories). It may well be that no one of the shock treatments brings about a long-range improvement or recovery or even an over-all decrease in the length of hospitalization; but it cannot be denied by anyone who has ever given shock treatment that it frequently does have an immediate, dramatic, beneficial effect. It is with this phenomenon that we are concerned.

In insulin, electric, and metrazol treatments and their modifications, there is at least a transitory change or, if you wish, damage to the cells. This need not be on a histological level or at least not on a histologically visible level—as was pointed out by Winkler and Frank (1948). The changes are manifest on the EEG and may possibly influence the enzyme metabolism of, for example, carbonic anhydrase. At any rate, it is probably the direct brain damage by the shock treatment and its influence on the id, ego, and superego balance that accounts for its beneficial effects. The exact nature of the process is, of course, unknown and perhaps is not the same in all cases. The shock therapies are still very crudely guided procedures, and there are great differences in the nature and the cerebral effect even of electric convulsive therapy, and wide variations in individual patients' responses to the treatment. However, schematically speaking at least, we might say that in some catatonics controlling areas related to superego functions are destroyed, and improvement might be ascribed to this decreased superego control. On the other hand, one might speculate that the occasional destruction of thalamic neurons leads to a decreased emotional push, thus allowing a beneficial solution of the conflict to be attained. Donnadieu and Hauser (1948) reported marked autonomic disturbance following electric convulsive therapy, suggesting thalamic involvement. Failures of treatment could be similarly accounted for: A patient may get more violent and disturbed if the treatment damages so much ego functioning and superego control that the id drives are now practically unlimited in freedom.

These are only speculations. One can cite some substantial evidence concerning the specific effect of shock on the ego. Some years ago, it was pointed out by Rodnick (1942) that the effect of electric shock seems to be a return from a more recently learned pattern to an earlier one. In other words, the ego leaves the psychotic compromise pattern for the one existing prior to the psychosis. This may lead either to a renewed breakdown following the previous course of illness or to improvement, particularly in light of environmental and psycho-therapeutic changes. Frosch and Impastato (1948), with whose theories many of the writer's notions independently coincide, believe that improvement following shock therapy may be caused by the temporary establishment of regressive de-fenses of the ego, ensuant to the organic confusion caused by the shock. The ego gets a breathing spell, so to speak, and is permitted some reintegration to a higher level. A similar explanation may apply to Kläsi's prolonged narcosis, namely a breathing spell for reintegration.

Lobotomy of all types is probably essentially effective to the extent to which the resulting changes balance the relationship of ego, id, and superego by affect-ing the organic substratum. In patients who, after lobotomy, become excessively uninhibited, it may be postulated that the controlling functions—roughly related to the superego—have been extinguished in too radical a fashion. If performed less radically, the patient may adjust without a psychosis, due to decreased guilt. A lobotomy performed on a patient who had had homicidal and suicidal impulses of uncontrollable strength apparently interfered mostly with thalamic conduction: She was still aware of these notions but felt them without compelling force. Thus one might say that lobotomies decrease superego or id forces surgically, thus allowing the ego to form better compromises, provided the ego itself, that is, the integrative function of the CNS, has not been too severely damaged.

Whatever the method of treatment, however, we may be certain that since schizophrenia is frequently the result of faulty inadequate development, or poor "psychodynamic learning," or diffuse brain damage, it is about as likely that it will be successfully prevented or etiologically treated by organic therapies as it is reasonable to expect that people will learn Spanish by injection or improve their English by taking pills. It is quite possible that some drug, or shock treatment, or surgical procedures may help integration by decreasing the tension between the motivational system—between id and superego, to use psychoanalytic terminology—and thus indirectly strengthen the ego. The tranquilizers may possibly be effective by decreasing "drive push." Barbiturates are possibly help-ful sometimes in decreasing "superego" forces in much the way alcohol does, and sometimes by decreasing excessively defensive ego functioning (as seen in intravenous sodium-amytal interviews). Surgical means may have a similar effect. But it is inconceivable at present that cases of insufficient progression and in-sufficiently defined ego boundaries, with poor concept formation, and a poorly defined secondary process will ever be improved except by learning the processes which they have previously failed to learn or which have been destroyed by organic processes. Furthermore, it is likely that even in cases of regression to schizophrenia (after previous progression to relatively good functioning), psycho-therapy will always be necessary to change the organizational weaknesses of the ego, to prevent a relapse if nothing else, even if somatic treatment managed to restore the equilibrium of forces to the point where the ego can function again.

PROGNOSTIC ASPECTS OF A MULTIPLE-FACTOR THEORY

It is one of the merits of a multiple-factor psychosomatic theory of schizo-phrenia that it helps one to understand the confoundingly wide range of prog-nostic possibilities in disturbances which today are lumped together as schizo-phrenia. While a previous survey showed reported rates of over-all improvement to vary from 22 per cent to 53.6 per cent, it should be understood that these figures are even more divergent than they appear: some authors may report that they had no complete recoveries at all, 5 per cent social recoveries, 10 per cent much improved, and 20 per cent slightly improved; other authors may speak of 30 per cent complete recoveries, and concomitantly higher figures for social recovery and improvement.

The prognosis of schizophrenia must involve consideration of organismic factors—be they congenital (genetic, intrauterine or intrapartum, or related to body build independent of the first three variables) or experiential, or a result of the interaction of these variables with each other or with intercurrent somatic illness.

In essence it can probably be said that the better the premorbid ego strength, the better the prognosis. This means that if the ego apparently had been good enough to withstand routine difficulties (but broke under a sudden onset of overwhelmingly adverse circumstances), it may also be presumed to have superior recuperative power. If, on the other hand, there has been a chronic onset, because of a psychological setting unfavorable to the development of a strong ego, or because of an insidious, slowly destructive organic disorder, or because of poor constitutional equipment, the chances for recovery are poor.

Appraisal of degree of ego disturbance in each clinical case should also be an excellent key to estimating changes for reversibility and restoration.

Recognition of the individual etiological factors in each case of schizophrenia and a genetic-quantitative appraisal of the degree of ego impairment involved should make prevention, diagnosis, prognosis, and treatment infinitely easier.

21

IS SCHIZOPHRENIA CURABLE?

Cure, in this chapter, is seen as a function of disease onset. If traumatic factors appear early in life, they will have a correspondingly greater impact and be less susceptible to reversal than if they appear late. Stability of personality presumably varies directly with age; more specifically, the integration and synthesis of ego function is presumably more advanced at a later period as compared to an earlier one. The importance of the synthetic function is thereby underscored; it stands as an important barrier against schizophrenia disintegration and must be supplied by therapy where it is lacking in nature.

THE ANSWER TO THE QUESTION, "Is schizophrenia curable?" seems to me to be clearly predicated on the definition of the two terms in the question—namely, "schizophrenia" and "curable."

Addressing myself to the first term, schizophrenia, I have to remind you of my concepts stated over the last fifteen years, called by such complex names as the "multiple-factor psychosomatic theory of schizophrenia" (Bellak, 1949b), or the "unified theory of schizophrenia" (1955a); the essence of what I believe is that schizophrenia is not one single disorder but the final common path of a number of etiological factors (1952a, 1958). The manifest picture represents a severe disorder of ego functions: in individual cases different ego functions are more or less severely involved, accounting for the variations we find clinically, though all of them share an over-all low ego strength. I have in the past (1958) attempted to define in relatively operational terms the various ego functions, how they can be measured, and how they contribute to a variety of schizophrenic syndromes. I will add only that I have recently found it useful to think of some general factors, G factors, as contributive, particularly disturbances of the "synthetic functions" of the ego and of the "stimulus-barrier functions" of the ego which may have familial, congenital, biological determinants, but may also be affected by experiential factors—as of course are many aspects of the causation of schizophrenia (see Chapter 19). In most people so afflicted, I believe that a subtle, unique interplay of biological, psychological, sociological, and other factors is responsible for the condition we see.

Now to the second term, "curable"; is schizophrenia curable? It seems to me that this term implies two propositions: (a) is the disorder, of whatever nature it is, reversible? and (b) how stable can we expect such a reversal to be?

Addressing myself to the aspect of reversibility, which I think is the simpler one to answer: Few people doubt that the manifest clinical picture can be reversible for shorter or longer periods. The question really revolves around the *degree* of reversibility and the subsequent stability. Unlike the perhaps strictest of Kraepelinian views (according to which there is some deterioration with each

---

NOTE: From an address before the American Psychotherapy Association, 1965, New York.

episode), I do believe that the manifest syndrome we label schizophrenia is reversible to where, at least by direct and perhaps also by subtle methods of inquiry, one may not be able to discover that somebody has had a schizophrenic episode. With regard to stability, one has to remember that *all* processes, be they biological, psychological, sociological, or physical, are a matter of interplay of dynamic forces—whether one thinks primarily of Selye's stress concept or the field concept of physicists and of Kurt Lewin in psychology, or of psychoanalytic psychodynamics. In terms of the latter, I have previously discussed that schizophrenia, like other disorders, is a more or less stable solution of the interplay of a variety of forces (Bellak, 1958, 1960), that the schizophrenias must be seen as one segment of a continuum that ranges from hypothetical normality on the left through the neuroses to schizophrenia on the right (see Chapter 20). Just as normal or neurotic attempts at adaptation may fail and lead to schizophrenic ones, so schizophrenic attempts may move toward the left to neurotic or normal ways of adapting and coping. It is, let me repeat, inherent in the concept of a process that we can only speak of *relative* stability of any constellation of forces, and this certainly holds for schizophrenics.

With these qualifications in mind, I do not hesitate to say that some schizophrenias are certainly curable—that is, reversible to where, by any method, the personality may not be distinguishable from the relatively normal—and that in some schizophrenics this reversal may be of a reasonable stability; that is, one may expect as much stability from it as from any process, including the psychodynamic constellations in "normal" people. However, in many other schizophrenics one may reach either only a partial reversibility or, if reversibility, a less stable arrangement of forces.

I can specify and say that the degrees of reversibility and stability, all other things being equal, are likely to depend primarily on the contribution of the G factors of the affliction, of the synthetic function and the stimulus-barrier function. Above and beyond that, I would say that the degree of reversibility and stability attainable will be less the earlier in the life history traumatic or pathogenic constellations played a role and the more severe these pathogenic constellations were. In turn, the relatively less general factors of biological and other kinds play a role, and the relatively less severe and relatively later in the individual life history the pathogenic constellations played a role, the more likely it is that schizophrenia is curable: that is, that someone afflicted with the schizophrenic syndrome can revert to, for all practical purposes, a form of functioning indistinguishable from the hypothetical normal, and with no more likelihood of showing a schizophrenic symptomatology again than the hypothetical normal.

Section V: Psychoanalysis and Creativity

THE CHAPTERS IN THIS SECTION represent attempts to apply psychoanalytic assumptions to nonclinical situations. Such an attempt may be read as a way of going beyond the surface and making a statement about the underlying process. For example, the detective story described in Chapter 24 may be *described* as a means of bringing about an increase and reduction of tension, or it can be *conceptualized* in such a fashion. In the first instance, we are providing a category for coding certain kinds of data; in the second, we are making a hypothesis about process which has specific testable consequences (for example, that the subjective pleasure of the reader would coincide with a drop in tension as indicated by some physiological index, and that both would be time-locked to a specific turn in the plot—for example, to the solution of the murder).

Psychoanalytic journals are filled with the first kind of essays, which are, in essence, little more than literary conceits and no more testable than any other literary exercise. Examples of the second are much less frequent and represent a larger commitment because they can be disproved. But if psychoanalysis is to be more than a school of literary criticism, then attempts of the second kind are clearly necessary; only they will test the theory.

The chapters in this section fall into the second category because they lead to testable hypotheses. Several approaches are possible. One can compare the literary assessment with what is known about the author's life, as in the case of Somerset Maugham; the more intimate the biographical details, the better. More to the point, one can study the story in relation to the author's life at the time and try to reconstruct the experiential context for the product. Ideally, this should be done by tracing the work from its beginning idea through to the final product. In this way we can study the interaction of reality with fiction in a way that we cannot by using conventional diagnostic instruments. Such attempts are particularly interesting when the work in progress was started but never finished, or started in one vein and then, as a result of some intervening circumstance, shifted drastically to quite another.

If the literary analysis has provided us with true insight into the author's dynamics, then we should be in a position to treat his creative work as systematically as we treat other behavior, accounting for both in terms of present and past determinants. This parallel, however, leaves out one thing: the fact that the work is often produced in an altered state of consciousness to which the determining principles of the author's life may not apply. Just as we cannot predict with any certainty what dreams may emerge at a given period of treatment, so it is difficult to make a clear link between cause and effect in creative work. (It may be that the complications provided by a changed state of consciousness may even override the problems imposed by the fact of multiple determination.) Be that as it may, the attempt can still be made and the possibilities have yet to be realized.

We have much to learn from the close interweaving of fact and fiction found in works about typical Victorian life and from such books as Lowes' treatment of the Coleridge notebooks (Lowes, 1927), and in some respects no psychological analysis has gone beyond Rowse's recent poem-by-poem exegesis of Shakespeare's sonnets in his attempt to put them in relation to Shakespeare's life (Rouse, 1963). Like carbon-14 tracing, the true excitement comes with the uncovering of new facts, and in this respect the pathogenic method has yet to show its true worth.

22

TOWARD SYSTEMATIC CONSIDERATION
OF THE NATURE AND GENESIS
OF THE CREATIVE PROCESS

If the creative process is the fossil of the creative act, as this chapter starts out by suggesting, it is a particularly awesome specimen and, more than most, is surrounded by the mystery and magic of the past. Toward it we are strangely ambivalent; on the one hand we want to account for its wonder, but on the other, we are wary of its mystery and treat it almost like a taboo object. Some of this ambivalence is reflected in the often-repeated assumption that psychoanalysis will destroy a person's creative powers, as if meddling with the mysterious will annoy the gods. As the last section of this chapter makes clear, there are reasons to think that creativity is often enhanced by treatment, and several instances are mentioned in which this was the case. In view of the large number of cases in which it has helped, it is perhaps symptomatic that the fear is still expressed—symptomatic of the underlying taboo. It goes without saying that a serious study of the effects of therapy on creativity is long overdue; perhaps it has not been attempted because of the same taboo.

One of the difficulties in studying the creative act is that its products wither so fast, and to that extent they resemble those fossils that deteriorate when moved from water into air. They wither in the sense that what was thought to be important and unusual is later seen to be quite ordinary. The truly creative work is best seen from a very long perspective, and if we wait that long for a judgment, all chances of studying the process are gone. If, on the other hand, we study the process on the spot, the chances are very good that the product we choose will not be creative in any lasting sense. Perhaps this paradox accounts for the difficulties in coming to grips with the problem.

SINCE CREATIVITY CONSTITUTES the essence of life itself, anything that might be said about it is necessarily fragmentary. Economic, historic, sociologic, biologic, and other aspects cannot be considered here. I want to permit myself, however, the luxury of an overview of at least six major variables of the psychological view of creativity: The psychological study of the *product of creativity,* the *creative process,* the *creative personality,* the *creative experience,* the *role playing* of the *creative person,* and the *relation of psychotherapy to creativity.*

In enumerating these facets of the topic, I wish to emphasize parenthetically that a discussion of creativity in a very general way often leads to much confusion: while the above-enumerated aspects of creativity are, of course, highly interdependent, they contain a measure of independence and need to be considered separately.

NOTE: From the *Journal of Projective Techniques,* 1958, 22, 358-380. Reprinted by permission of the publishers. Presidential address to the Society for Projective Techniques and the Rorschach Institute.

Aside from the limitations of the topic to the psychological and the restriction to six aspects of this level of behavior, I will further stress one particular view: the ego-psychological vantage point. I do not want to overlook other and greatly related propositions; however, the ego-psychological approach deserves special emphasis because it has been relatively neglected until now and offers special promise.

My topic makes it appropriate to comment on the creative aspects of this chapter. Little claim is made for the originality of this contribution (or for the exhaustiveness of treatment, or for adequacy of coverage of bibliographic references). Anyone working in the field of psychodynamics is likely to find, after the feeling of having made a new discovery, that Freud said it all long ago, and better.

In the particular field of creativity—and especially as related to art—it is likely that anything Freud did not elaborate, Ernst Kris has explored in detail, especially in his volume of papers on *Psychoanalytic Explorations in Art* (1952). It was Kris himself who, more than twenty years ago, introduced me to the concept of "afterdiscovery"—which happens in all fields, of course. Psychoanalytic authors, specifically, often start with premises taken from one of Freud's papers and proceed to what is, to the authors, honestly enough a new insight, a new discovery. Only later does it become apparent that Freud had elaborated the same point in some other paper of his, or that some other author had also proceeded from the same Freudian premises and arrived at the same concept; yet all concerned feel understandably very proprietary.

Much of what is often considered "unconscious plagiarism"—namely, a wholesale lifting of someone else's thoughts without conscious remembrance of the original source—is probably of the level of "afterdiscovery" or concurrent discovery of what is part of the *Zeitgeist*. It happens to all of us who are creative at all. One can take solace in the fact that such creative emergence of new configurations is such a small step removed from the original as to warrant little narcissistic investment.

THE PRODUCT OF CREATIVITY

The product of creativity is the *fossil* of the creative act. It has the advantage of all fossils—in holding still for study—and the disadvantage of permitting only retrospective, "postdictive" (G. W. Allport's [1942] term) inferences.

The product of the creative act is quite properly the first consideration of psychologists concerned with projective techniques; certain types of creative products are our daily concern. An advance in technique was attained when, in addition to test results, we learned to note all behavioral evidences of the creative act of responding to projective stimuli—as well as to study the evidence of the creative process in sequence analysis and also to analyze the standard defenses in the projective record.

Edward M. Burchard (1952) presented a scholarly paper, "The Use of Projective Techniques in the Analysis of Creativity," as his distinguished presidential address to the Society for Projective Techniques and the Rorschach Institute in 1952. His paper offered a lucid discussion and a careful review of the relevant literature available up to that time. He considered the topic broadly; however, I think he focused primarily on how to identify a specially creative person—how to infer unusual creative ability—from a projective record. Burchard did not find many encouraging data.

There may be at least four reasons for this fact: *First:* I believe that the unconscious and preconscious factors involved in creation often also necessitate a conscious factor—a mental set—and sometimes special cues to create; and that this mental set is often stimulus bound to a specific situation—the special workroom, the special view, isolation, noise, a drawing board, etc. Not only may the special set not be available in projective settings; our stimuli may not tap their resources. Only a part of that condition lies, I believe, in the fact that some of our stimuli, such as the TAT cards, are often considered unesthetic in nature by artists.

Second: creativity is often a process which has to reach the emergent level in its own course: the creative person sometimes has to be "moved" to create; in projective testing we *command* them to create. In analyzing projective records we assume that all forms of creativity are permanently operant variables of personality in all creative people. This assumption may hold true for some people; creativity may be cyclic or it may be sporadically emergent in others.

The *third* problem in making inferences from a creative product (of which projective techniques are one example) about the creative act and the creative personality is the fact that the product is an epiphenomenon, the Gestalt, the final configuration of many variables.

In this sense the creative product is similar to all data used for diagnosis, be it clinical, medical, psychiatric or, I think, geologic, economic, or of any other nature. We deal with a facet which is not only the resultant of many factors, but of many different ones in different cases. My own conception of schizophrenia (1958), similarly, is that the epiphenomenon may be the final common path of many different etiologies. Helen Sargent (1953) has splendidly illustrated, in her pyramid of diagnostic inferences, the multiplicity of levels involved in a diagnosis and the uselessness of expecting specific signs. We can think of hardly *any* clinical entities any more which can be reliably related to a few criteria. Not only love "is a many-splendored thing."

If we speak of the identification of creative ability—of the creative person as a specific problem of diagnosis just as in the diagnosis of schizophrenia or other syndromes—a few more general remarks are necessary here.

Behind the sign approach, behind the entire idea of diagnosis by relatively few variables of high abstraction, lies a misconception of the idea of determinism. It is as if in such a case, the nineteenth-century idea of a simple cause-and-effect chain of events were the conceptual frame of reference. I believe that such a misconception of determinism has been basic to some of the methodology of psychoanalytic practice as well as to diagnosis by projective techniques. Not only can probability theory be well applied to psychoanalytic psychodynamics—in therapy and in diagnostic testing—but it has some definite practical advantages for inferences from the latent to the manifest problem in testing. Some of the difficulties of identifying the creative personality by projective techniques are of this kind.

If one appreciates not only the multivalence of isolated behavioral signs, but also the vast variety of different variables resulting in a certain final common path (such as the creative product), it is not surprising to find some failures in common denominators among groups of creative people, if only relatively molar epiphenomenal criteria are studied. I will elaborate this point in the discussion of the creative personality.

A *fourth* level of difficulties in the diagnosis of creativity and any other diagnoses probably lies in the fact that our concept of diagnosis is still very much geared to the days of static psychology and descriptive psychopathology. We have learned to speak of adaptive syndromes rather than nosological entities and talk in terms of organismic defenses in psychodynamics as well as in medicine. Nevertheless, the whole concept of repeat reliability of personality tests is predicated upon the notion that the personality stays more or less the same and that if we have a good test the results ought to stay pretty much the same. One particular fallacy has already been widely recognized, namely, that different tests may explore different facets of the personality and therefore need not give identical results. It has not been recognized sufficiently that personality syndromes vary at different times and that the *extent of variability* over a period of time is probably one of the most important and least known personality indices.

If diagnosis is made in terms of ego functions it is obvious that these ego functions fluctuate all the time, in steady interaction with the momentary external changes of reality, most pronouncedly in the daily cycle, in the menstrual cycle, during the developmental stages of childhood, adolescence, maturity, involution, and senescence.

Some people have wider swings of ego functions than others and some ego functions swing more widely than others. Treating people everyday, one has a chance to observe the vast differences as well as the similarities: a patient who can hardly be trusted to find his way across the street one day may have excellent reality testing some other day. In that sense I would modify "once a schizophrenic, always a schizophrenic" to "once a schizophrenic, *maybe* some other time a schizophrenic."

Clinically, empirically, there is much case material to support the idea that at least in some people the degree of variability seems to be fixed: there are patients on record, schizophrenics, manics, neurotics who have had several episodes of disturbance, each of them going only so far and no further—running the same course over a lifetime. It seems as if there were some individual equilibrium which—as in the general course of pneumonia—leads to definite stages (before the antibiotics) with a final lysis if all goes well. There are some people who remain borderline schizophrenics all their lives and never go further. Therefore, I believe that no diagnostic statement is complete without a statement about the *probable stability or variability of the syndrome*. This should not be mistaken for a statement that there are no stable syndrome formations; there are stable and unstable ones, in different people.

Now that I have permitted myself this digression: what does it all have to do with the creative personality and with using the product of creativity, the projective-test protocol, for identifying the creative person? I am certain you have surmised: creativity may be a stable variable in some, present in relation to all stimuli at all times of the creative person's life; or, it may be a selective, only sporadically present personality syndrome in others. Therefore, it may be impossible to diagnose creativity in some people (known to be creative in some ways at some times) at certain times with certain tests. I have the unsupported notion that artistic perception—as one form of creative experience—may be a more stable variable than artistic expression. While the two cannot, of course, be very well separated, they may occur in relatively pure states in the critic on the one hand, and in the "primitive" artist on the other hand. Also, more often than not, in artists as well as in scientists, creative experience, creative conception may be pleasure, while expression may be labor.

Relatively little needs to be said about the dimensions of the product of creativity since relatively much has been said about them before. Principally, we could fairly well describe a piece of art or the creation of a new scientific Gestalt, or other creative products in terms of metapsychology: the adaptive, dynamic, economic, and structural aspects, as well as genetic and topographical factors. In connection with the latter, the contribution of preconscious mentation has been particularly stressed recently. While in earlier decades, the analysis of the libidinal content (of literature, sculpture, etc.) was in the foreground, ego-psychological considerations are more in focus today.

Long ago I spoke of adaptive, expressive, and projective facets in the Rorschach and TAT protocols (see Chapter 11). Later, I revised the idea of projective components to the wider frame of apperceptive distortion (Abt and Bellak, 1950). Now, I would like to broaden the base a little more by saying that under the adaptive components of the product we would subsume what was contributed by the autonomous ego functions, as Hartmann (1950a) has called them, the contribution of the relatively conflict-free sphere of the ego. Apperceptive distortion I would now wish to have understood as referring to all the factors which represent compromise formations of conflict of forces, including all the features of what is ordinarily considered defensive in psychoanalysis (and which are, of course, part of the adaptation, broadly speaking) and some that are not usually mentioned in clinical writings: principles of resolution formulated in Gestalt-psychological and learning-theory terms.

I have discussed degrees of participation of ego functions on a continuum in various creative products—problem solving, preconscious fantasy, daydreams, hypnagogic phenomena, and dreams. The concept of *vigilance* bridges adaptive and defensive factors: in certain stringent circumstances cognitive acuity is increased (the recognition of food by a hungry person), aside from the fact that compensatory projection may take place (as first clearly shown in the much overlooked work by Levine, Chein, and Murphy [1942]).

I believe that psychoanalytic hypotheses are the most useful ones for the understanding, prediction, and control of human behavior; I, of course, believe *ipso facto* that behavior on projective tests can be most usefully understood in terms of psychoanalytic theory; in turn, I believe that *all* psychoanalytic principles and concepts are discernible in projective testing.

The expressive aspect of the creative product is still the one that is relatively least explored. For a long time we have known some clinical features: the delicate, detailed productions of the obsessively inclined, the slapdash, broadly conceived work of the expansive, elated, or hysterical personality, etc.

Fries and Woolf (1953) have suggested that congenital activity types may be forerunners of expressive style (as well as a basis for choice of defenses). Spitz's (1951a) work has some potential bearing on psychoanalytic formulations of expressive behavior. Sheldon, Stevens, and Tucker (1940) suggest a relationship between somatotypes and expressive styles. Certain defenses seem to determine expressive style: denial leads to a centrifugal type of talking, whether in telling TAT stories or in hypomanic expression in any medium. Isolation may express itself in formal, emaciated, heaven-striving sculpture.

There seems little question that early libidinal overstimulation is likely to lead to great motor restlessness, and a great intensity in expression of any kind.

Again, I have to refer to the discussion of the creative personality for an elaboration of this point. Meanwhile it seems safe to say that the study of the expressive dimension has been the most neglected thus far, probably because ego-psychological considerations of the use of the motor apparatus have not been developed well enough. Both psychoanalytic studies proper and psychological methods, such as figure drawing, as well as the recent studies of psychomotor aspects of mental illness by King (1954), are likely to lead to further contributions in this area. I am especially hopeful that a systematic use of Mira's (1958) Myokinetic Psychodiagnostic Method (which we have finally succeeded in bringing to the American scene) will prove valuable. Clinical studies using the MKP, as already undertaken by Finn (1958), as well as careful longitudinal studies of child development by means of the MKP, should prove very helpful.

THE CREATIVE PROCESS

Much romanticizing has been done in the past, and not by poets alone, about the creative process. The essential contributions to its rational understanding have been made by Hartmann and by Kris, with their overlapping concepts of "self-exclusion of the ego" and "regression in the service of the ego." In short, the ego regresses or excludes itself, thus permitting an emergence of unconscious material. In a rapid oscillation, as Kris has pointed out, between regression and full vigilance, adaptive and emergent qualities of the creative product become integrated.

These concepts are by now well enough known not to need detailed discussion here.

If analogies help, one might compare this process to stepping back from a picture in order to lose sight of the details of brushstroke, to see all the facets of the whole. Nearly everyone has had the experience of acquiring new insights in a state of weakened ego functioning: in the process of falling asleep, while being very tired or intoxicated, etc. Of course, one's critical faculties are also impaired to the extent that something may appear to be brilliant to someone in that state which would appear inane to him in a fully functioning state; but that is not the whole explanation since people who have trained themselves to recall from hypnagogic states often record ideas which still seem very creative and useful the next morning.

Our main concern above was to stop speaking of "the ego" as an entity and to speak of different ego functions interacting at different levels of efficiency at the same time.

Second, some elaboration on the concept of "regression": some thought has been given to whether this involves primarily a topological regression or a temporal (ego) regression (to earlier points of libidinal organization). In the first case we are concerned with a change from the conscious to the preconscious or unconscious. In the second instance we are concerned with a regression to earlier, childhood levels of functioning. The distinction cannot be made quite definite since, by definition, nonconscious thinking involves primary-process thinking of infancy and childhood.

It will be more precise to say that a topological regression of the adaptive, cognitive processes (as one ego function) takes place which involves simultaneously a temporal regression to primary-process levels; the synthetic function does not regress at all but remains, or rises in fact, to optimal levels.

Increased emphasis has recently been placed upon the role of the preconscious in the creative process. The work and concepts of Fisher (1954), G. Klein (1956), and Kubie (1959) have suggested that not only is there much preconscious perception which constantly shapes integral parts of conscious mentation: Kubie particularly stresses the fact that conscious mentation is only a small sample of the stream of preconsciousness; electronic models, specifically of the scanning process, have been employed as analogies.

In describing regression in the service of the ego, we make specific use of Gestalt concepts in addition to psychoanalytic hypotheses. The conception of boundaries is not alien to psychoanalysis, since Freud and Federn and Schilder used it in various forms in relation to the self-concept. The concept of figures and ground, of their reversibility, of the degrees of clear definition of their relationship and their boundaries as well as the emergence of new wholes seems to be exceptionally useful for the understanding of the creative process.

I have had previous occasion (Bellak, 1954b) to discuss the creative process and the continuum from the purposive conscious problem-solving type of thinking to guided fantasy as in the projective techniques, daydream, preconscious fantasy, hypnagogic phenomena, and dream proper. What varies is the degree of participation of external stimuli via adaptive ego functions—highest in purposive behavior, lowest in the dream. "Good responses" to projective stimuli involve rapidly oscillating "regression in the service of the ego" as we have recast it above. Only in this way do we draw responses which are adaptively related enough to the stimulus: for instance, to give some "popular" responses on the Rorschach and yet permit enough emergence of preconscious or unconscious material to avoid sterile constriction of the impoverished ego (which expends most of its energy on countercathexis, on holding disruptive forces at bay).

Observing the relationship between regression and adaptation should be a good measure of a potentially creative, inventive, flexible mind. I do not think that we have better instruments than projective techniques for this purpose at present.

THE CREATIVE PERSONALITY

The attempt to define and circumscribe a concept leads very easily to statements by opposites and contrasts. It is interesting that by implication, at least, the creative person has been frequently compared to the noncreative, formal, administrative, well-organized one; e.g.: William James placed the "tough minded" and the "tender minded" into similar contradistinction as Schiller put the *Klassische* and the *Romantische* personality, and as Spengler conceived of the *Appolonian* and the *Dyonisian* types.

In more clinical terms, less rigidly bipolar (and rather in terms of a bimodal curve), I am inclined to associate the more creative person with the hysterical personality and the less creative one with the more obsessive character. It is my hunch that truly outstandingly creative people have a heavy component of both the rigid and the loose, in various temporal relations to each other, or else we have the critic, on the one hand, and the gifted dilettante on the other. Jones (1956), in his commemorative lectures on Freud, discusses the psychology of genius and the latter's occasional naïve, credulous attitude and subsequent acuity. By and large, though, creativity is associated with, though not identical with, the ability to bear ambiguity, to permit the regression of the adaptive ego functions in the service of the ego as discussed under the creative process.

The above are statements about certain dynamic aspects of the creative personality. It is tempting but difficult to attach value judgments, such as saying that the creative personality is more valuable than the "administrative" one. There may possibly be more admiration for the creative act than for the administrative one; though again, personality differences are likely to account for differences in values. Even the proposition that an insight, a new "aha" experience, beholding the creative act of the genius, gives exceptional pleasure is not quite tenable. Some people derive great pleasure from a well-ordered, smooth-running "machinery," be it metallic, or human, or reflected in the orderliness of beautiful crystals, or in conceptual or administrative activities. Furthermore, the "tough-minded," orderly, academic psychologists frequently feel disdain for the clinician who has greater tolerance of ambiguity—I suspect they have the disdain of the "clean" for the "dirty" (Bellak, 1956b).

It is already clear from our discussion of the creative *process* that regression in the service of the ego will not be useful unless there is a frequent oscillation to increased acuity, reality testing, and a good measure of organizational capacity as well as frustration tolerance.

Aside from these dynamic aspects, certain other characteristics can probably be described as applicable to most creative people, be they artists or scientists or active in other fields of endeavor. I believe it is useful to speak here of something like the "G factor" proposed for the conceptualization of intelligence. As elsewhere (Bellak, 1958), I would suggest that this G factor relates to a certain quality of the ego, a certain capacity for creativity, which is accompanied by and integrated with many s functions to account for specific aspects of creativity (following Spearman's concept of intelligence as G plus s_1, s_2, s_3, etc.), specific talents in different fields.

I am not sure what the G factor of creativity involves. There has been some suggestion that familial, genetic aspects may sometimes play a role. Whether inherited or acquired, the ability for *regression in the service of the ego* seems likely to be part of it, as much as is the ego function of *synthesis*.

Other general factors are likely to hold for all creative people. They probably share a more than average degree of narcissism; inasmuch as creativity can hardly become manifest without a mental set of wanting to produce and of valuing one's production (as an extension of oneself), this seems empirically a reasonable assumption. Such a set is likely to involve both a narcissistic involvement of the creative process and its specific features, e.g., the thought processes or esthetic perceptions, as well as a narcissistic overcathexis of the self (the clear-cut distinction of narcissistic cathexes of individual ego functions and of the self we owe to Hartmann [1953]). However, the narcissistic investment of the self is apparently not necessarily a part of the creative person: Einstein is said to have been unnarcissistic in that sense, not vain or exhibitionistic or arrogant in the way of Picasso or even in the way Beethoven is said to have behaved (Sterba and Sterba, 1954). It would not be wise, however, to separate artists from scientists in this respect because occasionally great scientists are not without considerable narcissism of the self.

Another general feature likely to hold, almost automatically, in relation to the above statements, is the fact that *object* relations are not likely to be at their best in creative people, as a result of their narcissism. This does not mean that they may not be sociable or what is known as extraverted: but in these latter we suspect that if one could study their fantasies and dreams they would appear to have poor object relations too.

In many creative people object relations are likely to be poor in terms of the analytic model of having achieved both "object constancy" (Hartmann, 1952) and genitality; they are, in fact, likely to have an overemphasis on certain pregenital aspects. E. Klein (1957) has suggested some general factors for creativity in the field of plastic art. He maintains that the child has a strong anthropomorphic relatedness to the world which is lost in the course of normal development, but which is retained in those who become plastic artists. These artists retain the child's interest in textures because of a difficulty in their relationships to people. He implies, in other words, a certain defensive failure of progression from a relationship with inanimate objects to a relationship with animate objects. To be sure, only in the schizophrenic is this failure to progress (according to Klein) primarily substitutive: in the artists he considers it largely additive.

This consideration brings us quite easily to a discussion of the s factors since, to a considerable extent, the specific pregenital function developed in a given person and even the specific type of object disturbance is likely to be highly correlated to the particular form of creativity.

To choose an easy example: the great dancer is likely to have a vast investment in her body, deriving a great measure of pleasure from rhythmic muscular activity; as we know, this often involves a lack of interest in heterosexual or any sexual genital activity despite the images the dancer creates for the audience. It is hard for the admiring male to understand that the ballerina's pleasure lies primarily in the feeling of overcoming gravity, of flying on her own, of marvelous command of her muscles. In the ideals of the textbooks she may have neutralized or sublimated a certain amount of direct (sexual) drive gratification for the sake of her dancing. In clinical fact, an outstanding dancer is particularly likely to have "invested" most of her drive, all hedonic tone, in muscle sense and in exhibitionism. In her case, the narcissism which we considered part of the G factor may take the special form of unconsciously conceiving of her whole body as a phallus (though she may, of course, not be without some feminine feelings, too). If this were s_1, s_2 might lie in a particularly great pleasure obtained in muscular discharge, and s_3 in exhibitionism, etc.

There is a usefulness in this kind of conceptualizing: each of these hypotheses includes a number of corollary hypotheses which permit certain predictions. Many of these predictions relate to behavior which constitute well-known psychoanalytic syndromes but which would not be apparent to the naked eye. Therefore, psychoanalytic language is more useful than it would be to say "she has such a great interest in dancing that she has no interest in men," etc. For instance, the body-phallus equation might permit us to understand why the dancer carries herself with an aggressive stance, why she has repeated dreams of breaking a leg or of having oozing holes in her body; why she should enjoy vigorous sexual foreplay but be unable to have an orgasm; why she might nevertheless be promiscuous, or more than usually homoerotic, why she should suffer from frequency of urination when aroused. We might even make some postdictions into her life history. Possibly she was born an active congenital activity type, as postulated by Fries and Woolf (1953). This might constitute a genetic or constitutional matrix for her choice of muscular activity. With or without that basis, we are likely to find, according to Spitz's hypothesis (1951a) concerning psychogenic diseases of infancy, that she had a mother whose attitude toward her oscillated between pampering and overt hostility, producing an infant with hypermotility, such as rocking in the knee-elbow position and other rhythmical movement. Superimposed upon these two facts (or sufficiently causative even without these two propositions) we may find that the dancer was exposed in childhood to a good deal of sexual stimulation by visual, auditory, and tactile stimuli; the young organism, unable to discharge this energy through its sexual apparatus, then behaves as though it were generally overloaded—like an electrical system—and discharges in almost random activity. If this simile strikes some as too fanciful, let me remind you that our conception of seizures is definitely predicated upon some such charge-discharge model.

By these hierarchical and collateral hypotheses we are able to construct some general theory of the nature of the creative ability manifesting itself in dancing. For this to include interpretive dancing or choreographic creation, we may have to add a few more s's related to literary talent. On the other hand, we can roughly differentiate the dancer from the actor by proposing that the latter usually has less of the muscular discharge syndrome and more of the voyeuristic-exhibitionistic charge, together with a tendency toward unreality and a make-believe emotional isolation that permits him to empathize by transitory identification, etc.

With all this wisdom we have not, of course, yet explained why our dancer became an artist rather than a person suffering from tics, restlessness, hypomania, etc. (dancing, of course, may successfully channelize what might otherwise become neurotic). The question is less unsettling than one might think because I suspect that a high correlation may be found between people who are dancers, and those who are not but who suffer from these symptoms: these restless neurotics will probably often have a propensity for dance and music, at least latently. Some of the determination of the choice of the epiphenomena may be of a cultural nature. A small hard core of information is still necessary. I have a notion that *"phase specificity"* (Hartmann, 1950b), i.e., in this case "overcharging" at a particular point of personality development, may be crucial. This idea requires validation by a study of a significant number of dancers. It is my guess that a set of factors involving difficulties in verbalization may be another s factor necessary to lead to muscular expression. Offhand, I would think that *oldest* or *only* children who did not find it easy to learn to speak (usually most easily learned from other, older siblings) would be more likely to combine the other factors mentioned in the syndrome "dancer." In other words, a disturbance of ego synthesis of the verbal-symbolic process together with the other factors mentioned might make a dancer. The same ego disturbance in the presence of withdrawal, lack of muscular charge, etc., might result in a mathematician such as Rosen (1953) described.

By and large, it appears that children with marked early object disturbances, with a lack of interest in and relationship to people, will turn interest and, in certain circumstances, creativity in the direction of the natural sciences: mathematics and its abstract symbols, physics and chemistry, seem to give them relief from oppressive conflicts with people. Those with a strong involvement with people and an inability to defend themselves against it by withdrawal into abstraction, tend toward the humanities, social science, and the arts. These hypotheses parallel to a certain extent the clinical finding that, generally, neurotics and psychotics do better on the verbal part of the Wechsler-Bellevue, and delinquents and psychopaths do better on the performance part. David M. Levy pointed out long ago that maternal overprotection leads to extensive and early verbalization (1943).

The relationship of the *creative personality to mental disturbance,* of genius to madness, has been frequently romanticized, sometimes not without a measure of satisfaction that, at least, the great have to pay for their gifts by being peculiar and disturbed.

In terms of ego psychology, I believe we can for once answer the question systematically and rationally. We have said that the creative process involves a partial regression of the adaptive ego functions. It is obvious that a relative ease of regression of the reality-testing aspects of the ego—such as is found in neurotics and borderline patients—would also enable them to see new configurations, new wholes, new answers. The gifted person, by virtue of being able to regress in the service of the ego, maintains relatively less firmly defined boundaries—of the self, of ideas—than does the average person. He makes less use of repression and therefore is relatively more likely to experience ego regression which might otherwise lead to neurotic or psychotic symptomatology. (It has also been said of the analyst that the constant use of emphatic ego regression and the need to have access to preconscious and unconscious processes constitutes a professional hazard.)

The answer to "madness and genius" is, then, that the creative person and the disturbed share the quality of ease of ego regression, of adaptive functions of the ego; they share the characteristic of less rigidly defined conceptual and perceptual boundaries and less strong countercathexis (by repression). However, disturbance and creative ability are not identical because the gifted person combines the ability for partial regression with an ability for synthesis, and an ability to increase again the adaptive capacity to the point of reality testing, criticism, and an ability to communicate.

To the extent to which regression of ego functions becomes broader and to the extent to which the return oscillation becomes impaired and the synthetic ability decreased—to that extent the gifted person resembles the disturbed individual.

In certain creative people much of the ego is incapacitated and only a small part—a few functions, including the creative one—is working well. We are familiar with this phenomenon in the ordinary, not especially gifted person who may be disturbed in every sphere of functioning, even to the point of delusions and hallucinations, and who may yet do a very good job as an economist, secretary, engineer, housewife, or physician. Similarly, in some people their specific creative ability may persist when the rest of the ego is severely disturbed. By the same token, and much more frequently, we find people whose ego is functioning very well in very many respects (particularly in reality testing by virtue of vigorous countercathexis and repression) at the cost of any creative regression in the service of the ego at all.

I am proposing here certain psychoanalytic hypotheses on a Spearman (see Wechsler, 1939) type of model of a G factor with a cluster of s (specific) factors; these hypotheses should lend themselves well to systematic experimental verification, possibly by factor analysis. I never did believe that there was any basic incompatibility between psychoanalysis and statistics, or rather, that statistics was useless. I merely believe that statistics, and specifically factor analysis and its relatives, is senseless without a workable theory of personality.

One could continue to describe in detail the particular factors in a creative engineer, outstanding photographer, a sculptor, an architect. In all instances one probably will find an early phase-specific development of certain ego functions related to the later choice of creativity. In a photographer, a patient of mine, to mention one detail, there was evidence of "perspective dreams" at least as early as age five: everything seemed in perspective, far away, sometimes small, accompanied by feelings of loneliness and fear. He was the youngest child by many years, of parents who brought him up kindly but with much emotional removal and an intellectual approach; emotional isolation under a veneer of good fellowship and a wish to be close characterized his object relations. I doubt that that would have been enough to make him a photographer, though he had good reasons for developing some voyeurism.

This patient lent himself particularly well to the proposition that the matrix might not at all necessarily have led to the specific choice of a certain vocation: the manifest choice was probably determined by the fact that an older brother had a great deal of interest in photography (but gave it up later when he could move to other interests). I think this patient had a factor pattern which could easily have permitted him to become a painter or a sculptor or even a musician.

After all, it is well-known that not only many artists, but many creative people generally, can be creative in several and often vastly different areas. It may not be fair to cite such rare examples as Leonardo da Vinci or Goethe: the latter thought for some time that his primary talent actually lay in painting rather than in writing; he was also creative and original as a scientist (he found the intermaxillary bone and, made independent contributions to other scientific fields). One frequently finds cross-talents in all fields of creativity.

The greatness of a creative person—as I have suggested in another context (1955b)—could be roughly estimated by the degree of "newness" of the configuration. In the case of scientists this is relatively easy. The time span which Einstein bridged with his insights covers the time since Newton; the time that will elapse before his contribution is radically superseded may serve as another criterion of the greatness of his creativity. Similarly, the fact that it took centuries to catch up with Leonardo da Vinci's technical creations might serve as a temporal measuring rod. The same might hold for a musician of Beethoven's status, etc.

In certain circumstances there may hardly be any previous stepping stone to a new insight, a new creation. When Einstein described his theory of relativity it took off from the existing Newtonian physics and was at least intelligible and acceptable to a good number of eminent contemporary physicists. When Freud stated his hypotheses concerning unconscious motivation, unconscious functioning, and the continuity of dynamic behavior, he had, in essence, no predecessors (except for isolated fragments of an unsystematic nature). If one should want to play at the game of measurement, it might be said that Freud's creative achievement was greater than Einstein's, by that criterion. The temporal measurement is, of course, not the only one—a popular way to measure creativity is by its impact on the contemporary scene or subsequent history.

In conclusion, some flights of fancy on the matter of the creative person: it will be well remembered that J. B. Watson was carried away, in his heyday of conditioning theory, to claim that given a child early enough, he could condition it to become anything one would care to choose. Today, we are both less sure of ourselves and also more fearful, for being closer to Orwell's *1984*.

In a very stimulating article, Professor Louis Hacker of Columbia University suggested "Oscars" be awarded for creative minds (New York Times, April 20, 1958). James Reston and Cyrus Sulzberger of the Times, themselves most eminently gifted, frequently allude not only to the need for exceptional intellectual capacities in politics, but, in one form or another, hope for a creative mind on the political scene (e.g., tangentially at least, James Reston, New York Times, April 20, 1958).

I think most competent psychologists could achieve some degree of agreement on educational conditions conducive to the development of a creative personality and on those circumstances likely to produce narrow, one-track minds. Unfortunately, producing generally happy, decent, and capable children may not be quite consistent with rearing outstandingly creative people. If our propositions concerning the G factor, the general aspects of the creative personality, hold true at all, it must be assumed that narcissism, the accentuation of partial pregenital drives, and the relative failure of phase-specific ego synthesis are not apt to arise in seemingly favorable circumstances. Could it be that highly developed cultures become decadent because their need for creative adaptation suffers from "disuse atrophy"? Could it be that modern American education produces children who are too happy to be creative? By and large I doubt it. We seem to have enough neurosis. If anything, the trouble lies more on the phenotypic level: in a culture which stresses conformity, other-directedness, creativity is likely to expend itself on the level of how better to conform rather than to be different. It is likely to manifest itself in administrative, mass-production levels of technicians rather than in bolder, individualistic, new configurations.

At the same time our increasing technical advances are likely to affect creativity adversely in a number of ways. One obvious fact is that creativity needs some measure of inner-directness, some isolation: the tremendous impact of constant sources of communication—of radio, TV, skywriting, number of publications—interferes with quiet fermentation.

Lamentation will not help and clocks cannot be turned back. Our energy will have to be applied to coping with this impact of technical advance on creativity. The development of teamwork may be one answer to it—the substitution of mutual external stimulation for internal stimulation. Let us hope there are other answers.

CREATIVE EXPERIENCE

In talking about creative experience one has to differentiate certain brief, all too transitory phenomena of *acute impact* from the experience of *sustained creative effort,* and from the *meaning* of the creative experience, as seen, on the one hand, by the creator and, on the other, by the observer.

(a) The *acute creative experience* certainly is always accompanied by the "aha" phenomenon, the feeling of sudden fit, the feeling of closure, a mingled sentiment of surprise, gratification, and elation. It would be hard to separate systematically this feeling about the creative experience from the feelings accompanying the attainment of closure in other circumstances—say of finally finding a way of solving a mathematical problem or finding the long-sought answer to a crossword puzzle. Romanticizing to the contrary, I suspect that the difference between that and Einstein finding his formula or a great artist finally hitting the right conception of his problem is a quantitative one, rather than a qualitative one: the greater the achievement, the sharper the feeling, most likely. It may well be that the meaning of the act of closure may supply additional qualities— i.e., if the final act of creating a sculpture has the meaning of giving birth, it is likely that an extra quality will be present that is absent in the crossword puzzle's solution. Most analysts have had patients for whom the solving of a puzzle, the attainment of a difficult school problem, had the unconscious meaning of winning out over the father, of gaining a phallus (or losing one, if it does not go well), and the difference is again likely to be more one of degree than principle.

A likely curve to plot for most creative experience is that the sharp feeling of elation is soon followed by some devaluation of the creation and of the self, with doubt, ambivalence, even depression ensuing. In part, we can understand the dynamics of this process as a transitory hypercathexis of the creation: like the similar process of love, it is likely to demand, by its own economic nature, a redistribution of energy—with many individual differences, naturally. Since there is doubtless a process of identification with the product, it seems reasonable to say that the amount of ambivalence and devaluation and depression is a function of the creator's attitude toward himself. A person characterized by a particularly effective process of relatively mild denial and somewhat excessive narcissism might maintain a rather high level of pride and happiness regarding his creation. For the relatively normal person, it all moves back into perspective, more or less.

The ego-psychological side of the acute creative experience is, of course, that the surge of the first elated feeling is facilitated by the ego's topological and temporal regression. As this state of affairs passes, an oscillation back to high adaptive functioning is likely to reduce the creative act to its proper proportions or even less—as if emergence from dulled cognitive functioning were invested with extra acuity by contrast.

The *sustained creative effort*—the nine-tenths of hard work that has been said to be the main ingredient of great achievements in all fields—is often part of a silent, preconscious grappling with the problem which eventually leads to the "aha" experience. Both the prelabor and the postcreative aspects are likely to be high in adaptive functioning of the ego, with smaller oscillations from high functioning to regression. If it is true that the "inspiration" is primarily of oral meaning, as Kris (1952) has suggested, or related to passive sexual traits or attitudes of passive aims (Jones, 1956) (this may relate to the high frequency of femininity in male artists), the sustained effort, libidinally speaking, seems to be related primarily to anal traits: cleaning up, attention to small detail, obstinacy, high frustration tolerance. Relating back to the conceptions of the creative personality, it certainly seems as if the oral people are most often especially endowed with ease of conception and frequency of "aha" experience and inspiration, with relatively less good follow-through; the reverse of this picture holds in the more anal person. Some creative persons seem to be lucky enough to have two distinct phases of activity—one of the acute creative experience, and another, temporally quite separated by hours, days, weeks, months, or years, of the sustained effort. The rhythm of creativity seems a highly personal one, since some people seem to create and improve by doing the "whole thing" over and over again, instead of starting with the product of one inspiration and consciously improving it. It is as if for some the entire first creative act were committed to a less-than-conscious memory, making it possible for them to emerge with one final optimal production. Aside from being characteristic of individual differences, it is very unlikely that there is any preference or advantage to one method over another.

The meaning of the creative experience will, of course, vary greatly from one person to another; we can only hope to mention a few of the more outstanding and more frequent propositions involved.

Sterba and Sterba (1956) have emphasized the *restitutive* meaning or function of the creative act in their discussion of Michelangelo; his sculpture seems rooted in his experience with the foster mother of stonemasonry setting. It has been said in the biography of a popular comedian that his antics are apparently directly related to the attempt to make his unresponsive mother laugh. In a patient of mine the tremendous urge to be an actor was very clearly related, by free associations and TAT, to the need to have the family's attention, particularly the mother's, in competition with the sister. The adaptive feature in the choice of the artistic expression is, incidentally, particularly clear in this patient's case: his first success came in singing; puberty brought an unfortunate change in voice and led to expression via acting.

The creative urge may certainly have *phallic* significance: many works are supposed to add up to "a long list" or a "long row" of achievements, which often translate themselves very obviously in dream symbolism into the possession of a big phallus. Needless to say, the meaning of creative experience may often lie at the core of a disturbance of creativity—if, for instance, the act of creation has a phallic or aggressive or oedipal meaning, it may have to be curtailed by the superego.

In others, creativity may be an outstandingly passive experience—an *oral* gift. Muscular activity or thinking may have strong unconscious masturbatory meaning. The creative process and its product may have the unconscious meaning of anality, of defecation, more or less closely related to ideas of giving birth. Popularly, the most often used simile for this is "giving birth" to an idea, a piece of art, etc. In such cases, the feeling of satisfaction, of having produced something, may soon be followed by a disturbing sensation of emptiness, depletion, lack.

Aggressive and aggressive-sexual oedipal meanings of the creative acts are not at all uncommon: "wrestling with an idea" is a common expression of this fact; the Sterbas point out that sculpture, the hammering away at rock, involves a good deal of aggression. Of course, literature may have the nature of aggressive revenge; finding the solution to a scientific problem may have all the earmarks of fighting with brother or father figures.

Klein, as mentioned, suggested that plastic creative experience may have the meaning of infantile object relations and of contact with a sensory world. Urethral and fecal meaning have been given to many artistic expressions. Bychowski has suggested that a feeling of omnipotence is a frequent concomitant of the creative act.

It is well to remember that reductionist formulas—"clay sculpture means playing with feces"—are, of course, uninformed oversimplifications which omit the majority of the relevant propositions.

THE OBSERVER

The role of the creative act for the observer has been mainly discussed in connection with artistic productions, of course, though Jones (1956) discusses the phenomenon in relation to scientific creativity in his discussion of Freud, and quotes Révész that the element of surprise is always an outstanding part of the observer's response.

The observation of the acute act of creation, or the acute exposure to a creation, is likely to be accompanied by an "aha" experience similar to that of the creator. The prolonged study of an idea, of a piece of art, probably produces more, smaller, more sustained feelings of gratification, by identification, empathy, and finally by total assimilation and familiarity.

Freud's economic model for the enjoyment of wit, comedy, and humor, in terms of saving of energy expenditures, can probably do duty for the pleasurable response to creative acts in creator and observer. (One might wonder if the mechanism of closure cannot be best studied in Freud's kind of energic-economic model).

Kris (1941) has made the main contributions to the understanding of the "aesthetic illusion" necessary to the enjoyment of drama, for instance.

His concept of "libidinization of anxiety" implies that anxiety which can be tolerated and the decrease of which can be anticipated, as in watching a drama or reading a novel, is pleasurable. It is very likely that this process of libidinization of anxiety plays a major role in creative acts of all kinds. A problem confronts us—be it in stone, choreography, physics, or psychoanalysis—and one enters into the solution of it with some tension and some anticipation of tension reduction by closure. The specific meaning of the creative act for different people contributes the specific features of the anxiety: oedipal, more plainly aggressive, fear of passivity, etc. This process holds as true for the creator as for the observer.

It might be said that most factors, "aha" experience, partial regression, etc., hold as true for the observer as for the creator, although usually in diminished degree. Indeed, the outstanding characteristic of artistic creations is the fact that the artist's accentuated, intense experience is communicated to the more plebian mind via the artistic creation, in whatever medium it may be expressed. It is the communicated experience that establishes the bond between artist and observer and lifts us "Michelangelos without hands" into heightened states of experience.

THE SOCIAL AND THE PRIVATE ROLE PLAYING OF THE CREATIVE PERSON

There is a never-ending public interest in the private role of the socially prominent person. The creative person, as one variety of the socially prominent person, may possibly even arouse more interest than most others. Somehow it seems more possible for the public to understand even Kings and Queens and multimillionaires than an Einstein or a Beethoven or a Freud. The interest in biography is undoubtedly predicated to a large extent on the wish to bridge the conceptions of the social and the private role. Gossip columns bridge the difference between the social and private role for contemporary luminaries.

To a certain extent, the social role of the great is probably predicated upon the childhood images of the parents: magically capable, knowledgeable, different. The famous person is the recipient of the parental role in the family romance, so to speak (Kris, 1952). He is, therefore, also expected to be pure—or immaculate, to be precise.

In the creative person, the social prominence is defined by the product of his creativity: his music, his painting, his formula, his writing. These creations produce certain responses in the populace; the latter thereupon constructs its fantasy image, disappointment and vengeance ensue (and a measure of satisfaction on the part of the population to have found him human, after all), if the private role does not live up to the social one, which, of course, it rarely, if ever can. Listening to Beethoven's 9th Symphony, it is hard to match the magnificent music with the image of the poor, suffering, paranoid, nasty, destructive man with the morbid attachment to his nephew that Sterba and Sterba (1954) describe.

It seems hard to comprehend that a specific creative ability may have a certain manifest autonomy (albeit latently integrated, understandably enough, with the rest of the person). If it is difficult for people to comprehend this, it is often hard for the creative person, himself, to come to terms with it. His creativity becomes anthropomorphized for him, invested with good and/or bad characteristics; and his self-conception, the role, he finds himself playing, may have a puzzling and sometimes destructive effect. Sometimes it seems indeed as if the attitude toward the self, influenced by the social role he plays, leads to such confusion of identity, such as a fear of not living up to the social role, that creativity —particularly in artists—may become destroyed. The court jester, the childhood crony, the intimate, the butler, are probably all forms of attempting to preserve identity and perspective, to avoid mistaking the social role for the private role:

because "that way madness lies," a feeling of unreality results, or a way of living the legend to the extent of losing the private role and all essential object relations and feelings that go with it.

THE RELATION TO CREATIVITY OF
PSYCHOANALYTIC THERAPY

The relationship of psychoanalysis (as a form of treatment) to creative ability is, as I have said, a complex one. One proposition is relatively simple: if creativity, artistic or otherwise, is strongly genetically determined, psychoanalysis will obviously not produce it or do away with it. On the other hand, even dyed-in-the-wool geneticists are nowadays aware of the effect of experiential factors upon the genetic Anlage; in that case, psychoanalysis as a process of reversing or restructuring experiential factors may affect creativity, for better or for worse.

Another relatively simple proposition is that if the creative process itself has neurotic implications, psychoanalysis or psychoanalytic psychotherapy can have a definitely beneficial effect. If successful creation in any medium has the meaning of a forbidden or frightening act, be it sexual, aggressive, passive, anal, or whatever, we are dealing with a variety of success neurosis. Inasmuch as this type of neurosis may involve the kind of superego constellation described as "moral masochism" and is likely to be characterized by the "negative therapeutic response" (where each advance in treatment is itself considered a forbidden achievement and is at first characterized by a worsening rather than an improvement in the patient), it is likely to be a difficult therapeutic process, but potentially a successful one.

Psychoanalytic treatment can also be very successful in broadening the creative scope. The photographer who was my patient could not work with older men owing to problems with his father; nor could he attain financial success for the same reason. Even the art medium he did work in successfully was too stereotyped, and improved greatly, by his own and other peoples' standards, in the course of treatment. The choice of subjects and the ability to convey feeling increased greatly for the sculptor who also had shrunk from attaining full success. The dancer became a more expressive, freer choreographer and less tired physically. The writer could address himself to other topics than the essential projection of his own neurotic problems (see Chapter 23). It is my guess that if Somerset Maugham (whose writings I greatly admire) had been analyzed, he would have broadened his themes beyond the almost stereotyped constellation of a woman being a man's (and his best friend's) downfall.

Psychoanalysis can increase frustration tolerance and enable some creative people to finish properly what they had to leave off too early; for instance, one consulting engineer approached puzzling problems in need of a creative approach with great creative ability but little patience and muddled those problems tremendously, until treated with some success.

And, of course, psychoanalysis can successfully deal with any number of ancillary problems affecting creative people, from impotence to insomnia, sometimes without even entering very much into the creative area.

A serious question has often been posed, however: whether analysis can possibly affect the creative process itself adversely: the question has to be answered in detail.

We all know that the reversibility of experiential processes by psychoanalysis has its limitations most of the time, unfortunately. It is very likely that most creative abilities are of an order of intensity and fixity and "primariness" to defy reversal by therapeutic process. Also, it has to be remembered that many of the creative abilities are likely to be of the order of autonomous ego factors of the conflict-free sphere of the ego, as described by Hartmann (1950a). The overwhelming chances are that creativity, if altered at all, will be enhanced indirectly, as described above, by a removal of neurotic encumbrances.

Nevertheless it is quite possible that some of the *enabling* aspects of the G factor may be so modified by the therapeutic process as to affect productivity.

Inasmuch as excessive narcissistic investment of the self and of certain ego functions, with concomitant impairment of object relations, is part of the G factor of the creative personality, inasmuch as psychoanalytic therapy usually has to involve an attempt to decrease at least the narcissistic investment of the self, and to improve object relationships (possibly at the cost of some investment of certain ego functions), it is quite conceivable and possible, I believe, that creative activity can be reduced by successful therapy.

In simple language, the creative person is primarily interested in himself and his creative process, whatever it may be. By implication this makes him often neglectful of other people, selfish, peculiar, and neurotic to the extent where his overcathexis of the self or of certain ego functions may lead to unpleasant manifestations of generalized oversensitivity, of feelings of unreality and depersonalization, etc. In the process of making him less self-centered, less sensitized, less infantile, one might well affect some of the *enabling conditions for his creative potential* (even if it is agreed that the creative activity itself cannot be diminished).

Not only that: in many ways the creative person is often "unselfish" in some ways, so involved with his concerns as to be unmindful of money, reason, comfort, rest, or self-preservation. A necessary part of all psychotherapy is reality testing: pointing out self-harming, self-crippling tendencies. In many ways "one has to be crazy" to be a greatly creative person who foregoes many of the available creature comforts. It is a moot point whether the true scientist, the true artist, attains such great pleasure from his work that other values pale in comparison. The fact is that if analysis may enable some creative people to lead happier lives in the more ordinary sense of the word, it is possible that it decreases the "enabling conditions" for creativity in others. The answer to this problem possibly lies in the consideration of specific parameters of the treatment of creative people: as careful an appraisal and planning of what to analyze and possibly what not to analyze as is possible in a process which has a certain momentum of its own. At any rate, with any given creative person the chances are so infinitely greater that psychoanalysis will help him *and* his creativity—rather than cause a decrease of the latter—that it seems one of the minor risks of life.

23

A PSYCHOLOGICAL STUDY OF THE
STORIES OF SOMERSET MAUGHAM:
A PROFILE OF A CREATIVE PERSONALITY

This chapter attempts to arrive at an overview of Somerset Maugham's personality through an analysis of ten of his stories. The underlying assumptions contained in the method used here (similar to that previously used by Freud in, for example, his analysis of Dostoevsky—Freud, 1928) are that the written story can be treated like a projective response; indeed, in this chapter a TAT summary form is used to organize the findings. Yet, as is pointed out elsewhere in, for example, his analysis of Dostoevsky—Freud, 1928) are that the written in response to a particular set of instructions. We can also add that a story is a finished literary product, often extensively rewritten; the TAT story is a one-time exercise. The projective aspects of a story are probably most visible in the first draft, but these are rarely available; to what extent elements of the first draft are contained in the final product is an extremely useful datum that is rarely, if ever, known. To the extent that polishing has taken place, any attempt to "read" the author's personality from the story is correspondingly diminished.

The diagnostic truth of a TAT assessment can be checked against the subject's performance in therapy; the truth of a pathographic impression is less easy to verify. In Maugham's case we know that his marriage was only partly successful, that he was detached in his personal relations, and that he traveled a great deal. These facts agree superficially with impressions gathered from his writings, yet the facts are also public information and may represent a certain rearrangement of the underlying truth. Here again we must deal with a public image, and hidden from us is the private side of the person that is so much the focus of psychotherapy. The problem is often confounded by the fact that biographical information is frequently derived from the subject's autobiography, which is itself a published work and subject to the same polishing, selection, and elaboration that goes into a short story. Any corroboration of a diagnostic assessment gained from his writings depends, then, on the agreement between two *published* works; some agreement is necessarily built in.

The interference underlying all these difficulties is the author's image of himself as a public figure—the narcissistic element in his work. Published materials are invaluable for telling us how much he wants to be seen; they are somewhat less useful in describing how he is when no one is looking.

I OWE MANY HOURS of diverse pleasure to Somerset Maugham. His deft portrayals of the human condition are a delight both in content and in form. If I now attempt a psychological analysis of some of these stories in the hope of a

NOTE: From *The Study of Lives*, edited by R. White, New York, Atherton Press, 1963. Reprinted by permission of the publisher and editor.

glimpse of the man who wrote them, I do so in a spirit much like his—one of curiosity and compassion, animated by a desire to understand the complexity of human lives. Regrettably, there will be no similarity in our styles.

The use of artistic productions as a basis for inferences about the creator is not new. Freud's study of Leonardo da Vinci (1910), of Dostoevski (1928), and of Jensen's *Gradiva* (1907), and especially his discussion of the relationship of daydreaming to creative work (1908) laid a foundation upon which has risen a host of such studies by other psychoanalysts (Greenacre, 1955, Hitschman, 1956). Nor is this so farfetched an exercise as it might seem. It is the task of science, after all, to provide hypotheses which permit the ordering of different observable facts into lawful relationships. Freud gave us the continuum not only between the child and the adult, between the waking thought and the dream, between the normal and the pathological, and between the visible and the unseen, but also between the man and his work, especially his creative work. He was aware, however, of the complexity of the creative process and himself suggested that there was more than a one-to-one relationship, that his view might prove itself to be too exiguous a pattern. Nevertheless, it may contain a first approach to the true state of affairs (1908, p. 151).

In his study of poets, Freud pointed out the effects of subjective experience on later perception. But he went beyond that. He suggested the possibility that a certain "bent"—a selective cognitive set—would lead to a subjectively meaningful choice of theme.

Pathographies of a psychoanalytic nature, although often persuasive clinically, nonetheless have troubled those concerned with the rigors of methodology. A suspicion of *post hoc, ergo propter hoc* reasoning has not been easily dispelled. It is understandable that Freud and his immediate followers thought in terms of the rather rigid determinism that was common at the turn of the century and largely along lines of motivation and drive expression in creative products. But current conceptual thinking revolves around the degrees of probability with which one fact may be predictably related to another. Ego psychology, itself a product of Freud's thinking, addresses itself to the adaptive, as well as the dynamic, genetic, economic, and structural aspects of all functioning. And of course it also takes into account as determinants of behavior the social setting in its broader cultural sense, the familial situation, the biological factors, and the physical environment.

This increased awareness of the complexity of behavioral determinants makes the task more difficult, but at the same time more gratifying. The problems one confronts in making inferences about Maugham as an individual from a study of his works are not so different from the contemporary problems of clinical psychoanalysis or the problems of psychological testing; the psychological analysis of purposeful literary production and the "story-making" involved in the Thematic Apperception Test, especially, share, in good measure, certain fundamental theories and techniques.

The Thematic Apperception Test (TAT), originated by Morgan and Murray (1935), consists of having the subject tell stories of what may be going on in response to a series of ambiguous pictures of people in different settings. The interpretation of these stories has been influenced by an increasing complexity of theory over the years. Originally it focused primarily on the motivational aspects of need and the perception of environmental stimuli (called "press" by Murray).

Ego-psychological thinking has extended the usefulness of the test by including interpretation of the defenses (see Chapter 11, and Bellak, 1950) and of apperception, which involves adaptive and expressive features (Bellak, 1954a, 1954b). An illuminating paper by Holt (1961) brought the cognitive approach to bear on the TAT, although the study revolved rather too extensively around the differences between TAT stories and fantasy, overshadowing the features in common.

The main point is simply this: literary product, TAT story, fantasy, and other acts are all products of the person involved, and as such must have a significant relationship to that personality. The only relevant question is one which centers on the problem of the complexity of that relationship and our ability to understand it. For many years, both as a psychoanalyst and a testing psychologist, I have been impressed by the continuity of the relationship among test products, artistic production, and the clinical data emerging in the psychoanalytic treatment of artists as patients.

The question of the validity of the interpretation of a test product or literary product, allowing for a complex interplay of many variables, seems to be primarily one of the logical and procedural tightness of the progression from observable fact to inference. This present attempt will be limited to one level of inference—from the story to the personality of the story-teller. It would be tempting to make a second order of inference—from the story to the genesis of the personality. The distinction between these two levels of inference is often not stated with sufficient clarity. A good deal of success can probably be achieved at the second level, but it involves another methodological step, which we must forego here.

The procedure I have found most helpful for the interpretation of the TAT is the use of a check form which provides a concrete frame of reference.[1] I shall attempt to use this same technique for the analysis of ten short stories by Somerset Maugham.

The initial step of this analysis concerns itself with determining the theme of a story on three levels. On the descriptive level one attempts simply to restate the gist of the story. On the interpretive level this statement is reduced in such a way as to eliminate particulars and establish the general psychological relationships that obtain in the story. A well-known tale can serve as an example: the story of the boy who cried wolf reduces itself to the statement that if you cry for help when you don't need it, you will not be believed when you really do need it. On the diagnostic level one begins to make clinical inferences, which involve a further translation of the theme into clinical concepts such as basic need, apperception, conflict, anxiety, defense, superego, and ego integration. In the wolf story one would notice that the superego is active and that anxiety is connected with dependence-inspired departures from the truth. The TAT form starts with the main theme stated at the diagnostic level, and its categories further aid one in capturing systematically other dynamic features. In our example we can note that a wolf is introduced and that the consequence of lying is being killed and eaten. We can make inferences as to certain ideas of death, certain ways of

---

[1] *Bellak TAT and CAT Blank* (C.P.S. Inc., P. O. Box No. 83, Larchmont, New York). See p. 347 for a shortened version.

dying (the fear of being devoured). The inevitability of the punishment and its rather unreasonable severity in relation to the nature of the crime would suggest a strict and primitive conscience.

The more samples of observed behavior of one person one has to draw upon, the greater the likelihood of making meaningful inferences. In TAT diagnosis a good many stories are used in order to detect the common denominators. In this literary analysis I want to follow the same procedure and analyze, albeit briefly and sketchily, ten of Maugham's stories. Maugham offers an abundance of riches. Volume I of the complete short stories contains thirty stories; Volume II, sixty-one (1953a, 1953b). Incidentally, Maugham's stories would delight any TAT psychologist by their degree of structure and the clear statement of theme. In his preface to the first volume the author tells us that the first of the stories of the first volume was written in 1919 and the last in 1931, and that they were written in the sequence in which they appear. In the preface to the second volume he simply says that these stories are the rest of the lot. They are much shorter than those of Volume I and apparently cover more time and traveled space.

It would be tremendously time-consuming to do even a most condensed analysis of ninety-one stories. Therefore, some sampling and selecting had to be done. I used a rather crude method of randomizing, and in Volume One picked stories by their numerical characteristics—1, 2, 11, 12, 21, 22. With the second volume, I asked my eight-year-old daughter to make a pencil mark at the margin of four different stories in the table of contents. I think that even the most statistically minded reader, if he knew Maugham, would not object to this simple procedure of selection. I think it will become quite clear that the themes and characteristics which become manifest in the selected stories have a great similarity to most of the rest of Maugham's writings, including his major work, *Of Human Bondage,* which is considered to be in large part autobiographical.

ANALYSIS OF THE STORIES

The first story in the volume, luckily enough, is "Rain"—luckily, because it is particularly widely known, as a movie as well as the original short story.

"RAIN"

Descriptive Theme. A zealous missionary, driven by great religious fervor, has always resisted the ordinary feelings of compassion, sex, and fear in his desire to rise above them for the sake of a stern religious morality. When he meets Sadie Thompson, a prostitute, he feels compelled to interfere with her activities in his efforts to save her soul (at the cost of great misery and actual danger to her). However, he finds himself increasingly attracted to her (note his dream of breastlike mountains, his remaining with her later and later into the night) and ultimately makes a sexual advance. He kills himself in consequence.

Interpretive Theme. If emotions are very strong, especially sexual ones, and one tries to control them while in intense contact with a woman, control may be destroyed as well as oneself.

SHORT FORM

BELLAK T A T and C A T BLANK

For Recording and Analyzing Thematic Apperception Test and Children's Apperception Test

Name_____Sex_____Age_____Date_____

Education_____Occupation_____; m. s. w. d. (circle one)

Referred by_____Analysis by_____

    After having obtained the stories analyze each story by using the variables on the left of Page 2. Not every story will furnish information regarding each variable: the variables are presented as a frame of reference to help avoid overlooking some dimension.

    When all ten stories have been analyzed it is easy to check each variable from left to right for all ten stories and record an integrated summary on Page 4 under the appropriate headings. That way a final picture is obtained almost immediately.

    Then, keeping Page 4 folded out, the Final Report: Diagnostic Impressions and Recommendations can be written on Page 1 for reference to Page 4. Page 5 gives available space for any other notations. The stories then can be stapled inside the blank against Page 5. For further instructions see Manual for TAT Interpretation, Psychological Corporation, by Leopold Bellak or Manual for the CAT, C.P.S. Inc. or *The TAT and CAT in Clinical Use*, pp. 282, Grune and Stratton, 1954, N.Y.C. by Leopold Bellak;

FINAL REPORT: Diagnostic Impressions and Recommendations

	Story No. 1	Story No. 2
1. Main Theme: (diagnostic level: if descriptive and interpretative level are desired, use a scratch sheet or page 5)		
2. Main hero: age____ sex____ vocation____ abilities____ interests____ traits____ body image_____ adequacy (√,√√,√√√) and/or self-image_____		
3. Main needs of hero: a) behavioral needs of hero (as in story): _____		
b) figures, objects, or circumstances *introduced*: _____ implying need for or to:_____		
c) figures, objects or circumstances *omitted*: _____ implying need for or to: _____		
4. Conception of environment (world) as: _____		
5. a) Parental figures (m____, f____) are seen as _____ and subject's reaction to a is _____ b) Contemp. figures (m____, f____) are seen as _____ and subject's reaction to b is _____ c) Junior figures (m____, f____) are seen as _____ and subject's reaction to c is _____		
6. Significant conflicts: _____		
7. Nature of anxieties: (√) of physical harm and/or punishment _____ of disapproval _____ of lack or loss of love ____of illness or injury _____ of being deserted _____of deprivation _____ of being overpowered and helpless _____ of being devoured _____other _____		
8. Main defenses against conflicts and fears: (√) repression_____ reaction-formation_____ regression_____ denial_____ introjection_____ isolation_____ undoing_____ rationalization _____other_____		
9. Severity of superego as manifested by: (√) punishment for "crime":_____ immediate_____just_____too severe_____ delayed_____unjust_____too lenient_____ delayed initial response or pauses,____stammer_____		
10. Integration of the ego, manifesting itself in: (√,√√,√√√) adequacy of hero_____ solution_____ adequate_____ outcome: happy_____ unhappy_____ inadequate_____ realistic_____ unrealistic_____ thought processes as revealed by plot being: (√,√√,√√√) stereotyped_____original_____appropriate_____ complete_____incomplete_____inappropriate_____		
Intelligence: (√) superior____above average____average____ below average____defective____		

Story No. 9	Story No. 10	SUMMARY
		1-3. Unconscious structure and drives of subject (based on variable 1-3)
		4. Conception of world:
		5. Relationship to others:
		6. Significant conflicts:
		7. Nature of anxieties:
		8. Main defenses used:
		9. Superego structure:
		10. Integration and strength of ego:

4

When you find need for more extensive notations on any story (e.g. the main theme) please use this page for this purpose. (The pages on which the TAT and CAT stories were recorded may be enclosed or attached to this Blank)

Diagnostic Level.   Presence of strong drives, aggressive and sexual. Attempted defenses are denial, repression, rationalization, withdrawal, and reaction formation. Adaptively tries to deal with his conflict by becoming a missionary. Fears loss of control over drives, especially sexual one. Fears destruction by women. Concern about self-destruction; suicidal ideas are present.

These bald statements leave out many subtleties of the story. Let me plead again the need for economy. However, I must, even though briefly, point out a few of the other features. The theme of the missionary is not the only one. He is not the only hero; Sadie Thompson is another.

Descriptive Theme.   A prostitute is reduced to a fearful clinging wreck by a zealous missionary bent on saving her soul, but she rises contemptuously when his moral principles collapse and ordinary lust shows through.

Interpretive Theme.   If a lustful woman meets a zealously moral man, she is reduced to weakness, but she recovers her strength if the man appears prey to lust.

Diagnostic Level.   Woman is seen as lustful, seductive. Moral man is seen as strong. Man unable to control his desires is seen as contemptible by women. Control is very important; its loss is contemptible.

Another subtheme is concerned with Dr. Macphail. One must consider him another identification figure for the author (of course, Maugham projects some of his own sentiments on all the figures). Let me simply remark that the doctor appears compassionate, but tries to remain uninvolved to avoid the discomfiture of too much emotion. He tries to accept with passivity the missionary, his own wife, and the world around him but finds himself uneasy. He engages in action in a desultory way (and with a good deal of conflict) only when he feels he can no longer avoid doing so.

The minor women characters in the story appear as controlling, either by their aggressive attitudes or by their moralistic ones. In fact, the most repetitive concern seems to be with emotions that could overcome one, especially with regard to women who tend to control.

Let me anticipate some broader inferences here by pointing out that the waitress, Mildred, in *Of Human Bondage* is not too different from Sadie Thompson in her effect on the protagonist. Nor is the principal character, Philip, himself a doctor, too different from Dr. Macphail. It is common knowledge that Maugham was a medical-school graduate.

"THE FALL OF EDWARD BARNARD"

In a general sense, one might describe this story as a not-so-gentle mockery of American culture, especially as seen through the bourgeois pretensions of wealthy women and their effect on men.

Descriptive Theme.   Edward Barnard is a traditional and upstanding young Chicagoan. Just as soon as he saves enough money from his work in Tahiti, he plans to return home and marry the beautiful, cultured, controlling, and ambitious Isabel. However, he comes to enjoy the easy and simple life of the islands, particularly the companionship of a half-caste girl. Unlike Isabel, she puts him at his ease.

Bateman Hunter, in love with Isabel, but friend to Edward also, is vaguely puzzled and distressed by Edward's change. He tries to persuade Edward to return home. When Edward renounces Isabel, Hunter himself returns to marry her. Isabel's dreams, as she embraces Hunter, are of business success, tea dances, and the look of distinction and solidity which horn-rimmed glasses will give her new fiancé.

Interpretive Theme. If one is caught in the demands of bourgeois culture, as represented by controlling, ambitious women, one may find life much happier in an undemanding culture (which permits more passivity) and with simpler women (who are no threat and do not make one feel inferior). A selfless male friend helps out reliably.

Diagnostic Level. An uneasiness about cultural demands. Sees women of society as subtly controlling, demanding, ambitious. Sophisticated women of this kind produce feelings of unease, inferiority. Attempts solution of anxiety and conflict by withdrawal (geographic and psychological) and by turning to more primitive women and less demanding societies. Uses rationalization, emotional isolation, and withdrawal as defense. A male friend is seen as selfless and dependable. Since we know something of the author's actual life history, we can add that his travels to primitive countries were adaptive ways of dealing with his problems. Writing was another way of dealing with his conflicts. He described writing *Of Human Bondage* as a cathartic experience. His friendships with men were often lifelong, his heterosexual relations apparently either transitory or distant and tempestuous (Maugham, 1962).

"THE YELLOW STREAK"

Descriptive Theme. Izzart, the handsome, English-educated son of a white father and half-caste mother, is constantly unnerved by the thought that someone will discover his mixed parentage. During a mission with Campion, a visitor to the Malayan jungle, the men are involved in a boating accident. Izzart is so intent on saving his own life that he ignores Campion's pleas for help. Miraculously, both men survive. Campion is publicly silent about Izzart's part in the near catastrophe, but, triggered by Izzart's fear and guilt, makes it privately plain to him that he attributes his cowardice to the "yellow streak"—the tainted blood.

Interpretive Theme. If a man is tainted by a (racially) inferior woman (mother), he fears his inferiority (the yellow streak) will emerge to his shame and peril. His fear that others will recognize this inferiority constantly haunts him.

Diagnostic Level. Feels inferior. Projects his feelings of inferiority on others. Inferiority is blamed on a woman, specifically his mother. Woman is seen as something inferior as well as a source of embarrassment and shame. The main concern is one of controlling emotion, particularly fear.

"P & O"

Descriptive Theme. Mrs. Hamlyn is returning alone to England from the tropics after twenty years of happy marriage. Her husband has fallen helplessly in love with another woman. She and her husband both view the intrusion of this new love as one would an illness—it is uncontrollable and one must bow before it. On shipboard she meets the vital and forward-looking Mr. Gallagher, a retired planter, who is going home to begin a new life. Mr. Gallagher has left behind his native wife, after making what he considered generous financial provision for her. His wife, however, became incensed and cast a spell upon him. When Mr. Gallagher sickens and dies on board, to the consternation of the ship's doctor, apparently as a result of this spell, Mrs. Hamlyn's own anger evaporates, and she feels great compassion for the love that, like an unrestrainable force (a spell) befell her husband.

Interpretive Theme. If love befalls one, it is like a sickness against which one is defenseless. If one fights a (native) woman's love, she will kill one. It is best to bow to uncontrollable emotions.

Diagnostic Level. Fear of emotion, particularly of heterosexual love. Fear of being overwhelmed by love (for woman). Fear of being killed by hate of woman. Defense used is emotional isolation and sublimation into compassion.

This story also involves the complexities of the caste system in British society, observations on emotional callousness, and the selfless relationship between simple men. Once again, a doctor (the ship's doctor—a sympathetic character) is cast into a hopeless conflict between passivity and activity.

"MR. HARRINGTON'S WASHING"

Descriptive Theme. Mr. Harrington is the prototype of the proper Philadelphian. He has a strong set of morals and principles of behavior, which he takes with him into the upheaval of revolutionary Russia. There he comes in contact with Alexandra, "a mad Russian," who has had a powerful effect on all sorts of men and whom he significantly nicknames "Delilah." Mediocre, resolute, stubborn, but rigidly sticking to his principles throughout, Harrington insists on getting his laundry before departing from unsafe Petrograd. Alexandra, who loyally accompanies him on this last mission, is attracted by a street crowd. Harrington, trailing behind her, is attacked and killed.

Interpretive Theme. If one has a strong set of moral and behavioral patterns, one is helped through many difficult situations. But one may also be led into absurdity. If one gets tangled up with a woman, she is likely to cause one's misfortune and death even though her intentions are the best.

Diagnostic Level. Conflict between conventional and less rigid behavior. Gentle mockery of bourgeois mind in unresolved conflict. Woman is seen as powerful and dangerous. Even when she means to be loyal and protective, she may be fatal.

The biographical background to this story, like that of several other stories, is related in Maugham's recent article (1962).

"FOOTPRINTS IN THE JUNGLE"

Descriptive Theme. Bronson, a plantation man, takes Cartwright, temporarily down on his luck, into his home in order to lend him a helping hand. In time, Cartwright and Mrs. Bronson have a love affair "swayed by turbulent passion." Although all three are basically decent people, Mrs. Bronson encourages her lover to kill her husband rather than risk discovery. The police chief learns of the crime, but there is insufficient evidence to bring the case to court. The new couple live on happily, since remorse for a crime does not seem to sit heavily if one can be absolutely sure one will not be found out.

Interpretive Theme. If a woman comes between two men, she causes trouble and death. Sexual passion may be the motive for murder even though the people involved were, and remain, perfectly decent people. They may not even suffer remorse.

Diagnostic Level. Sees women as causing trouble to men, as separating them, and as being fatal to them. There is the suggestion of an oedipal problem: one man must be killed for the other to get his woman. Passion is seen as overpowering, threatening to transcend control, specifically control of aggression. An unintegrated superego condones murderous aggression as an uncontrollable force.

"A FRIEND IN NEED"

Descriptive Theme. A seemingly pleasant, kind, middle-class sort of man is approached by an irresponsible, happy-go-lucky acquaintance who is in desperate need of a job. The former casually sends him to his death by proposing to him a dangerous swimming feat as the price for a job—a job which in fact he doesn't have to offer at all.

Interpretive Theme. If one is happy-go-lucky, one may be prey to the most incongruous hostilities of one's fellow man. This is probably due to disapproval and envy of an easy way of life and implied success with women.

Diagnostic Level. Fear of and desire for drifting, passivity. Sees people as incongruously and often casually cruel. This ascription of cruelty may be associated with concern over their envy and disapproval of happy-go-lucky ways and of success with women. The latter are felt as dangerous. There is fear of helplessness, guilt over sexual desires, and passivity, and a great deal of cruelty is projected on others.

"A ROMANTIC YOUNG LADY"

Descriptive Theme. The beautiful daughter of a duchess falls in love with a poor young man who returns her affection. Her mother disapproves and begs for help from a countess who employs the young man as mule-driver to her valuable and showy team. When the young man is made to choose between his beloved and his glamorous job, he chooses the latter.

Interpretive Theme. If a man has to choose between a woman and an esteemed job (with animals), he rather callously chooses the job.

Diagnostic Level. A sarcastic, low esteem is expressed for women. "There is not a pair of mules in the whole of Spain to come up to ours . . . one can get a wife any day of the week, but a place like this is found only once in a lifetime. I should be a fool to throw it up for a woman" (Maugham, 1953b, p. 321). So says the young man.

A subtheme is also concerned with the fact that the duchess and countess, though rivals previously, get together in this adversity. The beautiful young woman is met many years later, settled down comfortably as the stout, flaunting widow of a diplomat.

"THE KITE"

Descriptive Theme. A young boy, in joint venture with his parents, learns to love flying kites. As he grows older, this becomes the guiding passion of his and their lives. He meets a girl of whom his mother disapproves and, against her wishes, marries. His marriage is unhappy, his wife interferes with his kite-flying, and in anger he leaves her and returns to his parents. In retribution, his wife smashes his best kite. He retaliates angrily by choosing prison to the alternative of paying for her support.

Interpretive Theme. If a young man who has lived happily with his parents gets involved with a woman of whom they disapprove, the new woman may make him unhappy, interfere with his freedom, destroy the things he loves. Feels tremendous anger toward her.

You see, I don't know a thing about flying a kite. Perhaps it gives him a sense of power as he watches it soaring towards the clouds and of mastery over the elements as he seems to bend the winds of heaven to his will. It may be that in some queer way he identifies himself with the kite flying so free and so high above him, and it's as if it were an escape from the monotony of life. It may be that in some dim, confused way it represents an ideal of freedom and adventure. And you know, when a man once gets bitten with the virus of the ideal not all the King's doctors and not all the King's surgeons can rid him of it (Maugham, 1953b, p. 647).

This is what the narrator comments on the events he relates in the story.

Diagnostic Level. Tends to see life with parents as peaceful in infantile (sexually?) gratifying way. Woman is seen as making one unhappy, controlling one's life, interfering with infantile phallic pleasures and with man's freedom. Woman is seen as undermining his power. Conflict between monotony and adventurous, whimsical diversion. Woman is seen as plainly castrating, evil, controlling, interfering with narcissistic (sexual?) pleasures.

"THE HAPPY COUPLE"

Descriptive Theme. An apparently insignificant couple, in love with each other and warmly devoted to their baby, are found to have been the onetime doctor and female companion to an old lady they killed. Her inheritance enabled them to be married. At their trial, the jury found them not guilty despite overwhelming evidence, supposedly because of the fact that they had not had sexual intercourse during their long premarital relationship. The woman had been willing to commit murder to marry the man she loved, but not to have an illicit love affair.

Interpretive Theme. People are not what they seem. They may appear to be very decent people and yet commit murder. If people control their sexual desire, anything may be forgiven them. People are very strange. Sometimes one person must be disposed of for others to find happiness.

Diagnostic Level. Suspicious of people, of their deceptive appearances, of their complex natures which may conceal murderous aggression. The problem is of reconciling aggression and conscience. Unintegrated superego. Sex appears more prohibitive than aggression. Oedipal problem. Sees people as odd.

It is interesting to compare this story with "Footprints in the Jungle." In both instances one meets a quiet, pleasant, unobtrusive middle-aged couple who have committed murder in order to live with one another. In both stories, the murderers escape punishment for their crimes and live happily (though somewhat furtively) ever after. Once again, in "The Happy Couple," a doctor is the protagonist and is under the sway of love for a woman.

SUMMARY

UNCONSCIOUS STRUCTURE AND DRIVES (1-3)[2]

The author seems to have a continual struggle with aggressive and sexual drives. He feels strongly that their control is vital. Death follows loss of control. The character structure that has resulted from his attempts to deal with these problems is one of emotional isolation and detachment. He is an on-looker, peering in from the outside with considerable puzzlement and much suspicion of the barely repressed drives that lurk beneath the surface of his fellow men. And yet he is not without compassion. There seems to be a conflict between active participation in the demands of the world, especially those of bourgeois culture, and the giving in to passive desires, to the call of simpler living under more primitive circumstances. From the attempted resolution of this conflict arises the beachcomber, the wanderer, albeit in this case a highly sophisticated one. The self-image that results seems that of a mildly ineffective person who feels rather like a leaf in the wind and is not at all aware of his own strong emotions, especially of cruelty toward women.

CONCEPTION OF THE WORLD (4)

Puzzling, demanding, to be faced with wary eyes, full of surprises and over-whelming situations.

RELATIONSHIP TO OTHERS (5)

Urbane, mildly compassionate, warily expectant, but uninvolved manifestly; latent, strongly aggressive, hostile feelings toward women, projected onto them. Sometimes there is aggression toward men, though often men are seen as dependable if not affected by women.

SIGNIFICANT CONFLICTS (6)

Control versus lack of control of aggression and sex. Conflict between activity and passivity, between conformity and nonconformity, between identification as a man and as a woman.

NATURE OF ANXIETIES (7)

To be dominated, constrained, controlled, especially by women. To kill or be killed in triangular conflicts. To be embarrassed. To lose control of aggressive or sexual drives.

MAIN DEFENSES (8)

Reaction formation, emotional isolation, repression, and withdrawal from object relations. Extensive projection of aggression and sexual desires. Very superficial object relations.

SUPEREGO STRUCTURE (9)

An unintegrated superego; it is usually quite harsh, but occasionally, with a touch of cynicism or detachment, aggressive transgressions seem permissible, possibly more so than sexual ones.

---

[2] Numbered headings correspond to those of the TAT blank, p. 347.

INTEGRATION AND STRENGTH OF EGO (10)

The well-constructed stories show an ego strong enough to attain some closure and to maintain control. However, control is attained at the cost of considerable emotional isolation, of constriction and stereotyping of experiences, and of tangential relations to people. The self-image is one of a good deal of ineffectualness, but identification with the role of an urbane, controlled Englishman serves adaptively to maintain adequate functioning, which is enhanced by a very high intelligence and vast experience with the world.

FINAL REPORT

The author seems to have a continuous struggle with aggressive and sexual drives, feeling strongly that their control is literally vital, as seen in the stories "Rain," "The Happy Couple," "Footprints in the Jungle."

The character structure which has resulted from his attempts to deal with these problems is one of some emotional isolation and detachment, an onlooker looking from the outside in, not without compassion, with considerable puzzlement and a good deal of suspicion of the barely repressed drives that might lurk under the surface in his fellow man, as seen through the eyes of Dr. Macphail in "Rain," the narrator in "Mr. Harrington's Washing," and in the plot of "A Friend in Need."

There seems to be a conflict between active participation in the demands of the world, especially of the bourgeois culture, and the giving in to passive desires, generally, and the call of simpler living in more primitive circumstances, specifically, as in "The Fall of Edward Barnard" and "A Friend in Need."

The self-image that results seems that of a mildly ineffective person who feels somewhat like a pebble pushed about by the tides, e.g., "The Fall of Edward Barnard" and Macphail in "Rain."

Women are seen as domineering and demanding, such as Isabel in "The Fall of Edward Barnard," the women in "Rain," the wife in "The Kite"; or as leading to disaster—Sadie Thompson, "Delilah" in "Mr. Harrington's Washing." Women are also often seen as causing a feeling of inadequacy either as Edward Barnard in relation to Isabel or as in the case of Izzart's mother in "The Yellow Streak." Apparently, the author uses his defenses so extensively that he is not aware of his own strong aggressive drives, projected especially on women.

The constant conflict between activity and passivity, conformity and nonconformity, male and female identification can be seen all throughout the stories, with a fear of failure, of embarrassment and shame, a feeling of inadequacy constantly threatening to emerge.

When one is aware of some of the writer's life history, it becomes apparent that his defenses indeed necessitated a certain amount of constriction which led to rather restless, tangential relationships to people, traveling a good deal, almost by design an onlooker who participated only vicariously via his notebook in stories which, as seen in the sample examined, center on a relatively narrow range of themes. He was obviously able to function, nevertheless, by conforming with a character quite acceptable within the setting of the upper-crust Anglo-Saxon society—urbane, polished, knowledgeable, and, above all, not causing any difficulties by uncontrolled emotions. He was very sensitive and shy beneath this stiff-upper-lip front, and yet he was often involved in bloodcurdling and sometimes cold-blooded cruelties, as in his work as an intelligence agent. His own account of his married life suggests something less than affectionate warmth.

One wonders if the attempt to control all emotion might be related to the fact that some critics have spoken of Maugham as a great craftsman, rather than a great artist, feeling apparently that his stories lacked depth and were too neatly packaged. Could this same problem, especially in relation to women, also be related to his marital difficulties and to the fact that he wandered the earth so restlessly and aloof?

DISCUSSION

One may legitimately ask what bearing the procedure here followed might have on the broader problems of the analysis of literature and what light it might throw on the processes of creation.

In the case of writers, there are undoubtedly those, even of great stature and productivity, who have only one story to tell. There are others who cover a broad spectrum of content and form. The external features and the geographical settings of Maugham's stories vary a great deal. If one compares him, for instance, with Tennessee Williams, it is obvious that he is not constricted with regard to milieu. Williams almost always chooses the setting of the American South. Yet I believe that Maugham shares with Williams a constriction of essential subject matter. Whether the adventures are in Malaya or India, Chicago or Petrograd, the theme and its treatment stay fairly constant. Control of the emotions, the difficulties people get themselves into if they do not control them, and especially the dangers to men in their feelings for women are the leitmotivs that govern his work. A certain aloof compassion goes hand-in-hand with urbanity. Stylistically one always notes a form of prompt dispatch in the tightly organized plots. There is constriction here, a measure of stereotype, within the creative personality. We know something clinically about stereotypic thinking and feeling. The early psychoanalytic conception was one of fixation by overwhelming or repetitive experiences at certain genetic levels. I have found it more useful to think both psychoanalytically and in terms of Gestalt psychology: certain apperceptions, a complex Gestalt of past perceptions and adaptive and defensive features, seem to affect all contemporary apperception. This is more apparent in some people than in others.

In coarse clinical terms, the paranoid personality perceives a broad band of experiences in terms of suspiciousness, fear, and defensive aggression. The authoritarian personality (Adorno et al., 1950) and the closed mind which Rokeach describes (1960) have rigidly defined frames of reference within which all experience is organized. Freud, in his paper on the poet, mentioned perceptual selectivity with regard to the causal relationship between a writer's productions and his personality. In the case of Maugham, it seems that his stories are the result of such a selective viewing of life. They are the product of the forms of adaptation and defenses with which he tried to deal with his own life and his own emotional problems.

We have some clues about what these emotional problems might have been. There are some suggestive relations among his feelings for women, the loss of his mother at an early age, his aggression and his stammer, his personal shyness, his marital difficulties, and his restless wanderings. However, these conjectures with regard to causal interrelations to the early life history are not of central concern to us and could not progress beyond the usual state of loose guesses on the basis of limited material. I think we are on safer ground if we limit ourselves to inferences covering the relationship between literary production and the personality of the author.

However, it is always interesting to speculate: what if Maugham had been psychoanalyzed? How might analysis have affected his stature in literature?

Psychoanalysis is far from a panacea. It certainly cannot make creative a person who does not have creative potential. It can, and often does, improve the ability to translate potentiality into actual creativeness. The great similarity between the process of free association and creative writing has been remarked upon frequently (see Chapter 3). In the course of this process, changes go on which increase the freedom of access to one's unconscious. Whatever the limitations of the psychoanalytic process may be, it is usually superbly effective in dealing with the perceptual constriction which is the result of traumatic experience and with the defenses and character changes reactive to it. I would not hesitate to say that a successful analysis of Somerset Maugham would almost certainly have further improved his stature by increasing his emotional range and permitting a greater variability in essential themes and style. Almost certainly a successful analysis would have counteracted those features in his writing which some critics have claimed make him a superb craftsman rather than a great artist. I think the critics have overstated it, but what they say has a kernel of truth.

One can further speculate: in what way can the kind of story analysis we have done here contribute to the understanding and critical analysis of literature? The systematic frame of reference for analysis of literary products may be generally useful for any author's work. The range and depth of a literary piece are often at the center of critical appraisal, and a TAT type of analysis may well give a more reliable account than the customary free-style appraisal. Perhaps one of the reasons for widely differing critiques may be, at least in part, the lack of any base line of comparison.

The type of psychological analysis presented here may well throw some interesting light on the relationship between an author's personality and his work. I do not know that such enlightenment would add anything to the values of literature, but it might add some interesting facets to the story of man and his behavior.

On the other hand, I suspect that many an author might profit from an analysis of his work of the kind presented here. Certainly this should not be while the work is in progress; the increased awareness might interfere with the creative process. Maybe such an analysis would be useful after the first draft of a story or book has been written and the major, almost automatic, act of creation is over. With somewhat more certainty I feel that this type of psychological analysis would be salutary after a man has produced for a good many years and either comes to a standstill or feels it would be worthwhile to check his bearings. An increase in reality-testing, in cognitive acuity concerning one's own production might be of service to a writer who feels blocked at such an important turning point in his career.

24

ON THE PSYCHOLOGY OF
DETECTIVE STORIES

The build-up and relaxation of tension was viewed by Freud as one of the ingredients of a pleasurable experience, the sudden discharge of energy accounting for the subjective experience of satisfaction. This chapter applies this formulation to detective stories and suggests that one ingredient in their appeal is the tension produced by the unsolved incident, followed by the tension release that occurs on its solution. Part of the tension is produced by baffling the reader with a complex assortment of clues, as shown by the fact that when a story is read a second time there is much less uncertainty and a corresponding decrease in satisfaction emerges upon its resolution.

DETECTIVE STORIES, OR "MYSTERIES," are said to be the most popular literary product of our day. They seem to have a universal appeal to people of many diverse literary tastes. "Thriller" addicts are well represented among intellectuals for whom these stories constitute a quick form of relaxation, as well as among adventure-hungry youngsters and average readers of the more popular forms of fiction. It behooves a psychologist, then, to inquire into the dynamics of detective stories, particularly if he himself is an enthusiastic reader of this literature. We believe that what we shall have to say holds true generally, for practically all of this literature, from the classics of A. Conan Doyle to the Dime Novel, to current selections of the Crime Club.

The general structure may be broken down to the following: A crime is being committed; the criminal and certain aspects of the crime are mysterious; a usually well-known sleuth is on the trail and brings about an end which has the qualities of surprise and satisfaction. The treatment of the subject matter may then vary as far as the particular constellation is concerned, and in the extent of literary style and skill.

We believe that *two factors are important* in the psychological nature of the detective story: one is the *content* and the other is the *structure of it*.

The *dynamics of the content of detective stories* we believe is best understood in terms of psychoanalytic language. The criminal and aggressive proceedings permit a *fantasy gratification of id impulses*. In other words, first, the reader is permitted to identify with the criminal. This can safely be done because he is sufficiently removed from reality, and because soon the *superego is satisfied* that detection and punishment will follow. That is, after having identified with the criminal, the reader is permitted to identify with the detective.

Aside from this pacifying of the superego, identification with the sleuth also is pleasurable, *since he constitutes an ego ideal,* with the primitive, wish-fulfilling

---

NOTE: From the *Psychoanalytic Review,* 1945, 32, 403-407. Reprinted by permission of the publishers.

characteristics of a superman. In serials, for example, the detective is well-known, always wins, usually escapes danger, and knows all the answers, at times by means of unusual powers. This holds true for Sherlock Holmes, and it holds true for Ellery Queen, for Hercule Poirot, Agatha Christie, or Nero Wolfe, or Lord Peter Wimsey, and most of the others. In fact, it is often the nature of the sleuth that supplies the special delight, and many variations are possible. While Sherlock was so straightforwardly wonderful that he is now considered somewhat comical, Poirot and many others are outwardly very unassuming. This allows the reader to identify once more: "I am unassuming. If people only knew how wonderful I am under all this everyday appearance!"

The detective has often in addition other characteristics which are of a wish-fulfilling nature not germane to the detective story alone, but to all light fiction. Thus, many of the bloodhounds "really" are of a distinguished social class. In the mold of a Lord (Lord Peter Wimsey of Dorothy Sayers) or a famous official or a professor, or an internationally known personage, the reader feels himself lifted into the upper strata of society. Similarly, other gratifying devices of light literature may be added and superimposed on the mystery: love and lovers' plight are the most frequent ones.

Certain other fundamental processes help one to understand the delight found in detective stories. As Kris (1941) points out for the drama and other aesthetic experiences, it holds for our lighter brand of art that a *libidinization of anxiety* takes place: people like to play with anxiety as long as the dangerous situation is selected by themselves. *The unpleasurable may be felt as pleasure if the situation can be controlled.* This control is achieved by the ego by way of the protection of the "aesthetic illusion," as Kris calls it. In other words, one is constantly reassured that the situation is unreal and that one could leave the field of danger at will.

There exists some *clinical material* which substantiates our contentions and in part adds more information. Zulliger (1933) and Buxbaum (1941) published data of analyses of boys in whose lives and symptoms detective stories played a considerable role, of similar nature. The 12-year-old boy of Buxbaum had the fear that a man might leap on him and choke him. "He had a compulsion to read detective stories . . . he behaved like an addict who is afraid of going to pieces without his accustomed narcotic." The detective served as an ego ideal. He identified with the murderer, but also identified with the victim in his conflicts between aggression and passivity. The detective story provided a medium through which he could commit murder as well as be the victim. As detective he watched himself to save himself from his own murderous impulses. He was distressed by those stories which turned out badly because they failed their purpose of allaying his anxiety; in fact, such stories increased his anxiety. In both Buxbaum's and Zulliger's case, compulsion for detective stories is a form of defense against anxiety.

For the *structured dynamics* of the detective story, we believe the following is important: *tension and anxiety* are more or less skillfully increased and then *suddenly reduced*—the basic mechanism of pleasant experience. The cognitive aspect of the satisfaction with the solution is best expressed in terms of Gestalt psychology, namely, that *closure* is experienced. Reading mystery stories is one of the activities which supplies tension artificially and promises a prompt reduction. In part, it is the *anticipation* of tension reduction that is pleasurable. Reading detective stories is only one form of pleasurable activity in which there is such a wilful increase of tension with anticipated prompt reduction. The same mechanism holds true for the other most favored literary form of our time—the short story, and is also inherent in practically all forms of gambling.

The structural dynamics are the same for the short story and for the mystery story in the sense that the plot is quickly perceived and the pleasure which the solution offers can be derived in a short period of time. The same holds true for *games of chance,* from the pinball machine to horse races. One enters into some tension-arousing experience, the reduction of which may be anticipated as a near event. One engages particularly in such an activity if one has little frustration tolerance. This may hold true for some people perpetually while for others it may be only a transitory state. We would say that somebody has temporarily little frustration tolerance if he is in a state of fatigue. The tired businessman, the worn-out professional or politician, who grapples all day with long, drawn-out, frustrating experiences is in part actually and physiologically fatigued and partly wishes to relax with something that, after all, can be managed easily and will lead to a gratifying experience without fail and without too much delay. Thus, he may turn to the detective story where he can rely on this mechanism (aside from identifying with the aggression of the criminal and the wonderfulness of the superman-sleuth) or he may turn to a card game or some other form of gambling, or play or reading which permits quick gratification after short frustration.

In the habitual gambler or knight of fortune we deal with a person who persistently is not able to sustain much frustration, which is one of the aspects of his neurotic personality; frustration tolerance is one of the direct functions of ego strength. By ego strength again, we mean the degree of efficiency with which the ego, in the psychoanalytic sense, is able to discharge one of its functions, namely, mediation between id and superego, and between id and reality. A weak ego would then be little able to deal effectively with reality problems, since the primitive pleasure principle of the id would persistently interfere; a gambler is a person who has such a weak ego as to be unable to tolerate frustration for a long time and to pursue a goal undisturbed by internal and external distractions, and therefore has to engage in short-term propositions of the get-rich-quick formula. Even if he loses, this seems easier to sustain than persistent tension, particularly since his preferred method of dealing with this frustration is always another turn at the wheel. Aside from the structural aspects here as in the mystery, the identification with the grandiose—the winner—the millionaire, the daring adventurer, supplies gratification.

Finally, we believe that similar facts as described above hold true for the case of addictions. Here we are dealing with people who inherently have little frustration tolerance and by means of a drug manage to forget their frustrations for some time, permitting themselves rather unrestricted id activity such as aggressiveness, primitivity, immorality and feelings of grandeur. However, here we are dealing not with merely temporary, simple, substitute activity, but with a pathological withdrawal from reality and from frustration.

A word about the writers of detective stories: much has been said and written about the relationship between the artist and his creation. As I have stated elsewhere (see Chapter 11), we believe that each creative work has three aspects—adaptive, projective, and expressive.

By *adaptive aspects* of creative work we mean the part that constitutes problem solving; in the detective story, we mean the skillful construction of the plot, the conscious manipulation of the material in such a way as to arouse interest and to sell well.

By *projective aspects* we mean those parts which constitute the unwitting part of the writer's personality, where he projects his own needs, wishes, and sentiments into the plot and characters without being aware of it. Though this generally takes place to a considerable degree, the extent of it may vary from one story to another and from one author to another, depending in part on the personality structure and the temporary problems of the author. Taking Edgar Allen Poe as one extreme (probably in a class of his own) we find a maximum of projection, while mass-produced, technically skilled series probably show little projective material.

By the *expressive aspects* we simply mean that each author has his own way of expressing what he wishes to express, his own individual style.

BIBLIOGRAPHY

Abercrombie, M. L. J. (1960): The Anatomy of Judgment: An Investigation into the Processes of Perception and Reasoning. New York, Basic Books.

Abt, L., and Bellak, L. (1950): Projective Psychology. New York, Knopf.

Adorno, T., Frenkel-Brunswik, F., Levinson, D. J., and Sanford, R. N. (1950): The Authoritarian Personality. New York, Harper.

Alexander, F., and French, T. M. (1946): Psychoanalytic Therapy. New York, Ronald.

Allport, G. W. (1942): The Use of Personal Documents in Psychological Science. New York, Soc. Sci. Res. Coun. Bull., No. 49.

American Psychological Association (1954): Technical Recommendations for Psychological Tests and Diagnostic Techniques. Psychol. Bull., Supplement 51.

Arieti, S. (1955): Interpretation of Schizophrenia. New York, Brunner.

——— (1961): The loss of reality. Psychoanal. Rev. 48(3):3-24.

——— (1962): Hallucinations, delusions, and ideas of reference treated with psychotherapy. Amer. J. Psychother. 16:52-60.

Arlow, J. A. (1959): The structure of the *déjà vu* experience. J. Amer. Psychoanal. Ass. 7:611-631.

Auld, F., and Murray, E. J. (1955): Content-analysis studies of psychotherapy. Psychol. Bull. 52:377-395.

Bak, R. C. (1939): Regression of ego-orientation and libido in schizophrenia. Int. J. Psychoanal. 20:64-71.

Balken, E. R., and Masserman, J. H. (1940): The language of phantasy: III. The language of the phantasies of patients with conversion hysteria, anxiety state and obsessive-compulsive neuroses. J. Psychol. 10:75-86.

Bandler, B. (1960): Presidential address, American Psychoanalytic Association.

Barron, F. (1953): An ego-strength scale which predicts response to psychotherapy. J. Consult. Psychol. 17:327-333.

Baruk, H. (1949): The problem of will and personality. J. Nerv. Ment. Dis. 110:218-235.

Bateson, G., et al. (1956): Toward a theory of schizophrenia. Behav. Sci. 1:251-264.

Beck, A. T., Ward, C. H., Mendelson, M., Mock, J., and Erbaugh, J. (1961): An inventory for measuring depression. Arch. Gen. Psychiat. 4:561-571.

Bellak, L. (1948): Dementia Praecox. New York, Grune & Stratton.

——— (1949a): The use of oral barbiturates in psychotherapy. Amer. J. Psychiat. 105:849-850.

——— (1949b): A multiple-factor psychosomatic theory of schizophrenia. Psychiat. Quart. 23:738-755.

——— (1950): Thematic apperception: failures and defenses. Trans. N. Y. Acad. Sci. Ser. II, 12:122-126.

———, et al. (1952a): Manic-Depressive Psychosis and Allied Disorders. New York, Grune & Stratton.

——— (1952b): The emergency psychotherapy of depression. *In:* Specialized Techniques in Psychotherapy (G. Bychowski and J. C. Despert, Eds.). New York, Basic Books, pp. 323-336.

——— (1954a): A study of limitations and "failures": toward an ego psychology of projective techniques. J. Project. Techn. 18:279-293.

——— (1954b): The Thematic Apperception Test and the Children's Apperception Test in Clinical Practice. New York, Grune & Stratton.

——— (1955a): Toward a unified concept of schizophrenia. J. Nerv. Ment. Dis. 121:60-66.

——— (1955b): Review of *The Life and Work of Sigmund Freud*, Vol. 1, by Ernest Jones. New York Post, Sept. 18.

———, et al. (1956a): Rehabilitation of the mentally ill through controlled transitional employment. Amer. J. Orthopsychiat. 26:285-296.

——— (1956b): Comment on a letter by Carl R. Rogers concerning the lack of creativity in American psychology. Amer. Psychol. 11:156-157.

———, ed. (1958): Schizophrenia: A Review of the Syndrome. New York, Grune & Stratton.

——— (1959): Conceptual and methodological problems in psychoanalysis: the frame of reference of the monograph. Ann. N. Y. Acad. Sci. 73:973-974.

——— (1960): The treatment of schizophrenia and psychoanalytic theory. J. Nerv. Ment. Dis. 131:39-46.

——— (1961): Contemporary European Psychiatry. New York, Grove Press.

——— (1962): Testimony given at a hearing before a Subcommittee of the Committee on Appropriations, House of Representatives, Washington, D. C.

———, ed. (1964a): Handbook of Community Psychiatry. New York, Grune & Stratton.

——— (1964b): Correspondence in "Letters." J.A.M.A. 187(11):183.

———, and Ekstein, R. (1946): The extension of basic scientific laws to psychoanalysis and to psychology. Psychoanal. Rev. 33:306-313.

———, and Holt, R. R. (1948): Somatotypes in dementia praecox. Amer. J. Psychiat. 104:713-724.

———, and Jacques, E. (1942): On the problem of dynamic conceptualization in case studies. Character Pers. 11:20-39.

———, and Small, L. E. (1965): Emergency Psychotherapy and Brief Psychotherapy. New York, Grune & Stratton.

Bender, L. (1947): Childhood schizophrenia. Amer. J. Orthopsychiat. 17:40-56.

Benjamin, J. E. (1959): Prediction and psychopathological theory. In: Dynamic Psychopathology in Childhood (L. Jessner and E. Pavenstedt, Eds.). New York, Grune & Stratton, pp. 6-77.

Beres, D. (1956): Ego deviations and the concept of schizophrenia. In: Psychoanalytic Study of the Child, Vol. 11. New York, International Universities Press, pp. 164-235.

Bergler, E. (1950): Further studies on depersonalization. Psychiat. Quart. 24:268-277.

———, and Eidelberg, L. (1935): Der Mechanismus der Depersonalisation. Int. Z. Psychoanal. 21:258-285.

Bergman, P., and Escalona, S. (1949): Unusual sensitivities in very young children. In: Psychoanalytic Study of the Child, Vol. 3/4. New York, International Universities Press, pp. 333-352.

Bernfeld, S., and Feitelberg, S. (1934): Bericht über einige psycho-physiologische Arbeiten. Imago 20:224-231.

Bibring, E. (1953): The mechanism of depression. In: Affective Disorders (P. Greenacre, Ed.). New York, International Universities Press, pp. 13-48.

Bibring, G. L. (1949): Psychiatric principles in casework. J. Soc. Casework 30:230-235.

Blank, H. R. (1954): Depression, hypomania, and depersonalization. Psychoanal. Quart. 23:20-37.

Bleuler, E. (1911): Dementia Praecox or the Group of Schizophrenias. New York, International Universities Press, 1950.

Blos, P. (1962): The concept of acting out in relation to the adolescent process. Presented at the New York Psychoanalytic Society, September 25.

Blum, G. S. (1949): A study of the psychoanalytic theory of psychosexual development. Genet. Psychol. Monogr. 39:3-99.

———, and Miller, D. R. (1952): Exploring the psychoanalytic theory of the "oral character." J. Personality 20:287-304.

Boring, E. G. (1950): A History of Experimental Psychology, 2nd ed. New York, Appleton-Century-Crofts.

Braceland, F. (1951): Psychiatry and the science of man. Amer. J. Psychiat. 114.

Brenman, M. (1959): Discussion. In: Conceptual and Methodological Problems in Psychoanalysis (L. Bellak, Ed.). Ann. N. Y. Acad. Sci. 73.

———, Gill, M. M., and Knight, R. P. (1952): Spontaneous fluctuations in depth of hypnosis and their implications for ego-function. Int. J. Psychoanal. 33:22-33.

Brenner, C. (1957): The nature and development of the concept of repression in Freud's writings. In: Psychoanalytic Study of the Child, Vol. 12. New York, International Universities Press, pp. 19-46.

Breuer, J., and Freud, S. (1893-1895): Studies on Hysteria. Standard Ed., 2. London, Hogarth Press, 1955.

Brown, L. (1933): Mental aspect in the aetiology and treatment of pulmonary tuberculosis. Int. Clin. 3:149-174.

Bruetsch, W. L. (1940): Chronic rheumatic brain disease as a possible factor in the causation of some cases of dementia praecox. Amer. J. Psychiat. 97:276-295.

Bruner, J., and Goodman, L. C. (1947): Value and need as organizing factors in perception. J. Abnorm. Soc. Psychol. 42:33-44.

Burchard, E. M. L. (1952): The use of projective techniques in the analysis of creativity. J. Project. Techn. 16:412-427.

Butler, J. M. (1953): Measuring the effectiveness of counseling and psychotherapy. Personnel Guid. J. 32:88-92.

Buxbaum, E. (1941): The role of detective stories in a child analysis. Psychoanal. Quart. 10:373-381.

Bychowski, G. (1949): The ego of the brain wounded. Psychoanal. Rev. 36:333-343.

——— (1952): Psychotherapy of Psychosis. New York, Grune & Stratton.

Caplan, G. (1961): An Approach to Community Mental Health. New York, Grune & Stratton.

Chance, E. (1959): Families in Treatment. New York, Basic Books.

Chassan, J. B. (1956): On probability theory and psychoanalytic research. Psychiatry 19:55-61.

——— (1957): On the unreliability of reliability and some other consequences of the assumption of probabilistic patient states. Psychiatry 20:163-171.

——— (1959): On the development of clinical statistical systems for psychiatry. Biometrics 15:396-404.

——— (1960): Statistical inference and the single case in clinical design. Psychiatry 23:173-184.

——— (1961): Stochastic models of the single case as the basis of clinical research design. Behav. Sci. 6:42-50.

Clouston, T. S. (1863): Tuberculosis and insanity. J. Ment. Sci. 9(45):36.

Cobb, S. (1943): Borderlands of Psychiatry. Cambridge, Mass., Harvard University Press.

Cole, J. (1964): The efficacy of anti-depressant drugs. J.A.M.A. 190:448-455.

Coleman, R., Kris, E., and Provence, S. (1953): The study of variations of early parental attitudes. In: Psychoanalytic Study of the Child, Vol. 8. New York, International Universities Press, pp. 20-47.

Crafts, L. W., Schneirla, T. C., Robinson, Elsa E., and Gilbert, R. W. (1950): Recent Experiments in Psychology. New York, McGraw-Hill.

de Jong, H. (1945): Experimental Catatonia. Baltimore, Williams & Wilkins.

Deri, S. (1949): Introduction to the Szondi Test, Theory, and Practice. New York, Grune & Stratton.

de Saussure, R. S. (1929): Les mécanismes de projection dans les névroses. Ann. Medicopsychol. (Paris) 87:118-126.

Dollard, J., and Mowrer, O. H. (1947): A method of measuring tension in written documents. J. Abnorm. Soc. Psychol. 42:3-32.

Dombrose, L. A., and Slobin, M. S. (1958): The IES test. Percept. Motor Skills 8:347-389.

Donnadieu, and Hauser. (1948): Troubles vegetatifs persistants après Electrochoc. Ann. Medicopsychol. (Paris) 106:73-76.

Eissler, K. (1952): Remarks on the psychoanalysis of schizophrenia. In: Psychotherapy with Schizophrenics (E. B. Brody and F. C. Redlich, Eds.). New York, International Universities Press, pp. 130-167.

——— (1953a): Notes upon the emotionality of a schizophrenic patient and its relation to the problem of technique. In: Psychoanalytic Study of the Child, Vol. 8. New York, International Universities Press, pp. 199-251.

——— (1953b): The effect of the structure of the ego on psychoanalytic technique. J. Amer. Psychoanal. Ass. 1:104-143.

English, H. B., and English, A. C. (1958): A Comprehensive Dictionary of Psychological and Psychoanalytical Terms. New York, Longmans, Green.

Eron, L. D., and Ritter, A. M. (1951): A comparison of two methods of administration of the Thematic Apperception Test. J. Consult. Psychol. 15:55-61.

Escalona, S. (1948): Some considerations regarding psychotherapy with psychotic children. Bull. Menninger Clin. 12:126-134.

—————— (1952): Problems in psychoanalytic research. Int. J. Psychoanal. 33:11-21.

——————, and Heider, G. (1959): Prediction and Outcome. New York, Basic Books.

Eysenck, H. J. (1952): The effects of psychotherapy: an evaluation. J. Consult. Psychol. 16:319-324.

Federn, P. (1926): Some variations in ego feeling. *In:* Federn (1952), pp. 25-37.

—————— (1952): Ego Psychology and the Psychoses. New York, Basic Books.

Feigenbaum, D. (1936): On projection. Psychoanal. Quart. 5:303-319.

Fenichel, O. (1928): Organ libidinization accompanying the defense against drives. Collected Papers, Vol. 1. New York, Norton, 1953, pp. 128-146.

—————— (1945a): The Psychoanalytic Theory of Neurosis. New York, Norton.

—————— (1945b): Neurotic acting out. Psychoanal. Rev. 32:197-206.

Ferraro. A. (1951): Interpretations of cerebral histopathologic changes in cases of schizophrenia. J. Neuropath. Exp. Neurol. 10:104-105.

Fessel, W. J., and Hirata-Hibi, M. (1963): Abnormal leukocytes in schizophrenia. Arch. Gen. Psychiat. 9:601-613.

Finesinger, J. E. (1944): The effect of pleasant and unpleasant ideas on the respiratory pattern (spirogram) in psychotherapeutic patients. Amer. J. Psychiat. 100:659-667.

Fink, M., Jaffe, J., and Kahn, R. (1959): Drug induced changes in interview patterns, linguistic and neurophysiological indices. *In*: The Dynamics of Psychiatric Drug Therapy (G. J. Sarwer-Foner, Ed.). Springfield, Ill., Charles C Thomas.

Finn, M. (1958): The Mira (M.K.P.) Test. New York, Logos Press.

Finn, M. (1953): An investigation of apperceptive distortion in the obsessive-compulsive character structure by three methods, verbal, graphic-emotional and graphic-geometric, with special reference to a defense mechanism, reaction formation. Ph.D. Thesis, New York University library.

Fischer, R. (1954): Factors involved in drug-produced model psychoses. J. Ment. Sci. 100:623-631.

Fisher, C. (1954): Dreams and perception. J. Amer. Psychoanal. Ass. 2:389-445.

——————, and Joseph, E. D. (1949): Fugue with awareness of loss of personal identity. Psychoanal. Quart. 18:480-493.

Frank, L. K. (1939): Projective methods for the study of personality. J. Psychol. 8:389-413.

Freud, A. (1936): The Ego and the Mechanisms of Defense. New York, International Universities Press, 1946.

—————— (1949): Aggression in relation to emotional development: normal and pathological. *In:* Psychoanalytic Study of the Child, Vol 3/4. New York, International Universities Press, pp. 37-42.

—————— (1952): The mutual influences in the development of ego and id. Introduction to the discussion. *In:* Psychoanalytic Study of the Child, Vol. 7. New York, International Universities Press, pp. 42-50.

Freud, S. (1895a): On the Grounds for Detaching a Particular Syndrome from Neurasthenia under the Description 'Anxiety Neurosis.' Standard Ed., 3:90-115. London, Hogarth Press, 1962.

—————— (1895b): Project for a Scientific Psychology. Standard Ed., 1:295-397. London, Hogarth Press, 1966.

—————— (1896): The Aetiology of Hysteria. Standard Ed., 3:191-221. London, Hogarth Press, 1962.

—————— (1900): The Interpretation of Dreams. Standard Ed., 4 and 5. London, Hogarth Press, 1953.

—————— (1901): The Psychopathology of Everyday Life. Standard Ed., 6. London, Hogarth Press, 1960.

—————— (1905a): Three Essays on the Theory of Sexuality. Standard Ed., 7:130-243. London, Hogarth Press, 1953.

———— (1905b): Fragment of an Analysis of a Case of Hysteria. Standard Ed., 7:7-122. London, Hogarth Press, 1953.

———— (1907): Delusions and Dreams in Jensen's *Gradiva*. Standard Ed., 9:7-95. London, Hogarth Press, 1959.

———— (1908): Creative Writers and Day-Dreaming. Standard Ed. 9:143-153. London, Hogarth Press, 1959.

———— (1910): Leonardo da Vinci and a Memory of His Childhood. Standard Ed., 11:63-137. London, Hogarth Press, 1957.

———— (1911): Psycho-Analytic Notes on an Autobiographical Account of a Case of Paranoia (Dementia Paranoides). Standard Ed., 12:9-82. London, Hogarth Press, 1958.

———— (1911-1915): Papers on Technique. Standard Ed., 12:89-171. London, Hogarth Press, 1958.

———— (1913): Totem and Taboo. Standard Ed., 13:1-161. London, Hogarth Press, 1955.

———— (1914): Remembering, Repeating and Working-Through (Further Recommendations on the Technique of Psycho-Analysis II). Standard Ed., 12:145-156. London, Hogarth Press, 1958.

———— (1915a): Instincts and Their Vicissitudes. Standard Ed., 14:117-140. London, Hogarth Press, 1957.

———— (1915b): The Unconscious. Standard Ed., 14:166-204. London, Hogarth Press, 1957.

———— (1923): The Ego and the Id. Standard Ed., 19:12-66. London, Hogarth Press, 1961.

———— (1925a): An Autobiographical Study. Standard Ed., 20:7-74. London, Hogarth Press, 1959.

———— (1925b): Negation. Standard Ed., 19:235-239. London, Hogarth Press, 1961.

———— (1926): Inhibitions, Symptoms and Anxiety. Standard Ed., 20:87-172. London, Hogarth Press, 1959.

———— (1927): The Future of an Illusion. Standard Ed., 21:1-56. London, Hogarth Press, 1961.

———— (1928): Dostoevsky and Parricide. Standard Ed., 21:177-194. London, Hogarth Press, 1961.

———— (1930): Civilization and Its Discontents. Standard Ed., 21:64-145. London, Hogarth Press, 1961.

———— (1936): A Disturbance of Memory on the Acropolis. Standard Ed., 22:239-248. London, Hogarth Press, 1964.

Fries, M. E., and Woolf, P. (1953): Some hypotheses on the role of the congenital activity type in personality development. *In:* Psychoanalytic Study of the Child, Vol. 8. New York, International Universities Press, pp. 48-62.

Fromm, E. (1940): Escape from Freedom. New York, Rinehart.

Frosch, J., and Impastato, D. (1948): The effects of shock treatment on the ego. Psychoanal. Quart. 17:226-239.

Galton, F. (1879): Psychometric experiments. Brain 11.

Geleerd, E. R., Hacker, F., and Rapaport, D. (1945): Contribution to the study of amnesia and allied conditions. Psychoanal. Quart. 14:199-220.

Gill, M. M. (1963): Topography and systems in psychoanalytic theory. Psychol. Issues, 10. New York, International Universities Press.

————, Newman, R., and Redlich, F. C. (1954): The Initial Interview in Psychiatric Practice. New York, International Universities Press.

Glover, E. (1955): The Technique of Psychoanalysis. New York, International Universities Press.

Goldman, F. (1948): Breast-feeding and character-formation. J. Personality 17:83-103.

Goldstein, K. (1936-1937): The significance of the frontal lobes for mental performance. J. Neurol. Psychopathol. 17:27.

———— (1948): Language and Language Disturbances. New York, Grune & Stratton.

———— (1949): Frontal lobotomy and impairment of abstract attitude. J. Nerv. Ment. Dis. 110:93-111.

Gordon, H. L. (1948): Fifty shock therapy theories. Milit. Surg. 103:397-401.

Greenacre, P. (1947): Vision, headache and the halo. Psychoanal. Quart. 16:177-194.

—— (1950): General problems of acting out. Psychoanal. Quart. 19:455-467.

—— (1952): Some factors producing different types of genital and pre-genital organization. *In:* Trauma, Growth and Personality (P. Greenacre, Ed.). New York, Norton, pp. 293-302.

—— (1955): Swift and Carroll. New York, International Universities Press.

Group for the Advancement of Psychiatry (1957): Some Observations on Control in Psychiatric Research. Report No. 42.

Grummon, D. L. (unpublished): An investigation into the use of grammatical and psycho-grammatical categories of language for the study of personality and psychotherapy. Ph.D. thesis.

Haggard, E. G. (1946): Some conditions determining adjustment during and readjustment following experimentally-induced stress. *In:* Contemporary Psychopathology (S. Tomkins, Ed.). Cambridge, Mass., Harvard University Press.

Haigh, G. (1949): Defensive behavior in client-centered therapy. J. Consult. Psychol. 13:181-189.

Hare, A. P., Waxler, N., Saslow, G., and Matarazzo, J. (1960): Simultaneous recordings of Bales and Chapple interaction measures during initial psychiatric interviews. J. Consult. Psychol. 24:193.

Harris, R. E., and Christiansen, C. (1946): Predictions of response to brief psychotherapy. J. Psychol. 21:269-284.

Harrison, R. (1940): Studies on the use and validity of the thematic apperception test with mentally disordered patients: II. A quantitative validity study; III. Validation by the method of "blind analysis." Character Pers. 9:122-138.

Hartmann, H. (1922): Ein Fall von Depersonalisation. Z. Neurol. Psychiat. 74:593-601.

—— (1939): Ego Psychology and the Problem of Adaptation. New York, International Universities Press, 1958.

—— (1950a): Comments on the psychoanalytic theory of the ego. *In:* Psychoanalytic Study of the Child, Vol. 5. New York, International Universities Press, pp. 74-96.

—— (1950b): Psychoanalysis and developmental psychology. *In:* Psychoanalytic Study of the Child, Vol. 5. New York, International Universities Press, pp. 7-17.

—— (1952): The mutual influences in the development of ego and id. *In:* Psychoanalytic Study of the Child, Vol. 7. New York, International Universities Press, pp. 9-30.

—— (1953): Contribution to the metapsychology of schizophrenia. *In:* Psychoanalytic Study of the Child, Vol. 8. New York, International Universities Press, pp. 177-198.

—— (1955): Notes on the theory of sublimation. *In:* Psychoanalytic Study of the Child, Vol. 10. New York, International Universities Press, pp. 9-29.

—— (1956): Notes on the reality principle. *In:* Psychoanalytic Study of the Child, Vol. 11. New York, International Universities Press, pp. 31-53.

——, Kris, E., and Loewenstein, R. M. (1949): Notes on the theory of aggression. *In:* Psychoanalytic Study of the Child, Vol. 3/4. New York, International Universities Press, pp. 9-36.

Healy, W., Bronner, A. F., and Bowers, A. M. (1930): The Structure and Meaning of Psychoanalysis. New York, Knopf.

Hebb, D. O. (1958): The motivating effects of exteroceptive stimulation. Amer. Psychol. 13:109-113.

Hermann, I. (1929): Das Ich und das Denken. Imago 15:325-348.

Hilgard, J. R., and Newman, M. F. (1961): Evidence for functional genesis in mental illness. J. Nerv. Ment. Dis. 132:3-16.

Himwich, H. E. (1960): Biochemical and neurophysiological action of psychoactive drugs. *In:* Drugs and Behavior (L. Uhr and J. G. Miller, Eds.). New York, Wiley.

Hinsie, L. E., and Campbell, R. J. (1960): Psychiatric Dictionary, 3rd ed. New York, Oxford University Press.

Hitschmann, E. (1956): Great Men. New York, International Universities Press.

Hoffer, A., et al. (1954): Schizophrenia: a new approach. II: Result of a year's research. J. Ment. Sci. 100:29-45.

Hoffer, W. (1949): Mouth, hand and ego integration. *In:* Psychoanalytic Study of the Child, Vol. 3/4. New York, International Universities Press, pp. 49-56.

Hoffmann, E. P. (1935): Projektion und Ich-Entwicklung. Int. Z. Psychiat. 21:342-373.

Holt, R. R. (1943): Motivational factors in levels of aspiration. *In:* Summaries of Theses 1943-45. Cambridge, Mass., Harvard University Press, 1947, pp. 603-607 (Abs.).

——— (1956): Gauging primary and secondary processes in Rorschach responses. J. Project. Techn. 20:14-25.

——— (1960): Manual for the Scoring of Primary Process Manifestations in Rorschach Responses. Unpublished manuscript.

——— (1961): The nature of TAT stories as cognitive products: a psychoanalytic approach. *In:* Contemporary Issues in Thematic Apperceptive Methods (J. Kagan, Ed.). Springfield, Ill., Charles C Thomas.

——— (1962): A critical examination of Freud's concept of bound vs. free cathexis. J. Amer. Psychoanal. Ass. 10:475-525.

——— (1966): Beyond vitalism and mechanism: Freud's concept of psychic energy. *In:* Science and Psychoanalysis, Vol. XI. New York, Grune & Stratton.

Hook, S., ed. (1959): Psychoanalysis, Scientific Method, and Philosophy. New York, New York University Press.

Hoskins, R. G. (1946): The Biology of Schizophrenia. New York, Norton.

Hunt, J. McV., and Kogan, L. S. (1950): Measuring Results in Social Casework. New York, Family Service Association of America.

Jackson, D., and Weakland, J. H. (1961): Conjoint family therapy: some considerations on theory, technique, and results. Psychiatry 24, Suppl. to No. 2:30-45.

Jacobson, E. (1954): Transference problems in the psychoanalytic treatment of severely depressive patients. J. Amer. Psychoanal. Ass. 2:595-606.

——— (1957): Denial and repression. J. Amer. Psychoanal. Ass. 5:61-92.

——— (1959): Depersonalization. J. Amer. Psychoanal. Ass. 7:581-610.

Jahoda, M. (1958): Current Concepts of Positive Mental Health. New York, Basic Books.

Jones, E. (1953): The Life and Work of Sigmund Freud, Vol. 1. New York, Basic Books.

——— (1955): The Life and Work of Sigmund Freud, Vol. 2. New York, Basic Books.

——— (1956): Sigmund Freud: Four Centenary Addresses. New York, Basic Books.

——— (1957): The Life and Work of Sigmund Freud, Vol. 3. New York, Basic Books.

Katan, M. (1953): Schreber's prepsychotic phase. Int. J. Psychoanal. 34:43-51.

Kaufman, F. (1943): Methodology of the Social Sciences. Cambridge, Mass., Harvard University Press.

Kaufman, M. R. (1934): Projection, heterosexual and homosexual. Psychoanal. Quart. 3:134-136.

Kaywin, L. (1957): Notes on the concept of self-representation. J. Amer. Psychoanal. Ass. 5:293-301.

Kellam, S. G., and Chassan, J. B. (1962): Social context and symptom fluctuation. Psychiatry, 25:370-381.

Kety, S. (1961): An examination of current biochemical theories of schizophrenia. *In:* Chemical Pathology of the Nervous System. New York, Pergamon Press.

King, H. E. (1954): Psychomotor Aspects of Mental Disease. Cambridge, Mass., Harvard University Press.

Klein, E. (1957): Psychoanalysis and the plastic arts. Paper given before the New York Psychoanalytic Society, May 25.

Klein, G. S. (1951): The personal world through perception. *In:* Perception: An Approach to Personality (R. R. Blake and G. V. Ramsey, Eds.). New York, Ronald Press, pp. 328-355.

——— (1956): Perception, motives and personality: a clinical perspective. *In:* Psychology of Personality (J. M. McCary, Ed.). New York, Logos Press, pp. 121-199.

———, and Schlesinger, H. J. (1949): Where is the perceiver in perceptual theory? J. Personality 18:32-47.

Klein, M. (1932): The Psycho-Analysis of Children. London, Hogarth Press.

——— (1948): Contributions to Psycho-Analysis. London, Hogarth Press.

Knapp, P. H. (1960): Acute bronchial asthma: II. Psychoanalytic observations on fantasy, emotional arousal, and partial discharge. Psychosom. Med. 22:88-105.

Kraepelin, E. (1919): Dementia Praecox and Paraphrenia, tr. from the 8th German ed. Edinburgh, Livingstone.

Kris, E. (1941): Probleme der Ästhetik. Int. Z. Psychoanal. 26:142-178. Also in Kris (1952).

———— (1947): The nature of psychoanalytic propositions and their validation. *In:* Freedom and Experience (S. Hook and M. R. Konwitz, Eds.). Ithaca, New York, Cornell University Press.

———— (1952): Psychoanalytic Explorations in Art. New York, International Universities Press.

———— (1955): Neutralization and sublimation. Observations on young children. *In:* Psychoanalytic Study of the Child, Vol. 10. New York, International Universities Press, pp. 30-46.

Kris, M. (1957): The use of prediction in longitudinal study. *In:* Psychoanalytic Study of the Child, Vol. 12. New York, International Universities Press, pp. 175-189.

Kubie, L. S. (1952): Problems and techniques of psychoanalytic validation and progress. *In:* Psychoanalysis as Science (E. Pumpian-Mindlin, Ed.). Stanford, Cal., Stanford University Press, pp. 46-124.

———— (1958) Research into the process of supervision in psychoanalysis. Psychol. Quart. 27:226-236.

———— (1959): Discussion. *In:* Conceptual and Methodological Problems in Psychoanalysis (L. Bellak, Ed.). Ann. N. Y. Acad. Sci. 73.

Lashley, K. S. (1938): Experimental analysis of instinctive behavior. Psychol. Rev. 45:445-471.

Lasker, G. (1947): The effects of partial starvation on somatotypes. Amer. J. Physical Anthropol., 5:323-342.

Leider, A. R., et al. (1957): Report at the Annual Meeting of the American Psychiatric Association.

Leighton, A. H. (1960): An Introduction to Social Psychiatry. Springfield, Ill., Charles C Thomas.

Lemkau, P. (1958): Vital statistics of schizophrenia. *In:* Schizophrenia: A Review of the Syndrome. New York, Grune & Stratton, pp. 64-81.

Lennard, H., and Bernstein, A. (1960): Anatomy of Psychotherapy—Systems of Communication and Expectation. New York, Columbia University Press.

Levine, R., Chein, I., and Murphy, G. (1942): The relationship of the intensity of a need to the amount of perceptual distortion. J. Psychol. 13:283-293.

Levy, D. M. (1943): Maternal Overprotection. New York, Columbia University Press.

Lewin, B. (1946): Sleep, the mouth and the dream screen. Psychoanal. Quart. 15:419-434.

———— (1950): The Psychoanalysis of Elation. New York, Norton.

Lewy, E. (1954): On micropsia. Int. J. Psychoanal. 35:13-19.

Lilly, J. C. (1956): Mental effects of reduction of ordinary levels of physical stimuli on intact, healthy persons. A symposium. Psychiat. Ass. Res. Rep. No. 5:1-9, June.

Linn, L. (1953): The role of perception in the mechanism of denial. J. Amer. Psychoanal. Ass. 1:690-705.

———— (1954): The discriminating function of the ego. Psychoanal. Quart. 23:38-47.

Lord, E. (1950): Two sets of Rorschach records obtained before and after brief psychotherapy. J. Consult. Psychol. 14:134-139.

Lorenz, K. (1935): Companionship in bird life. *In:* Instinctive Behavior (C. Schiller, Ed. and Tr.). New York, International Universities Press, 1957, pp. 83-128.

Lowes, J. L. (1927): The Road to Xanadu. Boston, Houghton Mifflin.

Luria, A. R. (1932): The Nature of Human Conflict. New York, Liveright.

Magoun, H. W. (1952): An ascending reticular activating system in the brain stem. Arch. Neurol. Psychiat. 67:145-154.

Mahler, M. (1952): On child psychosis and schizophrenia. *In:* Psychoanalytic Study of the Child, Vol. 7. New York, International Universities Press, pp. 286-305.

————, and Elkisch, P. (1953): Some observations on disturbances of the ego in a case of infantile psychosis. *In:* Psychoanalytic Study of the Child, Vol. 8. New York, International Universities Press, pp. 252-261.

Mann, R. D. (1961): A Critique of P. E. Meehl's Clinical vs. Statistical Prediction. Ann Arbor, Mich., University of Michigan Mental Health Research Institute.

Maugham, S. (1953a): Complete Short Stories, Vol. 1. New York, Doubleday.

———— (1953b): Complete Short Stories, Vol. 2. New York, Doubleday.

———— (1962): Looking Back. Show: The Magazine of the Arts, 2, Nos. 6-8.

Meehl, P. E. (1954): Clinical Versus Statistical Prediction: A Theoretical Analysis and a Review of the Evidence. Minneapolis, University of Minnesota Press.

Meissner, W. W. (1966): The operational principle and meaning in psychoanalysis. Psychoanal. Quart. 35:233-255.

Mendelson, M. (1960): Psychoanalytic Concepts of Depression. Springfield, Ill., Charles C Thomas.

Menninger, K. (1954): Psychological aspects of the organism under stress. J. Amer. Psychoanal. Ass. 2:67-106, 280-310.

Meyer, J. E. (1961): Konzentrative Entspannungsubungen nach Elsa Gindler und ihre Grundlagen. Z. Psychotherapie 11(4).

Miller, J. G. (1942): Unconsciousness. New York, Wiley.

———— (1951): Objective methods of evaluating process and outcome in psychotherapy. Amer. J. Psychiat. 108:258-263.

Mira y Lopez, E. (1940): Myokinetic psychodiagnosis. Proc. Roy. Soc. Med. 33:173-194.

———— (1958): M. K. P.: Myokinetic psychodiagnosis. New York, Logos Press.

Mittelmann, B. (1954): Motility in infants, children, and adults: patterning and psychodynamics. In: Psychoanalytic Study of the Child, Vol. 9. New York, International Universities Press, pp. 142-177.

Morgan, C. D., and Murray, H. A. (1935): A method for investigating fantasies: the Thematic Apperception Test. Arch. Neurol. Psychiat. 34:289-306.

Morton, R. B. (1955): An experiment in brief psychotherapy. Psychol. Monogr. 69(1), No. 386.

Mowrer, O. H. (1940): An experimental analogue of "regression" with incidental observations on "reaction-formation." J. Abnorm. Soc. Psychol. 35:56-87.

———— (1953): Changes in verbal behavior during psychotherapy. In: Psychotherapy: Theory and Research (O. H. Mowrer, Ed.). New York, Ronald Press, pp. 463-545.

Murphy, L. (1956): Personality in Young Children. New York, Basic Books.

Murray, H. A. (1933): The effect of fear upon estimates of the maliciousness of other personalities. J. Soc. Psychol. 4:310-329.

————, et al. (1938): Explorations in Personality. New York, Oxford University Press.

————, and staff (1943): Thematic Apperception Test [31 cards, manual]. Cambridge, Mass., Harvard University Press.

Nachmansohn, M. (1925): Concerning experimentally produced dreams. In: Rapaport (1951), pp. 257-287.

Nagel, E. (1939): Principles of the theory of probability. In: International Encyclopedia of Unified Sciences, Vol. 1, No. 6. Chicago, University of Chicago Press.

Niederland, W. (1959): The "miracled-up" world of Schreber's childhood. In: Psychoanalytic Study of the Child, Vol. 14. New York, International Universities Press, pp. 383-413.

Nunberg, H. (1931): The synthetic function of the ego. Int. J. Psychoanal. 12:123-140.

———— (1956): Principles of Psychoanalysis. New York, International Universities Press.

Oberndorf, C. P. (1949): A Questionnaire Study on Evaluating Psychoanalysis. Yearbook of Psychoanalysis, Vol. 4. New York, International Universities Press.

———— (1950): The role of anxiety in depersonalization. Int. J. Psychoanal. 31:1-5.

———— (1953): A History of Psychoanalysis in America. New York, Grune & Stratton.

————, Greenacre, P., and Kubie, L. S. (1948): Symposium on the evaluation of therapeutic results. Int. J. Psychoanal. 29:7-33.

Office of Strategic Services, Assessment Staff (1948): Assessment of Men. New York, Rinehart.

Ostow, M. (1959): Use of drugs to overcome technical difficulties in psychiatry. In: The Dynamics of Psychiatric Drug Therapy (G. Sarwer-Foner, Ed.). Springfield, Ill., Charles C Thomas.

———— (1962): Pharmaceutical Agents in Psychoanalysis and Psychotherapy. New York, Basic Books.

Piaget, J. (1923): The Language and Thought of the Child. London, Routledge, 1932.

———— (1936): The Origins of Intelligence in Children. New York, International Universities Press, 1952.

———— (1937): The Construction of Reality in the Child. New York, Basic Books, 1954.

Pitts, W., and McCulloch, W. S. (1947): How we know universals: the perception of auditory and visual forms. Bull. Math. Biophys. 9:127-147.

Polatin, P., et al. (1944): Organic psychosis simulating dementia praecox: two cases with brain biopsy studies. Psychiat. Quart. 18:391-412.

Pollock, H., Malzberg, B., and Fuller, R. G. (1939): Hereditary and Environmental Factors in the Causation of Manic Depressive Psychosis and Dementia Praecox. Utica, New York, State Hospital Press.

Posner, P. A. (1940): Selfishness, guilt feelings, and social distance. Master's thesis, University of Iowa.

Prola, M., Rosenberg, S., Meyer, E. J., Zuckerman, M., and Bellak, L. (to be published): Brief Psychotherapy.

Rado, S. (1919): Clinical contribution to the paranoia question: a case of organ projection. Int. Z. Psychoanal. 15:44-46.

Rapaport, D. (1942): Emotions and Memory, 2nd unaltered ed. New York, International Universities Press, 1950.

————, ed. (1951): Organization and Pathology of Thought. New York, Columbia University Press.

Raskin, N. J. (1949): The development of the "parallel studies" project. J. Consult. Psychol. 13:154-156.

———— (Unpublished): Dissertation on psychology.

Redl, F., and Wineman, D. (1951): Children Who Hate. Glencoe, Ill., Free Press.

Reich, A. (1960): Pathologic forms of self-esteem regulation. In: Psychoanalytic Study of the Child, Vol. 15. New York, International Universities Press, pp. 215-232.

Reik, T. (1927): Psychologie und Depersonalisation. In: Wie man Psychologe wird. Vienna, Internationaler Psychoanalytischer Verlag.

Ribble, M. (1941): Disorganizing factors of infant personality. Amer. J. Psychiat. 98:459-463.

Riesman, D. (1950): The Lonely Crowd. New Haven, Yale University Press.

Rodnick, E. H. (1942): The effect of Metrazol shock on habit systems. J. Abnorm. Soc. Psychol. 37:560-565.

————, and Klebanoff, S. G. (1942): Projective reactions to induced frustration as a measure of social adjustment. Psychol. Bull. 39:489 (abs.).

Roizin, D., et al. (1945): Schizophrenic reaction syndrome in course of acute demyelinization of central nervous system. Arch. Neurol. Psychiat. 54:202-211.

Rokeach, M. (1960): The Open and Closed Mind. New York, Basic Books.

Rose, B. (1948): Wine, Women, and Song. New York, Pocket Books.

Rosen, J. (1953): Direct Analysis. New York, Grune & Stratton.

Rosen, V. (1953): On mathematical "illumination" and the mathematical thought process. In: Psychoanalytic Study of the Child, Vol. 8. New York, International Universities Press, pp. 127-154.

Rosenfeld, H. (1947): Analysis of a schizophrenic state with depersonalization. Int. J. Psychoanal. 28:130-139.

Rosenzweig, S. (1954): A transvaluation of psychotherapy—a reply to Hans Eysenck. J. Abnorm. Soc. Psychol. 49:298-304.

Rotter, J. B. (1940): Studies in the use and validity of the Thematic Apperception Test with mentally disordered patients: methods of analysis and clinical problems. Character Pers. 9:18-34.

Rowse, A. L. (1963): William Shakespeare: A Biography. New York, Harpers.

Runes, D., ed. (1942): Quotation from C. P. Herbart, Psychologie als Wissenschaft, Part III, Sect. 1, Ch. 15, p. 15. Dictionary of Philosophy. New York, Philosophical Library.

Sanford, R. N. (1936): The effects of abstinence from food upon imaginal processes. J. Psychol. 3:145-159.

———, Adkins, M., Miller, R. B., Cobb, E. A., and others (1943): Physique, Personality, and Scholarship. Washington, D. C., Society for Research in Child Development, National Research Council.

Sanua, V. D. (Unpublished): A comparative study of schizophrenics of different backgrounds (Italian, Irish, Jews, and Protestants). Progress Report, School of Social Work, Yeshiva University, New York, N. Y.

Sargent, H. (1953): The Insight Test. New York, Grune & Stratton.

Savage, C. (1955): Variations in ego feeling induced by D-lysergic acid diethylamide (LSD-25). Psychoanal. Rev. 42:1-16.

———, and Cholden, L. (1956): Schizophrenia and the model psychoses. J. Clin. Exp. Psychopathol. 17:405-413.

Schilder, P. (1950): The Image and Appearance of the Human Body. New York, International Universities Press.

Schneider, K. (1954): The problem of psychotherapy of endogenous psychoses. Deutsch Med. Wschr. 79:873.

Schwing, G. (1954): A Way to the Soul of the Mentally Ill. New York, International Universities Press.

Sears, R. R. (1936): Experimental studies of projection: I. Attribution of traits. J. Soc. Psychol. 7:151-163.

——— (1937): Experimental studies of projection: II. Ideas of reference. J. Soc. Psychol. 8:389-400.

——— (1943): Survey of Objective Studies of Psychoanalytic Concepts. New York, Social Science Research Council, Bulletin No. 51.

——— (1944): Experimental analysis of psychoanalytic phenomena. In: Personality and the Behavior Disorders (J. McV. Hunt, Ed.). New York, Ronald Press, pp. 306-332.

———, Hovland, C. I., and Miller, N. E. (1940): Minor studies of aggression: measurement of aggressive behavior. J. Psychol. 9:275-294.

Sechehaye, M. (1951a): Reality Lost and Regained: Autobiography of a Schizophrenic Girl. New York, Grune & Stratton.

——— (1951b): Symbolic Realization: A New Method of Psychotherapy Applied to a Case of Schizophrenia. New York, International Universities Press.

——— (1956): A New Psychotherapy in Schizophrenia. New York, Grune & Stratton.

Seeman, J. (1949): A study of the process of nondirective therapy. J. Consult. Psychol. 13:157-168.

Sheerer, E. T. (1949): An analysis of the relationship between acceptance of and respect for self and acceptance of and respect for others in ten counseling cases. J. Consult. Psychol. 13:169-175.

Sheldon, W. H., Stevens, S. S., and Tucker, W. B. (1940): The Varieties of Human Physique. New York, Harper.

Siegel, S. (1956): Nonparametric Statistics for the Behavioral Sciences. New York, McGraw-Hill.

Siipola, E. M. (1950): The influence of color on reactions to ink blots. J. Personality 18:358-382.

Silberer, H. (1909): Report on a method of eliciting and observing certain symbolic hallucination phenomena. In: Rapaport (1951), pp. 195-207.

Singer, J. L., and Opler, M. K. (1956): Contrasting patterns of fantasy and motility in Irish and Italian schizophrenics. J. Abnorm. Soc. Psychol. 53:42-47.

Snyder, W. U., et al. (1955): The role of Rorschach variability in the prediction of client behavior during psychotherapy. In: Group Report of a Program of Research in Psychotherapy (W. U. Snyder, Ed.). State College, Pa., Pennslyvania State University Press, pp. 60-74.

Spiegel, L. (1959): The self, the sense of self, and perception. In: Psychoanalytic Study of the Child, Vol. 14. New York, International Universities Press, pp. 81-109.

Spitz, R. (1945a): Hospitalism: an inquiry into the genesis of psychiatric conditions in early childhood. *In:* Psychoanalytic Study of the Child, Vol. 1. New York, International Universities Press, pp. 53-74.

———— (1945b): Diacritic and coenesthetic organizations. Psychoanal. Rev. 32:146-162.

———— (1946a): Anaclitic depression. *In:* Psychoanalytic Study of the Child, Vol. 2. New York, International Universities Press, pp. 313-342.

———— (1946b): The smiling response. Genet. Psychol. Monogr. 34:57-125.

———— (1951a): The psychogenic diseases in infancy. *In:* Psychoanalytic Study of the Child, Vol. 6. New York, International Universities Press, pp. 255-278.

———— (1951b): Purposive grasping. J. Personality 1:141-148.

———— (1957a): No and Yes. New York, International Universities Press.

———— (1957b): Die Entstehung der ersten Objectbeziehungen. Stuttgart, Ernst Klett Verlag.

Srole, L., Langner, T., Opler, M., and Rennie, T. (1962): Mental Health in the Metropolis. New York, McGraw-Hill.

Stamm, J. L. (1959): Depersonalization and the wish to sleep. Presented at the Midwinter Meeting of the American Psychoanalytic Association, Dec.

Starr, H. E. (1935): A study of experimentally induced projection of visual imagery. Psychol. Bull. 32:742 (abs.).

Stephenson, W. (1953): The Study of Behavior. Chicago, University of Chicago Press.

Sterba, E., and Sterba, R. (1954): Beethoven and His Nephew. New York, Pantheon Books.

Sterba, R., and Sterba, E. (1956): The anxieties of Michelangelo Buonarroti. Int. J. Psychoanal. 37:325-330.

Stern, W. (1913): The Psychological Method of Measuring Intelligence. New York, Warwick & York.

Stevens, S. S. (1951): Mathematics, measurement, and psychophysics. *In:* Handbook of Experimental Psychology (S. S. Stevens, Ed.). New York, John Wiley.

Strupp, H. (1957): A multidimensional system for analyzing psychotherapeutic techniques. Psychiatry 20:293-312.

———— (1960): Psychotherapists in Action. New York, Grune & Stratton.

———— (n.d.): A Clinical Picture of Claustrophobia. Film produced by the Veterans Administration.

Szondi, L. (1952): Experimental Diagnostics of Drives. New York, Grune & Stratton.

Tinbergen, N. (1951): A Study of Instinct. Oxford, Clarendon Press.

———— (1953): Social Behaviour in Animals. London, Methuen.

Tomkins, S. (1946): Contemporary Psychopathology. Cambridge, Mass., Harvard University Press.

Varendonck, J. (1921): The psychology of daydreams. *In:* Rapaport (1951), pp. 451-473.

von Bertalanffy, L. (1955): General system theory. Main Currents Modern Thought 2:75-83.

Watson, R., and Mensh, I. (1951): The evaluation of the effects of psychotherapy. I. Sources of material. J. Psychol. 32:259-273.

Wechsler, D. (1939): The Measurement of Adult Intelligence. Baltimore, Williams & Wilkins.

Weil, A. P. (1953): Certain severe disturbances of ego development in childhood. *In:* Psychoanalytic Study of the Child, Vol. 8. New York: International Universities Press, pp. 271-287.

Weiss, E. (1932): Regression and projection in the super-ego. Int. J. Psychoanal. 13:449-478.

Weisskopf, E. A. (1950): Experimental study of the effect of brightness and ambiguity on projection in the Thematic Apperception Test. J. Psychol. 29:407-416.

Werner, H. (1948): Comparative Psychology of Mental Development, rev. ed. Chicago, Follett.

Wexler, M. (1951): The structural problem in schizophrenia: the role of the internal object. Bull. Menninger Clin. 15:221-234.

Winkler, A., and Frank, K. (1948): Effect of electroshock convulsions on chronic decorticated cats. Proc. Soc. Exp. Biol. Med. 67:464-468.

Wright, B. A. (1941): An experimentally created conflict expressed in a projective technique. Psychol. Bull. 38:718 (abs.).

Wyss, D. (1958): Die Bedeutung der Associationstheorien für die Psychoanalyse. Confin. Psychiat. 1:113-132.

Young, K. (1927): Parent-child relationship: the projection of parents' ambition for fame, money, etc. on the child. Family 8:67-73.

Zilboorg, G. (1952): Some sidelights on free associations. Int. J. Psychoanal. 33:489-495.

Zulliger, H. (1933): Der Abendteurer Schundroman. Z. Psychoanal. Pädag. 7:357-377.

BIBLIOGRAPHY
of Leopold Bellak, M.D. (as of June 1967)

BOOKS

(1948): *Dementia Praecox: The Past Decade's Work and Present Status: A Review and Evaluation. New York, Grune & Stratton, 456 pp.

(1950) (Editor and contributor; with Lawrence Abt): *Projective Psychology: Clinical Approaches to the Total Personality. New York, Alfred A. Knopf, 485 pp.; paperback, Grove Press, 1959.

(1952): *Manic-Depressive Psychosis and Allied Disorders. New York, Grune & Stratton, 306 pp.

(1952) (Editor and contributor): †The Psychology of Physical Illness: Psychiatry Applied to Medicine, Surgery and the Specialties. New York, Grune & Stratton, 243 pp.; London, Churchill, 1953.

(1954): The Thematic Apperception Test and the Children's Apperception Test in Clinical Use. New York, Grune & Stratton, 282 pp.

(1958) (Editor and contributor; with P. K. Benedict): *†Schizophrenia: A Review of the Syndrome. New York, Logos Press, 1,010 pp.; now distributed by Grune & Stratton.

(1959) (Editor, conference chairman, and contributor): Conceptual and Methodological Problems in Psychoanalysis. Ann. N. Y. Acad. Sci. 76:971-1134.

(1960) (Co-editor of the American edition): Myokinetic Psychodiagnosis, by Emilio Mira y Lopez. New York, Logos Press.

(1961) (Editor): Contemporary European Psychiatry. New York, Grove Press, 372 pp.; hardcover and paperback.

(1964) (Editor and contributor): A Handbook of Community Psychiatry and Community Mental Health. New York, Grune & Stratton, 465 pp.

(1965) (with Leonard Small): †Emergency Psychotherapy and Brief Psychotherapy. New York, Grune & Stratton, 253 pp.

(1967): The Broad Scope of Psychoanalysis: Selected Papers of Leopold Bellak, ed. Donald P. Spence. New York, Grune & Stratton.

(Editor, with Laurence Loeb): The Schizophrenic Syndrome. New York, Grune & Stratton, to be published.

CHAPTERS IN BOOKS

(1949, 1950, 1951, 1952, 1953) (with Daniel Brower): Projective methods. (1954) (with Daniel Brower): Clinical psychology. (1955) (with Leonard Small): Projective methods. In: Progress in Neurology and Psychiatry, ed. E. A. Spiegel. 4:528-543; 5:528-543; 6:465-477; 7:511-520; 8:517-526; 9:554-555; 10:541-555. New York, Grune & Stratton.

(1950): Projection and the TAT. In: Recent Experiments in Psychology, rev. ed., L. W. Crafts, T. C. Schneirla, et al. New York, McGraw-Hill.

(1951): The analytic approach to the TAT. In: Thematic Analysis, ed. E. Shneidman, et al. New York, Grune & Stratton.

(1952): The emergency psychotherapy of depression. In: Specialized Techniques in Psychotherapy, ed. G. Bychowski and J. L. Despert. New York, Basic Books, pp. 323-336.

(1952): Thematic Apperception Test and other apperceptive methods. In: Progress in Clinical Psychology, ed. D. Brower and L. E. Abt. New York, Grune & Stratton, pp. 149-172.

(1955): Projective techniques in contemporary psychology. In: Present-Day Psychology, ed. A. A. Roback. New York, Philosophical Library, pp. 547-561.

---

* Selection of the Basic Book Club.

† Also published in Spanish.

(1956): Psychoanalytic theory of personality: notes toward a systematic textbook of psychoanalysis. *In:* Psychology of Personality, ed. J. M. McCary. New York, Logos Press, pp. 1-62.

(1960) (with C. Adelman): The Children's Apperception Test. *In:* Projective Techniques with Children, ed. Albert I. Rabin and Mary R. Haworth. New York, Grune & Stratton.

(1961): Foreword to The Psychological Test Report, by W. Klopfer. New York, Grune & Stratton.

(1962): The role of psychotherapy in community psychiatry. *In:* Current Psychiatric Therapy, ed. J. Massermann. New York, Grune & Stratton.

(1963): Somerset Maugham: a study of some of his stories. *In:* The Study of Lives, ed. Robert W. White. New York, Atherton Press.

(1963): Foreword to The Talking Cure, by Morton Hunt. New York, Harper & Row.

(1964): Depersonalization as a variant of self-awareness. *In:* Unfinished Tasks in the Behavioral Sciences, ed. A. Abrams. Baltimore, Williams & Wilkins.

(1965): Foreword, and The concept of acting out: theoretical considerations. *In:* Acting Out—Theoretical and Clinical Aspects, ed. Lawrence Abt and Stuart Weissman. New York, Grune & Stratton.

(1965): Foreword to The C.A.T.: Facts about Fantasy, by Mary Haworth. New York, Grune & Stratton.

(1966) (with Jacob B. Chassan): An introduction to intensive design in the evaluation of drug efficacy during psychotherapy. *In:* Methods of Research in Psychotherapy, ed. Louis A. Gottschalk and Arthur H. Auerbach. New York, Appleton-Century-Crofts, pp. 478-499.

(1966): Foreword to Research Design in Clinical Psychology and Psychiatry, by Jacob B. Chassan. New York, Appleton-Century-Crofts.

(1967): Bellak's viewpoint on mental health (transcript of an interview on WNYC-TV with Marvin Perkins). *In:* Viewpoint on Mental Health. New York City Community Mental Health Board.

An experimental study on brief psychotherapy and factors related to improvement in brief psychotherapy. *In:* An Evaluation of the Results of the Psychotherapies, ed. Stanley Lesse. Amer. J. Psychother., to be published.

Psychoses. *In:* International Encyclopedia of the Social Sciences. Crowell-Collier & Macmillan; to be published.

Papers

(1941): A possible dynamic explanation of variability in the I.Q. J. Abnorm. Soc. Psychol. 36:106-109.

(1942): An experimental investigation of projection (Abstr.). Psychol. Bull. 39:489-490.

(1942): The nature of slogans. J. Abnorm. Soc. Psychol. 37:496-510.

(1942): A note about the Adam's apple. Psychoanal. Rev. 29:300-302.

(1942) (with Eliot Jacques): On the problem of dynamic conceptualization in case studies. Character Pers. 11:20-39.

(1944): The concept of projection; an experimental investigation and study of the concept. Psychiatry 7:353-370.

(1945): On the psychology of detective stories and related problems. Psychoanal. Rev. 32:403-407.

(1946) (with Rudolf Ekstein): An extension of basic scientific laws to psychoanalysis and to psychology. Psychoanal. Rev. 33:306-313.

(1946) (with B. Parcell): The prepsychotic personality in dementia praecox; study of 100 cases in the Navy. Psychiat. Quart. 20:627-637.

(1947) (with Elizabeth Willson): On the etiology of dementia praecox: a partial review of the literature, 1935 to 1945, and an attempt at conceptualization. J. Nerv. Ment. Dis. 105:1-24.

(1947) (with Blaise Pasquarelli): A case of co-existence of idiopathic epileptic and psychogenic convulsions. Psychosom. Med. 9:137-139.

(1947) (with Rudolf Ekstein and Sydell Braverman): A preliminary study of norms for the Thematic Apperception Test (Abstr.). Amer. Psychol. 2:271.

(1948) (with Robert R. Holt): Somatotypes in relation to dementia praecox. Amer. J. Psychiat. 104:713-724.

(1948): A note on some basic concepts of psychotherapy. J. Nerv. Ment. Dis. 108:137-141.

(1949): The use of oral barbiturates in psychotherapy. Amer. J. Psychiat. 105:849-850.

(1949) (with Blaise Pasquarelli and S. Braverman): The use of the TAT in psychotherapy. J. Nerv. Ment. Dis. 110:51-65.

(1949): A multiple-factor psychosomatic theory of schizophrenia. Psychiat. Quart. 23:738-755.

(1950) (with Leah Levinger and Esther Lipsky): An adolescent problem reflected in the TAT. J. Clin. Psychol. 6:295-297.

(1950): The effect of situational factors on the TAT; a note on the TAT's of two Nazi leaders: Streicher and Rosenberg. J. Proj. Tech. 14:309-314.

(1950): Psychiatric aspects of tuberculosis. Soc. Casework 31:183-189.

(1950): Thematic apperception: failures and the defenses. Trans. N. Y. Acad. Sci. Ser. II. 12:122-126.

(1950) (with Sonya Bellak): An introductory note on the Children's Apperception Test (CAT). J. Proj. Tech. 14:173-180.

(1950) (with Florence Haselkorn): A multiple-service approach to cardiac patients. Soc. Casework 31:292-298.

(1954): A study of limitations and "failures": toward an ego psychology of projective techniques. J. Proj. Tech. 18:279-293.

(1955): Toward a unified concept of schizophrenia. J. Nerv. Ment. Dis. 121:60-66.

(1955): An ego-psychological theory of hypnosis. Int. J. Psycho-Anal. 36:375-378.

(1956) (with Bertram J. Black, Abraham Lurie, and Joseph S. A. Miller): Rehabilitation of the mentally ill through controlled transitional employment. Amer. J. Orthopsychiat. 26:285-296.

(1956) (with Florence Haselkorn): Psychological aspects of cardiac illness and rehabilitation. Soc. Casework 37:482-489.

(1956) (with M. Brewster Smith): An experimental exploration of the psychoanalytic process: exemplification of a method. Psychoanal. Quart. 25:385-414.

(1956): Comment on Carl Rogers. Amer. Psychol. 11:156-157.

(1956): Freud and projective techniques. J. Proj. Tech. 20:5-13.

(1958): Psychoanalytic principles discernible in projective testing. Amer. J. Orthopsychiat. 28:42-46.

(1958): Studying the psychoanalytic process by the method of short-range prediction and judgement. Brit. J. Med. Psychol. 31:249-252.

(1958): Henry A. Murray: an appreciation. J. Proj. Tech. 22:143-144.

(1958): Creativity: some random notes to a systematic consideration. J. Proj. Tech. 22:363-380.

(1959): The unconscious. Ann. N. Y. Acad. Sci. 76:1066-1081.

(1959) (with Herman Feifel, Bela Mittelmann, Bertram R. Forer, Walter G. Klopfer, and Eugene B. Brody): Psychological test reporting: a problem in communication between psychologists and psychiatrists. J. Nerv. Ment. Dis. 129:76-91.

(1959): Introduction: the frame of reference of the monograph. In: Conceptual and Methodological Problems in Psychoanalysis. Ann. N. Y. Acad. Sci. 76:973-975.

(1960) (with Bertram Black): The rehabilitation of psychotics in the community. Amer. J. Orthopsychiat. 30:346-355.

(1960): The treatment of schizophrenia and psychoanalytic theory. J. Nerv. Ment. Dis. 131:39-46.

(1960): A community mental health centre in a hospital. Brit. J. Med. Psychol. 33:287-290.

(1960): A general hospital as a focus of community psychiatry. J. Amer. Med. Assoc. 174:2214-2217.

(1961): Research in psychoanalysis. Psychoanal. Quart. 30:519-548.

(1961): Free association: conceptual and clinical aspects. Int. J. Psycho-Anal. 42:9-20.

(1961) (with Lee Salk and David Rosenhan): A process study of the effects of Deprol on depression. J. Nerv. Ment. Dis. 132:531-538.

(1961): Personality structure in a changing world. Arch. Gen. Psychiat. 5:183-185.

(1963): Acting out: some conceptual and therapeutic considerations. Amer. J. Psychother. 17:375-389.

(1963): Methodology and research in the psychotherapy of psychoses. American Psychiatric Association Research Report No. 17.

(1964) (with Jacob B. Chassan): An approach to the evaluation of drug effect during psychotherapy: a double-blind study of a single case. J. Nerv. Ment. Dis. 139:20-30.

(1964) (with Max Prola, Eva J. Meyer, and Marcia Zuckerman): Psychiatry in the medical-surgical emergency clinic. Arch. Gen. Psychiat. 10:267-269.

(1965): Intensive design drug therapy and the psychotherapeutic process. Psychosom. 6.

(1966): Effects of antidepressant drugs on psychodynamics. Psychosom. 7.

(1966) (with Marvin S. Hurvich): A human modification of the Children's Apperception Test (CAT-H). J. Proj. Tech. Pers. Assess. 30:228-242.

Papers Translated into Foreign Languages

(1956): Connaissance de l'homme: la theorie psychosomatique des facteurs multiples comme interpretation de la schizophrenia. Revue des Sciences de l'Homme et de Leurs Applications Pratique No. 15.

(1957): Freud y las técnicas projectivas. Revista de Psicologia, General y Aplicada, Madrid, 12:293-304.

(1959): Prédiction systématique au cours du processus psychothérapique et au cours d'autres processus d'interaction. l'Encephale. 48:361-376.

(1959): Biography and bibliography. Revue de Psychologie Appliquée, 9(3).

(1959): Una exploración experimental del proceso psicoanalítico. Revista de Psiquiatría y Psicología Médica, 4:457.

(1961): Freie assoziation. Psyche, Frankfurt.

(1964): Les urgences psychiatriques pour les médicins practiciens. Médicine et Hygiene, No. 649.

Tests

(1942): Scoring Key for Digit Symbol-Test of the Wechsler-Bellevue Intelligence Test. New York, The Psychological Corporation.

(1949) (with Sonya Bellak): The Children's Apperception Test: Pictures, Guide to the Interpretation Manual, and Analysis Sheets. Larchmont, N. Y., C. P. S. Inc. Also published in France, Italy, India, Australia, Germany, and Argentina.

(1950): An Introduction to the Children's Apperception Test. Larchmont, N. Y., C. P. S. Inc.

(1951): Bellak TAT Blank and Scoring Sheet, and Guide to the Interpretation of the TAT and Analysis Sheets. New York, The Psychological Corporation.

(1952) (with Sonya Bellak): The Supplement to the Children's Apperception Test (C.A.T.-S). Larchmont, N. Y., C. P. S. Inc. Second edition; published and translated in Australia, Italy, Germany, France, Japan, India and Argentina.

(1964): CAT-H (an adaptation of the CAT with human figures). Larchmont, N. Y., C. P. S. Inc.

TAT & CAT Blanks (short form). The CAT and related material are also published independently by: Centre de Psychologie appliquée, Paris, France; Organizzazioni Speciali, Italy; Verlag für Psychologie, Göttingen, Germany; Editoriales Paidos, Buenos Aires, Argentina; Australian Council for Educational Research, Melbourne, Australia; and an Indian adaptation by Manasayan, New Delhi, India.

Book Reviews

(1946): Young Man, You Are Normal (E. Hooton). Amer. J. Psychiat. 103:430-431.

(1948): Sexual Behavior in the Human Male (A. Kinsey et al.). Child Study Welfare League Amer. 17:15-16.

(1952): Psychotherapy with Schizophrenics (ed. E. B. Brody and F. C. Redlich). Amer. J. Psychiat. 109:477-478.

(1952): Psychological Analysis of Economic Behavior (Katona). Psychoanal. Quart., April.

(1952): The Bender Gestalt Test (G. R. Pascal and B. Suttell). Amer. J. Psychiat. 108:879.

(1955): The Life and Work of Sigmund Freud, Vol. 2 (E. Jones). N. Y. Post, Sept. 15.

(1957): The Life and Work of Sigmund Freud, Vol. 3. (E. Jones). Basic Book Service, Fall.

(1957): The Life and Work of Sigmund Freud, Vol. 3 (E. Jones). N. Y. Post, Oct. 13, p. M-11.

(1957): Medical Research: A Mid-century Survey, Vols. 1 & 2 (ed. E. E. Lape). Psychoanal. Quart. 26:272-273.

(1961): Anatomy of Judgment (M. J. J. Abercrombie). Psychoanal. Quart. 30:120-122.

(1961): Scoring Human Motives: A Manual (Dollard and Auld). Ment. Hyg., April.

(1962): Psychotherapy of the Psychoses (ed. A. Burton). Amer. J. Psychother. 16:526-527.

(1963): Creativity (Emanuel L. Hammer). J. Proj. Tech. 27:124-125.

(1964): Direct Psychoanalytic Psychiatry (John N. Rosen). Psychoanal. Quart. 33:281-283.

Object Relations Test (Philips). Int. J. Group Psychother.

The Stress of Life (Selye). Int. J. Group Psychother.

INDEX